FLIGHT INSTRUCTORS MANUAL

This manual has been approved by the U.K. Aircraft Owners and Pilots Association for use in conjunction with the AOPA Syllabuses for the Private Pilot, Assistant Flying Instructor, and Ground Instructor Certificate Courses.

FLIGHT INSTRUCTORS MANUAL

R. D. CAMPBELL

PUBLISHED BY:
THE CAMPBELL PARTNERSHIP

HATHERLOW
MERROW COMMON ROAD
GUILDFORD
SURREY, GU4 7BJ
ENGLAND

DISTRIBUTED BY:
POOLEYS

ESTREE AERODROME
HERTFORDSHIRE, WD6 3AW
ENGLAND
Telephone Number: 081 207 3749
Facsimile Number: 081 953 2512

First published in Great Britain by Aviation Training
Publications Ltd 1976.
Reprinted by Granada Publishing 1982
Reprinted with amendments by Collins Professional
and Technical Books 1985
Reprinted 1986
Reprinted with amendments 1988 by BSP Professional
Books
Reprinted 1990
Amended and reprinted by the Campbell Partnership
1994

British Library
Cataloguing in Publication data

Campbell, R. D. (Ronald D.)
            Flight Instructors Manual

ISBN 1 - 898567 - 05 - 0

Contents

Author's Note

This Training Manual is specifically written to cover the content and sequential layout of the Flight Training Sections in the U.K. Private Pilot Licence Syllabus and the U.K. Assistant Flying Instructor Syllabus. It will also be a useful reference work for the AOPA (U.K.) Ground Instructor Syllabus.

The layout and contents of this publication are intended solely as a guide to implement these syllabuses, and not to suggest that the format it follows is the only way to teach people to fly. There are many alternative ways of teaching efficiently and the exact method used will depend upon the personality and characteristics of both instructor and student. Nevertheless, planned instruction will need to conform to a syllabus which has been established and approved by the Civil Aviation Authority, and the manual seeks to conform in this respect. It also abides by good teaching practices and provides a systematic approach to the course content, both of which are essential if the required standard of flying training is to be achieved within the laid-down time of 40 hours.

One facet of a flying instructor's job is to teach the many learning items in logical sequence, another is to test for understanding, and a third is to analyse and advise the student on his progress. However, instructors have differing personalities which lend themselves to varying ways of presentation and accomplishment of their task. This manual should not therefore be used in a way which limits or inhibits instructors in the performance of their aim, but rather as an aid to elucidating and expanding upon those mandatory aspects of flying training required for the issue of the Private Pilot Licence.

This Instructor Training Manual has been produced in conjunction with a separate Student Training Manual. The two books are totally complementary and their use in an instructor/student environment will therefore be of valuable assistance to the planning and conduct of the student's flight training. The Student Training Manual contains four sections for each air exercise, Student's Guide, Long Briefing, Pre-Flight Briefing, and Flight Demonstration. The layout of these sections is similar to this Flying Instructor Manual and will therefore enable the instructor to direct the student's study to relevant sections at the appropriate stages of his training. In this way, the student's learning time will be utilised more effectively than in the case of random reading of the technical knowledge required for the promoting and developing of his pilot skills.

In some of the Long Briefings, formulae have been stated which will be of value to those interested in this aspect of aerodynamics and aircraft performance. However, such knowledge is not considered to be essential information, and the method of explanation in the Long Briefings is arranged so that the reader will understand the substance of the briefing, without necessarily being obliged to understand or use such formulae.

Flight safety is an ultimate objective of all those who work in aviation. The flying instructor's primary task is to teach his student to operate an aircraft efficiently with **safety**. A deep mathematical undertanding of the forces in the climb, or of abstract considerations relating to take-off and landing will have little influence on safety. However, being able to determine whether to use the best rate of climb speed, or the best angle of climb speed, together with a basic understanding of an aircraft's performance capability, would enable the pilot to decide, for example whether a short or soft field technique should be used for a particular take-off or landing. Such an ability to interpret and use the aircraft performance figures in a practical fashion will prove an invaluable asset to a pilot during training and afterwards.

The contents of each Long Briefing should not therefore be seen as an academic treatise on aerodynamics and aircraft power plants to be compulsorily learned. Although many aerodynamic and power plant considerations are covered, it is the principles of aircraft operation which should be emphasised to the student. In this same context it should be noted that it is not necessary for the detailed information given under the academic considerations to be committed to memory in order to obtain, renew or upgrade an Assistant Instructor Rating. A flying instructor should nevertheless have a broad appreciation of these considerations, as this will make it easier for him to understand the reasons behind the contents of the Air Demonstration, and to explain to the student why different operating techniques are used.

A private pilot eventually needs to absorb many learning items in order to operate his aircraft safely, and when these are listed, an appreciation of the flying instructor's task and responsibility towards his student begins to be fully realised. For example this manual contains 51 Pre-Flight Briefings to cover the Air Exercises contained in the Flight Demonstration sections. It must however be stressed that their inclusion, and the breakdown system used does not necessarily mean that 51 separate pre-flight briefings must be given.

Rather they provide a reference to the individual aims, descriptions, and contents from which any instructor can draw on to formulate his own lesson plan to suit his own style of presentation and the learning pace of his student. They can therefore be used individually or in combination, according to the dictates of the training situation. In this way, flexibility is achieved without missing out the essential components of the student's learning task.

With the exception of the Effects of Controls, the contents itemised in the Pre-Flight Briefing layouts are fairly detailed and are not intended to be written out in full during the actual briefing. It will therefore be necessary for the instructor to abbreviate his chalk/ perspex board presentation to suit his own requirements.

To be of practical value a Flying Training Manual must make reference to procedures relating to the operation of aircraft. This manual is not written around a particular aircraft type, but is for use in the wider sense. Therefore, due to the differences between aircraft of different makes and types, references to procedures must be made in an oblique fashion, to do otherwise would infer that the reader should automatically apply them to his own particular training aircraft whereas this will not always be correct. To overcome this problem, expressions such as 'if applicable', 'when available', and 'normally', are used. This avoids a pedantic inference that the procedure quoted is the one which the student must use. Reference is also made to 'Good Operating Practices' and although such items are common in most cases regardless of aircraft types and operating environments, there are times when differences will inevitably occur. The instructor must therefore be careful to interpret those differences as applicable to his own operating environment, aircraft type and stage of training.

Finally, although the prime objective of this manual is to guide the student instructor in the development of his teaching skill along established guidelines, and to determine what has to be taught within the flying section of the Private Pilot Course, it is nevertheless hoped that experienced instructors will find the contents and layout of this book a valuable aid memoire for their own knowledge and techniques.

R.D. Campbell DFC, AFC, FRAeS, MBAC

Acknowledgements

Acknowledgement is gratefully made to Mr W. G. Beadle for his encouragement and participation in the writing of this manual. Acknowledgements are also made to Mr A. McDonald C.Eng., F.R.Ae.S. of the Department of Design, College of Aeronautics, to Mr J. Jones M.A. (Cantab), and to those members of the Civil Aviation Authority, AOPA Instructor Committee, Panel of Examiners, and the staff of the many aircraft, aero engine, instrument and aircraft systems manufacturers whose advice and helpful suggestions were an important contribution.

Particular acknowledgement is also made to my wife, without whose patient tolerance this work could never have been completed.

The 'Flight Training' section of the U.K. Private Pilot Licence Syllabus lists the various 'Air Exercises' in the numerical sequence shown below:

EXERCISE   DESCRIPTION

1	Aircraft Familiarisation
2	Preparation For and Action After Flight
3	Air Experience
4	Effects of Controls
5	Taxying
6	Straight and Level Flight
7	Climbing
8	Descending
9	Turning
10A	Slow Flight
10B	Stalling
11A	Spin Recovery at the Incipient Stage
11B	Spinning
12	Take-off and Climb to Downwind Position
13	The Circuit, Approach and Landing
14	First Solo and Consolidation
15	Advanced Turning
16	Operation at Minimum Level
17A	Forced Landings without Power
17B	Forced Landings with Power
18	Pilot Navigation
19A	Introduction to Instrument Flying
20	Night Flying

FLIGHT INSTRUCTION

INSTRUCTOR'S MANUAL

AMENDMENT LIST No.	DATE INCORPORATED	SIGNATURE

Foreword

The purpose of all instruction is to help students learn, and the instructor's task is to see that learning occurs. When entering the field of instruction the professional instructor has to consider his own aims in the conduct of his task and one question he will need to ask himself is 'What must a flying instructor seek to accomplish?'. This question relates to education, which in general has three distinct objectives; the use of existing knowledge, the discovery of new facts, and the translation of knowledge and facts into action by the student.

These three purposes are directly applicable to flight instruction. Existing knowledge is used by both instructor and student alike. Research in the areas of aeronautics, engineering, medicine and psychology can uncover new facts about flying. Uncovering new facts and data which relate to flight instruction is generally, but not always, accomplished by governments, flying organisations and societies. Such information must be made available to those who can use it and this is usually accomplished through the medium of publications in the form of manuals, textbooks, and technical memoranda; and by aviation conferences, seminars and special courses.

Once ideas have been discovered and the knowledge disseminated, it becomes the responsibility of those who teach to see that their students interpret this information properly and effectively. The basic task of the flying instructor is to help students assimilate this knowledge so completely that all the flying they do will be guided by these facts. Facts and knowledge are important because they normally influence what people do. Unless prospective pilots learn to apply such information it is largely a wasted exercise. Pilots in their training must learn to do as well as to know.

Such is the nature of the flying instructor's job. This is why he teaches. Armed with knowledge and skill, the professional flying instructor approaches his task with the responsibility of teaching his students to perform in an aircraft in accordance with the proven facts. The facts of flight are mostly known, though not always understood. The ideas and principles of learning are becoming more widely

1

recognised. Flight instruction, therefore, is mainly a communication problem, so teaching and communication are almost synonymous in this respect.

The necessary training for pilot licences is established by Annex I of the International Civil Aviation Organisation (ICAO). This organisation formed in 1947 now has over 160 countries in membership.

The eighth edition of Annex I, which came into effect in 1989 made a number of changes to the training syllabi of various flightcrew licences. One major change was the introduction of a new subject 'Human Performance and Limitations'. This subject was included in order to ensure that pilots had a better understanding of human factors and so became more proficient at making judgements and decisions in aviation related operations. This new subject has now been incorporated in the UK pilot training syllabi. In order to bring the subject content to the attention of instructors an additional manual in the AOPA series has been published. This will give instructors details of the basic knowledge required to teach this subject and develop the necessary judgement skills in their students.

It is important to appreciate that this new knowledge requirement is not just an academic exercise, it is a serious attempt to cover the physiological and pscyhological aspects in relatively simple terms and to help pilots understand how to prepare themselves both physically and mentally to operate in the environment of flight.

Finally, if the flying instructor is to carry out his role in accordance with the legislation as laid down today, he will need to be a teacher, and that means more than just carrying out 'a recitation in the sky'. He must also keep abreast of progress at all times and above all he will need to ensure safety is brought into the cockpit, not only when he is flying with the student, but when the student is solo. Further to this if he is to be completely successful he must ensure safety in the cockpit after his student has acquired his Private Pilot's Licence and is carrying passengers.

Introduction

This book is written primarily for the use of the Flying Instructor undergoing training, it will also be of value during that period when he is obtaining experience in the instructional role. It must however be realised that no books, manuals or notes are a substitute for individual instructional experience, or to the application of common sense to the training task.

Whereas it is a common idea to tell qualified instructors 'what to teach' rather than how to teach, no book basically written for the new instructor will achieve its purpose if it ignores the principles of how to teach and therefore, the information which is contained herein attempts to cover, not only the what to teach but also in the early exercise Effects of Controls, some guidance is given on how to put across the Flight Demonstrations. This will, it is hoped, ensure the new instructor obtains a reasonable grasp of both the objectives and the implementation of some necessary teaching principles. Later on when he has gained experience he will still find the objectives and practical detail contained in this book, of value to him.

What follows will therefore, be used as a guide to flying instruction and even though the sequence recommended is of proven value it is not always necessary to use the precise form of the exercises shown, provided the purpose of the lessons is achieved and the instruction is given in a logical order.

This book is divided into a series of air exercises, each containing a Guide to the Instructor, a Long Briefing, a Pre-Flight Briefing and a Flight Demonstration. The flight exercises have been listed and then divided into separate demonstrations, which, when completed, cover the whole exercise.

This layout and sequence conform to the principles of good instruction, but in the field of flight training an instructor may of necessity modify these sequences in order to make the best use of the student's time and money. For example the weather will often interfere with introducing an exercise or part of an exercise and will thus disrupt the ideal progression. When the weather interferes in this way an instructor will need to use a little imagination in order to ensure his student receives maximum value from the flight, even though this means changing the order or content of a planned lesson after the take-off. However changing the order or content of a flight lesson should be done sparingly during the early training periods or confusion may easily occur. For this reason it is advisable to use the order laid down in the following sequences, until at least, the student has accomplished his First Solo flight.

A general description of the four sections; Instructor's Guide, Long Briefing, Pre-Flight Briefing and Flight Demonstration is shown below, these descriptions should be read carefully in order to understand the purpose behind such division and also how to use each section during your instruction.

The INSTRUCTOR'S GUIDE sections contain:
General advice to the instructor concerning the stage at which the exercise should be introduced. It includes points relevant to the teaching of each part of the air exercise, or which may amplify the content of the exercise. It also lists faults common to many students when learning, and suggestions on how to remedy them.

The LONG BRIEFING sections give details:
Of material which must be covered either in ground school or in a detailed briefing given by the flying instructor in order that the maximum benefit may be obtained from the air exercise. Coverage of these items will also help the student to acquire an adequate understanding of the principles on which aircraft are designed and flown. The briefing must take the student from the academic principles through to the practical application of the factors involved. Reference to all the relevant technical subjects should be included.

The PRE-FLIGHT BRIEFING sections form:
Lesson plans in outline, which should be used as a basis for briefing the student on how the flight demonstration will be presented. This type of briefing is essentially practical in nature and detailed reference to flight principles and other technical knowledge is unnecessary.

The FLIGHT DEMONSTRATION sections show:
Both the order and the content of the air demonstrations which form the flight syllabus. Whereas the first demonstration selected and shown in this section for any air exercise will always be the initial one, the following sequence of demonstrations may be varied according to circumstance, the weather or the student's rate of progress.

GENERAL PRINCIPLES

The long briefing should, if possible, be given before each new exercise is taught. It is a briefing which covers the principles associated with an air exercise and may take up to an hour to give adequately. Provided these briefings are not given too far in advance of the practical demonstration they can be given during periods of bad weather. The long briefing is an essential link between principles and practice, and as such is necessary if the student is to acquire an understanding of aircraft operation. The briefing should conclude on a practical note, one which relates as far as is possible to the teaching in the air.

The short pre-flight briefing should be given just before the flight demonstration so that it can take into account such variables as weather factors, local air traffic procedures and similar information. It should be a brief resumé of the flight with an outline of the points of each demonstration to be covered. Emphasis must be placed on how and when the student will participate.

Most of the air exercises should be broken down into several small demonstrations and so avoid the tendency among new instructors to try to cover all the points applicable to any one exercise in a single flight session, and which may as a result saturate the student to the detriment of his training as a whole. To assist the new instructor, the pre-flight briefing and flight demonstration sections of this manual show a suggested breakdown of the air exercises.

Immediately prior to the commencement of an air exercise the instructor should give a few words of introduction, notwithstanding the fact that a pre-flight briefing has been given. This short introduction will essentially be a review of how the demonstration will be unfolded, and can effectively involve student participation. For example, prior to the air exercise Climbing, he can be asked for the correct power setting and airspeed to be used during the demonstration. This short period of recall given by the instructor will be helpful to a student as many things may have occurred since the pre-flight briefing took place.

No details have been given of the post flight briefings as their content depends entirely upon the events which took place during the flight. Their omission from this manual does not imply a lack of importance. In fact the reverse is true. These briefings are an invaluable means of reviewing the student's progress, and also serve to clear up any misunderstandings or points of difficulty which the student may have.

The instructor's relationship with his students profoundly affects the progress they make. Instructors should do all they can to retain the interest of their students. The intensity of instruction can be increased with an apt student, and the sense of achievement he experiences from learning is a spur to further effort. However, it sometimes occurs through no fault of either the instructor or student, that antipathy arises between them. In such cases a change of instructor will be the only satisfactory course of action.

Student participation in the lesson is all-important. Students should be allowed to handle the controls as soon as possible when learning a new exercise, and to this end the essentials should be taught first and the refinements dealt with after the student has had some practice in the exercise. Students should be guided and encouraged to analyse their own faults and this practice should be continued during their solo flying.

Analysis of the student's performance is a vital function of the instructor's task. The development of ability to analyse faults and why they occur will only come from experience, therefore the new instructor should never hesitate to discuss his own student's performance and faults with more experienced instructors, as this will more easily speed up the new instructor's ability to analyse and correct student faults, and in turn lead to quicker progress by his students.

The instructor's flying must be accurate, and flights should be planned carefully so that the maximum amount of useful work can be done without taxing the student's capabilities. This planning should be such that it gives a logical development of the training. Instructors are responsible for choosing the best conditions for any demonstration, and should never teach when they know the weather or other conditions will spoil the value of the lesson and waste the student's flying time. For example, teaching the early exercises without a reasonable horizon considerably reduces their value.

Placing the aircraft in extreme attitudes should be avoided in the early stages of training unless the student appears to enjoy them, as the student's confidence may be undermined before it has had a chance to develop. Instructors should watch their student's reactions throughout the training, but should avoid giving them the impression that they are under observation.

Basic instruction should be made as simple as possible in presentation and no aid to instruction neglected. Learning is acquired through all the senses, and instructors in their teaching methods should ensure that their students use as many of these senses as possible. For example, it is possible for the student to see a manoeuvre performed, feel the movement of the controls and the response of the aircraft, and listen to the instructor explaining each event as it happens.

In this last item an instructor is faced with certain problems which in the main can be overcome by a little thought. For example, all the upper air exercises with the exception of spinning can be slowed down by the instructor's handling of the controls. By slowing down the control movements slightly, the instructor can more easily co-ordinate his words with the aircraft movements and so produce a smooth, easily understood 'explanation and demonstration'. This is much more desirable than a gabble of words which in many cases are not synchronised with the movements of the aircraft.

There are however, certain exercises which are controlled by a time factor such as 'the circuit', 'the landing phase', 'practice engine failure after take-off', and 'spinning'. In these circumstances the instructor must be careful not to cover too much detail in any one demonstra-tion, and should use several demonstrations to eventually cover all the points to be made. It must be borne in mind that many things which are commonplace and easily understood by instructors, are entirely new to a student and often difficult for him to understand.

A sense of airmanship should be developed throughout the training of a pilot. Individual skill is of little use if the pilot is a danger to himself and others. It is the awareness of the potentially dangerous situation and the decisive action taken to counter it which marks the sound pilot from the bad, the latter being better employed with a less lethal weapon under his control. *The teaching of airmanship is above all a matter of clear exposition and example displayed by the instructor.*

It is extremely important that the instructor should consider the previous paragraphs in relation to his task of teaching a pilot to fly. For example the private pilot is subject to a relatively short course of flying hours, and it is obvious from the beginning that in the time available it will be impossible to produce a pilot of great skill and ability. This can only come with increasing flying experience over many more hours than those provided for by a private pilot's course.

To sum up the problem briefly, it will be possible to teach the student the physical act of taking-off, flying from one place to another and landing again in a safe manner, provided the weather conditions remain suitable for his level of experience. This will also entail a sound knowledge of aircraft operation and handling of basic emergencies. However if the instructor can also instil a high standard of common sense and airmanship into his student he will have given him the greatest asset of all. He will in fact have given him an insurance policy which will stand him in good stead until he reaches a stage where his acquired skill and experience take over. He should then instinctively be able to keep out of trouble and will be endowed with a well-developed awareness of the need for safe flying.

Finally, this safety awareness will not be achieved if the instructor merely teaches his student to fly. Success will only be achieved if the student is taught to *operate an aircraft in safety and with confidence.* Although lack of skill is one factor in aircraft accidents, it is a relatively small one. The largest is a lack of knowledge or application of knowledge in relation to aircraft operation, either due to incorrect training or a lack of self discipline.

When a student receives his private pilot's licence and leaves the training environment an instructor will have little control over this area of self discipline. During training however, the instructor will have considerable influence over the way a student applies his knowledge. This area can be vitally affected by the instructor's training techniques, and it is not sufficient that the student only learns and practises drills and procedures in the cockpit. He must learn to implement them safely and efficiently, with understanding, in his area of aircraft operation.

For example, it is of no value for a pilot to obtain an aircraft's range or endurance figures from a Flight Manual unless he has also been taught that these figures are obtained by the use of 'lean mixture or best power mixture'. Further, in order to achieve such figures he must also have been taught how to use the mixture control during flight, or again, any attempt to use 'short take-off or landing techniques' through arbitrary methods without reference to the performance figures published for the particular aircraft type can only lead to accident inducing situations. These and many other operational aspects of flying must be adequately integrated into flying training techniques if the instructor is to realise his objective. This is basically to ensure that the training he gives will enable his student to operate his aircraft in a safe and efficient manner, and one which ensures his student can and will conduct himself in a way which does not hazard himself, other airspace users, the public at large and later on his passengers.

THE PLANNING OF FLIGHT LESSONS

The following points are written to assist the instructor in his preparation of flight lessons. Good lesson planning will always benefit the instructor's work and the student's performance.

The first step is to give careful consideration to the objective of the exercise(s) being taught. A lesson cannot be given efficiently if the instructor is vague about its end aim.

Next decide how long you will have and how far you will be able to go towards the accomplishment of the objective, upon deciding this you will have the particular aim of the lesson plan, which in turn will enable you to produce the structure of the intended briefing.

The content normally starts with a statement of the AIM followed by an explanation of exactly what air exercises are to be taught by the instructor and practised by the student during the flight. The body of the briefing should include how the flight will be conducted with regard as to who is to fly the aircraft and what Airmanship, Weather and Flight Safety aspects currently apply. The nature of the lesson will govern the order in which the constituent parts are to be taught.

All flights should be carefully planned so that the optimum amount of useful work can be done without taxing the student's capabilities. The planning should be such that it gives a logical development of the training and takes into account the priority of items to be taught. In sorting out these priorities, you should keep in mind that there are three classes of knowledge or skill:

1. Those items of knowledge or that level of skill which a pilot *must* know or achieve in order to operate an aircraft with safety.
2. Those items of knowledge or that level of skill which a pilot *should* know or achieve in order to reach a prescribed acceptable standard.
3. Those items of knowledge or that level of skill which would be *nice* to know or achieve.

The last mentioned class may only be achieved if sufficient training time permits but such time is rarely available during a private pilot's course. With this in mind an instructor should concentrate on items 1 and 2 and in this way ensure that he is planning to utilise the time he has available to the greatest advantage.

In relation to any training flight there will usually be two types of instructional presentation. One such presentation will be in the form of a detailed explanation and demonstration of an air exercise or part of an air exercise and the other type will be in the form of a commentary. For example, between specific exercises or parts of air exercises there will be opportunities to give a commentary on other aspects of the flight. During the first training flights this commentary would concern such items as; the direction to be taken to reach the holding point prior to take-off, the procedures to be carried out before take-off, and the method of leaving the circuit area. Other commentary points at this stage could include RTF procedures, orientation with regard to landmarks and any local airspace restrictions. These commentaries are equally as valuable as the main air lessons and should always be included. They form an integral part of your instruction technique and prepare the student for much of what is to follow during later exercises. Wherever possible they should be included in the lesson plan and given during briefings.

Having planned your lesson, follow it in the air and do not digress unless necessary for the benefit of the student. Recall should be used both in prior discussion of and the demonstration of any part of the flight exercise sequence. Instruction consists of both demonstration and explanation by the instructor, followed by practice and perform-ance evaluation by the student. The instructor must test for understanding and analyse the student's performance throughout the flight.

Remember to de-brief adequately after the flight, sometimes this may only take a few minutes when the performance of the student has been good, on the other hand it may take a lot longer to accomplish if the student has not learned to perform the manoeuvres or procedures correctly. The de-briefing should also include an indication of the intended air exercises to be covered during the next flight. In addition to giving a more positive approach to his training it will enable the student to prepare for his next flight lesson.

Before moving on to the next section, which concerns the translation of Flight Lesson Planning into actual Flight Instruction, it must be stressed that there are many acceptable alternatives when putting the Air Exercise Demonstrations into effect. The sequence in which the contents are taught, and the methods of expression used by different instructors may vary, and this will in no way detract from the value of the instruction. Standardisation of the instructor's task has merit within an acceptable limit, provided this does not result in dull, unimaginative teaching.

However, all good instructors will observe the basic tenet of sound teaching, which is the logical progression from the 'known to the unknown' and each demonstration must be in logical sequence. In general terms the real decision in whether or not the correct material and techniques are being used, can be revealed by asking the following simple questions:

● Is it true?
● Is it being put across in a logical sequence which makes sense to the student?
● Does it have both simplicity and impact?
● Has the student understood it?
● Has the rate of learning of the particular student been utilised efficiently?

If the answer to these questions is 'Yes' then good instruction has been given.

The sections headed 'Flight Demonstration' contain a layout of those demonstrations to be included under the particular exercise heading. The demonstration listed first under the exericse heading should always be given as the initial one, but the sequence in which the subsequent demonstrations for the exercise are dealt with may be varied according to the circumstances. These may be the weather conditions, the student's rate and stage of progress, or operational factors.

The layout of individual demonstrations within the appropriate air exercises indicates broadly how much to give at any one time, though for the reasons already mentioned, this amount may be varied. For example, with one student whose absorption rate is low, it would be inadvisable to give all of one demonstration, whereas an apt student may be given two demonstrations of any one exercise during the particular flight.

PRE-FLIGHT BRIEFINGS

The correct sequence of Flight Instruction is as follows:
● *Long briefing*
● *Pre-flight briefing*
● *Flight demonstration*
● *Post-flight discussion*

Your LESSON PLAN should contain the following headings or their descriptive equivalent.

- *Aim*   A positive statement of the aim of the flight.
- *What*   What you intend to explain and demonstrate.
- *How*   This section is the body of the briefing and outlines the sequence of the demonstration. It should include information on when the student will participate and how much practice time he will have available.
- *Airmanship*   The order in which Airmanship appears in this list of headings and the amount given, together with the degree of emphasis placed upon it, will vary dependent upon the particular exercise and the student's stage of training.

There is, for example, little to be gained by introducing Airmanship in depth at the beginning of the Effects of Controls, as the student will not be able to grasp the implications of Airmanship until he knows what he will be doing in the air. Whereas the introduction of Stalling will require Airmanship in the form of Safety Checks to be thoroughly covered at the beginning of the 'HOW' section.

Make the briefing practical. Refer to the weather and any effect this may have on the exercise. Tell him which aircraft will be used and the intended duration of the flight, together with any relevant ATC details such as the runway in use etc.

Limit the briefing time to 15–20 minutes, and avoid writing in great detail. The board should be used to show the basic outline of the air lesson, including relevant items such as airspeeds, power settings etc. From this basic outline expand the briefing verbally, implementing explanations with an aircraft model as necessary. Coloured chalk or marker pens should be used to bring important details into relief. Plan the use of the board to avoid erasing parts of the briefing, so that the entire briefing details are on the board at the finish. Avoid concentrating your attention on the board, remember it is the student who requires your attention.

When speaking, face the student as much as possible, and when using an aircraft model, hold it in such a way that references to direction make sense to the student. For example, if reference is made to the model moving left, it must move left as the student sees it.

Principles of Flight should be avoided where possible, and do not become involved with subjects not relevant to the exercise upon which the student is being briefed.

Remember above all that this period of ground instruction is essentially a practical one and directly related to the air exercise(s) about to be taught and practised.

FLIGHT INSTRUCTION POINTERS

> *FLIGHT INSTRUCTIONS consists of EXPLANATION and DEMONSTRATION by the INSTRUCTOR followed by PRACTICE and EVALUATION by the STUDENT.*

The general principles of Teaching and Learning as applicable to Flight Instruction are covered in the book 'Flight Training – Teaching and Learning'. However, the following pointers which have been obtained from experienced instructors will be of extremely good value to the embryo flying instructor.

IN-FLIGHT DEMONSTRATIONS

During flight training the student should understand not only why he is learning a particular exercise, but how that exercise fits into the overall training syllabus.

Do make sure your instructions are clear and explicit, and avoid phrases such as 'you have a go', 'its all yours', 'now its your turn'. A student cannot be expected to make a success of any task unless he knows exactly what he is to do.

Before fault analysis begins, give the student credit for those items which he has performed correctly. Any errors which he has made can then be pointed out followed by a positive statement on how such errors can be corrected or avoided during future practice.

Do not expect perfection after one attempt. Sort out the major errors one at a time and work down to the smaller ones in turn. Give the student an opportunity to analyse his errors and correct them, before you step in with guidance. In making your assessment of his ability, determine first, whether he has made any progress or whether he is consistently making the same mistake.

Good instruction technique demands that you break your demonstrations down into several parts whenever applicable. This allows the student to participate more quickly and avoids long instruction demonstrations in which the student feels he is taking no part.

Do not try to standardise the amount of instruction given on any one flight. The amount of instruction which a student can absorb on any flight will vary dependent upon the particular exercise, the stage of training, the weather conditions at the time, and the receptiveness of the particular student.

Preface the demonstration with a short introduction. This is not a briefing, and ideally should consist of no more than a few sentences to direct the student's thinking to the exercise planned. During the demonstration co-ordinate your words and actions, so that you speak as you do, and speak as it happens.

In the early stages back up your words with hand movements i.e., where applicable, physically point out the items to be observed in order to direct his eyes to them. Remember that communication in the cockpit is seldom as good as in the classroom. When you hand over control make sure you give the student a specific task in a way which will test his understanding, rather than just asking him to repeat your control movements.

STUDENT PRACTICE

Allow the student to fly the aircraft as frequently as possible.

Do not 'ride' the controls. Rather sit back and monitor and analyse his performance.

Do not nag. Aim to rectify major faults first and minor faults afterwards.

Take over control yourself before giving detailed advice in respect of his errors.

Minor faults are best handled by further student practice but when major faults occur, it is better to re-demonstrate rather than allow him to blunder along.

If errors are persistent, re-think and if possible use a different demonstration technique based upon the answers to the following questions:

Did you cover too much in one go?
Did you ask him to observe too many things at the same time?
Is he hearing you clearly?
Is he suffering from early nausea or discomfort?
Is he sufficiently relaxed?
Does he really understand you?

At the end of your demonstrations tie the component parts together and ensure the aim has been achieved.

DEBRIEFING

A student will be unable to respond efficiently to his instruction unless the instructor communicates after the air lesson as well as before and during the flight. Post flight discussion is a 'must' and the student needs to be told where his performance warrants improvement. Just writing comments on his record sheet will be inadequate.

Make the student give a constructive analysis of his performance at the end of the flight, and get him to analyse faults in the following order:

Symptoms – were they recognised?
Cause   – is this understood?
Result   – what would this have led to?
Correction – what technique should be used?
Prevention – for future practice.

GENERAL POINTERS

Do avoid using broad phrases which can be misleading. An example of this would be the bald statement 'during a turn you will always need to hold off bank with the ailerons'. This is an incorrect statement, as the need to hold off bank will be determined by the direction of propellor rotation (torque and slip-stream effect) in relation to the direction of turn, the aircraft speed and the power being used. The interaction of these effects will sometimes result in the need to 'hold off' bank and sometimes to 'hold on' bank. Confusion will however be avoided if the instructor simply states 'maintain the bank angle by the use of ailerons'.

If an aircraft were always flown perfectly during in-flight demonstrations the instructor would lose a valuable and very necessary opportunity to demonstrate how errors should be corrected. Therefore there will be times when errors become a fundamental part of a demonstration. In the event that two or more errors occur at the same time, the instructor must select his words carefully when explaining how to correct for these errors, or misunderstandings can easily occur. For example, a situation could occur during a demonstration of the landing approach phase where the aircraft is too high on the approach path and the airspeed is also too high. In this situation any attempt to cover both control corrections in one sentence could easily lead to the following remark:

'When you are too high, reduce the power and raise the nose to adjust the airspeed'.

The implications of such a remark are fairly obvious and could lead to the development of a dangerous situation when the student is flying solo. The correct method of handling this type of situation is to use two separate sentences, each one being aimed at the particular correction being made.

Remember, we all have the ability to talk a lot and say little, but a good instructor trains himself to talk little, yet say a lot. However, this does not mean that the use of cryptic comments is automatically good instruction. In addition, confusing and misleading terminology must be scrupulously avoided. Some of the classic but typically bad examples, together with the correct phrases are as follows:

INCORRECT	CORRECT
Roll on the ailerons	Use the ailerons to ....
Use upwind aileron	Move the control column (wheel) to the . . . right/left.
Use right aileron	Move the control column (wheel) to the right.
Apply back elevator	Apply back pressure to the control column.
Push the nose forward	Lower the nose.
Let the aircraft settle	Allow the airspeed to settle.
The horizon goes up	The nose goes down.
If you are overshooting you must overshoot	If you are too high, open the throttle and go round again.

Finally, the following list of Do's and Don'ts, although not exhaustive, will cover in a simple fashion many of the important items to be remembered during the giving of instruction.

DO	DON'T
Remember, that patience is the most important single quality that an instructor can have.	Use twelve words where six will do.
	Use words he may not understand.
Combine sequences when applicable, from various main exercises to form a complete flight lesson.	Ask him to do something he has not been shown and then criticise his efforts.
Make sure the student is comfortable and that he can hear you.	Forget you are looking for progress not perfection.
Make sure of your facts.	Expect too much from him.
Teach in simple terms.	Forget your own airmanship.
Give clear demonstrations.	Ride the controls.
Teach from the 'known to the unknown'.	Fly the aircraft yourself any more than is necessary.
Match your manner to his temperament.	Indulge in negative instruction.

DO	DON'T
Be sympathetic and understand his difficulties. Remember the problems you had when you were a student.	Talk at the student – talk with him, remember you are there to teach not just to tell.
Compliment the student when he gives a good performance.	Go too far from the airfield on his early flights, you may need to get back in a hurry if he feels unwell.
Clearly analyse student errors and give him positive advice on how to correct them.	Use sarcasm or ridicule in an attempt to assist his progress.
Encourage the student to think aloud.	Repeat demonstrations unless it is necessary to improve his understanding.
Set a good example, and if you do something you do not want him to repeat because of his limited experience, make sure he clearly knows why he should not do it.	Use repetitive explanations more than is necessary.
	Teach the student what has already been taught, or you will be using twelve words where six will do.

★ DO remember, it is the slow student who is in most need of ★ your teaching skills.

Aircraft Familiarisation

Instructor's Guide

The information and practices contained in this exercise will need to be spread over several training periods. The total content should however have been learned by the student before he can be considered competent to undertake his first solo flight.

The student should be taught those items which are normally used in flying the aircraft and also be given an explanation of constructional and technical details, such as the flying controls, and the fuel, oil, ignition and ancillary systems. Drills, checks and emergency procedures should be included at suitable stages during both the ground and flying periods of this exercise.

EXPLANATION OF THE AIRCRAFT

An explanation of such items as the main controls, trimming tabs, flaps, and engine controls should be given, but reference to the principles of flight, engines and instruments should be limited at this stage. A general survey of the aircraft should be covered as shown in the Flight/Owner's Manual.

EXPLANATION OF THE COCKPIT LAYOUT

A useful way of explaining the cockpit layout is to conform to the checklist. The value of systematic checks should be emphasised. When dealing with the engine and flight instruments, colour indications, aircraft placards and operating figures should be covered.

AIRCRAFT AND ENGINE SYSTEMS

Explain the function and operation of the aircraft systems and ensure that before 'First Solo' the student has sufficient practical knowledge to understand and operate the following systems and equipment (as applicable to the aircraft type):

Flying controls (including Flaps).
Engine controls.

Systems: Fuel.   Carburettor Heat.
                 Oil.   Instruments:
                 Ignition.   Pressure.
                 Mixture.   Vacuum.
                 Cabin Heating.   Electrical (inc. Radio).
                 Cabin Ventilation. Braking.
       Fire Extinguisher.
       First Aid Kit.
       Control Locks and Towbars.
       Other Systems as applicable to Type.

CHECK LISTS, DRILLS AND CONTROLS

Drills and checks must become instinctive, and the student must be sufficiently familiar with the cockpit layout to be able to quickly locate all controls and switches. The student should be encouraged to practise drills and checks with the aid of a check list whilst seated in the aircraft on the ground. Take the opportunity at this stage of explaining why drills and checks are an important part of his learning task. Ensure the student appreciates why check lists are of value to pilots, especially those who fly at infrequent intervals, a situation commonly forced upon private pilots by financial necessity.

It should also be remembered that at present the legislation concerning the privileges of private pilots allows them to operate any type of single-engined aeroplane the total weight of which does not exceed 5700 kg. This privilege of flying many different types of aeroplane without having to undergo dual conversion training highlights the importance of understanding and using check lists as a normal part of flying operations.

Finally, ensure the check list used is one designed for the specific type and model of aeroplane, as there can be nothing more confusing than using a check list which does not completely identify itself with the model of aeroplane being used and the specific services and equipment with which it is fitted.

DIFFERENCES IN THE INSTRUCTOR/STUDENT SEATING

When referring to the position of outside features relative to the cockpit structure or engine cowling, it is fairly easy for an instructor to appreciate that people of different heights have different 'eye levels'. What is not so easy to appreciate is that people of the same height can also have different eye levels due to differences in their respective leg or upper torso lengths. Instructors should therefore take care to check on this point before referring their students to the vertical position of outside references.

With side-by-side cockpit seating it must further be borne in mind that each of the two occupants will obtain a different view of the aircraft's attitude in relation to outside reference features.

For example when either person lines up the centre of the engine cowling with a reference feature ahead there will exist an angular difference between their lines of sight. This difference will also occur when lining up with a runway during an approach to land. The instructor must remember to make an allowance for this during his own demonstrations and also when the student is flying the aircraft.

A similar situation will exist whenever the aircraft is turning, in that the horizon line will appear in a different position relative to the engine cowling when turning to the left to that experienced when turning to the right.

Apart from the external differences the instructor, who will be sitting in the right hand seat, will find a relatively larger parallax error when using the flight instruments, and he will therefore have to learn to take this into account during his flying.

EMERGENCY DRILLS

In the early days of flight it could be said that every time an aircraft left the ground a state of emergency existed – today emergencies are the exception rather than the rule. Because of this the teaching of handling specific emergency situations can easily become neglected or given insufficient attention during training. Make it quite clear that emergency drills exist in case an emergency should arise, and not because it is always expected. It is also important to stress the prevention aspect by pointing out that most emergencies occur due to the pilot's mismanagement of the aircraft or its systems. For example, most engine failures today occur because of fuel mis-management, not because of mechanical failure. Emphasise that when an emergency occurs seconds will count, and that the position and use of equipment, and the correct drills must be known so thoroughly that carrying them out will be instinctive.

The following emergency drills must be learned and practised:

Action in event of Fire in the Air and on the Ground:
                    Engine Fire.
                    Cabin Fire.
                    Electrical Fire.
Systems Failure   (as applicable to type).
Escape Drills   Location and use of Emergency Equipment and
                    Exits.

The details of these actions and drills cannot be covered in this book due to differences of procedures, systems and equipment between different training aircraft. It is nevertheless vital to cover these items and the Flight/Owner's Manual must be consulted in this respect. All students should have a copy of the Flight/Owner's Manual for type, but an initial briefing by the instructor should be given in order to cover fully any questions which may arise.

During this training it is important to foster the student's keenness, as the main effort in learning these drills must come from him. The instructor must provide the stimulus and ensure that simulated minor emergencies are introduced early in the student's training. All the emergencies listed above must have been practised prior to 'First Solo'.

The procedure in the event of a failure of one or more of the aircraft systems will be guided by the information contained in the Flight/Owner's Manual for the specific type. However, this informa-tion is rarely finite and additional information compatible with the procedures used at the particular School or Club will need to be brought to the attention of the student.

Finally, an instructor must appreciate that accidents do not just happen, *they begin to happen*, and occurrences which are of minor importance to an experienced pilot could prove critical when the aircraft is being flown by a student and as a result lead to the development of an emergency situation.

NOTE:

In relation to aircraft Flight/Owner's Manuals, there are a large number of American manufactured training aircraft used in the U.K. Therefore, some of the technical terminology used in this

Training Manual reflects the terms used in the American aircraft manuals. This is done to avoid any confusion or misinterpretation while using such Flight/Owner's Manuals.

Aircraft Familiarisation

Long Briefing

OBJECTIVES

To acquaint the student with the aircraft, its controls, systems and equipment. It is not intended at this stage to do any more than explain in a brief manner how each control and system operates. Nevertheless it will be necessary to go into sufficient detail to ensure that the student understands the basic purpose and operation of the relevant items.

INTRODUCTION

The following briefing covers the aircraft structure and power plant, together with the various controls and systems.

EXPLANATION OF THE AIRCRAFT

The aircraft structure excluding the equipment and systems is called the airframe and consists of sufficiently strong members such as frames, bulkheads and longerons covered by sheets of aluminium. The engine is installed on a mounting which is attached to the main aircraft structure. For safety reasons a firewall is arranged between the engine and the cabin.

A cowling is fitted around the engine as an extension of the fuselage and maintains the smooth streamlined shape of the structure. The propeller is normally fitted with a tapered spinner to reduce turbulence at the propeller root.

An air intake is usually situated at the front of the cowling through which air passes into the engine and carburettor system. This air intake has a recessed filter to prevent dust particles being ingested into the power plant. Other openings in the front and/or side of the engine cowling are arranged to supply air for cooling the cylinders, alternator and radio, also to supply air for cabin ventilation. Further openings are fitted to provide air into the cabin and carburettor heating systems.

The wing structure, being the main lifting surface of the aircraft is very strong but light in weight. The surface is aluminium sheet and this is supported by internal members comprising of strong spars, ribs

Fig. 1-1

and stringers. It is usual to arrange a space within the wings to locate the fuel tanks. Ailerons and flaps are hinged along the trailing edge of the wing, the flaps being fitted to the inboard section, and the ailerons which are used in flight to control the aircraft's lateral level are fitted along the outboard wing section.

Fig. 1-2

The fuselage tail section consists of both fixed and moveable surfaces. The horizontal stabilizer has the elevators hinged to its trailing edge and the vertical stabilizer (fin) is fitted with a hinged vertical control surface known as the rudder. Some aircraft which need more powerful elevators at low airspeeds are fitted with an all-moving horizontal stabilator. A small auxiliary aerofoil known as a trimming control is normally fitted at the trailing edge of the elevators or the all-moving stabilator.

Fig. 1-3

Provision must be made for attaching wheels to the aircraft for taxying, take-off and landing. Most modern aircraft use what is termed the tricycle arrangement. This consists of two mainwheels and a nosewheel. The nosewheel is usually connected to the rudder pedals which are situated near the floor in the cockpit and movement of these pedals moves the nosewheel to obtain directional control whilst the aircraft is on the ground.

MAINWHEEL   NOSEWHEEL

Fig. 1-4

The shocks imposed on the mainwheels during landing and take-off are absorbed by using a spring steel strut or an oleo strut. Nosewheels use a basic oleo strut as this is the most practical method when directional movement is also required. A braking system is also incorporated in the landing gear assembly for additional control over the aircraft's speed when taxying or landing.

EXPLANATION OF THE COCKPIT LAYOUT

The cockpit of the aircraft contains all the controls and instruments which are used by the pilot to operate the aircraft. The main instrument panel is basically divided into sections containing the:

Flight Instruments.	Radio Equipment.
Engine Instruments.	Ignition and other Switches.
Ancillary Controls.	Engine Controls.

Fig. 1-5

The cockpit layout is individual to different types of aircraft and also varies between aircraft of the same type. The student must obtain a general understanding of all cockpit placards and the coloured markings on the instruments. He must also be able to quickly identify the controls, switches and instruments which are used during flight.

AIRCRAFT SYSTEMS

In order for the student to handle the aircraft safely on the ground and in the air he will need to have at least a basic and practical understanding of the following equipment:

Flying Controls (including Flaps).
Engine Controls.

Systems:	Fuel.	Carburettor Heat.
	Oil.	Instruments:
	Ignition.	Pressure.
	Mixture.	Vacuum.
	Cabin Heating.	Electrical (inc. Radio).
	Cabin Ventilation.	Braking.

Fire Extinguisher.
First Aid Kit.
Control Locks and Towbars.
Other Systems as applicable to Type.

The depth of knowledge which is necessary for you to be able to take decisions relating to the use of these systems and equipment will of necessity vary with the stage of training reached. You will however, need to have a sufficient understanding of the practical operation and use of the above listed items prior to 'First Solo'.

FLYING CONTROLS (INCLUDING FLAPS)

The control of the aircraft's attitude in flight is accomplished by the use of three primary control systems, the elevators, ailerons and rudder. A secondary control system, in the form of a trimming device, is usually fitted to the elevators and sometimes to the rudder and ailerons. Flaps are an auxiliary control system and are normally fitted to modern light aircraft.

ELEVATOR CONTROL SYSTEM

The elevators are used during flight to adjust the nose attitude in pitch. Two types of control surface can be used for this purpose, conventional elevators, or a moveable stabilator. The former consist of hinged aerofoils fitted at the rear of a fixed horizontal stabilizer. These elevators are operated by a forward or backward movement of the pilot's control column which transmits movement through a control stem, cables and pulleys, to the elevators. The latter type of control surface consists of a single horizontal stabilator which moves in one piece when operated by the control column.

Fig. 1-6   *Fig. 1-7*

AILERON CONTROL SYSTEM

The control column fitted to aircraft may be of two types, a single vertical column which can be moved to the left or right to alter the position of the ailerons, or a horizontal column which protrudes out of the instrument panel and which is fitted with a control wheel which can be rotated left or right to alter the position of the ailerons. Whichever type of control column is fitted, the left or right movement

ELEVATOR CONTROL SYSTEM

Fig. 1-8

controls the deflection of the aileron surfaces which are fitted to the trailing edges of the outboard wing sections. A typical control wheel installation is shown at fig. 1-9.

Rotating the wheel on the control column to the left causes the left aileron to rise and the right aileron to lower. This action makes the left wing drop and the right wing rise and induces the aircraft to bank to the left. The control wheel works in this manner regardless of the fore or aft position of the control column.

AILERON CONTROL SYSTEM

Fig. 1-9

RUDDER CONTROL SYSTEM
Fig. 1-10 illustrates a typical rudder system. The rudder pedals are situated forward on the cockpit floor and depressing (moving forward) the left pedal moves the rudder to the left and causes the aircraft to yaw to the left. A similar arrangement of cables and pulleys as fitted to the elevator and aileron systems is used.

On many aircraft the rudder pedals are hinged so that they can be tilted forward by toe pressure applied to the top of the pedal and this action operates the wheel brakes. (The braking system is covered later in this section.) One method of obtaining directional control on the ground is to connect the rudder system through to the nosewheel so that forward pressure on the left rudder pedal causes the

RUDDER CONTROL SYSTEM

Fig. 1-10

nosewheel to turn left and vice versa, this action gives much easier directional control during taxying, and in conjunction with appropriate brake co-ordination facilitates manoeuvring in confined spaces on the ground.

ELEVATOR TRIM CONTROL SYSTEM

All small aircraft are fitted with a trimming control system which is linked to the elevators or stabilator. Some aircraft also have trimming systems fitted to the rudder and sometimes the ailerons as well. The purpose of these trimming controls is to relieve control pressures and so assist the pilot. A conventional elevator trim tab system is illustrated at fig. 1-11 below.

A trim tab control wheel or lever is fitted in the cockpit and can be adjusted by the pilot. The wheel or lever is connected by cables to the elevator tab fitted to one or both elevators. Fitting a tab to one elevator is usually sufficient for most light aircraft.

Operation of the trim tab control changes the position of the trim

ELEVATOR TRIM CONTROL SYSTEM

WING FLAP SYSTEM

Fig. 1-11

Fig. 1-12

tab on the elevator and the correct use of this control during flight is to relieve any residual fore and aft control pressures on the control column which may exist after the pilot has used the elevators to make a change to the aircraft's attitude in pitch. A pointer device adjacent to the trim tab control is used to indicate the trim tab position, and this can be used by the pilot to pre-set the trimmer whilst on the ground and so avoid any adverse control forces during the take-off.

WING FLAP SYSTEM

Wing flaps when fitted, basically serve the dual purpose of producing extra drag so that the pilot can use a steeper approach path when coming in to land, and at the same time, because they provide added lift, they permit a slower approach speed to be used.

Flaps are operated either manually, electrically, or by the use of hydraulic or air pressure systems. There are several types of flaps which can be used on light aircraft, and normally they are fitted at the trailing edge of the inboard wing section.

A wing flap switch or lever is fitted in the cockpit together with an indicator to show how many degrees of flap have been selected. Dependent upon the type of system, flaps can be selected in any amount of degrees or by fixed increments such as 10 or 20 degrees etc. Before flight the flaps, as well as the other control systems, should be selected and tested for correct operation.

THROTTLE CONTROL SYSTEM

The engine power is regulated by a throttle valve inside the carburettor induction tube. This is popularly called the throttle butterfly. The position of this valve determines the rate and amount of air taken into the carburettor. The pressure drop in the vicinity of the throttle valve induces fuel from a storage chamber in the carburettor to flow into the induction tube and mix with the air.

Control of the throttle valve is by means of a linkage system from the carburettor to a throttle lever or knob inside the cockpit. Forward movement of this throttle control increases the amount of air entering the induction tube and causes an increase in engine power, a backward movement of the throttle control reduces the engine power.

When the throttle is opened suddenly the increased rate of airflow is so rapid that there is a slight time lag before the depression thus created at the throttle valve becomes sufficient to provide the correct mixture ratio. To avoid this situation and provide smooth engine acceleration, an accelerator pump is fitted integrally with the carburettor. This usually comprises a small cylinder and piston connected with the throttle system which delivers added fuel to the engine, and compensates for the deficiency caused by the lag.

CARBURETTOR SYSTEM

THROTTLE

BUTTERFLY
VALVE

ACCELERATOR
PUMP

Fig. 1-13

In order for the pilot to set a specific power setting and also to check the amount of power being produced a tachometer is fitted on the instrument panel. This instrument is calibrated in engine revolutions per minute (RPM) and the divisions between the calibration marks usually equal 100 RPM.

This instrument is also colour coded and shows a green arc for the normal power setting range with a red radial line to indicate the maximum RPM permitted. Some engines may have other restrictions such as a particular RPM range which should be avoided except for a permitted period of time, in which case a yellow arc will be used to enable pilots to clearly see this range. Other engines may be restricted to a 'Maximum Except Take-off Power' (METO). In effect this means that the engine may only be operated at a specified high power setting for a maximum period of five minutes. This limitation will vary with height and the RPM limitation becomes higher with increase in altitude. When this limitation is imposed it will normally be indicated by placarding the tachometer as well as being shown in the Flight/Owner's Manual.

Finally all throttle systems are equipped with a friction device which can be loosened by the pilot whenever he wishes to change power, and tightened again to avoid the throttle changing its selected position as a result of any vibrations experienced during flight.

THE FUEL SYSTEM

The function of the fuel system is to supply fuel to the engine at a sufficient rate of flow to satisfy all power demands by the engine from the idling setting through to the maximum power condition.

Basically it consists of one or more fuel tanks which hold the fuel and from which it is fed through pipes or hoses to the carburettor. Two types of fuel system are in common use in light aircraft, the 'Gravity Feed' system and the 'Fuel Pump' system.

The gravity feed system is normally used in high wing aircraft when the tanks are fitted in the wings and provide a head of fuel above the level of the engine. In low wing aircraft, the tanks which are normally fitted in the wings are below the level of the engine and a fuel pump must be used to provide fuel to the carburettor.

The gravity feed method shown in fig. 1-14 below is arranged so that it is above the vertical level of the carburettor, the resultant head of fuel pressure allows fuel to flow by gravity at a sufficient rate to satisfy all the needs of the engine. The fuel flows through a selector valve which is installed in the cockpit and thence to the carburettor. ON/OFF selection valves are a necessary item of an aircraft fuel system because in the rare event of an engine fire, the pilot will be

Fig. 1-14

able to isolate fuel flow from the source of the fire and therefore minimise danger.

Fuel systems may incorporate connected tanks from which the fuel flows to the engine through a common fuel selector cock, in this case both tanks are selected through a single ON/OFF selector cock, fig. 1-14 shows various selector cock methods. A second type of fuel selection system consists of two separate tanks with the facility to select both of them at the same time. If this facility is incorporated the tank selection cock will be marked LEFT, RIGHT, BOTH and OFF, as shown in fig. 1-14 (b). When non-connected tanks are used without the above type facility, the selector cock will only indicate individual tank selection and will be marked LEFT, RIGHT and OFF, as shown in fig. 1-14 (c).

One final point in relation to tank selection procedures, if a tank is mis-selected to the OFF position during flight the engine will continue to run until the supply in the fuel line is used up. The time taken for this fuel to be used will vary, and will be dependent upon the length of the line and the power being used. The important operational point being to ensure that the tank selection procedure has been carried out well before taking off or approaching to land. For this reason the reselecting of a fuel tank immediately prior to take-off or just before landing, may result in the engine stopping at a critical point in the flight.

Fuel gauges are fitted in the cockpit to enable the pilot to ascertain the amount of fuel contained in the tanks before and during flight. Whenever possible it is good practice to visually check the fuel contents prior to flight. When the fuel reaches the carburettor it is mixed with air and the resultant mixture is ducted into the engine cylinders where it is burned to provide the pressure needed to operate the engine. With the gravity feed system it is usual to provide a priming pump which is manually operated to supply the induction line with an initial mixture for engine starting.

In low wing aircraft where the tanks are fitted in the wings a 'Fuel Pump' system is used. This second type of fuel system utilises a fuel pump to transfer the fuel into the engine.

The fuel pump is arranged to operate integrally with the engine and is known as a mechanical fuel pump. However, unlike a gravity fuel system, a fuel pump can suffer mechanical failure, and because of this possibility, all systems which utilise a mechanical pump are also fitted with an auxiliary pump. These auxiliary pumps are normally electrically operated and their operation is controlled by a switch in the cockpit. Should a mechanical pump fail at altitude there will be sufficient time to bring the auxiliary pump into operation, but should the mechanical pump fail when the aircraft is at a low height, such as when taking off or approaching to land, there could be insufficient

FUEL PUMP SYSTEM

Fig. 1-15   Fig. 1-16

time to switch on the auxiliary pump, prime the system and get the engine working again, and because of this the auxiliary pump should always be switched to the ON position before taking off or approaching to land. Apart from the normal fuel contents gauges, pump type fuel systems also have fuel pressure gauges to enable the pilot to readily check if the fuel flow is being maintained correctly.

In order to ensure the pump capacity can supply the maximum flow demand required by the engine there is a need to arrange for a by-pass system to operate whenever the engine is using fuel at a lesser rate than is being supplied by the pump. In effect this is a simple piece of plumbing which diverts the excess fuel back to the supply side of the pump.

Drain plugs are arranged at suitable points in the system for servicing purposes and filters and strainers are fitted integrally to trap any foreign particles and water, both of which can cause irregular engine operation or in severe cases a complete engine stoppage. The straining check for water in the fuel system is particularly important when atmospheric conditions are conducive to the formation of condensation and when the aircraft has been left standing for a period with partially empty tanks. Fuel tanks must have a venting system to permit air to enter and occupy the space left as the fuel empties. If vents were not fitted a reduction of air pressure would occur in the tanks and the fuel flow would slow down and eventually stop. Fuel vents normally project out of the wing or fuselage and before every flight these should be carefully inspected to ensure they are clear and undamaged. The operation of fuel strainers to inspect for water is another important check to be made before flight.

Due to the variations between different fuel systems the Flight/Owners Manual must be studied carefully in order to learn how to operate the fuel system for each type of aircraft. Statistics reveal that a high percentage of 'in-flight' engine failures occur due to:

Mismanagement of fuel systems.

Inadequate pre-flight preparation.

Improper operation of the power plant controls.

The message which evolves from such causes of engine failure is very clear, it is that thorough pre-flight fuel system inspection, complete familiarity with the fuel system operation, and continuous 'in-flight' attention to fuel quantity, supply and consumption are all essential to safe aircraft operation.

Fig. 1-17

It is particularly important to appreciate that an aero engine is designed to use a specific grade of fuel. For many years the fuel specified for use in small aero engines was 80/87 grade, this fuel was then superseded by AVGAS 100L. However the higher lead content of AVGAS 100L was not considered to be compatible with the operation of the small piston engines used in light aircraft and has now been phased out and replaced by AVGAS 100LL (Low Lead). Aviation gasoline has a dye incorporated during manufacture as an aid to identification and AVGAS 100LL is coloured pale blue. Regulations require that the fuel grade specified for an engine is placarded adjacent to or upon the fuel filler cap, and it is the responsibility of the pilot to ensure the correct grade of fuel is used.

THE OIL SYSTEM

Oil is usually stored in a sump container at the bottom of the crankcase. The method of filling the sump is through a pipe which is accessible via a small door in the engine cowling. The oil cap at the top of the pipe is marked with the grade of oil to be used and normally incorporates a dipstick attached to the cap in order to check the oil and its level in the sump.

The main purpose of engine oil is to lubricate the moving parts of the engine and to cool the engine by reducing friction between moving parts and by radiating away heat that is collected by the oil as it circulates through the engine. If a flight is started with insufficient oil in the sump, serious consequences could occur.

TYPICAL OIL SYSTEM

Fig. 1-18

An engine-driven oil pump feeds oil under pressure to the engine bearings and other moving parts after which it drains back to the sump for re-circulation. Oil filters or screens are used within the system to collect any foreign or minute metal particles. The oil pump is designed to ensure an adequate flow of oil at all times and it can deliver more oil than is sometimes necessary, so an oil pressure relief valve is incorporated which allows some of the oil to be by-passed back to the sump whenever the flow exceeds the demand. Without such a valve, excessive pressures could build up within the system.

Two gauges in the cockpit inform the pilot of the oil pressure and temperature. These indicators are normally colour coded for easy reference with green arcs and red lines. The oil pressure gauge must be checked immediately after starting the engine, and if oil pressure is not indicating within one minute in winter and 30 seconds in summer, the engine should be shut down. Any time the gauge needles approach the red lines it is a warning that all is not well with the oil system. If the oil pressure indicates 'low' it is a sign that the oil pressure has dropped within the system, either due to a malfunction of the pump or to a shortage of oil. If the oil pressure drops substantially a check should automatically be made of the oil temperature gauge, because if the oil gauge is functioning correctly the oil temperature will be seen to rise rapidly and confirm troubles exist with the oil system. If, however the oil temperature remains normal, it is an indication that the oil pressure gauge itself is the most likely fault.

THE IGNITION SYSTEM

The function of the ignition system is to provide a rapid and continuous series of sparks to the points of the sparking plugs set into the cylinders of the engine. These sparks ignite the fuel/air mixture and they must be correctly timed in relation to each compression stroke of the engine, they must also be arranged to fire each cylinder in the correct sequence. These electrical sparks do not come from the aircraft's normal electrical system. The engine ignition system is completely separate and operates from two magneto systems attached to the engine. Therefore even if the aircraft's normal electrical system fails the engine will continue to function.

The basic components of the ignition system comprise two magnetos, two sparking plugs for each cylinder, an ignition lead for each sparking plug and ignition switches in the cockpit. In effect, therefore, there are two separate ignition systems, either of which will maintain the continuous operation of the engine should the other fail. The current for the ignition is generated from the two separate magnetos which are attached to the rear of the engine and driven through gears connected to the crankshaft. Magneto operation is timed to the engine so that a spark occurs only when the piston is in the proper stroke at a specified number of crankshaft degrees before the top dead centre piston postion.

The ignition switch in the cockpit has four positions, OFF, RIGHT, LEFT and BOTH. Many aircraft now use an ignition key starter

IGNITION DIAGRAM

Fig. 1-19

Fig. 1-20

system in which case a fifth position is included and marked START. In order to ensure that the starter motor has disengaged after starting the engine, key start systems are fitted with a red warning light and in these cases the first item to check after starting is that the red warning light has gone out. If it continues to remain illuminated after the engine has started it indicates the starter motor is still engaged, in which case the engine must be shut down immediately or damage will occur.

Before flight the ignition system should be tested, and during this test each magneto is selected individually to ensure that each circuit is functioning correctly. A slight power loss will occur when one magneto only is selected due to a slightly less efficient combustion when only one set of sparking plugs is working. If a large drop in power occurs the aircraft must not be flown until the problem is corrected. The permitted RPM drop will be given in the Flight/ Owner's Manual for type. Immediately prior to flight it is important to ensure that the ignition switch is selected to the BOTH position. It is equally important to ensure the switch is left in the OFF position when the engine has been shut down after flight. When an ignition key is used it should be removed after shut down. Another type of ignition switch system consists of two separate switches mounted side by side. When these are in the UP position the ignition is ON and when selected to the DOWN position the ignition is OFF. Either of these switches can be selected independently of the other. Finally the ignition system wiring has to be shielded to prevent interference with the aircraft radio. If this shielding breaks down an interference resembling static noise will be heard through the cabin speaker or the pilot's headphones.

MIXTURE CONTROL SYSTEM

The mixture control system is used to meter the amount of fuel passing through the main jet of the carburettor and regulates the fuel consumption rate. The mixture control knob is fitted adjacent to the throttle and is usually coloured red or blue.

Carburettors are calibrated for sea level operation, which means that the correct mixture of fuel and air will be obtained at sea level with the mixture control in the 'FULL RICH' position. As altitude increases, the air density decreases, which means that a cubic foot of air will weigh less at higher altitudes. As a result, when flight altitude increases, the weight of air entering the carburettor decreases, although the volume remains the same.

The amount of fuel entering the carburettor depends upon the volume and not the weight of air. Therefore, as the flight altitude increases, the amount of fuel entering the carburettor remains substantially the same for any given throttle setting if the position of the mixture control remains unchanged. Since the same amount (weight) of fuel is entering the carburettor, but with a lesser weight of air, the fuel/air mixture becomes richer as altitude increases.

To maintain the correct fuel/air ratio, the pilot must be able to adjust the amount of fuel being mixed with the incoming air as altitude increases. This is achieved by moving the mixture knob or lever situated in the cockpit and connected to the carburettor. A common system now used in light aircraft incorporates a simple shut-off needle in the body of the carburettor. The needle is tapered, and moving the mixture control knob or lever towards the lean position causes the needle to move further into an orifice and so reduce the amount of fuel flowing through the main jet. This reduction of fuel flow corrects the fuel/air ratio.

SIMPLE MIXTURE CONTROL SYSTEM

Fig. 1-21

Aero engines, just like car engines can suffer from a condition called 'DETONATION'. The term commonly used for car engines is 'PINKING'. Basically it is the result of a spontaneous explosion of the unburnt charge within the cylinder. It occurs if the temperature and pressure of the unburnt portion of fuel/air mixture reaches a critical value, and in this condition combustion will be spontaneous instead of at the normal rate. The result is a sudden and violent explosion of the charge instead of the relatively slow burning of normal combustion. Continuous operation when detonation is occurring will result in damage to the engine, causing a reduction in engine life or in severe cases a sudden and complete engine failure.

In car engines a characteristic 'pinking' noise signals that detonation is occurring and the car driver can take action to reduce power or to change gear. In an aero engine this 'pinking' noise cannot be heard and therefore the engine designer has to arrange a built-in method to avoid detonation. This is achieved by ensuring a richer mixture is supplied than that which is needed. The excess fuel acts as a coolant to the charge and prevents the mixture reaching a critical temperature. When aero engines are not operating at high power settings the danger of detonation recedes, and the excess fuel being used to guard against it is unnecessary, and under these conditions the pilot can adjust the mixture to make more efficient use of his fuel.

CABIN HEATING AND VENTILATION SYSTEM
Cabin heating systems installed in most light aircraft normally utilise a heat exchanger unit which is connected to the engine exhaust system. Fig. 1-22 shows a typical arrangement which consists of an external air scoop that takes in air and feeds it into a simple heat exchanger. The heat exchanger basically consists of two cylindrical shells. The inner one is connected with the exhaust system

CABIN HEATING AND VENTILATION SYSTEM

Fig. 1-22

to permit the escaping exhaust gas to pass through it before being ejected into the atmosphere, and this inner cylinder is therefore maintained at a high temperature. The intake air for the heating system is passed through the outer cylinder and is heated by conduction from the heated inner cylinder. The hot air so obtained is then ducted to vents inside the cabin. Such systems are simply controlled by a hot air knob or lever fitted inside the cockpit and the amount of incoming hot air into the cockpit can be adjusted from shut-off to maximum flow as desired.

An aircraft with a heating system will also have a cold air ventilation system. This normally comprises of external scoops through which the cold outside air is routed into the cabin and the amount of incoming air can be varied with the cockpit control. It is important to ensure that an adequate amount of fresh cold air is used whenever the cabin heating system is selected, as this will not only avoid any onset of 'heat induced' drowsiness to the pilot, but will also avoid stale odours and the possible onset of nausea in the passengers. A further very important reason for cabin ventilation is the possibility of carbon monoxide poisoning due to exhaust gases which may be vented into the cabin should a leak occur in the inner cylinder of the heating system, and although this is not common, the possibility of such an occurrence always exists.

THE CARBURETTOR HEAT SYSTEM

Under certain atmospheric conditions when the air humidity and temperature are within a particular range, there will exist the possibility of carburettor icing. This type of icing will produce a fall off in power, rough running and in severe cases the engine may stop.

To guard against these conditions aero engines in small aircraft are equipped with a carburettor heat system. A common method is by using a similar heat exchanger arrangement as used in the cabin heating system or a heater scoop placed adjacent to the exhaust system. The hot air so obtained is directed to the intake system of the carburettor via an air mixing unit as shown in fig. 1-23. The system is usually controlled by a push/pull knob or a lever which is mounted adjacent to the throttle. Pulling out the heat control knob opens the carburettor heat valve and allows the hot air to pass through the carburettor where it melts the ice, which mixes with the fuel as water and continues on to the engine cylinders. This action may cause temporary rough running dependent upon the amount of ice present at the time. In any event some loss of power will occur whenever carburettor heat is used, because hot air is less dense than cold air and as such less oxygen is available for the fuel/air mixture.

Carburettor heat should not be applied for long periods during ground operation as when hot air is selected the induction 'air filter'

TYPICAL CARBURETTOR HEAT SYSTEM

Fig. 1-23

is normally by-passed and unfiltered air will permit the ingestion of dust particles into the engine causing added wear to the pistons and cylinders.

THE PRESSURE INSTRUMENT SYSTEM

There are three instruments connected to the pressure instrument system, these are the ALTIMETER, VERTICAL SPEED INDICATOR and the AIR SPEED INDICATOR. The altimeter and the vertical speed indicator function by sensing the static pressure of air surrounding the aircraft. The static source is arranged either integral with a pressure head which measures both static and dynamic pressure and is mounted on the wing or fuselage or as a separate static point opening on the side of the fuselage, see fig. 1-24 (1). The air speed indicator is arranged so that it is connected to both the static source and the impact source (pitot tube) shown at (2) in fig. 1-24. The impact source is used to measure the dynamic pressure which in turn will show the indicated airspeed.

Fig. 1-24

Some aircraft are fitted with an 'alternate static air valve' in the cockpit. This is to provide a static air source should the external vent become blocked during flight. When the alternate static air valve is opened, cockpit air which is usually at a slightly lower pressure than the outside air is fed into the instruments. This causes a small error in the air speed indicator and altimeter readings, but such an error is not critical during 'visual flight' operations.

To prevent dust, insects etc. from entering the pressure head or pitot tube, a cover is normally placed over either of them whilst the aircraft is parked. It is essential to remove this cover prior to flight and also check to ensure the pressure head or pitot tube and the static vents are clear of dirt, water, insects etc. If any blockage occurs in these openings, inaccurate instrument readings will be obtained.

Finally, due to the sensitive construction of the pressure instruments pilots are advised against blowing into these openings to check if they are clear as excess pressures of this sort will cause damage.

PRESSURE STATIC SYSTEM   THE VACUUM SYSTEM

Fig. 1-25   *Fig. 1-26*

The gyroscopic instruments fitted to standard 'flight instrument panels' are in most cases operated by a vacuum system. The three basic gyroscopic instruments are, the Attitude Indicator (commonly called the Artificial Horizon), the Direction or Heading Indicator, and the Turn Indicator, the last named instrument is now gradually being replaced by a similar instrument known as a Turn Co-ordinator. These three types of instruments operate on the principle of gyroscopic rigidity and all utilise a spinning rotor. Normally the gyros of the attitude and direction indicators are driven by an air source and the turn indicator or turn co-ordinator by an electrical source. The reason for using two separate sources is that should one fail, the pilot will still have some gyro instrument reference.

THE VACUUM SOURCE

The function of the vacuum system is to supply a movement of air to drive the gyro instruments connected to it. To protect the internal mechanism of these instruments from dust, a filter system is incorporated. In some installations the air enters directly through a filter in the back of the instrument case and in others a single 'common filter' is used.

As the air flows from the instruments toward the vacuum pump it passes through a vacuum regulator. This regulator is spring loaded ad permits added air to enter the system whenever the vacuum pressure gets too high. This controlled air bleed keeps the vacuum pressure setting at the value recommended by the instrument manufacturer. A suction gauge is integral with the system and fitted in the cockpit so the pilot can check the operating pressure within the system at any time. Recommended vacuum settings vary slightly and range from 4.5 to 5.8 inches of mercury.

After passing through the regulator the air is taken through the vacuum pump and discharged to atmosphere. On some installations the pump is self lubricating by a sealed lubricant, on others the engine oil system is utilised, this results in some of the oil being mixed with air as it passes through the pump. After the air leaves the pump, it passes an air/oil separator where the oil is recuperated and returned back to the engine oil sump.

The correct functioning of the system is checked by noting the readings of the vacuum gauge, and by carrying out turns whilst taxying to ensure the instruments are giving the correct indications.

THE ELECTRICAL SYSTEM

Electrical energy is supplied by a 12 or 24 volt direct current system (most light aircraft use a 12 volt system) which is powered by an engine-driven generator or in later aircraft an alternator. An electrical storage battery serves as a standby power source, which supplies power to the system whenever the generator or alternator is inoperative. The battery also serves to provide the electrical current to the starter system, and for these reasons the electrical system should always be kept OFF when the aircraft is not in use.

A warning light or ammeter (and sometimes both) is provided in the system to warn the pilot when the generator or alternator is inoperative. Control of the charging current and voltage is automatically accomplished by a voltage regulator.

THE ELECTRICAL SYSTEM

Fig. 1-27

A master switch controls the entire electrical system with the exception of the ignition system which gets its electrical supply from the magnetos. Turning the master switch ON, supplies the electrical energy to all electrical equipment circuits. The following equipment and systems are typical of those which use the electrical system as a power source:

Landing Lights.	Wing Flaps System.
Taxy Lights.	Pitot Heat System.
Navigation Lights.	Stall Warning System.
Flashing Beacon.	Radio.
Instruments Lights.	Turn Indicator (or Co-ordinator).
Cabin Lights.	Fuel Gauges.
Clock.	Cigarette Lighter.

The energy obtained from the generator or alternator is supplied to a main bar (commonly called a BUS bar) through which the electrical

TYPICAL SWITCH AND FUSE PANEL

Fig. 1-28

services are supplied. The BUS bar leads are equipped with the fuse sockets on the instrument panel and these are marked off to identify the service(s) they protect, together with the appropriate fuse rating such as 5, 10, 15 amp etc. Aircraft fuses vary from simple cartridge types to manual and automatic circuit breakers.

ALTERNATOR

Fig. 1-29

Nowadays, alternators instead of generators are being fitted to light aircraft. They have the advantages of being lighter in weight, are less prone to overloading and have a relatively constant charge rate even at engine idling speeds. An alternator produces alternating current which is converted within the alternator assembly into the 'direct current' required to operate the aircraft's electrical equipment.

Unlike a generator the alternator requires current to excite it into action. This means that if at any time the battery becomes flat, starting the engine by 'hand swinging the propeller' will not bring the alternator into action. In order to use the electrical services, it will therefore be necessary to replace the flat battery with a fresh one, or use jump leads from a live battery to the discharged one in order to get the alternator working again. As some services are automatically live with the master switch in the ON position, such as turn co-ordinators, fuel gauges etc., it is important to be particularly careful to turn OFF the master/battery switch after shutting down the engine.

RADIO

One service which relies upon the aircraft electrical system is the aircraft radio. Today most light aircraft are equipped with a two-way radio communication system. Some are only equipped with a voice facility and others have both a voice facility and a radio navigation system. When both voice and radio navigation facilities are installed they are built side by side into the radio set. On one side is situated the VHF voice transmit and receiver element and on the other side is incorporated the radio navigation system known as VOR. Sometimes a single ON/OFF switch controls the whole set, and sometimes the voice communication and radio navigation elements have their own separate switches. In either case dual frequency selectors are incorporated.

TYPICAL VOICE/NAVAID ARRANGEMENT

Fig. 1-30

The volume control is usually integral with the ON/OFF switch and normally comprises a knurled knob which is rotated clockwise to switch the set ON and also increase the volume. An element called the SQUELCH control is fitted to all VHF aircraft radios; sometimes this is controlled manually and sometimes it is automatic. The SQUELCH is a device which assists to eliminate background static noise and it is important to adjust this after the volume level has been set. Frequency selection covers the band 118.0 to 135.95 Megahertz for voice transmissions. The correct frequency to use when contacting ground radio stations will be found in the U.K. A.I.P. The air publication CAP 46 covers the correct procedures to be used during radio telephony communications and should be referred to during training.

A microphone or headset is part of the radio equipment. The hand held or boom type microphone must be positioned and held correctly, approximately one inch away from the mouth when transmitting. It is not necessary to shout, and speech should be made clear and distinct, at normal conversation level.

THE BRAKING SYSTEM

Braking systems are operated either by cables or by the use of hydraulics. The most common is the hydraulic, but there are several variations in the methods of operation. They can either be actuated via a handbrake lever or by applying pressure to the tops of the rudder pedals. In the latter case a handbrake will also be incorporated for parking the aircraft.

Fig. 1-31

When brakes are controlled by the handbrake system, pushing forward on one or other of the rudder pedals will provide differential braking to assist the pilot when taxying in strong crosswinds or turning in confined spaces.

The toe operated brake system provides the same differential facility but the handbrake lever is only used when parking. The hydraulic brake system basically comprises of one or two master cylinders, and the action of depressing the toe pedal forces fluid from the master cylinder through the brake line to the brake pads which are an integral part of the main landing gear.

Fig. 1-32

If a leak occurs in the system, no pressure will be felt on the pedals when they are depressed. The pre-flight inspection should include a check on the visible brake lines and the area of the brake pad assembly. Traces of hydraulic fluid leaking from these areas is a sure sign that the aircraft brakes will be faulty.

FIRST AID KIT

The circumstances when first aid equipment must be carried are covered in Schedule 5 of the Air Navigation Order, but in any event a first aid kit should be carried at all times in training aircraft. The minimum scale of such equipment is indicated by this extract from the ANO:

First Aid Equipment of good quality, and sufficient in quantity, having regard to the number of persons on board the aircraft, and including the following:

FIRST AID KIT

Roller bandages, triangular bandages, adhesive plaster, absorbent gauze and cotton wool (or wound dressings in place of the absorbent gauze or cotton wool), burn dressings, safety pins, haemostatic bandages or tourniquets, scissors, antiseptic, analgesic, and stimulant drugs.

It would also be advisable to have a book on simple first aid included in the kit, and all the equipment should be stored in a suitable container which is readily accessible and easy to open.

Although private pilots are not examined in first aid, common sense dictates that they should have an elementary knowledge and where possible some practical instruction in this subject.

THE FIRE EXTINGUISHER

Although a fire inside an aircraft is a rarity, simple precautions include the requirement for having a small hand-held extinguisher fitted in the cockpit. This is clipped to a quick-release mounting attached either to the floor or a convenient place on the inside of the fuselage wall. Pilots should ascertain the position of this portable extinguisher and its method of release from its mounting during their internal checks prior to flight.

Normally some means of indicating its state of charge (such as a visual pressure gauge) is an integral part and usually attached to the top of the extinguisher, this also, should be checked during the pre-flight checks. Regulations require that a non-toxic substance is used and these contents are usually in power form.

In event of a fire occurring in the cabin the speed at which the extinguisher can be brought into operation will be most important, and it is at such times that a failure to understand the simple operating instructions will increase the hazards. Pilots should therefore practise the action of removing the extinguisher from its mounting, and carefully read and memorise the operating procedure.

During operation the powder should be aimed at the base of the fire, as the powder is used to produce a smothering action. It will also be important to warn passengers of the effects of releasing the powder into the cabin, which will quickly become filled with fine particles, reducing visibility and causing discomfort in breathing. Without such a warning the added element of panic could easily occur.

CONTROL LOCKS

All aircraft have some method of locking the controls while parked. These locking systems are primarily to prevent the control surfaces being damaged by wind gusts, and the actual equipment used varies from built-in systems to removable internal or external locks. It is an important and vital part of any pre-flight inspection to ensure these locks are removed or completely disengaged. After such locks are removed or disengaged the control surfaces must be checked for correct freedom of movement.

CHECKLISTS, DRILLS AND OPERATION OF COCKPIT CONTROLS

The primary purpose of checklists is to organise the order in which checks are carried out, they also reduce the possibility of omissions which can occur if one relies on the memory alone. Their use is particularly applicable when the pilot flies at infrequent intervals or if he operates in different types of aircraft. Some drills and checks should however be learned sufficiently well, so that any reference to a checklist is unnecessary. Such drills being those which are performed in busy circuit areas e.g. Pre-Landing Checks, the use of a checklist on such occasions would be detrimental to the pilot's lookout. The immediate actions to be taken in an emergency, such as 'engine failure during flight' should also be memorised as this will enable the pilot to carry out the initial procedure without the added workload of using a check-list. The checklist should however, be used after the initial emergency procedure has been completed in order to double check and ensure that all the correct actions have been completed.

When using checklists or carrying out drills from memory, the danger always exists of merely reading or reciting words instead of 'saying and doing', therefore it is particularly important to ensure that all cockpit checks involve physical actions, and not just recitations.

There is always the possibility of the pilot reaching out and selecting the wrong control, whether it be a knob, switch or lever, or having selected the right one, to move it the wrong way. Pilots must, therefore, develop the instinctive habit of re-checking their actions whenever moving kobs, switches, levers or similar controls.

Finally, efficient and safe cockpit organisation requires as a first essential the development of good habits. The sooner these good habits are established the more firmly they will become fixed and the safer the pilot will become.

EMERGENCY DRILLS

Certain drills are laid down to cover emergency situations. Due to the greater complexity of systems and equipment fitted in the modern training aircraft there is a greater variety of possible emergency situations. Emergencies vary in degree from a minor malfunction of an aircraft system to a major occurrence such as an engine failure or fire.

The procedures to adopt in event of any type of emergency, whether it be of a minor or major degree, must be learned and practised during the training period and at regular intervals thereafter. It is only by repeated practice that such situations can be contained and controlled efficiently.

The various emergency drills which are applicable to the flight exercises are covered in the respective Long Briefings, Pre-Flight Briefings and Flight Demonstrations. The emergency situations which are identified in this briefing are:

Action in event of fire – in the air and on the ground.
   Engine Fire.
   Cabin Fire.
   Electrical Fire.

Systems Failure – as applicable to aircraft type.
Escape Drills – the location and use of emergency equipment and
exits.

ACTION IN EVENT OF FIRE
The Flight/Owner's Manual will contain information on these
procedures, but this information varies between manuals, from a
sparse outline to a detailed step by step procedure. When only a
limited amount of information is available, the pilot will have to add
to such information from his own knowledge and experience. When
detailed information is available from the manuals it is advisable to
follow it as closely as possible, because the manufacturer would not
have included such detail in the manual without considerable
thought and knowledge of his product.

ESCAPE DRILLS
If an accident occurs the pilot must know how to leave the aircraft as
quickly as possible, he is also responsible for the safety of his
passengers. To this end, and if time permits he should ensure that
doors are unlocked prior to impact, this action will guard against the
effects of fuselage deformation which can lead to jammed doors and
prevent rapid exit by his passengers and himself. If doors or windows
are fitted with emergency releases the procedure for operating them
should be understood by the occupants of the aircraft. Finally, if
necessary the perspex fitted to light aircraft can be broken fairly
easily with a heavy object, such as a walking shoe or even the fire
extinguisher. However if this latter object is used, care must be
exercised to avoid operating the release mechanism.

Preparation For and Action After Flight

Instructor's Guide

It is important that the student wears appropriate flying clothing for the conditions of flight likely to be experienced, and that it fits and functions properly. His ability to learn can be considerably affected by discomfort, or the inability to hear properly. Flying boots are seldom necessary in light aircraft and only serve to make the student awkward with the rudder. If flying clothing is worn it should be comfortable, particularly the helmet or headset, which should fit properly and be adjusted correctly.

FLIGHT AUTHORISATION AND AIRCRAFT ACCEPTANCE

The student should be introduced briefly to such points of pre-flight planning as the weather, Air Traffic Control and airfield information pertinent to the flight. The use of the following documents and the appropriate actions with regard to them should be explained at this stage, also the pilot's personal equipment, e.g. maps etc., should be itemised and checked:

Certificate of Airworthiness.
Technical Log (if applicable).
Certificate of Maintenance Review and Release to Service
Aircraft Weight Schedule.
Flight Authorisation Sheet.

EXTERNAL CHECKS

A general check of the following points should be made:

The aircraft is on suitable ground and in a satisfactory position for starting.
Fire extinguisher is available.
The taxi path is unobstructed, remember to check the tailplane position with regard to adjacent obstructions.

A detailed check should then be made, conforming to the checks given in the check list or Owner's Flight Manual.

INTERNAL CHECKS

Carry out the internal checks as listed. The student should be given an active part which will not only help him to learn the checks that he must complete by himself in future, but will also familiarise him with the aircraft. Checks should be carried out by a student in stages, so that by the time he is ready for 'First Solo' he can carry out all the necessary checks and drills unassisted.

STARTING AND WARMING UP THE ENGINE

When demonstrating starting procedures the instructor should point out the safety aspects and any signals made between the pilot and ground crew. When possible the student should start the engine and carry out the necessary cockpit checks at the commencement of his first training flight. His fullest participation will be encouraged during the cockpit checks following starting the engine.

POWER CHECKS

The aircraft should be headed into wind and in the case of tail wheel aircraft the control column should be held fully back to avoid the danger of nosing over. Explain why such power checks should be made. Be careful when using narrow taxiways that the aircraft is not manoeuvered in such a way that the propeller is close to the edge.

RUNNING DOWN AND SWITCHING OFF

The procedure laid down in the handling notes or Aircraft Manual should be followed, and the correct procedure insisted upon at all times. Emphasis should be placed on the danger of leaving the ignition switches ON. In the case of aircraft which use a mixture control to stop the engine, ensure that the throttle is fully closed before operating the mixture control and that the ignition switches are moved to the 'OFF' position only after the engine has stopped. These two actions will ensure that the cylinders are starved of fuel and thereby reduce the risk of an engine firing if a person subsequently turns the propeller by hand. The mixture control should be left in the 'Full Lean' position after stopping the engine and if ignition keys are used these should be removed. Such actions will provide an additional safety factor.

LEAVING THE AIRCRAFT

The aircraft controls should be locked and the pitot cover placed in position. Brakes may be left off only when chocks are placed in front of, and behind the wheels. A brief external examination should be made before leaving the aircraft.

COMPLETION OF AUTHORISATION SHEET AND TECHNICAL LOG
Particular reference should be made to the recording of flying times in the authorisation sheet. The method of entering defects and the completion of the Technical Log (when applicable) should be explained.

CONCLUSION
This lesson will require repeated practice to perfect, and the instructor will insist upon the correct procedures being carried out. Bear in mind that everything in this exercise must be learned before the student's first solo flight but all the checks and procedures should be broken down in easy stages so that he will not find the task too difficult to assimilate.

Preparation For and Action After Flight

Long Briefing

OBJECTIVES

To teach the student how to prepare himself and the aircraft for flight. It will also include how to check and leave the aircraft after flight. As with 'Aircraft Familiarisation', the many items of this exercise cannot be learned in one lesson and need to be spread over that period of training prior to the first solo flight.

INTRODUCTION

Safe flying really begins on the ground. The attitude and habits developed by a pilot in the initial stage of training will tend to fix the standards he will achieve throughout his flying career. Therefore learning the correct procedures and techniques which are implemented prior to flight is a very important part of a pilot's training.

STUDENT COMFORT

A student who is seated comfortably in the aircraft will learn more quickly. Clothing should be compatible with the type of aircraft, and with the present modern cabin in which heating and ventilation are provided there is no need for heavy and cumbersome clothing. Ideally a pair of soft, lightweight gloves can be worn as they are useful in absorbing perspiration and keep the hands dry. They also give protection against burns in the rare event of a fire occurring in the cabin.

Although nowadays it is difficult to avoid wearing clothes made of nylon, it should be appreciated that nylon is virtually non-porous and as a result interferes with the breathing of the skin, it also melts rapidly if subjected to fire and can cause considerable damage to the tissues of the skin.

The main precaution in relation to comfort in cabin aircraft is to avoid wearing heavy clothes, as these can easily produce sweating and can lead to a feeling of nausea. Seating comfort is equally important and the student should not hesitate to take a little trouble and time to ensure that the seat is adjusted to his own requirements, both from a comfort point of view and an ability to reach and use all controls including full movement of the rudder pedals. After the seat adjustment has been made, the harness or lap straps can be secured about the body and adjusted.

Some aircraft are fitted with an 'inertia reel' shoulder harness, which can be tightened without restricting the body movements required for in-flight operations. If a fixed shoulder harness is fitted, it should be secured but the shoulder straps kept loose whilst on the ground because if a fixed shoulder harness is tightened at this stage body movement will be restricted, and the pilot may be unable to carry out his internal checks correctly. In these circumstances the harness must be tightened prior to take-off, and when at a safe height it can be relaxed again for greater comfort of the upper body. When using a shoulder harness type restraint ensure the lap strap portion is tightly drawn across the lap before tightening the upper straps. If this is not done the upper straps upon being tightened will raise the lap straps, and if this occurs the harness will be of little value when needed most, because a sudden deceleration will cause the body to slide down through the lower portion of the harness.

One final point in relation to both lap straps and harnesses, do make sure that the straps are not partially jammed down near the side of the seat, or caught in the cabin door. If either of these situations exists, an apparently tight strap will most likely become a loose one if strong turbulence is met or an accident occurs.

FLIGHT AUTHORISATION AND AIRCRAFT ACCEPTANCE
During this section of the briefing the student should be shown and have explained to him the following documents:

The Flight Authorisation Sheet.
The Certificate of Airworthiness.
The Maintenance Documentation.
Aircraft Weight Schedule.
A Technical Log (if used).
The local Flying Order Book.

All dual and solo training flights must be authorised on a suitable recording sheet. This sheet must contain at least the following information:

● The date.
● The aeroplane registration marks.
● The names of the instructor and student for dual flights, or the name of the student for solo flights.
● The exercise to be flown, or the route and destination aerodrome(s) to be visited.
● The authorising instructor's initial or signature.

- The initials or signature of the pilot in command both before and after flight.
- The intended duration of the flight.
- The total actual elapsed time of flight.
- Post-flight recording of any divergence from the intended exercise(s).
- If Technical Logs or other aircraft log books are not used, the Flight Authorisation Sheet may be used for the purposes outlined in The Air Navigation Order concerning defect reporting.

It is particularly important that any aircraft defects are entered on this sheet immediately after completion of the flight, and the attention of appropriate personnel drawn to the entry. If this is not done, a hazardous situation could occur during the next flight made by the aircraft.

A student should confirm his briefing and his knowledge of the exercises to be carried out during the flight by signing the Authorisation Sheet in the appropriate column prior to the flight.

Before accepting responsibility for the aircraft, he must check to see if any defects were reported by the previous pilot. Sometimes minor defects of a nature which do not seem to affect the safety of the aircraft will be reported. In these cases the student must consult an instructor for advice and confirmation that the aircraft is still serviceable to fly.

If the student is unable to carry out any of the authorised exercises, due to weather or for other reasons, he must ensure that this is clearly recorded on the authorisation sheet after landing.

A current Certificate of Airworthiness for the specific aircraft must be available for the pilot to check. The period of validity is shown on the reverse side of the Certificate. Apart from the date period, it is important to know that many Certificates of Airworthiness are issued with specific 'conditions and/or limitations' annotated upon them. The pilot should check such conditions/limitations to ensure that he complies with them during flight.

A Weight Schedule is part of the aircraft paper work, but apart from showing it to the student at this stage, an explanation of weight and balance should be left until a more suitable occasion.

Another item to be checked before flight is the Maintenance Document which is issued for a specific period, and a specific number of flying hours.

Some flying organisations use separate Technical Logs for each aircraft; if this document applies, then the student must be fully briefed on how to use it.

Finally the student must be introduced to the local Flying Order

Book, which he should read, understand and sign before being sent on his first solo flight.

After the student has been briefed on the authorisation procedure and aircraft documentation, the external checks should be commenced.

On approaching the aircraft it is important to note that it is standing in a suitable position for starting and taxying clear of the parking area. A walk around the aircraft noting its general condition, and examination of the specific items shown on the check list should then be made. Fuel state should, where possible, be visually checked by looking into the fuel tanks. The fuel and oil states should be determined as being sufficient for the flight and a check should also be made to ensure the nose wheel towbar, pitot cover, and external control locks (if fitted) are all removed. Either just before or just after entering the cockpit, the fire extinguisher and first aid kit should be checked as being available and serviceable.

Fig. 2-1

INTERNAL CHECKS

Upon entering the cockpit the seat, rudder pedals and harness should be adjusted to ensure that it is possible to obtain full rudder pedal movement. In those aircraft where full pedal movement is not permitted with the aircraft stationary, this check should be made shortly after taxying is commenced.

The internal checks should be done according to the check list for the specific type, and a meticulous and methodical procedure must be developed. If no check list is available, a systematic review of all instruments, controls etc. should be made, adjusting, setting or checking the appropriate item as the pilot comes to it. When this method is used, it is helpful to divide the sections of the control panel and instruments into groups, and to complete each section in turn before moving on to the next one. This internal check should include all items associated with the pre starting of the engine.

STARTING AND WARMING UP CHECKS

After the internal checks have been completed, a final look outside the aircraft should be made to ensure that it is 'All Clear'. One hand should be placed on the throttle and if a rudder pedal brake system is fitted, the feet should be near the brakes. A loud shout of 'Clear Propeller' should be made, followed by a pause before activating the starter mechanism.

Immediately following the engine start up, further checks must be carried out, such as monitoring the oil pressure and temperature gauges, the ammeter and suction gauge. A low power setting of approximately 1000 RPM is best until oil pressure comes up. As soon as the engine is running smoothly, the oil pressure should be checked, and if it does not rise to the specified value in about 30 seconds in the summer or 60 seconds in the winter, the engine should be shut down to prevent possible damage.

When ignition 'key start' systems are incorporated it is normal to fit a 'starter warning light'. This light comes on when the starter is engaged and goes out when the starter key is released. If this system is fitted, the first check after starting is to ensure the red warning light has gone out. If not, the engine should be immediately shut down as it indicates the starter mechanism is still engaged and consequent damage may result.

Following the engine starter light and oil pressure check, a reading of the oil temperature should be noted. The oil temperature is often slow to rise in cold weather, but normally if a steady reading is observed after engine starting it is acceptable. The ammeter should then be checked for a charge rate and if no charge is indicating it signifies a malfunction of the alternator/generator or ammeter gauge. This is the most appropriate time to ascertain the alternator/generator is working correctly, as the operation of the starter motor will have drained an appreciable current from the battery and if the system is working properly, a positive charge will be seen. Later on the charge rate will have topped up the battery and the ammeter will return to a near zero reading.

The next check is to note the reading of the vacuum gauge to ensure that the vacuum system is operating properly and driving the attitude and direction indicators. A final check of the engine should be made by selecting each ignition position in turn to ensure that both the left and right magnetos are working. If the selection of a single magneto causes the engine to stop, or if any malfunctions are noted from the previous 'after starting checks', the engine should be shut down and the matter reported to an instructor or the ground engineers.

Prior to taxying, the heading indicator should be reset with the magnetic compass and any other specific checks called for by the Flight/Owner's Manual/Pilot's Operating Handbook or Training Organisation operating instructions completed. The radio can then be switched on, and the appropriate frequency selected and a radio call made to ATC. This action will enable the pilot to obtain the altimeter setting, runway in use and taxying instructions.

Immediately after commencing to taxy and before leaving the parking area, the aircraft brakes should be tested and particular care taken when manoeuvring in the vicinity of other aircraft.

POWER CHECKS

Before take-off the engine should be briefly checked at a high power setting to ensure that the ignition and other systems are fully serviceable.

Good airmanship dictates that engine operation at high power should take place well clear of offices and other parked aircraft. It is therefore normal to taxy away from the parking area before commencing the 'power checks'. It is usually most convenient to carry out this check with the aircraft parked near to the take-off point of the runway in use (commonly called the 'holding point'). Apart from the airmanship aspect, delaying the power checks until the holding point is reached will give the engine longer to warm up and enable a more accurate analysis of the engine condition to be made prior to opening it up to a higher power setting.

Modern aircraft are designed to reduce cooling drag to an absolute minimum to obtain the maximum in aircraft performance. The net result is that during ground running and under certain take-off and climb conditions, the engine cooling is at a minimum.

Excessive ground running should be avoided. An air-cooled engine reaches operating temperatures under normal ambient conditions in only a few minutes. The initial sluggishness of oil circulation is taken care of in the engine design. In most cases, the time consumed in taxying to the assigned runway is sufficient for warm up, except during unusually cold conditions.

Most modern air-cooled engines are closely cowled and equipped with pressure baffles which direct the flow of air to the proper places in sufficient quantities during flight. On the ground however, much less air is forced around these baffles and through the cowling due to the design of propeller blades near the hubs, and any prolonged running causes serious overheating long before any indication of rising temperature is given by the oil temperature gauge.

If a cylinder head temperature gauge is fitted this will give a more accurate indication of the readiness of the engine to accept a high power condition. In the event that no cylinder head gauge is fitted the general rule is to ensure that when the engine is opened up to high power, there is no faltering from the engine or fluctuations in the oil pressure and oil temperature gauges.

The aircraft should be parked approximately into wind, well clear of the edges of taxyways and in an area where there are no loose stones or gravel. Loose stones and similar material can easily be picked up by the propeller when the engine is opened up to higher power, this can lead to damage to both the propeller and the airframe.

Note.   In cases where the wind direction parallels the taxyway, the aircraft should be manoeuvred so that it is parked at least 45 degrees to the taxyway centre line in order to prevent damage to following aircraft.

In the case of tail wheel aircraft, the control column should be held fully back during the engine run up. However, with tricycle type aircraft it is normal to hold the control column central unless wind conditions dictate otherwise. Prior to opening the throttle a final check that the oil pressure and oil temperature are within limits should be made followed by a good lookout either side and behind the aircraft. The power check should conform to that listed in the Flight/Owner's Manual with any additions required by local operating instructions.

The purpose of the magneto check is to determine that the ignition system is functioning properly and that the engine is firing correctly on all cylinders. If any cylinders however are not firing, the engine will suffer a large drop in RPM and run roughly. A small drop in RPM will normally occur when a single magneto is selected. This drop in RPM is a natural characteristic, and it is partly by the amount of this drop that the serviceability of the engine can be checked.

The power setting to carry out this test is laid down in the Flight/Owner's Manual. Normally two maximum allowable figures are given for the RPM drop. One is a maximum single RPM drop, and the other is the maximum difference permitted between the left and right magneto readings. This second figure is often quoted to eliminate the possibility of influences such as high ambient air temperature, humidity and density altitude giving a misleading impression of the actual engine condition. Taking these outside air influences into consideration a more valid check would be to measure the differential drop in RPM between the left and the right magnetos. The maximum permitted differential drop and the maximum single drop will be given in the Flight/Owner's Manual/Pilot's Operating Handbook.

Immediately the engine run-up power is set, the carburettor hot air system should be operated to ensure its serviceability and to remove any ice which may have formed, when cold air has been reselected the magnetos should then be checked.

NOTE: Even small amounts of carburettor ice can cause a misleading RPM drop and rough running when a single magneto is selected. For this reason it is usually better to operate the carburettor hot air system prior to the ignition check.

Whilst at high power, the engine oil pressure and temperature gauges should be read again to ensure that both are giving steady indications within the green arcs. This is the more appropriate stage for this check as any malfunction of the oil system will be more likely to manifest itself after a period of engine operation at high power. Finally the suction and ammeter gauges can be checked for correct readings before reducing power. The throttle should then be closed completely to check the engine still runs with the throttle in this position. The normal idling speed is approximately 500/600 RPM. If during these power checks, the prescribed limits of RPM, pressure, temperature, etc, are exceeded, the aircraft should not be flown. In these circumstances the appropriate defect reporting procedure (see page 2-12) should be adopted.

RUNNING DOWN AND SWITCHING OFF THE ENGINE

Upon returning to the parking area after flight, the correct running down and switching off procedure should be followed. If an engine is shut down when it is very hot, uneven cooling between the fixed and moving parts takes place, leading to deformation and engine damage, however, the taxying time after landing will normally have permitted the engine to cool evenly so that it can usually be shut down without delay after the aircraft is parked and the brakes are applied. The correct method of shutting down is detailed in the Flight/Owner's Manual and should be adhered to. Prior to closing the throttle and operating the Idle Cut-Off, the radios and other electrical services being used should be switched OFF and a final check of the engine instruments made to ensure the engine is continuing to function correctly.

It must be understood that there will always exist the hazard of an ignition system being 'LIVE' even with the ignition switches in the OFF position. This is due to the fact that the ignition switch system is different in at least one respect from all other types of switches, in that when the ignition switch is in the OFF position, a circuit is completed through the switch to ground. In other electrical switches the OFF position normally breaks or opens the circuit. A defect such as a broken ground wire in the ignition system could lead to a situation where the ignition system will be live although the ignition switches are in the OFF position. Handling the propeller on these occasions could cause the engine to fire and seriously injure the handler. For this reason propellers must be handled with extreme caution and must always be treated as live. A good practice is to momentarily switch OFF each magneto individually and then BOTH to establish the serviceability of the ignition system prior to shut down. If the engine continues to run with both switches OFF it will indicate that the ignition system has gone 'Live' and this must be reported immediately.

In the case of an aircraft which utilises an 'Idle Cut-Off' for engine shut down, ensure that the throttle is fully closed before operating the mixture control and that the ignition switches are moved to the OFF position only after the engine has stopped. These two actions will ensure that the cylinders are starved of fuel and thereby reduce the risk of an engine firing should the propeller subsequently be turned by hand. The mixture control should be left in the Idle Cut-Off position after stopping the engine and if ignition keys are used these should be removed. Such actions will provide an additional safety factor should the propeller be handled manually afterwards.

LEAVING THE AIRCRAFT, PARKING, SECURITY AND PICKETING

It is the final responsibility of a pilot to carry out a brief external examination of the aircraft before leaving it safely parked. Brakes should be firmly ON and the control locks placed in position. The pitot cover should be fitted if available and the aircraft parked in a safe position. If the aircraft has to be left out over night, precautions against high winds should be made by placing chocks in front of and behind the wheels, and tying the aircraft firmly down by some form of picketing. After the final flight of the day, it is advisable to have the fuel tanks topped up to prevent condensation occurring in the tanks over night.

COMPLETION OF THE AUTHORISATION SHEET AND AIRCRAFT SERVICEABILITY DOCUMENTS

The flight time and exercises carried out should be entered on the authorisation sheet together with a statement of the aircraft's serviceablity. Any defects should be clearly written down and an instructor informed. The pilot should then enter the flight details in his personal log book and have the entry signed by his instructor, or in the event of a solo flight by his authorising instructor.

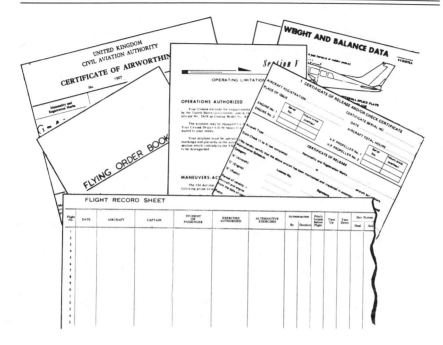

UNITED KINGDOM
CIVIL AVIATION AUTHORITY

CERTIFICATE OF AIRWORTHIN

No. 1907

Nationality and
Registration Marks

FLYING ORDER BOOK

WEIGHT AND BALANCE DATA

Section V

OPERATING LIMITATION

OPERATIONS AUTHORIZED

Your Cessna exceeds the requirements
by the United States Government and is re-
tificate No. 3A19 an Cessna Model No. A

The airplane may be equipped for
Your Cessna Dealer will be happy to a
suited to your needs.

Your airplane must be operate
markings and placards in the airplane
section which contradicts the FAA
to be disregarded.

MANEUVERS-AC

The 150 Aerobat
following gross weigh

CERTIFICATE OF RELEASE AND/OR CHECK CERTIFICATE

FLIGHT RECORD SHEET

Flight No.	DATE	AIRCRAFT	CAPTAIN	STUDENT OR PASSENGER	EXERCISES AUTHORISED	ALTERNATIVE EXERCISES	AUTHORISATION		Pilot's Initials Before Flight	Time Up	Time Down	DAY FLYING	
							By	Duration				Dual	Solo
1													
2													
3													
4													
5													
6													
7													
8													
9													
0													
1													
2													
3													
4													
5													

Air Experience

Instructor's Guide

OBJECTIVE

To introduce and accustom the student to the environment of the cockpit, the sensation of flying and the aspect of the ground as seen from the air.

Instruction is not normally undertaken on this flight but it can nevertheless be a valuable lesson. It gives the instructor an opportunity to assess the student's temperament, to some degree and to decide on the manner of approach suitable for subsequent instruction, also the student gains knowledge of the aircraft and its operation by watching the instructor, and becomes accustomed to the new environment and the sensations associated with flying, before having to concentrate on learning. If the student already has previous flight experience in light aircraft, then this flight should be integrated with the air exercise 'Effects of Controls'.

The duration of the flight is variable and should be designed to suit individual students. After the student has adjusted himself to the environment and sensation of flying, encourage his interest by getting him to read some of the instruments and identify ground features.

The student should be watched for signs of airsickness and the flight should be discontinued if necessary. If possible, the flight should be planned to keep the aircraft in the vicinity of the airfield – so that a quick return can be made at any time if the student shows signs of physical discomfort, and in this respect the importance of 'prevention being better than cure' cannot be over emphasised as airsickness at this stage could easily turn his interests away from flying. If however, the student is actually sick, the instructor should avoid showing any great concern.

Later on in the flight, encourage the student to handle the controls and point out the light forces and movements needed to alter the aircraft's attitude. If the student's interest is fostered and he enjoys this first flight, it will form a good foundation for subsequent instruction.

Effects of Controls

Instructor's Guide

This is the student's first lesson in the air and teaching should not be hurried. It is important not to ignore points which seem obvious to the experienced pilot, for example, the direction of movement of the rudder pedals and trimming controls. A clear understanding of the principles taught in this lesson is an essential foundation for all later exercises. It will normally be necessary to use more than one flying period to cover the exercise adequately.

Whilst the instructor is giving demonstrations the student should in most cases be following through lightly on the controls. This will be a valuable aid to his appreciation of the direction, rate and amount of control movement being used. It must nevertheless be appreciated that he will not obtain any feeling of the control pressures which the instructor applies. There will be occasions when the student should be told to leave the controls alone and these in the main will occur during the 'observation' periods which will normally occur at the introduction stage of a flight exercise.

During this exercise, the student will need to be shown the correct way to hold the control column and how to place his feet on the rudder pedals. Rudder pedal movement is best accomplished through the balls of the feet with the heels resting on the floor. If the student keeps his heels off the floor it becomes very difficult for him to use the rudder correctly for balanced flight.

Finally, whenever the student is flying the aircraft encourage him to think in terms of control pressures rather than control movements and ensure that no harsh or extreme movements of the controls occur, such as would cause the student discomfort or unpleasant sensations.

AIRMANSHIP

At this early stage, airmanship points, other than the necessity to keep a good lookout, should be left until the student is more familiar with the aircraft and its environment.

'LOOKOUT' is one of the many points of airmanship which must be continually stressed during the student's training. It should however, be understood that the mere mention of the word 'lookout' from time to time is a poor substitute for that of ensuring the student is trained to scan correctly and quickly see other aircraft in his vicinity. In the initial stages, it will help if the instructor manoeuvres the aircraft so that the student clearly sees other traffic in his area. This should be followed by pointing out the relationship of other aircraft in terms of both height and distance, and a simple introduction to the 'clock code' method of reporting can be made.

During the student's initial attempt at the early air exercises his attention will be mainly diverted to the task in hand. On these occasions it should be made clear that the instructor will be primarily responsible for lookout.

BEFORE THE EXERCISE
The Long Briefing should cover the following:

Objectives.
The function of the Primary Flight Controls –
    when laterally level and banked.
The further effects of aileron and rudder.
The effects of:
    Inertia.
    Airspeed.
    Slipstream.
    Power.
    Trimming Controls.
    Flaps.
Operation of the Mixture Control.
Operation of the Carburettor Heat Control.
Operation of the Cabin Heat/Ventilation Controls.
The effects of other controls as applicable to aircraft type.
Airmanship.

The short Pre-Flight Briefing should be based upon the relevant parts of the Long Briefing and the Air Exercise to be covered. It should be appreciated that this exercise must be covered fairly thoroughly if not fully before further exercises can be taught. It will usually be necessary to spread the contents of this exercise over two flight periods.

DURING THE AIR DEMONSTRATION
Explain the use of the horizon as a reference for judging the attitude of the aircraft and use features of the aircraft, such as the nose, windscreen frame, cockpit coaming or engine cowling, to relate the aircraft attitude to the natural horizon.

Allow the student to try for himself all the effects demonstrated (with the exception of the further effects of ailerons and rudder) before proceeding to the next stage. Give him sufficient time to become accustomed to the handling of the controls and to appreciate their effects. It is important to ensure that the aircraft is correctly trimmed before handing over control and that the student knows the correct method of 'Handing Over and Taking Over Control.'

Primary Effects

Before demonstrating this sequence make sure that the student can hear clearly, is relaxed, and knows how to hold and move the controls, and that the seat and/or rudder pedals are adjusted correctly.

When teaching the effect of the rudder emphasise that its prime function is to balance the aircraft's flight and not to control direction.

Point out that the response of the aircraft to control movements depends on the rate and amount of control movement.

Further Effects

The student should be made aware that no other control is being moved but the one demonstrated. This can be ensured if the instructor and student take their hands or feet off the control which is not being demonstrated. During the demonstration of the further effects of the ailerons, instructors must avoid instinctively applying back pressure on the control column when banking the aircraft, as this application of back pressure would result in a positive reduction in the further effect being demonstrated, namely yaw. If back pressure is applied it will be necessary to use steep bank angles for this demonstration, but if one considers the effect of a steep bank angle on a student who is probably flying for only the second time in his life, it will be realised that an extreme bank attitude will most likely take his mind completely off the point being taught.

Effect of Airspeed and Slipstream

Although control response varies with changes in airspeed all controls remain effective over a wide range of speeds and little difficulty will be experienced by the student in appreciating this demonstration. However, the effects of slipstream are less convincing, but can be reviewed later if necessary, when the gliding exercise is covered. The application of power from the gliding condition results in a positive force being required to prevent the nose of the aircraft rising above the horizon. This force is greater than that caused by the effect of power alone and its intensity is due to the effect of slipstream over the elevators and trim tab. The latter will have been used fairly coarsely to hold the aircraft in the gliding attitude.

The Effects of Trim

Trimming controls are designed to relieve the pilot of unnecessary pressures on the flying controls. Ensure the student clearly understands that the initial adjustment of attitude is always made by means of the primary controls, and then the trimmers are adjusted until 'no load' is felt on the controls.

The 'no load' position of the trimmers can only be fully appreciated if the control column is held correctly and, if rudder trim is applicable, when the feet are rested lightly on the pedals.

The Effects of Flap

Depending upon the type of flaps fitted, selecting several flap positions in this demonstration may tend to be confusing and to have insufficient emphasis. It is therefore suggested that the demonstration is limited to the selection of the half and full flap positions. Before using flaps stress the importance of remaining within the flap limiting speed. When flaps are lowered or raised, there will be a change in the position of the centre of pressure, the angle of downwash, the drag force and the position of the drag line, these four factors will interact to produce a change in the pitch attitude of the aircraft. Point out that the direction and amount of change will vary between different types of aircraft.

Use of the Mixture Control

There is a tendency amongst some instructors to avoid teaching the student the use of the mixture control. Whereas this type of thinking may have been justified when using the older and smaller type of aero engine, the design philosophy of current light aero engines demands knowledge of mixture control operation, particularly at heights above 4/5000 feet where engine rough running due to an over rich mixture can easily occur and mixture control operation becomes a requirement.

Whilst the student under training will be unlikely to fly at heights in excess of 5000 feet he will more likely do so when he has acquired his private licence and undertakes longer cross country flights. Further, it is important to appreciate that the fuel consumption figures obtained from the tables and graphs in Flight/Owner's Manuals are normally only valid when using mixture control. A student who does not understand and learn to operate the mixture control system during training will not be capable of conducting safe flight operations once outside the supervision of the training environment. However, at this early stage it would be advisable to limit the coverage of mixture control to an explanation of its use during starting and running down the engine and the dangers of using it inadvertently. Later it should be covered in greater detail and for this purpose a supplement has been included at the end of the Long Briefing.

Use of Carburettor Heat
The operation of this control should be shown together with its effect upon engine power. The instructor should demonstrate its effect upon actual carburettor icing at the first opportunity.

For similar reasons as described under 'Use of the Mixture Control' it would be advisable to spend a separate lecture period to ensure a thorough understanding of carburettor icing, its prevention and the remedial actions which can be taken, and for this purpose a further supplement has been included at the end of the Long Briefing.

Cabin Heating and Ventilation
When a cabin heat system is installed, the operation of its controls should be clearly shown together with the use of any cabin ventilation controls. It should also be pointed out that cabin heat should not normally be used without adequate cabin ventilation.

AFTER THE FLIGHT
The post-flight discussion is an important part of your teaching technique, during which the standard of achievement attained by the student during the flight should be reviewed. He should be encouraged to analyse his own performance, and must be left with a clear impression of whether or not he has met the standards required for the particular flight. The technique of conducting the post-flight discussion can be varied slightly to suit the temperament of the student. For example, underconfidence can be met with encouragement, and praise given for any aspect of his performance where merited.

Effects of Controls

Long Briefing

OBJECTIVES

This briefing is to introduce the student to the aircraft controls, their method of operation and how these controls affect the aircraft during flight.

INTRODUCTION

The flight path of an aircraft through the air can be resolved into three planes of movement; the pitching plane about the lateral axis, the rolling plane about the longitudinal axis and the yawing plane about the vertical (normal) axis.

FUNCTION OF THE PRIMARY CONTROLS

An aircraft is controlled in these planes of movement by means of the flying controls. Conventionally, the elevators control it in pitch, the ailerons in roll and the rudder in yaw.

The three planes of movement are considered as being fixed relative to the aircraft and the pilot. Therefore, if the aircraft is banked, the pitching plane is inclined to the vertical, but the effect of the elevator will still produce the same movements of the nose relative to the pilot and the aircraft, i.e. pitching. Further, whatever the attitude of the aircraft, the control movements will always produce the same pitching, rolling or yawing movements relative to both the pilot and the aircraft.

FURTHER EFFECTS OF AILERONS AND RUDDER

There is an inter-relationship between the actions caused by operating the ailerons and the rudder, in that the secondary effect of aileron movement is to create yaw, and the secondary effect of rudder is to create bank.

Effect of Bank

If an aircraft is flying along a straight path and bank is applied by use of the ailerons, it will sideslip towards the lower wing. As a result of this sideslip the sideways pressure of air upon the keel surface of

THE AIRCRAFT AXES

Fig. 4-1

Fig. 4-2

Fig. 4-3

Fig. 4-4

the fuselage behind the centre of gravity will tend to yaw the aircraft into the direction of sideslip.

The degree to which this yaw occurs is dependent upon the angle of slip and the relative area of keel surface behind the centre of gravity. The greater this keel surface the greater will be the yaw produced. The result of this yaw will cause the nose to drop and a descending spiral will commence.

The yaw resulting from the application of bank is called the further effect of ailerons, it should however, be noted that it is only indirectly the result of aileron movement. As will be seen later, this effect of aileron is an important consideration in the achievement of balanced flight.

In early aircraft another yaw effect was produced when the ailerons were used suddenly. This effect known as 'Aileron Drag' caused the aircraft to yaw slightly in the opposite direction to that of the intended turn. However, aileron drag on the modern aircraft has been virtually eliminated by improving the design of the ailerons and by using a differential action coupled with 'Frise' design. The arrangement with a differential aileron system is that the downgoing aileron (which increases the induced drag) moves a lesser amount than the upgoing aileron. Frise effect is produced by having the lower leading edge of the upgoing aileron protrude into the airflow and so produce slightly more drag. The result of these design features is to provide

BANK LEADING
TO SIDESLIP...

...FOLLOWED BY YAW

Fig. 4-5

an equal amount of drag from both the upgoing and downgoing ailerons.

Despite the incorporation of both these design features there will still be a slight adverse yaw produced whenever the aircraft is banked. When an aircraft starts to roll the lift vectors on the downgoing wing are inclined forward and those on the upgoing wing are inclined backwards as shown on the diagram below.

Relative
airflow

Up-going
wing

Down-going
wing

Fig. 4-6   Relative airflow

As a result of these two vectors a yawing moment is introduced. The two moments will tend to turn the aircraft to the right when the wings are in the process of being rolled to the left and vice versa. This change in heading is in the opposite direction to that in which the pilot wishes to turn the aircraft and is therefore called 'Adverse Aileron Yaw'.

Effect of Yaw

If an aircraft is yawed by rudder alone it will tend to bank. The reasons for this further effect of rudder is that the outer wing obtains more lift than the inner wing for the following reasons:–

When an aircraft is yawed about the normal axis there will occur a small differential in the speed of airflow over the left and right wings.

Inertia causes the aircraft to continue for a short time along its original direction of flight. The effect of this upon dihedral or other methods used for lateral stability is to create a small increase in the angle of attack of the outer wing and the opposite on the inner wing. There will also be a minor masking of the airflow on the inner wing.

Fig. 4-7

Together these effects are pronounced and cause the aircraft to adopt a banking attitude followed by the nose dropping and the onset of a descending spiral.

EFFECT OF INERTIA

An aircraft, like all other masses, possesses inertia, it tries to continue on its original path even when the controls are operated to change that path. Thus, when the controls are moved there will be a lapse of time, even after the attitude has altered, before the flight path changes. This time lag will naturally vary with the size of the aircraft, and will be almost negligible in training aircraft but appreciable in the heavier and/or faster types.

EFFECT OF AIRSPEED
The effectiveness of the flying controls depends on the speed of the airflow passing over the control surfaces.

Fig. 4-8 Low Airspeed – Less Effective Controls

Fig. 4-9 High Airspeed – More Effective Controls

The greater the airspeed the more effective are the controls. At higher speeds, as well as becoming increasingly effective, the controls tend to become very firm and heavy, whilst at lower speeds they become light and sloppy. With the possible exception of the rudder they usually become ineffective below the landing speed.

EFFECT OF SLIPSTREAM
Slipstream increases the effective airflow over the control surfaces it envelopes, usually the elevators and rudder. Throttling back will therefore reduce the effectiveness of these controls. The ailerons are outside the area of slipstream influence and will remain unaffected by changes in throttle setting. The effect of slipstream is most clearly observed when entering the climb or glide from level flight.

The spiral path of the slipstream as it passes the vertical stabilizer, creates an angle of attack, which in turn produces a horizontal 'lift' or sideways component which tends to yaw the tail as shown in fig. 4-10. This angle of attack will vary with both RPM and airspeed. The lower the airspeed the tighter the 'coils' of slipstream will be, increasing the angle of attack relative to the vertical stabilizer. This, combined with a reduction in the directional stability of the aircraft at lower airspeeds will cause an increase in the yaw effect from the horizontal force.

At higher airspeeds the slipstream spiral becomes elongated and its angle of attack relative to the vertical stabiliser becomes less, resulting in a smaller horizontal 'lift' or sideways force. This, together with the increased directional stability of the aircraft at higher airspeeds causes the horizontal force and its effect upon the aircraft to diminish, and yaw is less pronounced. It can therefore be seen that during normal flight operations the largest yaw effect will occur when the aircraft is climbing.

In fig. 4-10 the propeller rotation is clockwise as viewed from the cockpit. This causes a slipstream direction which produces a force to the right at the tailplane. The effect of this is to cause the nose of the aircraft to yaw to the left.

Fig. 4-10

EFFECTS OF POWER
In all aircraft, changes in engine power have a definite effect upon longitudinal trim. An increase of power usually results in a nose up change of trim, and a decrese in power in a nose down change.

On propeller driven aircraft, changes in engine power can also effect the directional trim. An increase of power will usually cause a yaw in the opposite direction to the rotation of the propeller. This is particularly noticeable in single engined aircraft due to the slipstream effect on the keel surface, and the changed angle of attack on the vertical stabilizer.

HIGH POWER

RUDDER AND ELEVATORS
MORE EFFECTIVE

AILERONS ARE NOT
AFFECTED

Fig. 4-11

LOW POWER

RUDDER AND ELEVATORS
LESS EFFECTIVE

AILERONS ARE NOT
AFFECTED

Fig. 4-12

Fig. 4-13

Fig. 4-14

When propeller rotation is clockwise, an increase of power will result in a nose-up moment followed by yaw and roll to the left (Fig. 4-13).

When propeller rotation is clockwise, a decrease of power will result in a nose down moment. If right rudder or right rudder trim is being used at this stage, the aircraft will also tend to yaw and roll to the right (Fig. 4-14).

EFFECT OF TRIMMING CONTROLS

Trimming controls are designed to relieve the pilot of sustained loads on the flying controls. The correct method of use is to select the required attitude by the use of the primary flying controls, and then to adjust the appropriate trimmer until no pressure is needed on the control column or rudder pedals. Changes in trimmer position are normally required after changes in power, speed, and flap setting, and also after a variation of the aircraft's disposable load.

When an up position of the elevators is required to hold the nose in the level flight attitude............

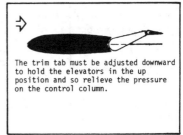

The trim tab must be adjusted downward to hold the elevators in the up position and so relieve the pressure on the control column.

Fig. 4-15

Trimming controls are a great help to the pilot, but as they are powerful and sensitive, they should be used carefully. Mishandling can lead to reduced aircraft performance and may also cause undue stress loads on the airframe. Trimming controls should not be used to relieve control loads of transient nature.

Fig. 4-16

EFFECTS OF FLAPS

Although many different forms of wing flaps are used on aircraft, they are all designed to vary the lift and/or drag. By increasing the lift, the flaps reduce the stalling speed and so enable the aircraft to fly safely at lower airspeeds. By increasing the drag, and acting as airbrakes, flaps make it necessary to glide at a steeper angle to maintain a given speed.

Figure 4-17 shows the effect of the wing curvature and angle of incidence producing an angle of downwash over the tail surfaces. The Centre of Pressure (C.P.), and the Drag force (D) in the mean 'drag line' position are also shown.

Fig. 4-17

The following diagram shows the flaps in the lowered position. When flaps are lowered, they cause a change in the position of the Centre of Pressure, and alter the angle of downwash over the tailplane. The total drag is increased and the drag line lowered. These four major effects usually cause a pitching moment to take place. When the pilot resists this pitch change and holds the aircraft in its original attitude a lower airspeed will result.

Fig. 4-18

On the majority of modern aircraft, the initial application of flap will increase the lift without causing much increase in the drag. However, a setting which varies with different aircraft will be reached, beyond which the lowering of further flap will start to make a substantial increase in the drag with little further increase in lift. This increase in drag will continue in proportion to the amount of flap lowered, but no appreciable increase in lift will occur after flap angles of about 60 degrees have been reached. The largest change of attitude usually takes place within the first 20 degrees or so of flap application, and may be nose down or nose up in direction, dependent upon the aircraft type.

The maximum permitted speed for the operation of flaps will be given in the appropriate Flight/Owner's Manual, and in modern aircraft this speed (V_{fe}) will also be displayed on the air speed indicator as the top of the white arc. This maximum speed limitation is imposed to avoid excessive stresses on the aircraft and to the flap operating mechanism.

OPERATION OF THE MIXTURE CONTROL

The use of this control will be applicable to the particular type of aircraft. At this early stage of training there is little value in learning its use with regard to fuel consumption, or operation at higher altitudes. However, during this exercise, the student should learn to appreciate that the mixture control is used for the following basic purposes:

1. To shut down the engine on the completion of each flight, and to shut down the engine as a specific emergency procedure during flight.
2. To achieve fuel economy during flight.
3. To maintain the correct fuel/air ratio when the aircraft is climbing above 5000 feet.

The explanation of 2 and 3 will be left until later and are given in the supplement to this exercise, but the reasons for using the mixture control to shut down the engine need to be known at this stage.

Figure 4-19 shows an illustration of the mixture control system. When the mixture control knob is set at the full rich position the tapered needle in the carburettor fuel metering system is withdrawn, allowing a maximum rate of fuel flow to be available when the throttle is opened. This position is normally used at low altitudes and for starting up, taking off and landing. When the mixture control knob is moved towards the full lean (idle cut-off) position, the tapered needle moves further into the fuel metering orifice and reduces the rate of fuel flow. When the knob is in the 'idle cut-off' position all fuel flow to the carburettor is cut off and the engine will stop.

Full rich

Fig. 4-19

With earlier engines the method of shutting down was basically to turn OFF the ignition switches, however, if there was any incandescent carbon deposit on the pistons or cylinder head it could cause a form of intermittent engine firing called pre-ignition. Due to the irregularity of this type of engine firing a harmful strain was imposed on the engine. To obviate this occurrence an 'idle cut-off' system was introduced, whereby no fuel was available for continued engine firing once the mixture control was placed into the 'idle cut-off' position. An added benefit with this system is that in the event of an engine fire during flight the engine could be shut down more quickly, and the possibility of the fuel spraying from a loose or cracked carburettor joint is eliminated.

NOTE: Several accidents have occurred during flight in the past due to the mixture control being inadvertently operated, instead of the carburettor heat control. Special care must be taken to avoid a mistake of this nature.

OPERATION OF THE CARBURETTOR HEAT CONTROL

The operation of this control and the circumstances under which it is used will vary slightly from one type of aircraft to another, and detailed reference to the particular Flight/Owner's Manual will need to be made. Therefore, at this stage it will be necessary to follow the instructions given in the aircraft manual. Basically the purpose of the carburettor heat control is to afford protection from ice forming within the carburettor system, and to remove such ice if it should form.

When the heat is applied there will normally be a drop in power due to the lower density of heated air. The 'Hot Air' position should not be selected for any length of time while the aircraft is on the ground with the engine running, this is because with hot air selected the engine air filter system is by-passed and dust particles will be ingested into the engine, causing unnecessary abrasive wear to the moving parts. This will however be of secondary importance should ice form within the induction system during ground operations.

It is vitally important to understand and appreciate the problems and the technique for the prevention and removal of carburettor ice as soon as possible during training, and in any event before the 'First Solo' flight. Therefore, the detailed information on carburettor icing which is contained in the supplement to this briefing must be learned as soon as practicable.

CABIN HEATING AND VENTILATION CONTROLS

The method of operating these controls will depend upon the specific aircraft type and the Flight/Owner's Manual will contain the necessary information. It should, however, be understood that the heat exchangers which supply heated cabin air are normally heated by the engine exhaust gases, and any cracks in the heat exchanger canister or associated pipes can lead to carbon monoxide fumes entering the cabin leading to a physical deterioration of the pilot. Because of this possibility, and in order to ensure mental alertness, the cabin cold air ventilation system should always be used in conjunction with the cabin heating system.

AIRMANSHIP

Airmanship will form part of every flight but on this first instruction exercise the student will only be briefly introduced to a few of the items which come under this heading. The items covered at this stage will normally be confined to the necessity for a continuous and adequate lookout, the maintenance of general orientation within the local flying area, and the procedure to adopt when taking or handing over control of the aircraft.

Supplement No. 1

MIXTURE CONTROL

The design philosophy of the current light aero engine demands an adequate knowledge of mixture control operation in order that the engine can be handled efficiently and correctly. This is particularly true for flight operations conducted above 4/5000 feet where engine rough running can easily occur if the mixture control is not used correctly. Although in the early stages of training a student will be unlikely to operate at heights above 5000 feet he will more likely do so when he has acquired his Private Pilot's Licence and undertakes long cross-country flights. Further, it must be appreciated that the fuel consumption figures obtained from the tables and graphs in Flight/Owner's Manuals are normally based upon the correct use of the mixture control system. A student who does not learn and understand the correct use of the mixture control during training will not always be capable of conducting safe flight operations once outside the supervision of the training environment.

Basically the mixture control is used to vary the fuel/air ratio for three separate reasons:

1. The fuel/air ratio in all reciprocating aero engines is set to give an over-rich mixture, and the actual degree of richness varies with the throttle setting, being greatest at full power operation. The purpose of this arrangement is to reduce the possibility of detonation, pre-ignition and overheating occurring in the cylinders. However, when operating at cruise power settings with an engine in normal condition the possibility of these factors occurring will be remote. Therefore it is acceptable for the pilot to achieve greater fuel economy by using the manual mixture control to achieve the correct mixture strength. Further to this, the excess fuel flow as a result of an over-rich mixture leads to plug fouling and excess carbon forming on the piston heads and valves. Therefore good engine handling dictates the use of correct mixture control operation in order to maintain the efficiency and life of the engine.

2. As the aircraft climbs the surrounding air density decreases and without some means of adjustment the fuel/air ratio will become too rich, and the engine will suffer a loss of power. This power loss will be indicated by a gradual drop in RPM (when a fixed pitch propeller is fitted) followed eventually by rough running.
3. When the 'Idle Cut-Off' position is used it provides an efficient method of stopping the engine.

There are several ways of determining the correct setting for the mixture control when it is appropriate to use it. However, the following represents the simplest method in small training aircraft which are not normally fitted with cylinder head temperature gauges or exhaust gas analysers.

1. Set the throttle as required.
2. Accurately note the RPM.
3. Move the mixture control towards the LEAN position slowly.
4. If mixture control is required it wil be indicated by a rise in RPM.
5. If a rise in RPM occurs, continue moving the mixture control towards the LEAN position until the highest RPM figure is achieved, and until further movement of the mixture control would cause a drop in RPM.
6. Once the RPM peak is passed, move the mixture control slightly towards the RICH position until the peak RPM is restored (this is to ensure that the engine is not in a critically lean condition where detonation may occur).
7. The above steps will need to be repeated whenever altitude or power are changed.

The above procedure can be used to obtain 'best power mixture' and also to avoid the engine running rough during a climb in excess of 5000 feet. Further, it will give a more economical fuel consumption at cruise power settings below 75% power at any height, and reduce the possibility of excess carbon deposits being formed on the plugs, piston heads and in the cylinders.

Although this manual is not designed to give a comprehensive and detailed explanation of engine efficiency and fuel/air ratios the following will be of interest and value to any pilot under training.

In an internal combustion engine the greatest heat energy derived from the burning of the combustible mixture occurs at a fuel-to-air ratio of 1 part fuel to 15 parts air, or expressed another way, 0.067 lbs of fuel to 1 lb of air. This is the chemically correct or ideal mixture strength where all the fuel and air is converted into heat energy i.e. no fuel is wasted. If this fuel/air ratio is changed so that the proportion of fuel to air is increased, then excess fuel will be passed through the engine in an unburnt state.

The mixture of 0.067 is a theoretical point that can only be demonstrated on a single cylinder in a laboratory. In engines with more than one cylinder, the variations in fuel distribution between the cylinders makes it difficult to evaluate the fuel/air ratio in each cylinder. This matter of distributing correct and equal amounts of fuel and air to the various cylinders is one of the greatest problems facing the aircraft engine manufacturers. Because of the unequal fuel/air ratio delivered to the various cylinders, the pilot who practises using extremely lean mixture settings, so increasing the proportion of air to fuel without reference to additional engine instrumentation could experience a situation where, for example, all cylinders in the engine are operating at normal temperatures – except for one hot cylinder, where the exhaust valve and seat are red hot.

By calibrating and adjusting the carburettor to give a slightly over-rich mixture the engine designer is able to overcome the problem of having one or more cylinders receiving a mixture ratio which is too lean. By further enriching the mixture the designer can guard against detonation, pre-ignition and excessive cylinder head temperatures when the engine is operating at very high power settings. It can be seen from this that all aero engines generally operate with an enriched mixture from idling through to full power.

Figure 4-20 illustrates the effect of excess fuel or excess air upon engine power. It will be seen that the engine produces its best power at a fuel/air ratio of approximately 0.080 lbs of fuel to 1 lb of air and therefore this represents a mixture setting where the demands of

Fig. 4-20

efficient power production and fuel economy are both fairly well satisfied.

Although it is possible to achieve greater fuel economy by reducing the mixture strength to 0.067, it is difficult to ensure this value of fuel/air ratio to all the cylinders of an engine equipped with a simple carburettor. Indiscriminate leaning is not conducive to efficient and safe engine handling, and special instrumentation such as exhaust gas analysers would be necessary. These types of instrument are not normally fitted in simple training aircraft, so a good general purpose fuel mixture will be as shown at 0.080 in the diagram.

The information contained in this supplement illustrates some of the principles involved in mixture control operation, however the Flight/Owner's Manual or the Engine Manual for the specific aircraft or engine type must be the basic reference document when employing mixture control techniques. Finally it must be clearly understood that the figures for range and endurance as given in tables or graphs in aircraft manuals are normally only applicable when mixture control is utilised.

CARBURETTOR HEAT CONTROL

The use of this control will vary with the aircraft type, and the procedure concerning when and how it is used must be obtained from the relevant Flight/Owner's Manual.

When certain atmospheric conditions of temperature and humidity occur, ice can form in the carburettor system. The vaporization of fuel combined with the expansion of air as it passes through the carburettor causes a sudden cooling of the fuel/air mixture, and in small aero engines this temperature drop can be as much as 20 degrees Centigrade. Water vapour contained in this air is condensed by the cooling and if the temperature in the carburettor reaches the freezing level or below, moisture is deposited as frost or ice on the inside of the carburettor passages and/or the throttle butterfly valve. Even a slight accumulation of this deposit will reduce power and in large amounts may lead to complete engine failure.

Dry days, or days when the outside air temperature is well below freezing, are conditions not conducive to carburettor icing, but if the outside air temperature is about −6°C to 30°C with visible moisture or high humidity, carburettor icing can occur. If the outside air temperature is much lower than −6°C any water droplets will condense directly into minute ice particles which will pass through the induction system without adhering to the inside of the carburettor passages and carburettor icing will not occur. Most modern aircraft have an outside air temperature gauge fitted inside the cockpit, and the outside air temperature can be monitored from this instrument.

Fig. 4-21

Fig. 4-22

The pilot first becomes aware that carburettor ice may be forming by one of two indications. On aircraft equipped with a fixed pitch propeller, a loss of engine RPM appears on the tachometer at an unchanged throttle setting. In the case of aircraft equipped with a constant speed propeller, a loss of manifold pressure is noted. There is no reduction in RPM in an engine fitted with a constant speed propeller since propeller pitch is automatically adjusted to compensate for the loss of power, thus maintaining a constant RPM. In either of the two cases, a roughness in engine operation will develop as the ice accumulates. It should be noted that a pilot scans the flight instruments more frequently than the engine instruments and therefore he will most probably notice any small drop in power output, initially through the indications of an airspeed reduction when height is held constant or, a gradual height loss when the airspeed is kept constant.

To prevent or remove ice, a carburettor heat system is installed (a typical system is shown in fig. 1-24). Pulling out the carburettor heat knob opens the carburettor heat valve, allowing hot air to pass through the carburettor where it mixes with the fuel and melts the ice. *It is vitally important to appreciate that carburettor icing can occur without visible moisture being present in the atmosphere..*

Application of carburettor heat allows hot air to enter the carburettor system, but an engine which has been throttled back for a short while may not be able to supply air at a sufficient heat to melt the ice quickly, therefore it is usually advisable to select 'Hot Air' whenever the engine is being operated at reduced power settings. Carburettor icing can be particularly hazardous if it forms at low power settings or with the throttle fully closed. The reason for this being that in a low power condition there will be little if any warning given i.e. during descents with little or no power being used there will be no clear indication of power loss or rough running. Further to this, the throttle butterfly valve will be in the nearly or fully closed position and only a small amount of ice will be needed around the periphery of the butterfly valve to stop the engine completely.

Fig. 4-23

If carburettor heat is applied after ice has already formed, the RPM may momentarily decrease and then increase as the ice melts, a further increase in RPM will occur when the carburettor air is returned to the 'COLD' position.

If 'Hot Air' is selected after a large quantity of ice has formed, the engine will run very rough or momentarily stop. The pilot should be aware that this is a natural occurrence whenever a large amount of ice melts into water and is ingested by the engine. During this period the carburettor air must be left in the 'HOT' position.

When applying carburettor heat as a precaution, partial application may be desirable in an aircraft which is known to suffer a substantial power loss when full heat is applied. This practice however, may tend to induce carburettor icing by warming air which was below the temperature range for ice formation and raising it up into the ice formation range. The Flight/Owner's Manual must be checked to determine the correct procedure for the aircraft type.

The carburettor heat control should not normally be used during taxying unless ice formation is suspected, since the air from the carburettor heat system is normally unfiltered. Taxying with unfiltered air could cause dirt, grass cuttings etc., to get into the engine cylinders and cause the cylinder walls and piston rings to develop excessive wear.

To sum up, the carburettor heat control is used:

(a) As a preventive measure against carburettor ice forming, particularly during prolonged descents or, when approaching to land.

(b) To positively remove ice which has formed in the carburettor system.

Due to the variable factors involved in the formation of carburettor ice, e.g. outside air temperature, adiabatic cooling, evaporation cooling and atmospheric humidity, it is not easy for the pilot to forecast when such conditions will occur. He must therefore remain on guard against such a possibility occurring during every flight. The remedial actions which are available whenever icing does occur are as follows:

First   Use full heat to clear any icing which has formed, then;

(1) If recommended by the aircraft manufacturers, use partial heat to prevent recurrence (the amount will have to be determined by trial and error).

(2) Alter the power setting or if applicable use mixture control. The evaporation of fuel normally accounts for some 70% of the temperature drop in the carburettor and therefore a power change can often have a positive effect upon the internal temperature of the carburettor. The greatest effect upon temperature change is usually made by increasing power.

(3) Alter the altitude at which the aircraft is flying. This however is usually a somewhat restricted remedy against ice reforming as the normal outside air temperature change is only 2° C per 1000 feet and the constraints of a 'safe height to fly' when reducing altitude and the fairly widespread existence of 'controlled airspace' when increasing altitude do not normally allow for much height variation.

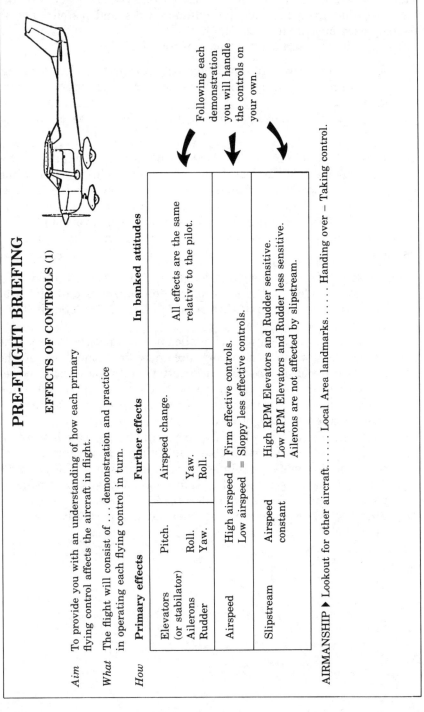

PRE-FLIGHT BRIEFING

EFFECTS OF CONTROLS (1)

Aim To provide you with an understanding of how each primary flying control affects the aircraft in flight.

What The flight will consist of . . . demonstration and practice in operating each flying control in turn.

How

Primary effects		Further effects	In banked attitudes
Elevators (or stabilator)	Pitch.	Airspeed change.	All effects are the same relative to the pilot.
Ailerons	Roll.	Yaw.	
Rudder	Yaw.	Roll.	
Airspeed		High airspeed = Firm effective controls. Low airspeed = Sloppy less effective controls.	
Slipstream	Airspeed constant	High RPM Elevators and Rudder sensitive. Low RPM Elevators and Rudder less sensitive. Ailerons are not affected by slipstream.	

Following each demonstration you will handle the controls on your own.

AIRMANSHIP ▶ Lookout for other aircraft. . . . . Local Area landmarks. . . . . . Handing over – Taking control.

PRE-FLIGHT BRIEFING

EFFECTS OF CONTROLS (2)

Aim   To provide you with an understanding of how the operation of the supplementary controls and systems affect the aircraft in flight.

What   The flight will consist of . . . demonstration and practice in operating the supplementary controls and aircraft systems.

How

	Effects	Summary
Power	Increase throttle setting – Pitch . . Yaw . . and Roll. Reduce throttle setting – Pitch . . Yaw . . and Roll. A correctly trimmed aircraft will maintain its attitude.	Use all main controls to hold attitude whenever power is changed. The need to retrim. Use main controls to obtain the attitude, then use trim controls to relieve pressures.
Trim	If the nose rises – forward trim is required. If the nose lowers – rearward trim is required.	
Flaps	Flap limiting speed – top limit of the white arc. Whenever flaps are lowered or raised a change in Pitch will occur.	Lower airspeed for original nose attitude when the flaps are down.
Mixture	Operation – The need for caution.	Cabin heating/ventilation – Operation and effect.
Carburettor Heat	Operation and effects.	

AIRMANSHIP ▶ Lookout for other aircraft. . . . . Local Area landmarks. . . . . Handing over – Taking over control.

Effects of Controls

Flight Demonstrations

INTRODUCTION

Ensure that the student can hear clearly and tell him to stop you if he fails to understand any part of the demonstration being given. Remind the student of the primary purpose of the exercise, which is to show him the correct method of holding and moving the controls and to see the effect of their movement upon the aircraft in flight. Ask him to particularly note the small and gentle control movements which are needed.

Resume:

The primary controls; elevators, ailerons and rudder will be demonstrated first, then the effect which the airspeed and slipstream have upon them.

ELEVATORS

INSTRUCTOR'S NOTE: Refer the student to the attitude of the nose in pitch, relative to the natural horizon and also note the airspeed.

DEMONSTRATION

These are operated by the fore and aft movement of the control column.

When the control column is moved forward the nose of the aircraft will lower. If the control column is held in this new forward position the nose will remain in this lower attitude.

Note the airspeed has now increased.

Return the aircraft to level flight.

When the control column is moved back the nose of the aircraft will rise. If the control column is held in this new aft position the nose will remain in a higher attitude. Note the airspeed has now decreased.

SUMMARY: The elevators control movement in the pitching plane and also affect the airspeed.

STUDENT PRACTICE Ask the student to raise the nose and hold it in a particular attitude as directed by you. After returning it to the level attitude ask him to lower the nose and again hold it in a particular attitude as directed by you. Finally ask him to return the aircraft to the level flight position.

INSTRUCTOR'S NOTE: When asking the student to operate the controls, it is important to give him a specific task, this will enable the instructor to 'test for understanding' and quickly correct any misconceptions which may have occurred. For example, asking the student at this stage to just move the control column forward will at best only prove that he understands your request, but you need to know if he understood your demonstration. You will only ascertain this by asking him specifically to lower or raise the nose and having altered the aircraft attitude to hold it for a short while in its new position. Although in this context it may appear to be a simple point, specific requests of this nature should become a fundamental principle of your instruction technique.

AILERONS

INSTRUCTOR'S NOTE: Ask the student to note the position of the cockpit coaming line or some other convenient datum in relation to the natural horizon, to establish the wings are laterally level.

DEMONSTRATION
These are operated by the lateral movement of the control column (or rotation of the control wheel).

When the control column is moved to the left, the left wing goes down – the aircraft is now banked to the left. If the control column is now moved back to the neutral position this bank will remain constant. Movement of the control column to the right will raise the left wing and as the wings become level again the control column should be returned to the neutral position.

Repeat this explanation and demonstration to the right.

SUMMARY: The ailerons control movement in the rolling plane.

STUDENT PRACTICE Ask the student to bank in specific directions and ensure he notes your lookout prior to each manoeuvre.

RUDDER

INSTRUCTOR'S NOTE: Select a reference feature ahead, one which the student can clearly see. Ensure the wings are kept approximately level throughout the demonstration in order that the yaw can be seen clearly. If the aircraft is allowed to bank the student may have difficulty in appreciating the yaw during this early stage of his training.

DEMONSTRATION
When pressure is applied to the left rudder pedal the nose moves across the horizon to the left, this is known as yaw. If this pressure is removed the yaw stops and the aircraft continues in a straight line again.

Repeat this explanation and demonstration to the right.

SUMMARY: Although the rudder can create yaw, it is not normally used in this sense. However because the rudder can create yaw, it can also be used to prevent yaw and it is in this latter sense that the rudder is mainly used during flight.

STUDENT PRACTICE Ask the student to apply rudder in specific directions, and then centralise it again.

INSTRUCTOR'S NOTE: Throughout these demonstrations the student should be obtaining an appreciation of the amount and rate of all the primary control movements relative to the amount and rate of the aircraft's response.

EFFECT OF THE PRIMARY CONTROLS WITH THE AIRCRAFT BANKED

DEMONSTRATION
The aircraft should now be placed in a shallow banked attitude and each of the three primary controls operated to show the student that when the aircraft is banked, all three controls still operate in their normal sense 'relative to the pilot'.

SUMMARY: The effects are in relation to the aircraft axes and not necessarily to the natural horizon.

STUDENT PRACTICE Ask the student to place the aircraft in a shallow banked attitude and then operate all three controls in turn.

FURTHER EFFECT OF AILERON AND RUDDER

INSTRUCTOR'S NOTE: Make it clear to the student that you will only be using one control at a time during the following demonstration. This will be more clearly appreciated if you keep your feet off the rudder whilst demonstrating the further effect of ailerons and removing your hand from the control column when demonstrating the further effect of rudder. It must also be remembered that in modern aircraft there will be very little adverse yaw (opposite to bank) when the ailerons are used. The main effect will be sideslip in the direction of bank, leading to yaw and a spiral descent.

DEMONSTRATION: AILERONS

When the aircraft is banked by the use of ailerons a yaw will occur in the direction of the lowered wing leading to a spiral descent.

SUMMARY: Ailerons produce roll as a primary effect and yaw as a secondary effect. A spiral descent will follow.
   Instructor demonstration only – no student practice.

DEMONSTRATION: RUDDER

When the aircraft is yawed by the use of rudder a roll in the direction of the yaw will follow. This effect will cause the nose to drop and a spiral descent will follow.

SUMMARY: Rudder will produce yaw as a primary effect and roll as a secondary effect. Eventually a spiral descent will occur.
   Instructor demonstration only – no student practice.

EFFECT OF AIRSPEED

INSTRUCTOR'S NOTE: Maintain a constant throttle setting throughout this demonstration and place the aircraft into a trimmed attitude to give first a high airspeed, and then a low airspeed. It is not necessary to use very high or very low airspeeds during this demonstration, the object will be achieved provided the two speeds chosen are some 40 knots apart. Make sure only the student is handling the controls when you ask him to feel their responsiveness. If an aural stall warner is fitted, mention to the student that this may sound during the demonstration.

DEMONSTRATION
The effectiveness of the controls is dependent upon airspeed. At higher speeds they are firm and effective, with small control movements producing a positive response from the aircraft. At lower speeds they are less effective and larger control movements are required to achieve aircraft response.

You will note the speed is now ... knots and my movements of the elevators, ailerons and rudder produce a firm and responsive change to the aircraft's attitude.

STUDENT PRACTICE   Ask the student to operate all three controls and note their effectiveness.

You will now note the speed is ... knots and my movements of the elevators, ailerons and rudder, although large, produce a small response from the aircraft. They also feel 'sloppy' to handle.

STUDENT PRACTICE   Ask the student to operate all three controls again and note their reduced effectiveness and 'sloppy' feel.

Resume normal cruising flight.

SUMMARY: From this it can be seen that the primary flying controls rely upon airspeed for their effectiveness and if a pilot allows the speed to become too low he will lose control of the aircraft.

EFFECT OF SLIPSTREAM

INSTRUCTOR'S NOTE: Maintain a constant airspeed throughout this demonstration. The normal gliding speed would be quite suitable for this purpose. Ensure the aircraft is trimmed correctly for both the high power and low power condition before handing over control to the student.

DEMONSTRATION
The slipstream energy from the propeller passes over the tailplane surfaces and therefore the greater the RPM the greater the effectiveness of the elevators and rudder. The ailerons are situated outside the slipstream zone and are not affected by changes in RPM.

You will now note the airspeed is ... knots and the RPM ...

STUDENT PRACTICE   Ask the student to operate all three primary controls and note their effectiveness.

Maintaining the same airspeed close the throttle and re-trim.

STUDENT PRACTICE   Ask the student to operate all three controls again and note the aileron feel is unchanged but the elevators and rudder have become less effective.

SUMMARY: It can now be appreciated that any change in power setting will affect the responsiveness of the elevators and rudder.

INSTRUCTOR'S NOTE: During the next three demonstrations which cover the Trimming Controls, Power and Flaps, (Part Two of the Effects of Controls) the instructor should clearly show the effects on the aircraft attitude of the control being operated, but when the student takes control more benefit will be obtained if he is directed to operate these supplementary controls while he is using the primary flying controls to maintain the aircraft's attitude.

Effects of Controls – Part Two

EFFECT OF POWER
INSTRUCTOR'S NOTE: Ensure the aircraft is correctly trimmed in level flight at cruising speed. Remove your hand and feet from the controls when increasing and decreasing power.

DEMONSTRATION
From cruising flight increase to high power. Note the nose rises, followed by bank and yaw to the left.
   Resume level flight at cruising power.
   From cruising flight decrease power. Note the nose lowers and this is possibly followed by a slight bank and yaw to the right.
   Resume level flight at cruising power.

SUMMARY: Whenever power is altered it will be necessary to adjust all the primary flying controls to maintain the aircraft in a constant attitude.

STUDENT PRACTICE   Direct the student to select different power settings whilst maintaining the aircraft's attitude.

EFFECT OF THE TRIMMING CONTROLS

INSTRUCTOR'S NOTE: Bear in mind the primary purpose of this demonstration is merely to show the effect of the trimming tab(s), the operation of the trim control and the principle behind their use. During that period when the student is being taught to relieve control pressures on the primary controls it will speed up his learning if you point out the direction and approximate amount of trim control movement.

DEMONSTRATION

From trimmed cruising flight raise the nose slightly and allow the airspeed to reduce. Release the control column and the nose will lower – the student will clearly see that back pressure will be required to keep the nose in the higher attitude.

Raise the nose to the original high attitude and demonstrate the correct trimming procedure. Point out that the primary controls are used to establish the required attitude and the trimming control is used to relieve the residual control pressure.

Return the aircraft to the cruising flight attitude but do not re-trim.

STUDENT PRACTICE   Ask the student to hold the aircraft in the cruising attitude and note the pressure required on the control column. Direct the student to re-trim until a no-load condition exists on the control column.

Finally point out the importance and the sensitivity of the trimming control by making the student hold the level flight attitude in pitch whilst you wind on sufficient nose-up trim to permit him to appreciate the strong loads which can be imposed if the correct trimming procedure is not carried out.

INSTRUCTOR'S NOTE: If the training aircraft is fitted with a rudder trimmer a shortened version of the above demonstration in the yawing sense will normally be sufficient.

EFFECT OF FLAPS

INSTRUCTOR'S NOTE: As with the previous parts of this exercise the demonstration of flaps at this stage is to show the effect they have upon the aircraft's attitude. The various reasons for flap operation and the amount of flap required should be covered as appropriate in subsequent exercises.

DEMONSTRATION

In trimmed level flight note that the airspeed is within the flap operating range and remove your hand and feet from the controls.

Ask the student to note the aircraft's attitude and trimmed

condition. Point out the flap switch/lever and flap indicator.

Select half flap and note the aircraft's change of attitude. Return the aircraft to the original attitude and re-trim. Note the airspeed is now lower.

Again leave the control column free and select the rest of the flaps. Note once more the pitch change of the aircraft. Return the aircraft to its original attitude and re-trim. Note the further lowering of the airspeed and call the student's attention visually to the flaps down position pointing out that the lower airspeed is due to the lowered flap which gives an appreciable increase to the aircraft's drag.

STUDENT PRACTICE   Ask the student to take control and maintain the aircraft's attitude whilst he raises the flaps to the halfway position and then re-trims. After this ask the student to again hold the aircraft's attitude constant whilst he raises the flaps fully and then re-trims.

DEMONSTRATION
Finally, with the aircraft trimmed in level cruising flight select the flaps fully down. Re-trim and leave the control column free. Raise the flaps fully in one selection and point out the marked change of attitude and height loss. Ensure the student appreciates the results of this incorrect procedure for raising the flaps.

SUMMARY: The use of flaps affect the pitch attitude of the aircraft and the airspeed. The operational use of flap will be covered later in subsequent exercises.

EFFECT OF THE MIXTURE CONTROL

INSTRUCTOR'S NOTE: At this stage it is too early to introduce the use of the mixture control for efficient engine operation or for fuel economy. However the danger of inadvertently moving this control to the 'Lean' or 'Idle Cut Off' position should be covered and with American-built engines this danger can be demonstrated at a safe altitude.

DISCRETIONARY DEMONSTRATION
Reduce power to a low cruise setting and then lean the mixture until rough running is clearly heard. Point out that the engine would stop if further leaning was carried out.

SUMMARY: The detailed and correct use of the mixture control will be covered later on in the student's training.

EFFECT OF THE CARBURETTOR HEAT CONTROL

INSTRUCTOR'S NOTE: If carburettor icing occurs during this flight then it would be sensible to explain and demonstrate the use of this control. However if this opportunity does not occur the demonstration should be confined to 'Hot Air' selection, and its effect upon the engine RPM.

DEMONSTRATION

When carburettor icing occurs, note the indicated RPM, and then select carburettor heat. Note the immediate drop in RPM which will normally be followed by a very slight rise if icing had existed. Reselect 'Cold Air' and note the RPM rises to a higher figure than that noted originally.

Point out that if considerable icing had been present rough running of the engine would have been heard. The selection of 'Hot Air' at this stage may temporarily worsen this rough running condition and in the event of a large ice build up in the carburettor the engine may even stop firing for a moment or two when 'Hot Air' selection is made. This period will normally be very brief and the heat control should be left at 'Hot' during this period.

CABIN HEAT AND VENTILATION CONTROLS

INSTRUCTOR'S NOTE: The operation of these controls can easily be forgotten during your air demonstrations but in the closed cabin type aircraft in common use today they are an important feature and should be properly understood by the student.

DEMONSTRATION

Point out the various control knobs and ensure the student has operated them before the conclusion of this flight. Stress the necessity of having 'Fresh Air Inlets' at least partially open whenever the cabin heating system is being used and if a windscreen de-misting system is available make sure he understands how to operate it.

Taxying

Instructor's Guide

Introduce this exercise as early as possible, gradually increasing the student's responsibilities as proficiency increases. Allow the student to taxy on all possible occasions and resist the temptation to take over control in order to save time.

The order in which this exercise is taught depends on many variables, in addition to the student's progress and ability. Lessons should therefore be adapted to the prevailing circumstances. Whenever possible, carry out the initial taxying lessons in an open area on the airfield where there is plenty of space to manoeuvre.

AIRMANSHIP

Stress the need for a continuous lookout, coupled with reasonable but safe taxying speeds. The pilot is at all times responsible for the safety of the aircraft, and although marshalling signals should in general be obeyed, in this respect they are advisory and not mandatory.

Serviceability checks of the appropriate flight instruments such as the Attitude Indicator, Heading Indicator, Turn Co-ordinator and Magnetic Compass should be introduced as soon as possible consistent with the student's stage of progress and in any event by the time he goes on his 'First Solo'.

BEFORE THE EXERCISE

The Long Briefing should cover the following:

Objectives.

Pre-Taxying Checks.

Starting, Control of Speed and Stopping.

Engine Handling.

Control of Direction and Turning (including Manoeuvring in Confined Spaces).

Parking Area, Procedures and Precautions.

Effects of Wind.

Effects of Ground Surface.

Freedom of Rudder Movement.

Marshalling Signals.

Instrument Checks.
Airmanship and Air Traffic Control Procedures.
Common Errors.
EMERGENCIES – Brake or Steering Failure.

The short Pre-Flight Briefing should be based upon the relevant part of the Long Briefing and the Taxying Exercise to be covered.

DURING THE EXERCISE
The emphasis in taxying should be placed on the need for care, as aircraft are not ideally suited to movement on the ground because of the following factors:

The aircraft's keel surface makes it susceptible to weathercock effect in brisk to strong winds.
The application of power or brakes needs time to take effect.
Tailwheel type aircraft can cause problems due to the position of the Centre of Gravity and the effect of inertia.

Starting, Control of Speed and Stopping.
When introducing this portion of the exercise it will be helpful to utilise a fairly straight portion of a taxyway unless operating from a grass airfield, and also ensure that you will not be causing an obstruction to following aircraft.

Parking Area Procedures and Precautions
This part of the exercise should only be covered in detail after the student has had some practice at taxying the aircraft.

EMERGENCIES
It will not be sufficient to teach the emergency procedures solely during classroom periods. The student must be kept on the alert for the eventuality of an emergency occurring, and to this end the instructor should simulate emergency situations from time to time during dual instruction, ensuring that the correct procedures are put into effect by the student. When demonstrating brake failure near obstacles, greater teaching value will be achieved if the instructor actually switches OFF the engine and brings the aircraft to a stop at least once when covering this emergency situation. However when this is planned ensure you will not cause inconvenience to other aircraft.

COMMON ERRORS
● Application of brakes without first reducing power.
● Fast taxying when time is pressing.

● Using brakes and power together.
● Failure to observe movement of other taxying aircraft, or missing R/T calls made by Air Traffic Control.
● Lack of anticipation when straightening the aircraft after a turn.
● Lack of anticipation of the 'weathercock effect' during moderate to strong crosswind conditions.
● Failure to look behind to ensure the tailplane will remain clear of obstructions when turning in congested areas.

Taxying

Long Briefing

OBJECTIVES

To control the aircraft safely whilst on the ground under its own power, and to handle such emergencies as Brake Failure or Steering Failure.

INTRODUCTION

The control of aircraft on the ground entails safe handling whilst taxying at comparatively slow speeds. An aircraft requires control in direction and rate of movement, and such control is obtained through the independent use of the rudder pedals, engine thrust, and brakes, or any combination of these.

PRE-TAXYING CHECKS

The internal checks after engine starting should be completed and when applicable the necessary radio communication with ATC established before taxying is commenced.

In areas where aircraft normally park, space is often limited and it is therefore important to ensure that it is all clear around the aircraft before the brakes are released. The position of any obstructions and other aircraft should be noted and considerable care should be used when turning. Remember the tailplane is some distance behind the pilot's seat and a pilot who turns his aircraft tightly can easily foul the tailplane on obstructions or other aircraft. The use of power should be the minimum required to prevent the danger of the propeller slipstream damaging other aircraft, and also the inconvenience of blowing dirt and similar material into hangars.

STARTING, CONTROL OF SPEED AND STOPPING

More power is required to start the aircraft than to keep it moving because of the initial power requirement to overcome inertia. Once the aircraft is moving, power will need to be reduced to avoid accelerating to an unmanageable speed. During the early stages of taxying practice, speed assessment is best obtained by judging the speed of the aircraft in relation to the ground close to the aircraft.

Brakes are used to reduce speed only after the throttle has been closed. Avoid using power and brakes together except when necessary to assist turning the aircraft in confined spaces.

Power and brake applications should always be smooth, and with tailwheel aircraft the control column should be held back when either are applied. Harsh braking, excessive use of power and failure to keep the control column back separately or together, may cause the aircraft to nose over.

The forward view from nosewheel aircraft is very good, but with tailwheel aircraft the nose obstructs the forward vision, and weaving the nose of the aircraft is therefore necessary to obtain the clear lookout essential for safe taxying under all conditions. A careful lookout for obstacles and other aircraft on the ground should be maintained at all times. When taxying, pilots must be prepared to give way to aircraft approaching to land or taking off. On most aircraft it is advisable to taxy with the flaps up and the hatches or windows closed.

To stop the aircraft, the throttle should be closed first and the brakes applied smoothly and symmetrically. When the aircraft has been brought to a stop the parking brake should then be applied and the throttle set to 1200 RPM. With tail wheel aircraft the use of the parking brake while the aircraft is still moving can tip the aircraft onto its nose, therefore especial care should be exercised with this type.

ENGINE HANDLING

The throttle should always be used smoothly and abrupt applications of power avoided. The engine should be allowed to warm up for a few minutes before commencing to taxy. The engine 'warm up' period should be made at approximately 1200 RPM to allow cold oil to thin out and pass freely through the various passages inside the engine.

Many air cooled engines are closely cowled and designed with baffles which direct the flow of air around the cylinders during flight. When the aircraft is on the ground much less air is available and prolonged running may cause serious overheating. This overheating can occur before any indication of rising temperature is given by the oil temperature gauge. If a cylinder head temperature gauge is fitted this will be a more reliable source for any indication of overheating.

Many low powered modern engines are designed to be operated with very short warm up periods, the initial sluggishness of the oil being taken care of in their basic design. In which case it is not normal to fit a cylinder head temperature gauge, but nevertheless good engine handling considerations still apply and prolonged running on the ground, particularly at high power and high ambient temperatures must be avoided.

The use of carburettor heat normally involves by-passing the main induction air filter and therefore during carburettor heat operation dust particles etc, will be ingested by the engine causing increased wear of the cylinder walls and pistons. Therefore, apart from checking its operation before flight, ground operation should only take place when engine icing occurs or is suspected.

When the engine is idling at very low RPM, carbon deposits build up on the sparking plugs which in turn will reduce the engine efficiency and power output when the throttle is fully open. A minimum idling RPM will be laid down in the Flight/Owner's Manual; normally this RPM is approximately 1200 and should always be set when the aircraft is kept stationary with the engine running.

CONTROL OF DIRECTION AND TURNING

Rudder and differential brake are used as the normal means of controlling direction and turning, a push force to the rudder pedal being applied in the direction of the required turn. The rudder pedal movement required to enter and straighten out from turns must be anticipated. The amount and direction of the control movements used will depend upon the strength of the wind and its direction in conjunction with the direction of the turn. When controlling direction in tailwheel aircraft the rudder will often need to be used to its limit. If rudder alone will not turn the aircraft, more engine thrust or the use of differential braking will normally produce the required results. With nose wheel aircraft control is simplified by the use of a steerable nosewheel operated through the rudder pedals. Due to the fact that nosewheel aircraft can be operated in stronger wind conditions than tailwheel aircraft, extra care must be taken not to take advantage of this by taxying at high speeds which would reduce the safety factor.

When manoeuvring in confined spaces the tail can swing out quite sharply and this must be anticipated in order to avoid adjacent obstacles. When using differential braking in these conditions a locked wheel must be avoided unless it is absolutely necessary to ensure the safety of the aircraft. Locking a wheel when turning causes a sideways stress on the tyre which in turn can produce a hazard during take-off or landing when weakened tyre sidewalls could rupture.

PARKING AREA PROCEDURES AND PRECAUTIONS
The brakes must be checked immediately upon commencement of taxying out from or into the parking area. When an aircraft is parked on sloping ground the use of chocks is advisable to guard against the inadvertent failure of the parking brake. A small chock placed appropriately in front of or behind the nosewheel of tricycle undercarriage aircraft will be satisfactory for this purpose. Whenever the aircraft is to be left out in the open and unattended for some time it should be properly secured and tied down.

EFFECT OF WIND
The control of the aircraft on the ground will be affected by the speed and direction of the wind. When taxying into wind the controls will be more effective than when taxying downwind. Extra caution is required in light aircraft when taxying in a crosswind. When on the ground, aircraft have a natural tendency to line up with the wind due to the larger keel surface behind the centre of gravity. The stronger the crosswind the greater will be this tendency, and in strong winds the pilot may find himself unable to control this effect. Tailwheel aircraft are more prone to difficulties when taxying in crosswinds and although nosewheel aircraft have a greater steering capability there may be times when differential brake will be needed to maintain direction. This is due to the strength of the wind on the keel surface of the aircraft causing the nosewheel to be forced sideways. Such an effect will be more common on wet grass than for example dry hard taxyways.

WIND

USE UP AILERON ON LH WING AND NEUTRAL ELEVATOR

USE UP AILERON ON RH WING AND NEUTRAL ELEVATOR

USE DOWN AILERON ON LH WING AND DOWN ELEVATOR

USE DOWN AILERON ON RH WING AND DOWN ELEVATOR

Fig. 5-1

CODE

WIND DIRECTION ▶

Strong quartering winds are probably the most difficult for taxying. In these wind conditions the elevators should be held in the down position and the aileron on the side from which the wind is coming should also be held down. Figure 5-1 shows how to position the flying controls during windy conditions. Finally, whenever gusty conditions are experienced the pilot should be especially alert for 'weather-cocking effect' and a slower taxying speed adopted.

EFFECTS OF GROUND SURFACE

Extra care must be taken when taxying over rough or soft ground surfaces, and ridges and ruts should be crossed at a 45° angle. Speed must be kept very low and a sharp lookout maintained for any holes or 'bad ground' markers. When taxying over loose stony soil or gravel it should be borne in mind that the propeller tips will pick up small stones and similar material which can damage the propeller and other parts of the aircraft.

All aircraft with a tricycle landing gear will have a relatively small clearance between the propeller and the ground and this is another reason for keeping the taxying speed low when crossing rough ground, also the shocks to the landing gear and particularly the nosewheel are multiplied by the square of the taxying speed.

When taxying over wet grass the braking effectiveness is seriously reduced, and this is an important consideration when slowing down at the end of a landing run. The transition from a wet grass surface to a wet tarmac surface will cause any braking action to suddenly become more effective and could easily tip a tailwheel aircraft onto its nose, or cause nosewheel damage to a tricycle type. Although these factors are fairly elementary, they can be easily forgotten when a pilot is in a hurry, or during the stress of a particular landing situation.

MARSHALLING SIGNALS

These signals are devised to enable a form of communication to exist between the pilot and the groundcrew directing the aircraft's movement on the ground. They are laid down in detail in 'The Rules of the Air and Air Traffic Control Regulations' and are also shown in 'The United Kingdom Air Pilot'. Pilots must become conversant with

COME
AHEAD

STOP

these signals in order to control the aircraft safely when being directed and manoeuvring in parking areas.

INSTRUMENT CHECKS

An opportunity is afforded when taxying to check the indications of certain flight instruments such as the attitude indicator, direction indicator, magnetic compass and turn and balance indicator (or turn co-ordinator). These checks however, should be carried out after the aircraft is clear of the parking area. Essentially these checks consist of turning the aircraft to the left whilst checking that the turn indicator shows a turn to the left with the ball of the balance indicator moving to the right, and the direction indicator and magnetic compass show a decrease of heading. A right turn is then initiated to check a correct indication of these instruments in the opposite direction. The attitude indicator should remain relatively steady during both these turns. If incorrect indications are received from any of these instruments the intended flight should be cancelled unless the instructor decides the particular instrument is not required for the safety of the flight.

AIRMANSHIP AND AIR TRAFFIC CONTROL PROCEDURES

The pilot is captain of the aircraft at all times. This applies equally on the ground and in the air. During the period when the aircraft is operating upon the airfield manoeuvring area it is the responsibility of the pilot to maintain a visual and listening watch for light signals or radio messages from the Air Traffic Controller. The signals given by ground marshallers and Air Traffic Controllers are usually of an advisory nature and it is up to the pilot to decide the best course of action. For example, upon the receipt of the 'Clear Take-Off' call from Air Traffic Control it is still up to the pilot to ensure that the approach path is clear of other aircraft approaching to land and that the take-off path is clear. Common sense, self discipline and courtesy are all hallmarks of the good pilot and they apply equally on the ground and in the air. Fast taxying is foolhardy and can lead to taxying accidents, this particularly applies when taxying in the vicinity of obstructions and other aircraft. A final note concerning airmanship during taxying is that special care must be taken when in the vicinity of areas where other aircraft may be carrying out engine power checks. Ground engineers and pilots often run-up engines in the vicinity of hangars and the propeller wash from mulit-engined aircraft can easily cause light aircraft to be blown over. Further to this, many light aircraft operate from the same airfields as jet aircraft and the jet blast behind such aircraft can exceed 80 m.p.h. within 120 feet of their engines during the application of thrust to start their taxying operations.

EMERGENCIES

The emergencies covered during the Taxying exercise will be:

(1) Nosewheel steering failure or when applicable tailwheel castoring failure.
(2) Brake failure.
    (a) Near obstructions.
    (b) Away from obstructions.

Nosewheel Steering Failure: If at any time the steering mechanism or linkage to the nosewheel fails, the use of differential braking action will usually be sufficient to maintain directional control. Should an unserviceability of this nature occur whilst taxying prior to take-off the flight must be cancelled and the aircraft taxied cautiously back to the parking area. Should the nosewheel become locked the aircraft must be stopped, Air Traffic Control informed and the engine shut down.

Tailwheel Castoring Failure: In the event of this occurrence the advice given under nosewheel steering failure should be followed, but if strong crosswind conditions prevail the advisability of shutting down the engine and waiting for assistance should be considered. Taxying should never be continued if the tailwheel castoring mechanism becomes locked.

Brake Failure: The main factors affecting the action to be taken in the event of brake failure are:

    (a) The amount of clearance from other aircraft and obstructions.
    (b) The wind strength and direction.
    (c) The nature of the ground surface and gradient.
    (d) The smaller turning effect of use of power without brake, particularly in tailwheel aircraft.

Basically there are two situations which decide the procedure to be adopted if brake failure occurs:

When the aircraft is near obstructions: In this situation there is a strong possibility of the aircraft colliding with obstructions or other aircraft, and if this does occur the rotating propeller will cause the most damage. Therefore whenever obstructions are in the immediate vicinity the aircraft should be steered into the nearest safe open area and the temptation to use power to assist in turning the aircraft should normally be resisted. The ignition should be switched off as quickly as possible, and when the aircraft has stopped Air Traffic Control should be informed and the rest of the closing down procedures put into effect. The control locks should then be placed in position and the pilot should wait with the aircraft until assistance arrives. No attempt should be made to taxy the aircraft back to the parking area without assistance.

When the aircraft is clear of obstructions: If a brake failure occurs out in the open and away from obstructions, or on the manoeuvring area, the aircraft should be allowed to slow down and then taxied into a position clear of the take-off and landing area. Grass surfaces provide a reasonable braking action, and therefore where it is safe to do so, the aircraft should be steered onto adjacent grass areas where it will quickly come to a stop. Air Traffic Control should then be informed and a request for assistance made. The normal engine stopping procedure can then be carried out. The control locks can be placed in position and when the wind is brisk or strong the aircraft should be turned manually into the wind direction. The pilot should then wait by the aircraft until assistance arrives. No attempt should be made to taxy the aircraft back to the parking area without assistance.

PRE-FLIGHT BRIEFING

TAXYING

Demonstration 1.

Aim To teach you how to move the aircraft safely under its own power on the ground

What The method of Starting, Controlling Speed and Stopping the aircraft.

How Starting, Control of speed and Stopping. Aircraft stationary and in a clear area.

Starting
Close the throttle.
Rudder pedals central.
Brakes released.
Open the throttle sufficiently to get the aircraft moving (inertia effect).
Reduce power slightly.

Control of speed
Speed controlled with throttle and brakes.
Too slow – Increase power.
Too fast – Reduce power and use brakes gently.
More power required if uphill or into wind.
Less power required if downhill or downwind.
Engine handling – smooth and gentle throttle movements.

Stopping
Close the throttle.
Rudder pedals central.
Brakes as necessary – smooth operation.
When aircraft stops – select parking brake.
Open throttle to 1200 RPM.

Airmanship
Maintain correct taxying speed.
If in doubt, bring the aircraft to a stop.

Demonstration 2.

AIM To teach you how to control direction and to turn the aircraft safely.

What The method of controlling direction and turning the aircraft on the ground.

How Control of Direction and Turning.

Control of direction
Once the aircraft is moving, the rudder pedals are used to control direction.

Turning
Applying pressure to the left rudder pedal will cause the aircraft to turn to the left.
Applying pressure to the right rudder pedal will cause the aircraft to turn to the right.
Cenralising the rudder pedals wil enable the aircraft to continue straight ahead.
Anticipation will be required to straighten up on a specific heading.

Turning in confined spaces
Differential brake will be required to carry out tight turns.
Slower speed is necessary and care must be used to ensure the tail clears obstructions.
Slight increase in power will be required to maintain aircraft movement.
Avoid locking a wheel during the turn.

Airmanship
Lookout – Remain well clear of obstructions.
        Right of way rules.
Maintain correct taxying speed.
If in doubt, bring the aircraft to a stop.

PRE-FLIGHT BRIEFING
TAXYING

Demonstration 3.

Aim   To teach you how to taxy the aircraft safety in various taxying conditions.

What   The correct procedures used to control the aircraft during various taxying conditions.

How   *Parking Area Procedure and Precautions:*
         The use of marshalling signals.
         Brake test prior to leaving or entering parking areas.
         Lookout – ahead and to either side and ensure the tail is clear of obstructions whilst turning.
         Rudder freedom – ensure full travel.

         Instrument Checks: When clear of obstructions:
         Turn Co-ordinator, Heading Indicator and Magnetic Compass, Attitude Indicator.

         Engine Handling:
         Avoid long stationary periods whilst facing downwind.
         Review of Oil Temperature/Pressure gauges.
         Avoid use of carburettor heat unless carburettor icing is suspected.

         Effect of Wind:
         Taxying upwind/downwind – use of elevators.
         Taxying crosswind – use of ailerons and alertness for weathercock action. Use of differential brake.

Effect of Ground Surface:
Downhill gradient or smooth surface – less power will be required.
Uphill gradient or grass surface – more power will be required.
Rough ground should be crossed at an angle with the control column held firmly back.
The effect of braking action will change when crossing from grass to tarmac and vice versa.
Avoid harsh braking on wet grass.

Airmanship
Lookout – anticipation of other aircraft movements. Avoid fast taxying speeds and be alert for ATC instructions by light signals or radio.

PRE-FLIGHT BRIEFING
TAXYING

Demonstration 4.

Aim   To teach you the correct procedures to adopt should nose wheel steering failure or brake failure occur whilst taxying.

What   The demonstration and practice of EMERGENCY procedures.

How   *Nosewheel Steering Failure:*
If loss of steering occurs taxy cautiously back to the parking area by judicious use of power and differential brake.
If steering jams, inform Air Traffic Control – switch OFF the engine and wait for assistance.

Brake Failure: Near Obstructions. . . . .
Throttle closed – magneto switches OFF.
Steer the aircraft into an open area.
When the aircraft is stationary;
Inform Air Traffic Control.
Complete the engine shut down procedures.
When strong winds prevail, turn the aircraft into wind by hand.
Remain with the aircraft until assistance arrives.
Do not taxy without manual assistance.

Brake Failure: Away from Obstructions. . . . . .
Reduce speed.
Inform Air Traffic Control.
Taxy clear of the manoeuvring area and stop the aircraft into wind and where it will not obstruct other aircraft.
Complete the normal engine shut down drills.
Remain with the aircraft until assistance arrives.
Do not carry out any further taxying until manual assistance is available.

Airmanship. . . .   Application of all normal airmanship considerations during the performance of these procedures.

Taxying

Flight Demonstrations

INTRODUCTION

The contents of the total taxying exercise may be divided into four specific demonstration groups as follows:

1. Starting, Control of Speed and Stopping.
2. Control of Direction and Turning.
3. Parking Area Procedures and Precautions, including Taxying Considerations of a General Nature.
4. Emergency Situations and Procedures.

It will however be logical to introduce some of the items in demonstration 3 as a commentary during those periods when demonstrations 1 and 2 are being given.

Airmanship items which are applicable to the safe handling of aircraft on the ground will normally be covered at the appropriate times and as such will be integrated into a number of taxying periods.

DEMONSTRATION 1. STARTING, CONTROL OF SPEED AND STOPPING

Flight Lesson	*Demonstration Sequence*
Starting	Throttle friction loose. Throttle closed. Rudder pedals central. Control column neutral (or as required for aircraft type, e.g. tail-wheel). Lookout behind, to each side and ahead. . . . If clear. . . . Increase power smoothly until the aircraft is moving forward. Reduce power slightly once the aircraft is moving.

Control of speed	Maintain lookout. Note the correct taxying speed.
Allow the aircraft to slow down. Increase the speed to more than acceptable	If the aircraft slows down, increase the power as required. If the aircraft begins to move too fast, reduce power to maintain a safe taxying speed.
Emphasis point.	Fast taxying must be avoided at all times.
Stopping	To stop the aircraft, close the throttle. If taxying on grass the aircraft will stop fairly quickly. If taxying on smooth surfaces such as tarmac, brakes will normally be required to assist the aircraft to stop. Brakes, when used should be applied smoothly and together. After the aircraft has stopped, apply the parking brake, and increase power to 1200 RPM.
Emphasis points	Harsh braking must be avoided. Power must be re-set to 1200 RPM.
Student practice of Starting, Controlling Speed and Stopping.	

Following this demonstration the student will on all possible occasions be allowed to start, control the speed and stop the aircraft himself.

DEMONSTRATION 2.   CONTROL OF DIRECTION AND TURNING

Flight Lesson	*Demonstration Sequence*
Nosewheel steering	Rudder pedals are used in the conventional sense to control direction. With nose wheel steering a good directional response exists. Note the amount of anticipation required to straighten out on a particular heading.
Tailwheel aircraft	Rudder pedals are used to obtain control of direction. The aircraft reaction is sluggish but can be improved by the use of throttle and differential brake.

	Note the amount of anticipation required to straighten out on a particular heading.
Turning in confined spaces	The need for slow speed and sufficient tail clearance from obstacles. Use of differential brake in direction of the turn. Additional power needed to maintain aircraft movement. The need to avoid locking a wheel during tight turns.
Emphasis points	The tailplane must be kept clear of obstacles and a locked wheel should be avoided.
Student practice of Controlling Direction and Turning.	

DEMONSTRATION 3.   PARKING AREA PROCEDURES AND PRECAUTIONS (including Rudder and Instrument Checks, Engine Handling and the effects of Wind and Ground Surface).

Flight Lesson	*Demonstration Sequence*
Leaving the parking area	Pre-Taxy checks, completion of internal checks and procedures. Check list and other equipment, maps etc.) securely stowed. Marshalling signals (when applicable). Clear all round aircraft. Throttle closed. Brakes released. Power as required to start moving. Close the throttle – Test the brakes. Rudder check – Full and free movement. When clear of the parking area, Instrument checks.
Engine handling	Smooth use of throttle. Monitor engine oil pressure and temperature gauges. Avoidance of long stationary periods with the aircraft facing downwind. Avoidance of carburettor heat unless necessary.

Effects of wind	Tendency for speed to increase when taxying downwind. Tendency for speed to decrease when taxying upwind.

During crosswind conditions	Weathercock tendency,
	  Use of flying controls.
	  Use of differential brake.
	  Anticipation of weathercock action.
	Turns into wind will tend to tighten.
	Turning downwind will tend to reduce the turn rate.

Effect of ground surface	With uphill gradient more power will be required. With downhill gradient less power will be required and braking action may be necessary. When taxying on grass, more power will be required than for smooth hard surfaces. When taxying on wet grass braking action will be poor and harsh brake application should be avoided. When taxying over rough ground the speed must be kept low and pronounced ridges should be crossed at a 45° angle with the control column held back.
Emphasis points	Use of controls relative to the effects of wind and ground surface. Airmanship points relative to engine handling, other aircraft, obstructions and ATC instructions.

Student practice of Taxying under various conditions of wind and ground surface.

DEMONSTRATION 4.   EMERGENCY PROCEDURES

The extent to which these procedures can be carried out will depend upon the airfield situation and the taxying environment. However, where possible they should be demonstrated at least once during a student's training.

| Flight Lesson | Demonstration Sequence |
| Steering failure | In this event, taxy cautiously and use differential braking to control direction. |

	If difficulty is experienced, clear the manoeuvring area (if possible) and inform ATC. Complete the normal running down checks and switch OFF the engine. Stay with the aircraft and wait for assistance.
Brake failure	

Near Obstructions	Throttle closed and magneto switches OFF.
	If possible, steer the aircraft into an open area.
	When the aircraft stops,
	  Inform ATC.
	  Complete the engine 'shut down' procedure and wait for assistance.

Away from Obstructions	Reduce speed by closing the throttle. Inform ATC. Taxy clear of the manoeuvring area. Position the aircraft facing into the wind. Complete the normal 'shut down' procedure and wait for assistance.
Emphasis points	When near obstructions, switch the engine OFF as quickly as possible. Under no circumstances attempt to taxy back to the parking area without manual assistance.

Student practice of Emergency Procedures when suitable conditions occur.

Straight and Level Flight

Instructor's Guide

There are many requirements for accurate straight and level flight, and a high standard should eventually be required. During this early stage of training the instructor should continually check to ensure the student remains relaxed and holds the controls correctly. This monitoring action by the instructor will be invaluable to the student's rate of progress.

Probably the most important factor which affects the student's rate of progress is continuity of training. This continuity is naturally dependent upon the student's finances and the time he has available, and a third factor is the weather. All these variables are outside the instructor's control, but in relation to weather, and in an attempt to maintain continuity and avoid students being disappointed, instruction is often given during periods when unsuitable weather conditions exist, for example persistent haze. During such periods every effort should be made to climb above the haze layer to provide a horizon line, but when this is not possible it should be appreciated that sometimes it will be of more value to descend to lower altitudes where the student can gain a better impression of the aircraft's attitude by reference to the ground. Such altitudes must however, take into account the height of obstructions in the local flying area.

Instruction should whenever possible be arranged so that each manoeuvre, flight experience or procedure is an extension of the student's previous learning and accomplishments. For example this flight exercise should follow on naturally from the Effects of Controls exercise and reference to this previous exercise should be made whenever applicable. To illustrate this, it is during the 'control of lateral level and balance' in straight and level flight that the information given regarding the 'further effects of aileron and rudder' during the Effects of Controls exercise becomes of practical value, and this is something that the student must appreciate if he is to understand how his control actions can achieve proper co-ordination.

AIRMANSHIP
Stress the importance of maintaining a good lookout. Never lose a

suitable opportunity to point out other aircraft, and use these occasions to stress the need for constant vigilance. Continue to develop the student's proficiency in using the clock code system of reporting aircraft and encourage him to report other aircraft and assess their position and also their distance and level.

Towards the end of this exercise an introduction should be made to the need for regular checks such as:

Fuel state and consumption rate.
Engine oil temperature and pressure.
Alternator charge rate.
Suction gauge reading.
Indications of carburettor icing.
Synchronising of the heading indicator with the magnetic compass.

During the resetting of the heading indicator it is particularly important that the student learns to maintain the wings level and use the heading indicator to hold an accurate heading prior to reading the magnetic compass.

BEFORE THE EXERCISE
The Long Briefing should cover the following:

Objectives.
The Forces.
Longitudinal Stability and Control in Pitch.
Relationship of the Centre of Gravity to Control in Pitch.
Lateral and Directional Stability.
Attitude and Balance Control.
Trimming.
Power Settings and Airspeeds.
Drag and Power Curves.
Range and Endurance.
Airmanship.
Common Errors.

The short Pre-Flight Briefing should be based upon the relevant part of the Long Briefing and the Air Exercise to be covered.

DURING THE AIR DEMONSTRATION
At the commencement of the exercise, point out the attitude of the aircraft to the natural horizon both in relation to pitch and lateral level. Emphasise the need to form correct habits while this exercise is being taught. A lack of understanding, or the failure to develop good habits during the teaching of straight and level flight will adversely affect the student's future flying techniques and delay his immediate progress.

ATTITUDE AND BALANCE CONTROL

Introduce the exercise by adopting straight and level flight at cruising power and trim the aircraft. From this lead on to the various outside observations in relation to correct attitude in pitch, lateral level and balance. Follow this by referring to the altimeter, heading indicator and balance indicator. Cross relate the airspeed of the aircraft to the power setting being used.

During the initial straight and level demonstration and practice it will normally be advisable to set a constant power and teach the maintenance of constant altitude before progressing to constant height at a selected airspeed. A constant airspeed is often difficult to achieve in a small aircraft because even minor turbulence will lead the student into the common error of 'chasing the airspeed' to the detriment of maintaining a constant altitude. Therefore the collective attainment of constant altitude and speed should be left until later.

Ensure the student understands how to detect unbalance and demonstrate that if marked unbalance occurs the sensation of yaw can be felt, and when the wings are level the yaw can be seen. Slight unbalance is more difficult to detect, and reference to the balance indicator is necessary to confirm accurate balanced flight, but this should not be over emphasised in the initial demonstration or his standard of lookout will suffer due to over-concentration on the balance indicator.

When demonstrating lateral level, direction and balance, the student should be reminded of the demonstration given during the Effects of Controls, i.e. use of aileron creates a slight yaw and use of rudder also creates a rolling action. This recall will assist the student to understand why the use of aileron and rudder must be co-ordinated in order to achieve lateral level, direction and balance.

The inherent stability of the aircraft can be demonstrated by flying with the hands and feet off the controls, and with the aircraft correctly trimmed for the level flight attitude.

After practice at maintaining straight and level flight, the student should be given practice at correcting errors. This is best done by the instructor upsetting the attitude, power and trim, and asking the student to return the aircraft to straight and level flight. As the student becomes more proficient, draw his attention to the use of the flight instruments in greater detail to obtain precision flight, but remind him not to 'dwell' upon them or his standard of lookout will suffer.

It would be wrong to assume the student will automatically maintain his heading during his early attempts at straight and level flight. Therefore as soon as the student has grasped the fundamental control actions required for straight and level flight he should be taught how to use the controls in order to bring the aircraft back to the original heading. In the initial practice of this procedure a visual reference point should be used.

TRIMMING

Get plenty of emphasis on the need to trim correctly. Remember that although he learned the purpose and the action of the trimming controls during Effects of Controls it is only during his practice of the air exercises Straight and Level, Climbing and Descending that he is able to develop a full appreciation of how to trim the aircraft correctly and accurately. Ensure the student appreciates the need to let the airspeed settle to a steady value following an attitude or power change before the aircraft can be accurately re-trimmed. It is quite a common error with some students to attempt to re-trim whilst the aircraft is still changing its speed.

POWER SETTINGS AND AIRSPEEDS

For many years the basic concept that elevators control airspeed and power controls height has been accepted by many pilots, whereas in fact there can be occasions when the opposite holds good and height may be controlled by the use of the elevators.

During Climbing a pilot who wishes to maintain a given airspeed with climbing power set will do so by the use of the elevators. During Gliding the same will apply. If however he wishes to change his airspeed whilst maintaining level flight he will use the power to give him more thrust or less thrust and his elevators to adopt the new attitude to maintain level flight at the changed power setting.

From this basic understanding of the use of power and elevators emerges the correct concept that 'Attitude plus Power equals Performance' in other words to adopt a specific airspeed and hold a specific altitude it will be necessary to alter the power setting and control the attitude with the elevators at the same time. In addition to this, the use of ailerons and rudder will be required in order to maintain a balanced flight condition.

Straight and Level Flight at Selected Airspeeds

If straight and level flight is to be maintained correctly, the power cannot be changed without also changing the speed, and the speed cannot be changed without changing the power. Therefore this Manual treats the Effect of Changing Power as an integral function of the Air Demonstration 'Straight and Level Flight at Selected Airspeeds'. When teaching this section of straight and level flight make it quite clear that if power is reduced and the attitude held constant the aircraft will descend or if power is increased and the attitude held constant the aircraft will gradually climb, therefore in order to maintain height and change the airspeed the power and the elevators will have to be adjusted at the same time.

Two Speeds for One Power Setting

For any one power setting within a given range there will be two speeds at which level flight is possible. In modern low drag aircraft however, the variation in nose attitude associated with these two speeds is quite marked, and the incorrect nose high attitude can easily be seen when in level flight. However this difference in nose attitude is far less apparent during manoeuvres such as steeply banked turns, and in low powered aircraft during such turns a student may get the aircraft into an incorrect nose high attitude. This could result in a low speed condition possibly leading to a Stall/Spin situation.

A demonstration to emphasise this possibility to the student can be achieved by using a low cruising power during the initial stages of a turn so that the airspeed lowers as altitude is maintained. The power used for this demonstration will depend upon the characteristics of the particular aircraft type, but in this low speed condition a relatively gentle and continuous backward movement of the control column can bring the aircraft to a stall, often with an associated rapid wing drop. At this stage of the student's training it will be too early for him to appreciate the significance of this possibility and the flight demonstration to cover it should be left until the stalling exercise is covered.

RANGE AND ENDURANCE

Although an integral part of the straight and level flight exercise, this lesson does not fit into the form of a very practical air demonstration. It would usually be sufficient therefore, to cover the points pertaining to flight for range and endurance in the form of a ground lecture at a later stage. The student should then be shown how to select the correct speeds for the flight conditions required by reference to the appropriate Flight/Owner's Manual and the practical aspect of both range and endurance can then be implemented prior to and during navigation flights.

COMMON ERRORS

● Difficulties experienced with balancing the aircraft are usually due to the wings not being levelled accurately or not maintained in the level condition, the wings not being held level whilst eliminating yaw or the rudder not being used correctly.

● Despite careful instruction, some students tend to develop the habit of making partial changes of attitude with the trimming controls. This action is not always easily apparent and should be watched for carefully. In this respect instructors should be careful to show as clearly as possible the correct use of the trimming controls during the initial demonstration.

• The student often fails to maintain his periodic checks in relation to fuel state, oil temperature and pressure etc.

• Prior to re-setting the heading indicator many students tend to watch the magnetic compass instead of maintaining a constant heading by reference to the heading indicator and as a result never learn to do this check with accuracy.

• The standard of the student's lookout will inevitably be poor during the early stages of this exercise, but in the latter stages the instructor must demand constant vigilance from the student.

Straight and Level Flight

Long Briefing

OBJECTIVES

The objectives in this exercise are to teach the student an understanding of the factors which affect the aircraft during straight and level flight, together with how the flying controls and instruments are used to acheive and maintain a constant height, heading and airspeed with the aircraft in balance. It is during this exercise that the student will be introduced to the co-ordinated use of the controls and an understanding of aircraft performance.

INTRODUCTION

Straight and level flight involves keeping the aircraft laterally level with the height and direction constant. The aircraft will be in equilibrium when the lift equals the weight and the thrust equals the drag, this being recognised by the pilot when the airspeed and height remain constant. Accurate straight and level flight is essential for precise flight such as that required for reliable navigation and for obtaining the best performance from the aircraft.

This is a student's first exercise in co-ordination, and therefore it is the basis upon which subsequent instruction is built. Many variable factors are involved in this flight condition, attitude in pitch and roll, power setting, airspeed, height and direction all being important. An alteration to one normally affects the others. For example, an increase in power will produce an increase in airspeed or height or a combination of both; a change in attitude may vary height, airspeed and direction; an increase in airspeed will cause a reduction in height unless power is increased.

THE FORCES

In order to maintain a condition of horizontal level flight the lift produced must be equal to the weight of the aircraft (Fig. 6-1).

In order to obtain the aircraft's forward movement through the air, thrust is achieved through the use of the engine and propeller. When the speed is constant the thrust will exactly equal the drag produced from all sources, including the aircraft's resistance to the airflow (Fig. 6-2).

Fig. 6-1

Fig. 6-2

When Lift = Weight and Thrust = Drag, a condition of equilibrium will result and only small control movements and adjustments will need to be made to maintain this condition.

The study of aircraft equilibrium and stability can become a very complex subject but although a pilot does not need to have the detailed knowledge required of an aircraft designer he should nevertheless have a basic understanding of the principles involved in stability and control. These principles will be of practical benefit to any pilot and will assist in his appreciation of those factors involved for example, in the stability about the three axes, control of the aircraft throughout its speed range, and the method of correctly loading passengers and baggage.

All these items are of primary importance to safe flight, and a lack of comprehension of these factors can completely negate the designer's efforts to provide the pilot with a safe and stable aircraft.

In flight the aircraft is controlled about three axes, the lateral (pitching axis), the longitudinal (rolling axis) and the vertical (yawing axis). The aircraft must also have adequate stability to maintain a uniform flight condition and recover from the disturbing influences of rough air. It is also necessary to provide sufficient stability to minimise the workload of the pilot and give proper response to the flying controls throughout the speed and loading range of the aircraft.

LONGITUDINAL STABILITY AND CONTROL IN PITCH
The main factors which influence longitudinal stability are the relative positions of the Centre of Pressure (lift) and the Centre of

Gravity (weight) together with the design of the tailplane and elevators.

Longitudinal stability is initially achieved by arranging the forces so that the centre of weight acts ahead of the centre of lift. This distribution of Lift and Weight creates a nose down moment which is compensated for by the action of the horizontal tailplane. The angle at which the tailplane is set causes it to carry a download (or negative lift force).

This arrangement of forces including the action of the tailplane will ensure a stable or nose down movement of the aircraft whenever the engine is throttled back as shown in fig. 6-3.

L

Lift/Weight
couple = a
nose down moment W

Down load on
tail compensates
for nose down
moment

Fig. 6-3

In some cases, notably with high wing aircraft it is possible to arrange for a high drag line and a low thrust line, this results in a small nose up couple which counteracts some of the effect of the strong nose down couple of lift and weight. When this arrangement is adopted the down load produced by the tailplane will be less.

L

Thrust/Drag
couple = a
nose up
moment

T   D

Lift/Weight
couple = a
nose down
moment   W

Fig. 6-4

If the Lift/Weight couple was arranged to be in the reverse order ie. Weight behind Lift then the arrangement would be an unstable one as shown in fig. 6-5.

Lift/Weight
couple = a
nose up moment

Unstable in
pitch

Fig. 6-5

In this situation the inherent tendency would be for the nose to rise. When this happens the airspeed would lower and the tailplane and elevators would become less effective, a situation which would be classed as unstable.

Having arranged for a stable action in pitch by placing the weight in front of centre of lift it must be realised that in practice the exact positions of the centre of gravity and the centre of lift will vary during flight. This is due to variations in angle of attack, weight, airspeed and the use of flaps etc. The designer therefore ensures that the balance action of the tailplane and the effects of the elevators will be sufficient to control the aircraft's attitude at the lowest speed of flight, provided the centre of gravity limits have not been exceeded by incorrect loading of passengers or baggage.

Apart from balancing the residual unbalanced couples of the four forces the tailplane is designed to provide longitudinal balance whenever disturbing influences of the air are encountered. Basically this is effected by setting the mainplanes and tailplane at different angles of incidence (see fig. 6-6).

When the aircraft is disturbed by a gust it will take up a different attitude, but due to inertia it will remain temporarily on its original flight path. The result of this is that both the mainplanes and tailplane will have a changed angle of attack. If the changed attitude is in a nose up direction the angle of attack of the mainplanes and tailplane will be increased by the same amount. As an example, assume the mainplane angle of incidence is $+4°$ and the tailplane angle of incidence is $+2°$ (tailplane incidence is normally negative due to reasons already explained but for simplicity of illustration $+2°$ is assumed for this example. Assuming a $2°$ increase in angle of attack occurs due to a gust it can be seen that this represents a

Mainplane - 50% change
in angle of attack

Tailplane - 100%
change in angle
of attack

6°

4°

2°

4°

Fig. 6-6

change in the mainplane angle of attack by 50%, whereas a 2°
increase in angle of attack of the tailplane would represent an
increase of 100%.

Therefore, due to the different angles of incidence and different
values of angle of attack, a greater proportional increase of lift will
occur on the tail. The tail will therefore rise and result in a lowering
of the nose. In other words the aircraft will tend to return to its
original trimmed position. Although there are other factors involved
the above explanation illustrates the basic principle of the tail
restoring action in pitch.

RELATIONSHIP OF CENTRE OF GRAVITY TO CONTROL IN PITCH

All aircraft are designed to be longitudinally stable over a limited
Centre of Gravity range. If the Centre of Gravity moves outside this
range the performance of the aircraft and the pilot's control over its
attitude will be limited and in serious cases the aircraft's attitude
will be uncontrollable.

If the aircraft is loaded so that the Centre of Gravity is at its
forward limit the aircraft will be most stable. If disturbed in flight it
will quickly return to its original attitude. However, if the forward
limit is exceeded the aircraft will become tiring to manoeuvre in pitch
due to its strong longitudinal stability. It can also become uncontrollably nose heavy, particularly at lower airspeeds when elevator
control is less effective, as for example during the landing phase. It is
in this situation that full up elevator may not be capable of creating a
round out prior to touchdown.

When the Centre of Gravity is moved aft the degree of longitudinal
stability decreases, which means the aircraft will take longer to
resume its original attitude when disturbed. If the Centre of Gravity
position moves aft of the rear limit the aircraft will become
uncontrollably tail heavy, the nose will rise and the aircraft will
eventually stall. It can be seen from these considerations that the

Action of Forward   Action of Aft
Centre of Gravity   Centre of Gravity

Fig. 6-7

correct procedure for ensuring that Weight and Balance is within the permitted limits is extremely important. Reference to the Flight/ Owner's Manual and the Weight and Balance Schedule must be made collectively in order to obtain the specific information relating to a particular aircraft. Supplement No. 2 at the end of this briefing contains information regarding Weight and Balance calculations.

LATERAL AND DIRECTIONAL STABILITY

During the demonstration of the 'Effects of Controls' the further effects of aileron and rudder were shown. It was noted that the use of aileron to produce roll also caused yaw to occur and the use of rudder to produce or reduce yaw also caused the aircraft to move in the rolling plane.

Similarly, movement of the aircraft about the vertical or longitudinal axis is inter-related in that yaw effects roll and roll effects yaw. Therefore lateral and directional stability effects are interrelated and movement of the aircraft in either one of these planes automatically effects the stability characteristics of the other.

Lateral Stability

The lateral stability of an aircraft involves the rolling moments produced by sideslip. A sideslip tends to produce both a rolling and yawing motion and if a favourable rolling moment can be made to occur through basic design geometry a sideslip will tend to return the aircraft to a laterally level attitude.

The design features which are normally used on light aircraft to achieve a favourable rolling moment are, a high wing relationship to the Centre of Gravity, Geometric Dihedral or a combination of both these features.

The high wing arrangement results in a Centre of Gravity below the wing which therefore acts like a pendulum, the high wing offering a resistance to the airflow and thus acts as a type of pivot about which the Centre of Gravity acts. This effect upon lateral stability is however by itself somewhat limited and tends to produce an oscillating motion.

Geometric dihedral however offers a more positive action and is accomplished in the following manner. The wings are arranged to produce an angle to the plane of symmetry as indicated in fig. 6-8.

Dihedral Angle

Plane of Symmetry

Fig. 6-8

Whenever a wing drops the aircraft will sideslip in that direction due to the tilted lift line in relation to the weight.

L

Sideslip Component

W

Fig. 6-9

Figure 6-9 illustrates this effect. A sideways component is producd and Lift being inclined, has a shorter vertical component and is no longer sufficient to balance the Weight. The result of this is to cause the aircraft to sideslip in the direction of the lower wing. The effect of sideslip is to change the direction of the relative airflow which now comes from ahead and slightly from one side as shown in fig. 6-10.

This produces a greater angle of attack to the lower wing and a lesser angle of attack to the raised wing. The lower wing therefore obtains more lift than the higher wing and a tendency to restore the aircraft back to its laterally level position occurs. In this situation a very minor masking of the airflow occurs on the higher wing due to fuselage interference, but at the small sideslip angles incurred in this

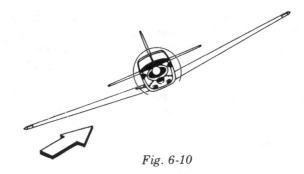

Fig. 6-10

lateral stability consideration the effect of such masking can be virtually ignored unless the aircraft is placed into a positive sideslip by the pilot.

It can be seen from the foregoing that geometric dihedral has a beneficial effect upon lateral stability but its actual restoring action is limited due to the fact that if the wing was returned to the laterally level position by the dihedral effect, inertia would cause the rising wing to continue beyond the laterally level position and the opposite wing would drop. This would produce a cycle known as oscillatory instability (commonly called Dutch Roll). This is a condition which would make the pilot's task in relation to the maintenance of lateral level more difficult. An aircraft with strong lateral stability would also be more difficult to manoeuvre in roll. The designer will therefore normally limit the dihedral angle to one which will give an aircraft a tendency to resist a rolling motion set up by disturbances of the air.

To sum up, it can be stated that the amount of effective dihedral will vary with the type and purpose of the aircraft. Normally the effective dihedral is kept low since a strong rolling tendency due to sideslip can lead to Dutch Roll, a difficult rudder co-ordination in rolling manoeuvres and place excessive demands on lateral stability during crosswind take-offs and landings.

Directional Stability

The directional stability of an aircraft is essentially 'weathercock stability' and concerns movement about the vertical axis and its relationship to yaw and sideslip angle.

An aircraft which possesses directional stability will tend to maintain its heading or damp out any tendency to diverge from its heading should it be disturbed. The vertical tailplane (fin) and that area of the fuselage behind the Centre of Gravity are the primary surfaces which control the degree of directional stability. Whenever an aircraft is sideslipping or yawing the vertical tailplane will experience an angle of attack as shown in fig. 6-11.

Fig. 6-11

Due to inertia an aircraft will continue for a short while along the original flight path after its heading is disturbed, this will produce a relative airflow which results in a horizontal lift force setting up a restoring moment about the Centre of Gravity. This tends to return the aircraft to its original flight path. This corrective action will be increased by the effect of airflow direction upon the side surface of the fuselage behind the Centre of Gravity and the greater this area the stronger the restoring effect.

Spiral Instability
As stated at the beginning of this section on stability there are many interrelated factors affecting the adequate provision of both lateral and directional stability. Due to the conflicting aerodynamic needs between these two stabilities in relation to sideslip and yaw, most aircraft are designed to have a lateral stability which will not overcome the properties of directional stability. This results in the aircraft having a weak spiral divergence, i.e. if a wing should drop, the aircraft will eventually go into a gentle spiral descent unless checked by the pilot.

ATTITUDE AND BALANCE CONTROL
Initially level flight is maintained by consciously noting the relationship of parts of the aircraft to the natural horizon, and cross referring to the altimeter, heading indicator and balance indicator to confirm that level flight is being achieved and maintained. The first demonstration will therefore start by the instructor placing the aircraft in the correct straight and level attitude, then pointing out the following observations:

The nose attitude in pitch relative to a constant altimeter reading.
The laterally level attitude with a constant heading and the aircraft in balance.
The power selected and the airspeed obtained.

When the aircraft is correctly trimmed it will normally fly 'hands off'.

It is customary to use a moderate power setting for the initial demonstration of straight and level flight, so the first demonstration will be done at normal cruising power.

At Normal Cruising Power
This means flying straight and level using a power setting which is within the economical cruising range as specified in the Flight/ Owner's Manual for the aircraft type.

Once the power setting has been adjusted, straight and level flight may be achieved by:

Controlling the attitude in pitch by use of the elevators so that the aircraft neither gains nor loses altitude.

Controlling the attitude in roll by use of the ailerons so that the aircraft remains laterally level.

Balancing the aircraft by the use of rudder so that it is flying without slip or skid.

The aircraft must be kept laterally level to fly straight, as even a small angle of bank will cause the nose of the aircraft to yaw in the direction of the lower wing. It is possible to counteract this yaw with opposite rudder so that it may appear to be flying straight and level, a condition often described as flying with crossed controls. It is an inefficient condition of flight and a fault which students should be careful to avoid.

When an aircraft is flying without any side-slip so that its path of flight is in line with its longitudinal axis, balanced flight has been achieved. Most propeller driven aircraft have a yawing tendency due to the effect of the slipstream from the propeller on the keel surface, and this tendency must be counter-acted by the use of rudder.

Provided the aircraft is held level laterally and the rudder is used to prevent yaw the aircraft will be in balance and it will also maintain a constant heading.

It has already been stated that if the wings are kept level and the heading remains constant the aircraft will be in balanced straight and level flight. If marked unbalance occurs it can be detected by the physical sensation of yaw or in cases of small unbalance it will be seen by a change of heading with the wings level or the ball balance indicator being out of centre. When using the ball to detect or correct unbalance, rudder will be required the same side to which the ball has moved i.e. if the ball is left of centre, left rudder pedal pressure will be required. Slight unbalance is always difficult to detect without reference to the balance indicator.

When making any corrections to lateral level or unbalance the student must remember the further effect of ailerons and rudder, in that the use of ailerons also creates a slight yaw and the use of rudder also creates a slight roll, therefore a movement of one will always require a compensating movement of the other.

Effect of Inertia

Whenever changing attitude to straight and level flight there will be a short time lapse before the airspeed settles to a steady figure. This is due to the inertia of the aircraft, and it is essential after adjusting the attitude to wait until the airspeed is steady. Failure to do this will result in a tendency to chase the airspeed to the detriment of maintaining a constant altitude.

TRIMMING

Once the pilot has assumed the correct attitude and the appropriate airspeed for the power used has been reached, the final stage is trimming. Because of its stability, an aircraft which is well trimmed tends to remain steady of its own accord, unless it is disturbed by alterations in power, air turbulence or changes in the disposition of the load it carries. It follows therefore, that frequent use of the trimmer controls is necessary to adjust for changes in power load and airspeed, in order to maintain accurate straight and level flight, and is one of the essentials of good flying.

POWER SETTINGS AND AIRSPEEDS

During flight, aircraft spend a good proportion of their time flying straight and level. Therefore, it is essential that the pilot should know how to handle his engine so as to produce power most economically for this flight condition. In most light aircraft the maintenance of the correct fuel/air ratio with variation of altitude or power is achieved by the use of a manual mixture control. This can be used to obtain the best power/mixture which will give a slightly higher airspeed for a given throttle setting within the cruise power range. The use of the mixture control in this way will also achieve better fuel economy. The correct method of using the mixture control has been outlined in the supplement to the Effects of Controls.

Drag and Power Curves

When the aircraft is in steady level flight the basic condition of equilibrium must prevail, hence in steady level flight at any airspeed the lift will equal the weight and the thrust will equal the drag. With piston engined aircraft the power required for this condition can be shown in the form of a performance curve. Fig. 6-12 illustrates the relationship of power required to aircraft speed.

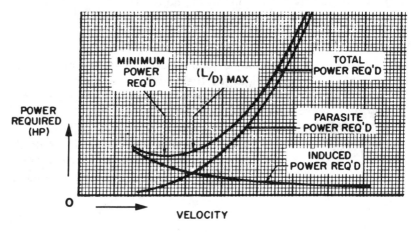

Fig. 6-12

The power required curve will be related to the specific configuration, weight and altitude flown, and if it is required to operate the aircraft at a particular speed a specific power requirement will exist as shown in fig. 6-13.

When flying at a speed corresponding to A in the diagram a particular power will be required, if the aircraft's speed is to be changed to that shown at B then a different power will be required. A change of airspeed to that shown at B will also require a change in the angle of attack in order to maintain a constant lift equal to the aircraft's weight. Similarly, to fly at speed C a change in power and angle of attack would again be necessary and in this case the aircraft would be flying in the vicinity of the minimum flying speed for the particular aircraft and the major portion of the power required would be due to induced drag. The actual minimum speed in level flight is not usually defined by power required since for practical purposes conditions of stall, or stability and control usually predominate.

The maximum level flight speed for the aircraft will be obtained when the power required equals the power available as shown at D in

Fig. 6-13

the diagram. From the foregoing information it can be seen that aircraft are therefore capable of being flown at various airspeeds in level flight, and the actual speed achieved will be dependent upon the all up weight and the configuration and the power selected.

Straight and Level Flight at Selected Airspeeds

It has been seen that one aspect of an aircraft's performance is its capability to fly at different airspeeds in level flight. This capability is achieved through a combination of aerodynamic and power plant characteristics. The aerodynamic characteristics generally define the power requirement for specific conditions of flight, and the matching of the aerodynamic configuration with the power from the engine will be needed to obtain such performance requirements in terms of airspeed, aircraft range and endurance, and manoeuvres such as climbing, turning and descending.

During level flight the aircraft is normally operated in a clean configuration throughout the cruising range and with one which gives a good Lift/Drag ratio. In order to adopt a specific airspeed and hold a constant altitude it will be necessary to alter the power setting and the attitude at the same time. In addition to this, the use of aileron and rudder will also be required to maintain the aircraft in balanced flight without slip or skid.

When adopting straight and level flight at a different airspeed it should be appreciated that if power is reduced and the aircraft attitude held constant the aircraft will descend or if power is increased and the attitude held constant the aircraft will climb.

Therefore, in order to maintain altitude and also change the airspeed the power and the elevators will have to be adjusted at the same time.

Two Airspeeds for One Power Setting

For any one power setting within a given range there will be two speeds at which level flight is possible. Figure 6-14 shows the power required to overcome the drag at different airspeeds.

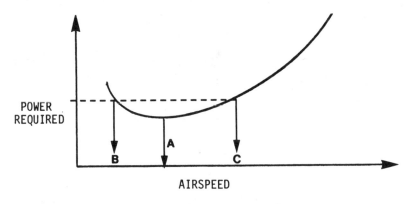

Fig. 6-14

The bottom of the curve A shows the particular aircraft endurance speed which relates to the minimum power required to maintain the aircraft in level flight. On either side of this curve at B and C it can be seen that for the same power setting two different airspeeds can be achieved. The lower of these speeds will occur with the aircraft flying at a high angle of attack and the higher of these speeds will represent the correct attitude for level flight. Although this variation between aircraft attitudes is quite marked whilst in normal level flight it is far less apparent during manoeuvres such as steep turns. It is during this latter type of manoeuvre that a student can more easily get the nose of the aircraft in the higher and wrong attitude which will result in a lower speed and a critical control condition which may lead to the aircraft stalling. The possibility of this situation occurring will largely depend upon the particular drag and power required characteristics and is more likely to occur with low powered aircraft.

Straight and Level Flight in Different Configurations

If flaps or landing gear are lowered during flight the drag of the aircraft will be increased and the effect of this is shown in fig. 6-15.

The upper drag curve shows that the added drag compatible with flap or landing gear selection will require an increase of power in order to maintain a pre-selected airspeed. It can also be seen that if the airspeed is increased the additional drag will increase at a

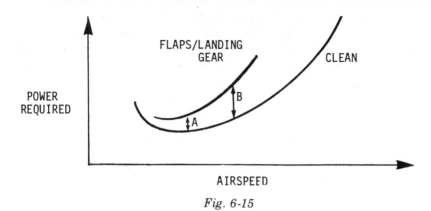

Fig. 6-15

greater rate than the normal drag increase when the aircraft is in the clean configuration. This can be seen from the lines at A and B in the diagram.

Apart from additional drag the lowering of flaps will also create a pitch change due to the associated movement of the wing centre of pressure, the drag line (and the amount of drag), and the variation of the downwash angle. The interaction of the changes to these four factors will determine the strength of the pitch change and the direction of such change i.e. nose up or nose down.

The operation of a retractable landing gear (if fitted) will also cause pitch changes to occur, though these changes are usually of a minor nature.

USE OF THE INSTRUMENTS TO ACHIEVE PRECISION FLIGHT

Precision flight is achieved by the combined use of both visual (outside reference) and instrument reference, with sufficient attention being paid to the aircraft instruments to achieve accurate heading, balance, airspeed and altitude. The attitude indicator can be referred to at this stage but it must be appreciated that the use of the instruments in this way must on no account be considered as an exercise in instrument flying. It is also important that precision flight is not achieved to the detriment of a good standard of lookout, and therefore the periods of reference to the instruments must be of a fleeting nature rather than long observations.

RANGE AND ENDURANCE

To fly for maximum range, that is, to cover the greatest distance through the air on the fuel available, the best compromise between the separate considerations of engine, airframe and weather must be determined. Airframe considerations require the aircraft to be flown at an angle of attack which gives the best lift/drag ratio, usually a positive angle of about 4 degrees. As the pilot is unable to measure the angle of attack whilst in flight, this angle is interpreted in terms of airspeed in the Flight/Owner's Manual/Pilot's Operating Handbook for the type, in which range curves or numerical graphs are shown so that it is possible to read the correct airspeed, power setting and fuel consumption.

CRUISE PERFORMANCE

ALT.	RPM	% BHP	TAS MPH	38.8 Gal Endurance Hours
	2500	75	130	3.7
2500	2350	▶63	118	4.4
	2200	53	107	5.2
	2525	75	131	3.7
3500	2400	65	121	4.3
	2250	55	110	5.0
	2550	75	132	3.7
4500	2400	63	120	4.4
	2250	53	109	5.2
	2600	77	135	3.7
5500	2450	65	123	4.3
	2300	55	112	5.0
	2600	75	134	3.7
6500	2450	▶63	122	4.4
	2300	54	111	5.1
	2600	73	133	3.8
7500	2450	62	121	4.4
	2300	53	111	5.1

Fig. 6-16

Engine considerations primarily require that a power setting within the cruising range be used and one which will permit the use of mixture control. Although there are other considerations such as the use of low RPM, and operation at a height which requires a throttle setting compatible with a fully open carburettor butterfly for the particular range speed, such factors have little practical benefit or influence on range for simple training aircraft. Therefore, in the case of low horsepower engines these additional factors can be ignored and the actual altitude chosen will in the main depend upon such items as terrain clearance, the floor of any controlled airspace en-route and the prevailing weather conditions.

When flying for maximum endurance, considerations of distance are not applicable. The requirement is to remain airborne at the

ALTITUDE	RPM	% BHP	TAS MPH	GAL/ HOUR	38 GAL (NO RESERVE)	
					ENDR. HOURS	RANGE MILES
2500	2700	87	139	9.6	3.9	545
	2600	78	133	8.6	4.4	590
	2500	70 *	128	7.7	4.9	630
	2400	63	122	▶7·0	5·4	655
	2300	57	116	6.6	5.7	665
	2200	51	109	6.2	6.1	665
5000	2700	81	138	8.9	4.3	585
	2600	73	133	8.1	4.7	630
	2500	66	128	7.4	5.1	655
	2400	60	121	6.8	5.6	675
	2300	54	114	6.4	5.9	675
	2200	48	107	6.0	6.3	675
7500	2700	76	138	8.4	4.5	630
	2600	69 *	133	7.6	5.0	660
	2500	63	126	▶7·1	5·4	675
	2400	57	119	6.6	5.8	685
	2300	51	112	6.2	6.1	685
10,000	2700	72	138	7.9	4.8	665
	2600	66	131	7.3	5.2	685
	2500	59	124	6.8	5.6	695
	2400	54	117	6.4	6.0	700
	2300	48	110	6.0	6.3	700
12,500	2650	65	132	7.2	5.3	695
	2500	56	122	6.5	5.8	710
	2400	51	115	6.2	6.2	710

Fig. 6-17

appropriate power to ensure the least rate of fuel consumption. The engine has to do less work at altitudes near sea level than at higher altitudes where the aircraft must fly at a greater true airspeed in air of reduced density to develop the same amount of lift. Therefore, with piston engine aircraft endurance decreases with altitude. However, as with the case of range flying, this effect is very small.

Figure 6-17 shows an example of fuel consumption and range figures taken from a representative small training aircraft. Such aircraft are normally limited to flight operations below 10,000 feet due to the lack of oxygen systems. The figures in this example are closely comparable to other training aircraft and reveal the very small benefit derived from variation of altitude when flying for range or endurance. For example, in the range column of fig. 6-17 it can be seen that flying at a typical range power setting of 70% BHP the gain in range between flying at 2500 feet (630 miles) and flying at 7500 feet (660 miles) is some 30 miles over approximately 5 hours, i.e. 6

miles of extra distance achieved per every hour of flight. Bearing in mind the considerable effect which wind can have upon range it will be seen that the variation of strength of the head or tail wind component with change of altitude will be of far greater importance than the minute benefit of greater engine efficiency with increase of altitude.

It can also be seen from the same table that by using an endurance power setting of 63% at 2500 feet and 7500 feet the gain by flying 5000 feet lower down is 0.1 of a gallon of fuel per hour. Reference to the table shown in fig. 6-16 further shows that the difference in fuel consumption between 2500 feet when operating at 63% power is nil. Therefore in the case of endurance flying in a light training aircraft the insignificant gain in endurance by flying low down is totally outweighed by consideration of minimum Safety Altitude.

AIRMANSHIP

This will be a student's second or third flight and 'Lookout' will begin to take on a wider meaning. The development of the *See and Avoid* concept and the application of Visual Flight Rules will from this stage onwards have a greater part to play in the learning of good airmanship. In relation to the *See and Avoid* concept, constant vigilance must be maintained by pilots in order that they not only see other aircraft, but can take appropriate avoiding action in time. Cockpit 'look in' time must be kept to a minimum and the aircraft flown in such a manner that it remains well clear of cloud. For example, it is of little use remaining clear of cloud if a pilot flies too close to the base or in such close horizontal proximity to cloud that when another aircraft is seen there is insufficient time to take safe avoiding action.

The student should also gradually become more aware of the proximity of his aircraft to the base of airways or the limits of other controlled airspace, and to Danger or Prohibited Areas.

Towards the end of this exercise the student will be introduced to the need for periodic checking of fuel state and consumption rate, engine oil temperature and pressure, alternator charge and suction readings, and for indications of carburettor icing and re-synchronising the heading indicator with the magnetic compass.

PRE-FLIGHT BRIEFING
STRAIGHT AND LEVEL FLIGHT
Demonstration 1.

Aim To teach you how to attain and maintain straight and level flight at normal cruising power.

What The co-ordination of the controls together with the use of the flight instruments to attain straight and level flight and confirm that it is being maintained.

How Initial demonstration of straight and level flight.

Observations: Recognition of the correct pitch and lateral attitude with the aircraft in balance. Note the RPM selected and the airspeed attained. The aircraft will be trimmed and only small control pressures will be required to maintain the flight attitude.

Attainment of Level Flight in Pitch.	*Attainment of Lateral Level, Direction and Balance*	*Co-ordination of Aileron and Rudder*
Pitch attitude selected.	Select wings level attitude.	Use of ailerons alone will produce a yaw.
Use of elevators and throttle.	Use of rudder to prevent yaw.	Yaw will be prevented by the correct use of the rudder.
Cross check with altimeter.	Cross check by visual heading.	Apply rudder in the same direction as the control column.
Adjust attitude as necessary.	Reference.	
Trim out control pressure.	Cross check with balance indicator.	
Student practice.	Student practice.	Student practice.

Consolidation: Attaining and maintaining straight and level flight in pitch, lateral level, direction and balance using ailerons, rudder, elevators, throttle, altimeter and balance indicator.

Student practice.

Airmanship Continued use of the clock code for reporting other aircraft. to *See and Avoid*, and the application of Visual Flight Rules. Orientation and avoidance of controlled airspace and similar areas.

PRE-FLIGHT BRIEFING
STRAIGHT AND LEVEL FLIGHT
Demonstration 2.

Aim   To teach you: (a) How to regain a reference altitude and heading.
                             (b) How to fly the aircraft at selected airspeeds.

What   (a) The method to be used for regaining a reference heading.
                             (b) The method of establishing a specific airspeed in straight and level flight.

Airmanship Responsibility for LOOKOUT. Visual Flight Rules. Orientation and avoidance of controlled airspace etc.

How *Regaining a Reference Altitude and Heading*

If the aircraft ascends/descends in relation to the reference altitude:

Return the aircraft to its original altitude by small adjustments of the attitude in pitch. Depending upon the amount of height loss/gain a power adjustment may be required at the same time.
A small anticipation of the 'level off' altitude will be required.

If the aircraft moves off the reference heading:

Return the aircraft to its original heading by co-ordinated use of ailerons, rudder and elevators.
A small anticipation of 'roll out' heading will be required.

Student practice.

Flight at Selected Airspeeds

Increase of power will result in a higher airspeed.

Increase the power – the nose rises.
Prevent pitch change.

The airspeed will increase and a lower nose attitude will be required to maintain a constant altitude.

Inertia – allow time for the new airspeed to be determined.

Re-trim.

Student practice.

Reduction of power will result in a lower airspeed.

Reduce the power – the nose lowers.
Prevent pitch change.

The airspeed will decrease and a higher nose attitude will be required to maintain a constant altitude.

Inertia – allow time for the new airspeed to be determined.

Re-trim.

Student practice.

PRE-FLIGHT BRIEFING
STRAIGHT AND LEVEL FLIGHT
Demonstration 3.

Aim   To teach you: (a) To maintain straight and level flight in different aircraft configurations.

(b) To achieve a condition of precision flight.

What   The method used to: (a) Maintain altitude, heading and balance whilst controlling the airspeed during the lowering or raising of the flaps and/or landing gear.

(b) Relate visual horizon references with the instrument indications to achieve more precise flight than can be obtained by outside visual reference alone.

Airmanship   Continued maintenance of Lookout, orientation and avoidance of controlled airspace and similar areas and cloud

How

Changing Configurations

Airspeed within the flap lowering limits.
Select flap and maintain attitude.
Note: Lower airspeed and gradual loss of height.
Increase power and adjust attitude to maintain height at the required airspeed.
Re-trim.

Maintaining level flight raise flap and adjust power for airspeed required.
Re-trim.

If a retractable landing gear is fitted repeat the above – lowering and raising the gear.

Student practice.

Precision Flight

Confirmation of aircraft attitude and performance by reference to the flight instruments.
Attitude indicator – heading indicator.
Turn/balance indicator or turn co-ordinator.
Re-setting the heading indicator by reference to the magnetic compass:

Maintaining the wings level hold a constant heading by reference to the heading indicator.
After 15-30 seconds read off heading from the magnetic compass.
Re-set heading indicator as required.

The development of instrument scanning and the use of instrument checks in relation to the engine and ancillary systems. Lookout is maintained by the use of only momentary glances at individual instruments.

Student practice.

PRE-FLIGHT BRIEFING
STRAIGHT AND LEVEL FLIGHT
Demonstration 4.

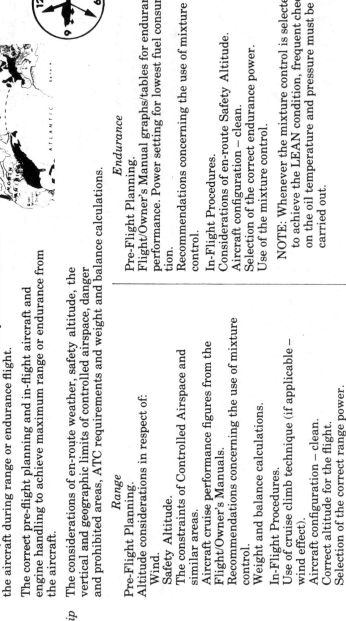

Aim To teach you how to obtain the maximum cruise performance from the aircraft during range or endurance flight.

What The correct pre-flight planning and in-flight aircraft and engine handling to achieve maximum range or endurance from the aircraft.

Airmanship The considerations of en-route weather, safety altitude, the vertical and geographic limits of controlled airspace, danger and prohibited areas, ATC requirements and weight and balance calculations.

How

Range

Pre-Flight Planning.
Altitude considerations in respect of:
Wind.
Safety Altitude.
The constraints of Controlled Airspace and similar areas.
Aircraft cruise performance figures from the Flight/Owner's Manuals.
Recommendations concerning the use of mixture control.
Weight and balance calculations.

In-Flight Procedures.
Use of cruise climb technique (if applicable – wind effect).
Aircraft configuration – clean.
Correct altitude for the flight.
Selection of the correct range power.
Precise flight – accurate trimming.
Use of mixture control.
Use of cruise descent (if applicable).

Endurance

Pre-Flight Planning.
Flight/Owner's Manual graphs/tables for endurance performance. Power setting for lowest fuel consumption.
Recommendations concerning the use of mixture control.

In-Flight Procedures.
Considerations of en-route Safety Altitude.
Aircraft configuration – clean.
Selection of the correct endurance power.
Use of the mixture control.

NOTE: Whenever the mixture control is selected to achieve the LEAN condition, frequent checks on the oil temperature and pressure must be carried out.

Straight and Level Flight

Flight Demonstrations

INTRODUCTION

The contents of the total straight and level exercise may be conveniently divided into four specific demonstration groups as follows:

1. Attaining and Maintaining Straight and Level Flight.
2. Regaining a Reference Altitude/Heading.
   Straight and Level Flight at Selected Airspeeds.
3. Straight and Level Flight in Different Configurations.
   Instrument Indications in Straight and Level Flight.
4. Straight and Level Flight to obtain Range or Endurance.

Whereas demonstrations 1, 2 and 3 will all need to be covered early in the course it is suggested that demonstration 4 be left until the appropriate moment, e.g., the pilot navigation stage.

Airmanship items will be introduced and developed at appropriate moments during the demonstrations.

DEMONSTRATION 1.   ATTAINING AND MAINTAINING STRAIGHT AND LEVEL FLIGHT

Flight Lesson	*Demonstration Sequence*
A demonstration of straight and level flight Place the aircraft in straight and level flight at normal cruising power	Student Observations: Recognition of the correct pitch and lateral attitude, relating the fixed parts of the aircraft to the natural horizon. Pitch attitude for a constant altimeter reading. Wings laterally level with the heading constant and balance indicator ball central. Note RPM selected and the airspeed attained.

	If correctly trimmed the aircraft will fly 'Hands Off', and only small control pressures are needed to maintain this flight condition.

Attainment of straight and level flight in pitch
Make a small but positive change in the pitch attitude, power and trim
	Re-select the correct pitch attitude and power.
	    Use of elevators and throttle.
	    Cross check with the altimeter for constant altitude indication.
	    Adjust attitude as necessary.
	    Trim.
	Note the use of control pressures rather than movements.

Student practice: The student should now practise the selection of the correct level attitude in pitch, adjusting the power and retrimming. During this period the instructor will normally assume the general responsibility for lookout so that the student can concentrate on flying the aircraft.

Attainment of straight and level flight with regard to lateral level, direction and balance Lower one wing to disturb the lateral level and fly the aircraft out of balance	Use the ailerons to level the wings and with the wings level use the rudder to prevent any change of heading (yaw). When the wings are level and the heading is constant the aircraft will be in balanced flight. Cross refer to the balance indicator.

Student practice: The student should now practise selecting the correct lateral level and maintain heading and balance. The instructor will remain primarily responsible for the lookout.

Correct co-ordination of aileron and rudder Allow one wing to drop and use the ailerons alone to bring the aircraft back to laterally level flight	If ailerons alone are used to level the wings a yaw will be produced. Yaw is prevented by the use of rudder. Therefore both ailerons and rudder must be used whenever altering the attitude of the wings, i.e. If the control column has to be moved to the left to level the wings, then under normal conditions left rudder will also be required. If the control column has to be moved to the right, then right rudder will also be required.

	When ailerons and rudder are used in co-ordination the wings can be levelled without yaw occurring. Therefore, ailerons and rudder are used together to obtain and maintain lateral level, direction and balance.
Disturb the aircraft's attitude both in pitch and lateral level	Use the ailerons and rudder together to level the wings and maintain balance. Application of rudder in the direction of the balance (ball) indicator. Use of the elevators to achieve level flight in pitch. Adjustment of power and trim as required.

Student practice: The student should now practise obtaining and maintaining straight and level flight in the lateral and pitching planes whilst keeping the aircraft in balance. At this stage the student should start sharing the responsibility for lookout.

DEMONSTRATION 2.   REGAINING A REFERENCE ALTITUDE AND HEADING

Flight Lesson	*Demonstration Sequence*
Returning the aircraft to its original altitude	
Allow the aircraft to descend below the reference altitude	To return to the original altitude whilst maintaining heading and balance. Increase power if and as required (compatible with the amount of height loss) and adjust the nose attitude to achieve a small climb rate. Small airspeed variations are acceptable while restoring the air craft to the correct altitude. Maintain a cross reference with the natural horizon (attitude in pitch, wings level and direction constant) and the altimeter. On reading the reference altitude adjust power and pitch attitude as necessary to maintain level flight. Use ailerons and rudder throughout to maintain laterally level flight together with a constant heading and balance.
Allow the aircraft to ascend above the reference altitude	To return to the original altitude whilst maintaining heading and balance. Decrease power if and as

required (compatible with the amount of height gain) and adjust the nose attitude to achieve a small descent rate.
Small airspeed variations are acceptable while restoring the aircraft to the correct altitude.
Maintain a cross reference with the natural horizon (attitude in pitch, wings level and direction constant) and the altimeter.
On reaching the reference altitude adjust power and pitch attitude as necessary to maintain level flight.
Use ailerons and rudder throughout to maintain laterally level flight together with a constant heading and balance.

Student practice: The student should now practise regaining and maintaining a reference altitude whilst sharing the responsibility for lookout.

Returning the aircraft to its original heading

Lower one wing and allow the aircraft to turn away from its original heading

To return to the original heading, whilst maintaining altitude, gently bank the aircraft in the required direction by co-ordinated use of aileron, rudder and elevator.
Just before the original heading is reached, start centralising all three controls whilst maintaining co-ordination.
If the correct anticipation is used the aircraft will arrive on the original reference heading as the wings become level.

Student practice: The student assumes responsibility for the lookout and practises regaining a reference heading.

STRAIGHT AND LEVEL FLIGHT AT SELECTED AIRSPEEDS

Achieving different airspeeds whilst maintaining level flight

Commence from level flight at normal cruising power, and increase the power to a higher setting

Note the power selected and the airspeed obtained.
an increase of power will produce a nose up change in pitch. Resisting the

	pitch change will cause the airspeed to increase. Increased airspeed will result in added lift causing the aircraft to gradually climb. Therefore, at higher power settings the nose attitude will have to be lowered to maintain a constant altitude, and retrimming will be necessary. Time should be allowed for the airspeed to settle down at the new higher figure before the aircraft can be finally retrimmed Increase of power will require movement of elevator, aileron and rudder to maintain straight and level flight.
(Fixed Pitch Propeller)	The RPM selected will increase slightly with the increase of airspeed. Finally, note the new higher airspeed obtained for the particular RPM reading.
Reduce the power to a low RPM cruise setting	Reduction in power will cause a nose down change in pitch. Resisting the pitch change will cause the airspeed to reduce. Reduced airspeed will result in a reduction of lift causing the aircraft to gradually descend. Therefore at lower power settings the aircraft nose will have to be held in a higher attitude to maintain altitude, and retrimming will be necessary. Time should be allowed for the airspeed to settle down at the new lower figure before the aircraft can be finally retrimmed. Reduction of power will require movement of elevator, aileron and rudder to maintain straight and level flight.
(Fixed Pitch Propeller)	The RPM selected will decrease slightly with the decrease of airspeed. Finally, note the new lower airspeed obtained for the particular RPM reading.

Student practice: The student should now practise flying at specific airspeeds (as selected by the instructor) whilst maintaining straight and level flight.

DEMONSTRATION 3.   STRAIGHT AND LEVEL FLIGHT IN DIFFERENT CONFIGURATIONS

Flight Lesson	Demonstration Sequence
Altering the aircraft configuration whilst in level flight In level flight select a power setting compatible with the airspeed(s) for flap and/or landing gear operation This demonstration can be repeated through various flap settings and when applicable with the landing gear lowered.	Note the airspeed in level flight for the particular power selected. Lower partial flap whilst maintaining the aircraft attitude. Retrim. Note the lower airspeed. Maintain level flight and increase the power to return the airspeed to its original value. Note the amount of additional power required. Maintain level flight and raise the flap. Adjust the power to maintain the airspeed. Retrim.

Student practice: The student should now practise maintaining
    constant airspeeds during changing configurations and adopting
    selected airspeeds during configuration changes. The student contin-
    ues his responsibility for the lookout.

PRECISION FLIGHT

Instrument indications during straight and level flight
 	
 The use of Flight, Engine and Aircraft System instruments
	Attitude Indicator.
	 Heading Indicator.
	 Turn and Balance Indicator or Turn Co-ordinator.
	 The development of instrument scanning in relation to Precision Flight.
	 Re-setting the Heading Indicator by reference to the Magnetic Compass:
	    Hold the wings level,
	    Hold the heading constant,
	    Refer to the magnetic compass,
	    Re-set the heading indicator.

Instrument checks of engine and ancillary systems:
    Oil pressure and temperature.
    Cylinder head temperature (if applic-
    able). Ammeter, Suction and other
    instruments applicable to type.
The maintenance of lookout is achieved
by the use of momentary glances at the
instruments.

Student practice: The student should now incorporate the concept of
Precision Flight during his future handling of the aircraft in straight
and level flight.

DEMONSTRATION 4.   RANGE AND ENDURANCE

Flight Lesson	*Demonstration Sequence*

Aircraft performance in relation to range or endurance
 	
Straight and level flight to obtain best range or endurance
	Pre-flight planning to establish the best power settings and airspeeds as given in the Flight/Owner's Manual. The altitude selected will depend upon the considerations of the performance aspect required i.e. range or endurance, and will include:
	    The effects of wind,
	    The selection of a Safety Altitude, and
	    The constraints of controlled airspace en-route.
	The aircraft should be flown in a clean configuration.
	Use of mixture control:
	    Set the power for the required airspeed.
	    Trim.
	    Re-adjust the power as necessary and retrim accurately.
	    Note the RPM and move the mixture control slowly towards the LEAN position.
	When its application is required the use of the mixture control usually results in a slight rise in RPM to a peak increase, after which further application leads to a decrease in RPM.
	If a rise in RPM occurs continue

moving the mixture control towards the LEAN position.

Note the peak RPM just before the RPM start to reduce. Move the mixture control towards the RICH position until just forward of the position which gave peak RPM.

Whenever the power setting or altitude is changed the above steps will have to be repeated.

Changes in mixture strength can alter engine temperatures, therefore careful monitoring of the appropriate gauges will be necessary following such changes.

Student practice: In the practical sense the practice of range or endurance will normally be confined to cross country flights. The procedures can however be practised on suitable occasions during flights in the local area.

Supplement No. 2

WEIGHT AND BALANCE

LIMITATIONS ON AIRCRAFT WEIGHT
A limitation is imposed on the all-up weight at which any aircraft is permitted to operate. This limitation depends on the strength of the structural components of the aircraft and the operational requirements it is designed to meet. If these limitations are exceeded, the operational efficiency will be impaired and the safety of the aircraft may be at risk.

The lift of an aircraft depends on the design of the wing, the airspeed, and the density of the air. The lift generated by the wing of the aircraft is the primary force available to counteract weight and maintain the aircraft in flight. If the lift is less than the aircraft weight in level flight and no additional power is available the aircraft must descend.

The design of the wing on any particular aircraft limits the amount of lift available at any given speed and the available power from the engine limits the speed at which the wing can be made to move through the air. These two basic factors determine the amount of lift produced to balance the aircraft's weight.

When the aircraft is operated in atmospheric conditions where the air is less dense than the International Standard Atmosphere the aircraft performance will be reduced. The effect of this performance reduction is particularly important during the take-off and initial climb. Therefore before flight the pilot must ascertain that the all-up weight of the aircraft is within the correct limits and applicable to the conditions in which it is operated. He must also appreciate the probable hazardous effects on aircraft performance if the permitted all-up weight or centre of gravity limits are exceeded.

Pre-flight planning should include a check of the aircraft performance charts to determine if the aircraft weight could contribute to a hazardous flight condition. Payload, passengers, baggage, cargo and fuel load must be adjusted to provide an adequate margin of safety. In this respect it should be understood that in most general aviation aircraft it is not possible to fill all seats, baggage space and fuel tanks and remain within the approved weight or balance limits. In many four seat aircraft, the fuel tanks may not be permitted to be filled to capacity when a full complement of passengers and baggage is to be carried. Aircraft are generally designed so that a full complement of passengers can be carried on short flights but not on extended flights when a full fuel load will be needed.

The effects upon the performance characteristics of an overweight aircraft are a:

Higher take-off speed
Longer take-off run
Reduced rate and angle of climb
Lower maximum ceiling altitude
Shorter range
Reduced cruising speed
Reduced manoeuvrability
Higher stalling speed
Higher landing speed
Longer landing roll

LIMITATIONS IN RELATION TO AIRCRAFT BALANCE

Balance refers to the location of the centre of gravity (c.g.) of the aircraft. It is of primary importance to the safety of flight. Whilst it is necessary to ensure that the maximum all-up weight of an aircraft is not exceeded, the distribution of permissible weight, i.e. the balance of the aircraft, is equally important.

It is not possible to design an aircraft in which the lift, weight, thrust and drag forces are always in a natural state of equilibrium during straight and level flight; the centre of pressure and the drag line vary with changes of angle of attack and the position of the centre of gravity depends on the load distribution. It is necessary therefore to provide a force to counteract unbalancing couples that may be set up by these forces. This is the function of the tailplane, which together with the elevators and trimmers, can offset any pitching moment set up by the movement of the centre of pressure or the drag line. It is also able to counteract any of the unbalance or unstable tendencies caused by movements of the c.g., provided that these movements are confined within certain limits.

There are forward and aft limits beyond which the c.g. should not be located for flight. These limits are established by the aircraft manufacturer and published on a weight and centre of gravity schedule which is issued for individual aircraft. Information relating to examples of working out weight and balance problems is contained in the Flight/Owner's Manual.

A restricted forward c.g. limit is specified to ensure that sufficient elevator deflection is available at minimum airspeed. When structural limitations or large stick forces do not limit the forward c.g. position, it is normally located at the position where full up elevator is required to obtain a high angle of attack for landing.

The aft c.g. limit is the most rearward position at which the c.g. can be located for the most critical manoeuvre or operation. Aircraft static stability decreases as the c.g. moves aft, and the ability of the aircraft to right itself after manoeuvring or after disturbances by gusts is correspondingly decreased.

If after the aircraft is loaded, the c.g. does not fall within the allowable limits, it will be necessary to shift loads before flight is attempted. The actual location of the c.g. can be determined by a number of factors under the control of the pilot. Positioning of baggage and cargo items, assignment of seats to passengers according to weight, and arranging for the fuel load to be carried are all items under his control. The pilot may also be able to make selective use of fuel from various tank locations, a factor which may have to be considered in maintaining a safe condition of aircraft balance.

The all-up weight of an aircraft will vary during flight due to the consumption of fuel and oil. The alteration of all-up weight due to this fuel and oil consumption will usually change the position of the c.g. unless the c.g. of the fuel and oil is coincident with the aircraft's c.g., fuel tanks are normally aligned close to the mid point of the basic c.g. in order to keep the c.g. changes from this source to a minimum, but when fuselage fuel tanks are fitted they can result in large changes of c.g. position as the fuel is consumed. Any movement of the passengers or crew during flight will also cause changes in the position of the aircraft c.g.

The Air Navigation Order requires that before take-off the commander of an aircraft shall satisfy himself that the load carried by the aircraft is of such weight, and is so distributed, that it may be safely carried on the intended flight. Therefore, before every flight it is the captain's responsibility to ensure that his aircraft is loaded in such manner that the all-up weight is not exceeded and that the position of the centre of gravity remains within the limits for the particular aircraft.

In order to understand the principles of weight and balance calculations a pilot will need to be familiar with the following terms:

Centre of Gravity (c.g.)   The point about which an aircraft would balance if it were possible to suspend it

	at that point. It is the mass centre of the aircraft or the theoretical point at which the entire weight of the aircraft is assumed to be concentrated.
Centre of Gravity Limits	The specified forward and aft points beyond which the c.g. must not be located during flight.
Centre of Gravity Range	The distance between the forward and aft limits.
Arm (moment arm)	The horizontal distance, from the reference datum line to the c.g. of the item. The sign is (+) if measured aft of the datum and (−) if measured forward of the datum.
Datum (reference datum)	An imaginary vertical plane or line from which all measurements of the arm are taken. The datum is established by the manufacturer. After the datum has been established, all moment arms and the location of the permissible range must be taken with reference to that point.

Station	A location in the aircraft which is identified by a number designating its distance from the datum. The datum is therefore identified as zero. The station and arm are usually identical i.e. an item located at station +50 would have an arm of 50 inches.
Moment	The product of the weight of an item multiplied by its arm. Moments are expressed in pound inches or metric equivalent kg. m.
Moment Index (or index)	The moment divided by a constant such as 100, 1000, or 10,000. The purpose of using a moment index is to simplify weight and balance computations where heavy items and long arms result in large, unmanageable numbers.
Reduction Factor	The constant which, when divided into a moment, results in an index.

| Mean Aerodynamic Chord (MAC) | The c.g. limits are sometimes specified as a percentage of mean aerodynamic chord. The MAC is specified for the aircraft by determining the average chord of a wing. |

The aircraft weight and balance schedule will contain information relating to the following terms:

Basic Weight	The basic weight is the weight of the aircraft and all its basic equipment and that of the declared quantity of unusable fuel and unusable oil. In the case of aircraft of 5700kg (12,500lb) maximum authorised weight or less it may also include the weight of usable oil.
Basic Equipment	This consists of the unconsumable fluids, and equipment which is common to all roles for which the operator intends to use the aircraft.
Variable Load	Variable load is the weight of the crew and of items such as the crew's baggage, removable units and other equipment the carriage of which depends upon the role for which the operator intends to use the aircraft for the particular flight.
Disposable Load	This is the weight of all persons and items of load, including fuel and other consumable fluids carried in the aircraft, other than the basic equipment and variable load.

Note: To obtain the total loaded weight it is necessary to add to the basic weights of the variable and disposable load items to be carried for the particular role for which the aircraft is to be used.

Fig. 6-18

Flight/Owner's Manuals vary in their methods of presenting weight and balance information but most of them show a weight and balance envelope (see fig. 6-18) so that a pilot can quickly check if the weight and balance is within limits after making his calculations. These calculations must commence by referring to the Weight and Balance

Schedule for the particular aircraft. The following information outlines the steps to be taken to determine the actual weight and balance of the aircraft.

Referring to the Weight and Balance Schedule and the aircraft Flight/Owner's Manual:

1. List the aircraft Basic Weight, Variable Load and Disposable Load.
2. Multiply the weights by their arms to get the moment of each item.
3. Add the respective weights to get the total loaded weight of the aircraft.
4. Add the moments to get the total moment.
5. Divide the total moment by the total weight to obtain the arm of the c.g. of the aircraft.
6. Compare the total weight obtained in step 3 to the maximum authorised all-up weight.
7. Compare the calculated c.g. arm obtained in step 5 to the approved c.g. range of the aircraft.

If both the weight and position of the c.g. are within the permitted limits the aircraft is safe to fly. If however the actual weight is greater than the maximum authorised weight or the calculated c.g. position is outside the permitted limits the disposable load must be adjusted accordingly.

Although it will be sensible to enter the weights of the various items first and then check that the total weight is within limits before carrying out the moment arm calculations, it must not be assumed that because the actual total weight is below the maximum all-up weight allowed the c.g. will also be within the permitted limits.

Remember the calculations must determine two items:

(a)   The total all-up weight

(b)   The actual position of the c.g.

EXAMPLE OF A WEIGHT AND CENTRE OF GRAVITY SCHEDULE

Reference   : BA/123.
Produced by   : Balanced Aircraft Ltd.
Aircraft Designation   : Pivot 00.
Nationality and Registration Marks   : G-BZZZ.
Constructor   : General Aviation.
Constructor's Serial Number   : 432L.
Maximum Authorised Weight   : 758 kg. (1690 lb.)
Centre of Gravity Limits   : Refer to Flight Manual
                                                reference No. AV50.

PART A   BASIC WEIGHT

The basic weight of the aircraft as calculated from the weighing report supplied
by General Aviation reference W/Bal. 00.
dated 27 March 1985 is   : 1190 lb.

The Centre of Gravity of the aircraft in
the same condition at this weight with
landing gear extended is   : 38.5 in. aft of datum.

The Total Moment about the datum in
this condition is   : 45815.0

Note: The datum is at fuselage station
0.0 and is situated at the front face of
the firewall. This is the datum defined
in the Flight Manual. All lever arms
are distances in inches aft of datum.

The basic weight includes the weight
of 21 lb. unusable fuel and total oil and
the weight of items as indicated on the
attached Basic Equipment List (not
included in this example).

PART B   VARIABLE LOAD

The weight and lever arms of the variable load are shown below.
The variable load depends upon the equipment carried for the
particular role.

ITEM	WEIGHT lb.	LEVER ARM in.	MOMENT lb./in.
Pilot	Actual	39.0	Actual

PART C LOADING INFORMATION (DISPOSABLE LOAD)

The total moment change when the landing gear is extended in lb/in. is :N/A. The appropriate lever arms are:

ITEM	WEIGHT lb.	LEVER ARM in.	CAPACITY Imp. Gal.
Fuel: Main Tanks	135	42.0	18.75
Aux. Tanks	N/A	—	—
Engine Oil: Included in the basic weight.		—	—

Note: In some cases oil may not be included in the basic weight and in these circumstances this will have to be included in the disposable load calculation.

Baggage: In Cabin.	120 (max)	60.0	
Passenger: Row 1.	Actual	39.0	

Fuel density 7.2 lb./gal. and oil density 9.0 lb./gal.

Note: To obtain the total loaded weight of the aircraft, add to the basic weight, the weights of the variable and disposable load items to be carried for the particular role.

This Schedule was prepared (date) .... and supersedes all previous issues.

Signature .... etc, etc.

The following weight and balance calculations are worked out with reference to the example Weight and Balance Schedule on page 6-43. The aircraft load in this case consists of the pilot, one passenger, full fuel tanks and no baggage.

Dividing the total weight into the total moment gives the position of the c.g. in this case it is + 38.88 ins aft of the datum. Reference to the Centre of Gravity moment envelope contained in the Flight/Owner's Manual (fig. 6-19) shows that the maximum all-up weight permitted

	ITEM	WEIGHT lb.	ARM	MOMENT
Basic weight	Aircraft	1190.0	+ 38.5	45815.0
Variable				
load	Pilot	160	+ 39.0	6240.0
Disposable				
load	Fuel	135	+ 42.0	5670.0
	Oil (included in the basic weight)			
	Passenger (one)	160	+ 39.0	6240.0
	Baggage	nil	—	—
	TOTAL	1645.0	—	63965.0

is 1690 lb., therefore the calculated weight of 1645 lb. is within limits. A further check of the moment envelope shows that at 1645 lb. with a total moment arm of 63965 the loaded aircraft is within the authorised weight and balance envelope and can be operated in the Utility Category. If the weight and moment had fallen in the Normal Category section of the envelope the weight and balance would still have been within limits but certain manoeuvres, for example spinning, would not be permitted.

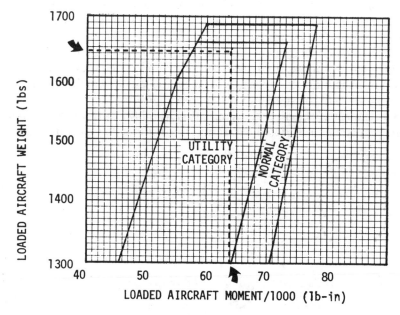

Fig. 6-19

The term 'Category' in relation to 'Utility', 'Normal', and 'Aerobatic' indicates the types of manoeuvres which can be carried out in a particular aircraft in that category. Its meaning in this case is quite different from the definition of Category in the Air Navigation Order which relates to the purposes for which the aircraft can be used, e.g. Transport Category, Aerial Work, Private etc.

The terminology used to define whether certain manoeuvres are permitted varies in different countries. In the U.K. the terminology as laid down in the British Civil Airworthiness Requirements is, Aerobatic, Semi-Aerobatic and Non-Aerobatic. Many countries however use the terms Aerobatic, Utility and Normal. These terms do not always relate to each other in an identical fashion. The term Aerobatic is virtually synonymous in all countries, and the terms Non-Aerobatic and Normal also mean the same thing; however the term Utility is not the same as Semi-Aerobatic. Semi-Aerobatic means that the aircraft is permitted to carry out certain standard aerobatic manoeuvres, but an aircraft in the Utility Category would only be permitted to carry out spinning and certain other manoeuvres as listed in the Flight/Owner's Manual. (Note that spinning is classified as an aerobatic manoeuvre.)

Some aircraft are permitted to operate in either one of two categories and sometimes in all three. The reason for this is to widen the operational use of the aircraft, for example, the manufacturer may wish to produce an aircraft which is capable of meeting basic training requirements and also be used as an air tourer. This latter purpose would be better accomplished if it could carry say, four persons and their baggage. Whereas it would be possible to design the aircraft with the appropriate seating and baggage space, the operation at the all-up weight will normally put a restriction on the more vigorous flight manoeuvres such as spinning, etc.

Nevertheless if the aircraft is operated at a lower all-up weight and within a specified restricted c.g. range this could safely permit limited

BASIC WEIGHT (includes unusable fuel/oil)

VARIABLE LOAD
Pilot/Crew and
their equipment

DISPOSABLE LOAD
Usable fuel
Passengers
Baggage/Cargo

TOTAL ALL UP WEIGHT

aerobatic manoeuvres such as spinning to be carried out. In some aircraft the weight and range of the c.g. may be restricted still further to make it possible to extend the operational capability of the aircraft to carry out normal aerobatic manoeuvres.

In view of these variations to the operational category of the aircraft it will be necessary for the pilot to establish the particular category in which the aircraft falls when the weight and balance calculations have been made prior to flight.

A final cautionary note concerns the stowing of baggage. It is not sufficient just to ensure that the baggage weight and stowage position does not cause the weight and balance limits to be exceeded if during flight it is not secured properly. A shift in the position of loose baggage can destroy the purpose of the balance calculations and also loose baggage could lead to injury of the pilot or the passengers in the case of an accident.

Climbing

Instructor's Guide

The main effort from the student during the initial practice of this exercise will occur during the entry to and levelling off from the climb. Once he has established the climb his training workload is reduced. Therefore little value will be obtained from long continuous climbs during this early practice. More efficient use of the time available will be achieved by using short climbs which will give him more opportunities to practise entering the climb and levelling off.

The student will need to have mastered the task of climbing accurately prior to his introduction to the Take-off, Circuit and Landing stage, but during the period between his introduction to climbing and the consolidated circuit lessons he will have many opportunities to practise the climb. Because of this the individual climbing demonstrations and the practise of them can be spread over several hours of flying. The instructor should ensure that the training is planned accordingly and he should avoid combining all the facets of climbing into one or two lessons.

Remember during your instruction that he has already been taught the basics of straight and level flight, so do not over instruct, but give him the opportunity of demonstrating that he has grasped and understood the method of changing and maintaining attitude in relation to pitch, direction and balance. For example it would be superfluous to tell him at this stage to apply back pressure to the control column to raise the nose because he should already be aware of this from his previous instruction, rather he should be told the correct order in which his actions should be made i.e. power before raising the nose etc.

Before each flight, where a particular type of climb, e.g. cruise climb or maximum angle climb is to be taught, review the practical use and ensure the student understands the purpose of the procedure to be followed in order to achieve the performance desired.

AIRMANSHIP
Ensure the student appreciates the necessity for a careful lookout all round the aircraft prior to entering the climb. The area ahead and to

either side of the intended climbing path is of particular importance. The possibility of the student concentrating on maintaining the correct climbing attitude to the exclusion of where his climbing path is taking the aircraft is a real one and a few words about the dangers of inadvertently entering cloud should be included at some stage of the exercise. During the climb it is very easy to develop the bad habit of only looking ahead and to one side, i.e. in the area of the reference feature which has been selected to maintain the heading. A conscious effort must be made to develop the 'roving eye' technique to cover the area either side and ahead of the nose.

Introduce the practical considerations of the use of the Area and Airfield QNH and check that he understands the purpose of these altimeter settings during visual flight operations. It is also important to remain aware of the aircraft's proximity to airways and similar controlled airspace. The lower levels of airways are sometimes based on Area QNH and sometimes on flight levels. The lower limit or floor of a Terminal Area is normally based upon the QNH of an airfield below that TMA. This should be borne in mind if climbing with an altimeter setting which is different from that used to determine the base of any adjacent controlled airspace.

Although the view up and along the climbing path covers the same area in relation to the aircraft's flight path as when in level flight, it is advisable to avoid climbing on a constant heading for more than short periods. In the early stages small changes of heading can be accomplished by the student lowering the wing slightly (as when regaining a reference heading during straight and level flight) this will achieve an alteration of heading and permit clearing the blind spot beneath and ahead of the aircraft nose.

BEFORE THE EXERCISE
The Long Briefing should cover the following:

Objectives.
Forces.
Relationship between Power/Airspeed and Rate of Climb (Power Curves).
Effect of Flap.
Engine Considerations.
Effect of Altitude.
Maximum Rate of Climb.
The Cruise Climb.
Maximum Angle of Climb.
Airmanship.
Common Errors

The short Pre-Flight Briefing should be based upon the practical aspects of that part of the Long Briefing in relation to the Air Exercise to be covered. Ensure the student understands how to use the Flight/Owner's Manual in order to obtain the relevant speeds and the associated performance figures.

DURING THE AIR DEMONSTRATION

Emphasise the correct principle of Attitude + Power = Performance and that the attitude must be adopted and maintained before the airspeed can stabilise. If the student over concentrates on the airspeed indicator his attitude will usually vary and he will tend to start 'chasing the airspeed'.

Avoid teaching too much during the initial climb entry demonstration. Such items as oil temperature and pressure checks, although very important, should be left until the student has at least had practice in entering the climb and levelling off.

Avoid the illusion of thinking the student will automatically use the trim correctly to completely remove any pressure on the control column because he has used it during straight and level flight. Correct trimming is a very important function of accurate flight and therefore it is important for the student to appreciate the finer points of trimming as soon as possible. To this end the instructor should take a little time to re-trim the aircraft during his demonstration and ensure the student notes the approximate amount of trim movement used.

Make it quite clear that the controls are used to change or maintain the attitude in exactly the same way they were used for straight and level flight and although more rudder pressure will normally be required during the climb the method of achieving balance is unchanged.

LEVELLING OFF

Students will find the maintenance of altitude by changing attitude as the speed increases difficult at first and emphasis on accurate altitude maintenance should be left until they are generally proficient at levelling off.

EFFECT OF FLAP ON THE CLIMB

The effect of climbing with flaps down can often be shown in terms of performance if a vertical speed indicator is fitted. However, a relatively calm day is required for this part of the demonstration to be shown clearly. During the flight demonstration when first raising the flaps allow the student to see for himself the direction and amount of pitch change before demonstrating how to control the aircraft in this situation. This method will ensure a better understanding of what is involved. However when this presentation is employed in aircraft which have a strong pitch change during flap operation care must be taken to take control of the aircraft before its attitude change becomes too marked.

MAXIMUM ANGLE OF CLIMB
This type of climb is normally used to clear obstacles shortly after take-off. At lower altitudes the best angle of climb speed will be lower than that for the best rate, and reduces the ground speed which gives more time to gain height before the obstruction is reached. The benefits achieved by the best angle of climb technique are usually quite small bearing in mind the circumstances under which this type of climb is normally used, e.g. an obstacle climb out from a small field. The lack of available performance figures in the Flight/Owner's Manual, together with the practical difficulties in estimating the actual take-off distance, obstacle height, wind strength and direction etc., dictate that the benefits anticipated should be estimated with caution.

FUTURE LESSONS
By the time the climbing exercise is introduced the student will be at the stage where (whenever practical) he should be given a short and simple introductory demonstration of the flight exercises to be covered in the next air lesson. Care should however be exercised to avoid any great detail or the student may become confused and the value of such demonstrations will be lost.

COMMON ERRORS
• Many accidents are attributable to poor climb techniques and lack of accurate airspeed control when the aircraft is near the ground. As this exercise progresses stress should be laid on correct procedures and accuracy in flying. Most students tend to chase the airspeed as a result of paying insufficient attention to attitude. Ensure the student appreciates the difficulties he will make for himself if he does not hold a constant attitude long enough for the airspeed to become established at a constant figure.
• Many students fail to anticipate and correct yaw during power and airspeed changes. This is further aggravated by the changing rudder effectiveness when power or airspeed are altered and also the reduced visual reference to the natural horizon when in the climbing attitude. This latter effect makes it more difficult to maintain a wings level condition together with constant heading and balance.
• When teaching the climb at a specific power setting a fixed pitch propeller will incur a drop in the original RPM selected as the speed is reduced to that required for the climb. Emphasise this point to ensure the student re-establishes the RPM chosen for the climb

except in cases where full throttle is already being used.

• Students often have difficulty with accurate trimming because they attempt to trim out the control pressures before the airspeed has settled to a constant figure, or due to allowing the attitude of the aircraft to change slightly during the trimming operation.

• Some students develop a tendency to neglect to check engine oil temperature and pressure readings when concentrating on flying the aircraft. All students should be reminded, as soon as practical, of the vital importance of not exceeding the laid down engine temperature and pressure limitations.

• Performance considerations in respect of the climb rate, cruise climb and angle of climb will often become neglected due to their lack of practical application during the early stage of the student's training. Reference to this type of aircraft performance should be repeated at a later stage of the course, e.g. after first solo and before cross country operation is undertaken. The student must be given some practice at interpreting the Flight/Owner's Manual for the relevant performance figures for the particular type.

• It is fairly common for students to get into the habit of raising the flap during the climb without first referring to the airspeed. This should be watched for carefully and emphasis given to the importance of having an adequate airspeed prior to retracting the flaps or a sudden sink will result. Such a sink could lead to the student applying back pressure which will in turn result in a lowering of the airspeed, and when the aircraft is near the ground a situation of this nature could be dangerous.

BEST RATE OF CLIMB

Climbing

Long Briefing

CLIMB DATA

GROSS WEIGHT POUNDS	AT SEA LEVEL & 59°F			AT 5000 FEET & 41°F			AT 10,000 FEET & -12°F								
	BEST CLIMB IAS MPH	RATE OF CLIMB FT/MIN	GAL. OF FUEL USED	BEST CLIMB IAS MPH	RATE OF CLIMB FT/MIN	FROM S.L. FUEL USED	BEST CLIMB IAS MPH	CLIMB FT/MIN	FUEL USED	IAS MPH	CLIMB FT MIN	FUEL USED	IAS MPH	RATE OF CLIMB FT/MIN	FROM S.L. FUEL USED
2200	84	1770	2	81	1420	3.0	77	1080	4.1	75	750	5.4	71	400	7.1
2700	90	1320	2	87	1030	3.3	84	740	4.9	81	450	6.9	78	160	10.5
3200	96	1000	2	93	740	3.8	90	480	6.1	88	220	9.7	--	---	---

NOTE: FULL THROTTLE, 2625 RPM, MIXTURE AT RECOMMENDED LEANING SCHEDULE, FLAPS UP. FUEL USED INCLUDES WARM-UP AND TAKE-OFF ALLOWANCE.

OBJECTIVES

Primarily the purpose of this exercise is to teach the student how to initiate normal climb entry, maintain the climb and level off. Later the exercise will include the effect of flaps and altitude on climb rate, together with the method of establishing the aircraft in the climb with flaps down in preparation for 'going round again' and how to return to the normal climb in the aircraft clean configuration. Finally the student will be taught the cruise climb and maximum angle of climb techniques. Airmanship and engine considerations will form an integral part of the total exercise.

INTRODUCTION

Normal climbing flight is achieved by the expenditure of propulsive energy over and above that which is needed to sustain the aircraft in level flight. Another method of gaining height is by raising the aircraft's nose, utilising airspeed to zoom to a higher altitude. This process can only be a temporary one in which the associated reduction in speed (kinetic energy) is converted into height (potential energy).

Correct climbing flight is therefore a steady process during which additional propulsive energy is converted into potential energy. Climbing performance also involves a flight condition where the aircraft is in equilibrium as height is gained.

THE FORCES

The direction in which the three forces, Thrust, Lift and Drag, will act will be dependent upon the aircraft flight path. Weight however will always act downward perpendicular to the horizontal. When the aircraft is in a climb the geometric relationship of the forces will be as shown in fig. 7-1.

Unlike level flight, it can be seen that during the climb a component of weight will be acting backwards along the flight path and this component will in effect be additional to aerodynamic drag.

The fundamental process of climb performance is the application of additional thrust over and above that required to maintain level

Fig. 7-1

flight at the same airspeed. During a steady climb the aircraft is in equilibrium. In the case of small aircraft which have moderate angles of climb the vertical component of lift is very nearly the same as the total lift force.

The effect of the weight being inclined backwards along the flight path means that this must be compensated for by increasing the thrust by a greater amount than is needed merely to balance the aerodynamic drag. For the benefit of those who are interested in the mathematics of climbing the summation of the forces along the flight path in a steady climb with a small inclination of flight path from the horizontal (low performance aircraft) is as follows:

$$T = D + W \text{ SIN } \gamma$$

$$
\begin{aligned}
\text{where } T &= \text{thrust available} \\
D &= \text{drag} \\
W &= \text{weight} \\
\gamma &= \text{flight path inclination} \\
&\quad \text{(angle of climb in degrees)}
\end{aligned}
$$

Although this summation neglects some of the factors involved, such as the inclination of the thrust line relative to the flight path, changes in the induced drag, and lift not being equal to weight, etc., all of which may be important in high performance aircraft, the basic principle shown still defines the relationship of those factors affecting the aircraft climb performance.

The vertical velocity (rate of climb) of an aircraft depends upon its flight speed and the inclination of the flight path. The definition of 'velocity' relates to both speed and direction so that the rate of climb is the vertical component of the flight path velocity.

RELATIONSHIP BETWEEN POWER/AIRSPEED AND RATE OF CLIMB

The balance of the forces to achieve equilibrium is more complicated than in level flight because the inclination of the thrust line from the horizontal introduces a component of thrust which adds to the lift

Fig. 7-2

produced from the wings. Therefore during climbing flight the wing lift will be less than the weight.

To obtain a rate of climb it is necessary to consider the airspeed at which the aircraft will be flown. A rate of climb will be achieved at any airspeed provided there is a surplus of power available after the power required to overcome drag has been met. It can therefore be seen that at any airspeed the rate of climb depends upon the excess power in hand, that is, the difference between the actual power which is available and that power required to maintain that speed in level flight.

When the excess power is zero the rate of climb will be zero and this will for example occur when the aircraft is flying at its maximum speed in level flight. When the power available is greater than the power required this will permit a rate of climb compatible with the amount of excess power. This relationship provides the basis for an important aspect of normal flight technique, i.e. for a condition of steady flight the power setting is the primary control of rate of climb or descent.

Figure 7-3 represents typical performance curves for a light aircraft and provided the airspeed is between A and B the aircraft will have a climb performance. However, the closer the airspeed gets to A or B the less will become the rate of climb. The recommended speeds for rate of climb, cruise climb, or angle of climb are given in the Flight/Owner's Manuals.

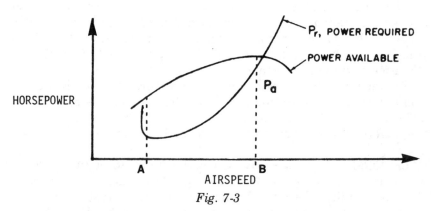

Fig. 7-3

Entering and Maintaining the Normal Climb
Once the Airmanship considerations of Lookout, the direction of climb in relation to controlled airspace, the vicinity of cloud and the selection of a reference feature for maintenance of heading have been completed, the aircraft is placed in the climb by the following method:

Climb Entry

Power –   Climbing power is selected whilst carefully keeping the wings level, the direction constant and the aircraft in balance.

Attitude –   The aircraft nose is raised to the approximate climbing attitude and then held steady until the airspeed settles to a constant reading. If this airspeed is not the correct climbing airspeed the nose attitude will have to be readjusted accordingly.

Trim –   Once the correct airspeed has been established the aircraft should be trimmed correctly for a condition of 'no load' on the flying controls.

The correct climb attitude with the wings level, heading constant and the aircraft in balance is maintained by the use of elevators, ailerons and rudder in a similar manner as when in straight and level flight. During a climb the higher nose attitude obscures the view directly ahead of the aircraft and as such it is a little more difficult to use the horizon line to maintain the correct pitch and wings level attitude, and it is necessary to use that portion of the horizon line which extends out either side of the aircraft nose. The rudder is still used to maintain balance and provided the wings are held level and the heading remains constant the aircraft will be in balanced flight.

With the higher attitude of the nose a reference feature directly ahead of the aircraft will not be seen, so in the initial practice of this exercise it will be necessary for the student to select a reference feature to one side and well ahead of the aircraft to ensure the heading is being maintained. Later the use of the heading indicator will be introduced and this will permit greater heading accuracy.

The aircraft is returned to level flight by the following method:

Levelling Off
Attitude –   The nose is lowered to the attitude required for flight at normal cruising power and held in this position.

Power –   As the speed approaches the normal cruising airspeed the cruising power should be selected. In the same way as for the climb entry care must be taken to keep the wings level and to maintain the heading and balance during this change of power. At this stage cross reference must be made between the nose attitude and the altimeter to ensure the correct attitude for constant altitude at the power selected has been chosen. If the altitude is not maintained the nose attitude will have to be re-adjusted accordingly.

Trim — Once the correct attitude has been selected and the altitude remains constant the aircraft should be re-trimmed for this flight condition.

Levelling Off at a Pre-selected Altitude
With small training aircraft the rate of climb is relatively low and no great difficulty is normally experienced by levelling off at the same time as the required altitude is reached. However a smooth and more precise technique can be achieved if a small anticipation factor is employed. This anticipation factor should relate to the actual rate of climb at the time and if the figure of 10% of the rate of climb is used as a lead factor to commence the levelling off action this will result in a smoother and more gradual transition from the climb to level flight, e.g. if the rate of climb is 500 f.p.m. then start slowly levelling off 50 feet before reaching the required altitude.

This technique has two added benefits in that it is the one used during instrument flying, and a lead factor of approximately 10% will also produce a rate of control movement during levelling off which will be virtually constant for all types of aircraft regardless of variation in rates of climb.

MAXIMUM RATE OF CLIMB
One of the more important items with respect to climb performance is the maximum rate of climb airspeed (Vy). Fig. 7-4 shows that in the case illustrated the speed of 80 coincides with that point where there exists the greatest difference between power required and power available. Climbing at speeds either side of 80 will result in a reduced climb rate.

The power available curve for a piston engine/propeller aircraft will show a variation of propulsive efficiency with variation of airspeed. If the propeller efficiency were constant over the aircraft speed range the best rate of climb speed would be coincident with the minimum power required speed. The actual propeller efficiency however varies with the aircraft speed and will produce a lower power available at lower speeds. Therefore the largest difference between the power available and power required curves occurs at a higher speed than that for minimum drag.

In the example shown at fig. 7-4 the airspeed of 80 represents the

Fig. 7-4

maximum rate of climb speed for the aircraft concerned. However due to the related shape of the power available and power required curves there is normally sufficient latitude in most light aircraft for small variations of climbing speed to be used without significantly reducing the rate of climb.

EFFECT OF WEIGHT

A change in the aircraft weight affects both the angle and the rate of climb. An increase of weight will reduce the maximum rate of climb and (depending upon the shape of the power available and power required curves for a particular aircraft) the optimum rate of climb speed may be higher than when the aircraft is at a lesser weight. Reference to the Flight/Owner's Manual for the aircraft type will need to be made to establish the correct climbing speed for the particular all-up weight of the aircraft.

EFFECT OF FLAPS

For a given speed the selection of optimum lift flap will give added lift with only a small increase of drag. Therefore it is possible to obtain the original amount of lift at a lower airspeed. At this lower airspeed the total aerodynamic drag may be less, and if this were the case in a particular aircraft the power required for level flight at this lower airspeed would also be less, resulting in more power being available for the climb. This would mean that there would be more thrust available to act against the aircraft weight, and as a result the aircraft would climb at a steeper angle. The rate of climb however is a function of both angle and airspeed and because of the lower airspeed with flaps down the rate of climb will usually be reduced.

Therefore at normal cruising altitude there is no advantage in climbing with partial flap, but when flying near the ground, particularly after take-off, a steeper angle of climb may be of importance in clearing obstructions. Provided it is beneficial to use flaps in this situation (the Flight/Owner's Manual will indicate this) their use will normally be of value, provided a lower climbing speed is used. Following such a take-off and when a safe height has been reached the flaps should be raised and a normal climb adopted.

When the flaps are lowered beyond the optimum setting for maximum lift, a considerable increase in drag occurs which needs more thrust to balance it. Therefore the amount of thrust available to act against weight becomes less and it is no longer possible to maintain the steep angle of climb. Thus it is wrong to climb with a flap setting greater than the optimum. At times when a climb must be started with this amount of flap down, as when 'going round again' following a mislanding, the flaps should be raised to the optimum setting as soon as a safe airspeed has been attained.

Climbing with Flaps Down
The purpose of this demonstration is to give the student an appreciation of the effects on the performance of the aircraft whilst climbing with the flaps lowered and also to provide him with the opportunity to practise raising the flaps during a 'go round again' situation following a landing or mislanding.

The effects of climbing with the flaps down and the associated change of pitch attitude, rate of airspeed variation for a constant attitude, together with the direction and rate of pitch change when the flaps are raised will depend upon the characteristics of the particular aircraft and the type of flaps fitted.

This exercise will commence from normal climbing flight and if possible in relatively smooth air conditions. After noting the rate of climb the flaps should be lowered to an appropriate setting (depending upon aircraft type) whilst the normal climbing airspeed is maintained. It will be seen that the rate of climb will now be reduced. If the speed is now reduced by a small amount (5 – 10 knots) the rate of climb will increase slightly, therefore it will be more efficient to use a slightly lower airspeed when climbing with the flaps down. The actual airspeed used will depend upon the particular aircraft type.

Recovery to the Normal Climb
Leaving the control column free raise the flaps and note the direction and rate of change in the pitch attitude. Having noted the

effect of raising the flaps the aircraft should then be returned to the normal climbing attitude.

The flaps should again be selected and the aircraft attitude adjusted to maintain the flaps down climbing speed. At this stage the flaps should be raised and at the same time the correct pitch attitude to give the normal climbing speed should be adopted, after which the aircraft can be re-trimmed.

ENGINE CONSIDERATIONS

 During the climb the engine will be operating very close to or at a full power condition. For this reason care must be taken to monitor the oil temperature and pressure gauges at frequent intervals to ensure that these remain normal. Where applicable the cylinder head temperature gauge must also be included in this check. With the present day modern aero engine, any indication on the gauges which show the engine is approaching a limiting condition should be treated as unusual and power accordingly reduced.

Use of the Mixture Control
As the aircraft climbs the surrounding air density decreases and without some means of adjustment the fuel/air ratio will become too rich, and the engine will suffer a loss of power. This power loss will be indicated by a gradual drop in RPM (when a fixed pitch propeller is fitted) followed eventually by rough running.

The fuel/air ratio in all reciprocating aero engines is set to give an over rich mixture, and the actual degree of richness varies with the throttle setting, being greatest at full power operation. The purpose of this arrangement is to reduce the possibility of detonation, pre-ignition and overheating occurring in the cylinders.

However, due to the reducing air density which is experienced as an aircraft climbs, the engine power output gradually decreases. For example the maximum power output at 5000 feet is approximately 75% of that obtained at sea level and because of this the possibility of detonation and pre-ignition occurring at full power decreases with height. Due to the over rich mixture which occurs when the manual mixture control is left in 'Rich' an added loss of power is experienced during climbing and above 5000 feet this over rich condition manifests itself by a positive drop in RPM (fixed pitch non-supercharged engines) followed by rough running.

Therefore when climbing above 5000 feet it is normally recommended that the pilot adjusts the fuel/air ratio by the use of the manual mixture control. The method of using the mixture control is given in Supplement 1 on page 4-19.

EFFECT OF ALTITUDE

At altitude and due to the lower air density a higher angle of attack will be needed for any given TAS. This normally increases the total drag force and more power will be required. The power available from the engine is dependent upon the amount of air (by weight) which can be provided to it and the power output will reduce with increase of altitude unless a supercharger is used.

Most light training aircraft are fitted with normally aspirated engines and therefore the maximum power available will start to decrease from sea level upwards. It can therefore be seen that an increase of altitude generally results in an increase of power required and a decrease of power available. When an aircraft reaches its absolute ceiling it will be flying in close proximity to the stalling angle of attack and it will only be capable of flying at one speed.

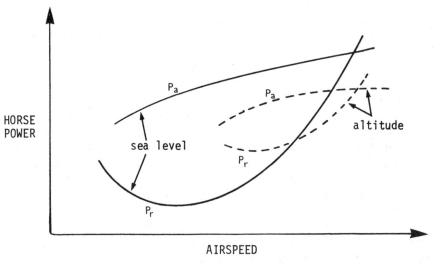

Fig. 7-5

In fig. 7-5 the dotted lines show the effect of altitude upon the horse power required and available curves. The gradual closing of the curves for power required and power available as altitude is gained will eventually mean that there will be no excess power available for climbing when the aircraft reaches its absolute altitude, and the power curves at the maximum height at which the aircraft is capable of flying will appear as shown in fig. 7-6. Even in small training aircraft absolute altitude will occur above 10,000 feet but as these aircraft are not normally equipped with oxygen systems or equipment this altitude will not usually assume any importance during training. However there are many advanced single and multi-engine aircraft which have the capability of meeting such oxygen requirements and when these are used, it is important during pre-flight planning to bear in mind the effect of altitude on aircraft performance.

AIRSPEED

Fig. 7-6

For a given IAS under standard atmospheric conditions TAS increases with altitude and as a result affects the characteristics of the performance curves. As the pilot uses indicated airspeed he will need to decrease this speed slightly as altitude is gained during a long climb. A rule of thumb method of estimating the correct indicated climbing speed for height is to reduce the best climb speed IAS at sea level by 1 m.p.h., or (1kt) per 1000 feet gained. However as stated earlier the related shape of the power available and power required curves normally allow sufficient latitude for small variations of climb speed to occur without significantly affecting the rate of climb, and because of this there is little need to consider climbing airspeed reductions unless operating above 5000 feet

Before leaving the consideration of the effect of altitude upon climbing performance it is pertinent to consider the effcts of Density Altitude. This is the pressure altitude corrected for deviations from the standard temperature, i.e. if the temperature at a given height is different from that relating to the Standard Atmosphere the density altitude will be different from the pressure altitude. Low atmospheric pressure, high temperature and high humidity all produce a decrease in air density which results in a high density altitude. In other words if the atmospheric conditions are such that the density is less than standard then the performance of the aircraft is reduced and the rate of climb will be less.

The effects of a high density altitude can be significant when applied to the performance characteristics of an aircraft. The performance figures given in the Flight/Owner's Manuals are based upon a standard atmosphere and if the actual density of the air is less than this then the performance figures given are greater than can actually be achieved. For example if an aircraft requires a take-off distance of 1200 feet at sea level under standard conditions, it will need a longer distance to take-off if the temperature is above standard or the airfield is above sea level. The extra distance required if the aircraft were taken off from an airfield at 4000 feet a.m.s.l. with a surface temprature of 36° C is 1200 × 2.2 or 2620 feet. Whereas in the U.K. airfield elevations are fairly low and temperatures of 36° C are rare this would not be so in Southern Europe, where many airfields are well above 1000 feet a.m.s.l. and the mean summer temperature (excluding spain) is 32°C.

OAT

Fig. 7-7

THE CRUISE CLIMB
The object of a cruise climb is to obtain a reasonable rate of climb as well as to travel at a higher forward speed than in the normal climb. Its practical value lies mainly in cross country flying where it is often of benefit to climb at a slightly less rate and travel further during the climbing period. Provided a reduced power is acceptable during the climb another benefit would be that the mixture control could be employed leading to a more economical operation.

For most small aircraft an increase of speed of 20 knots above the normal climbing speed will usually lead to a reduction in the rate of climb by approximately 7% but an increase of forward speed by some 25%. Subject to the prevailing wind conditions, operating height to be reached and the length of the flight, this method of climbing may show greater advantages over the normal climb technique.

MAXIMUM ANGLE OF CLIMB
The maximum angle of climb concerns obstacle clearance. The maximum angle of climb airspeed (V_x) would occur where there exists the greatest difference between the *thrust* which is available during the climb and the *thrust* which is required. Reference to the summation of the climbing forces shows that the following relationship exists to express the trigonometric sine of the climb angle,

$$\sin \gamma = \frac{T - D}{W}$$

This simply states that for a given weight, the angle of climb (γ) depends on the difference between thrust and drag (T − D), or excess thrust. In other words when the excess thrust is zero the inclination of the flight path is zero and the aircraft is in steady level flight. When the thrust is greater than the drag, the excess thrust will allow a climb angle depending on the value of excess thrust.

Figure 7-5 illustrates the climb angle performance with the curves of thrust available and thrust required versus airspeed. The thrust required, or drag curve is assumed to be representative of a typical propeller driven aircraft. The thrust available curve shows the typical propeller thrust available which is high at low speeds and decreases with an increase in velocity.

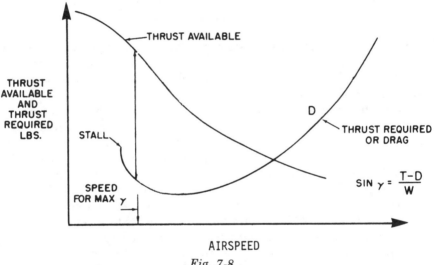

Fig. 7-8

The best angle of climb speed will therefore be lower than the best rate of climb speed and reference to the Flight/Owner's Manual will be needed to determine the exact figure.

Whereas the maximum rate of climb is related to maximum height gained in a minimim time, the best angle of climb is concerned with maximum height gained in relation to the minimum distance travelled. Due to the marginal benefits obtained from this latter type of climb, aircraft manufacturers seldom publish any specific information relating to this type of aircraft performance. The following table however gives some simple arithmetical calculations to show that the benefits are small and that considerable care must be used in deciding upon the value of its practical application in relation to the clearance of obstacles immediately after take-off. (This is covered later during the take-off exercise.)

Assume climb rate ... 500 f.p.m. at 70 m.p.h.

SPEED M.P.H.	DISTANCE FEET	TIME SECONDS	HEIGHT GAIN FEET	VERTICAL DIFFERENCE FEET
70		9.74	81.16	
	1000			13.50
60		11.36	94.66	
70		12.85	107.08	
	1320 ($\frac{1}{4}$ mile)			17.92
60		15.00	125.00	

Bearing in mind that the rate of climb will probably be a little less when the best rate of climb speed is not used, it can be seen that the practical benefits achieved by using the maximum angle of climb speed are rather small.

From the practical viewpoint the effect of wind is the largest single factor in determining the angle of climb for a small aircraft. To appreciate this, consider the effect on the climbing angle when climbing in zero wind conditions and into a headwind of 26 kts (30 m.p.h.). Ignoring the small slant angle of the climb path and assuming a climbing speed of 60 m.p.h. it would take one minute to cover one mile in conditions of zero wind. The same climb conducted into a headwind of 26 kts would take two minutes to cover one mile. If the rate of climb were 500 feet per minute at an airspeed of 60 m.p.h. it will be seen that in zero wind the aircraft will reach 500 feet in one mile and with a headwind of 26 kts it will reach 1000 feet in one mile. Wind therefore becomes a very important consideration in the practical application of obstacle clearance.

During a maximum angle of climb the lower airspeed will provide less engine cooling but as this type of climb is normally only used to ensure greater obstacle clearance immediately following a take-off, the length of time spent at this lower airspeed is extremely short and in these circumstances no additional engine handling considerations should apply.

USE OF THE INSTRUMENTS TO ACHIEVE PRECISION FLIGHT
Precision Flight has already been defined during the Long Briefing for Straight and Level Flight. During the climb the airspeed indicator will tend to be monitored more frequently than during level flight in order to accurately maintain the correct climbing speed. It must

however be appreciated that the concept of attitude flight still applies and the temptation to 'chase the airspeed' must be resisted. The correct method of making airspeed corrections is to alter the attitude in the required direction in pitch and whilst holding the new attitude constant allow the airspeed to settle to its new constant figure. This action is repeated whenever the airspeed moves away from the correct figure and the correct position of the index aircraft of the attitude indicator above the artificial horizon line should be noted, together with its lateral level indications.

 Throughout climbing the aircraft is in a condition of high power and relatively low airspeed. This means that the slipstream effect is fairly strong and a conscious effort must be made to remember that greater rudder pressure will be required to maintain balanced flight. Bearing in mind the need to keep the wings level and the further effect of rudder application, together with the restricted view of the horizon line, a further conscious effort must be made to ensure the wings are kept level during this added rudder application.

On aircraft fitted with American built engines the direction of yaw will be to the left and right rudder pressure will be required. If this yaw is not corrected and the wings are being held level the balance indicator ball will be out of centre to the right indicating that right rudder will be required. When a rudder trimmer is fitted it will need to be re-adjusted once the aircraft is in the climb.

Finally, a greater use of the aircraft instruments increases cockpit 'look in' time and as a result the standard of Lookout can easily deteriorate. Therefore reference to the instruments must be kept as brief as possible compatible with achieving the purpose of precision flight.

AIRMANSHIP

As with any other flight manoeuvre Lookout will be of primary importance both before and during the climb. A careful lookout must be made around the aircraft and particularly up ahead and to either side of the intended climbing path. The climb must not be commenced until it has been established that the climbing path is clear of other aircraft, cloud and controlled or other special airspace.

Although the high nose attitude in the climb obscures reference to the horizon line ahead the area of the pilot's visibility in relation to the aircraft flight path is the same as when in straight and level flight.

Fig. 7-9

However unlike level flight is has become the accepted practice during a prolonged climb to change the aircraft heading from time to time to clear the blind spot beneath the nose.

It is also during this flight and those which follow, that the rules of avoiding other aircraft can be applied, and in the case of converging or approaching head-on to other aircraft, a simple memory guide such as 'on the right all right' will be found useful and will act as a quick reminder for the taking of decisions regarding the right of way rules for aircraft avoidance.

During the climb the engine is being operated at a high power setting and it is a good practice to check the engine temperature and pressure at more frequent intervals than when in normal cruising flight. If cooling gills or shutters are fitted then consideration should be given to their operation as required from the readings of the cylinder head temperature gauge.

Once the aircraft has left the airfield traffic area the altimeter should normally be re-set to the Area QNH in order to obtain altitude information in relation to the terrain over which the aircraft is flying. Outside controlled airspace and above 3000 feet a.m.s.l. many pilots set the altimeter to 1013 mb., in which case the flight level of the aircraft is read from the altimeter. Unless special operating circumstances dictate the use of flight levels it is usually more convenient to use the relevant Area QNH during training as in these circumstances the aircraft rarely maintains a constant heading or height for more than a few minutes at a time and this therefore restricts the application of the 'Quadrantal Rule'.

PRE-FLIGHT BRIEFING
CLIMBING
Demonstration 1

Aim   To teach you how to attain and maintain the normal climb and how to return the aircraft to level flight.

What   Climbing is a condition of flight during which the aircraft gains height at a constant rate, airspeed and heading with the aircraft in balance. It is a fundamental procedure which is used in various forms to reach appropriate altitudes for various flight operations.

Airmanship   Ensure the area above, ahead, and to one side of the intended flight path is clear of other aircraft, cloud and controlled or similar airspace.

How

Climb Entry
Select a reference feature ahead and to one side for the purpose of maintaining a heading.
Lookout, clear area ahead, above, and to either side of the intended climb path.

Power.   Select climbing power, maintaining lateral level, direction and balance.

Attitude.   Adopt the approximate climbing attitude and maintain this until the airspeed settles to a constant figure.
Re-adjust the attitude as necessary to achieve the correct climbing speed.

Trim.   Re-trim as required to relieve the control pressures.

Student practice.

Maintaining the Climb
Lookout maintained.
Use elevators, ailerons and rudder to maintain the correct speed with the wings level and heading and balance constant.
Cross refer between the nose attitude and the ASI to maintain the correct climbing speed.

Engine considerations – as applicable to type.

A prolonged climb will necessitate heading changes or a temporary lowering of the nose to clear the area of the blind spot beneath the nose.

Student practice.

Levelling Off
Maintaining the lookout.

Attitude. Adopt the level flight attitude for normal cruising power.
As the airspeed approaches the cruise speed.

Power. Select cruising power, maintaining lateral level, heading and balance. Cross refer between the nose attitude, the horizon and the altimeter.
Re-adjust the nose attitude as necessary to maintain constant altitude.

Trim. Re-trim to relieve the control pressures.

Student practice.

PRE-FLIGHT BRIEFING

CLIMBING
Demonstration 2.

Aim

To teach you:

(a) To level off at a pre-selected altitude.

(b) To climb with the flap lowered and how to raise the flap whilst returning to the normal (clean) climb condition.

What

(a) A transition from the climb to level flight at a precise and pre-determined altitude.

(b) A condition of climbing flight during which the aircraft is flown initially with flap down, followed by the flap being retracted whilst the aircraft is safely returned to the normal (clean) climb condition with a minimum reduction in the rate of climb.

Airmanship Lookout considerations and avoidance of cloud, controlled airspace etc, and the use of altimeter settings.

How *Levelling Off at a Pre-selected Altitude*

During the climb. . . .

As the selected altitude is approached commence gently levelling off, co-ordinating the change in pitch attitude to give a zero climb rate at the pre-selected altitude.

Maintaining a cross reference between the pitch attitude and the altimeter, smoothly reduce the power to that required for cruising flight.

Small attitude adjustments will be required during the change from climbing to cruising power.

Re-trim as required.

Student practice.

Climbing with Flap Down and Returning to a Normal Climb

During the climb. Note the rate of climb. Lower partial flap. Maintain normal climb speed. Re-trim. After the flap is lowered note the reduced rate of climb.

Reduce the speed to that recommended for climbing with flap. Note the slight improvement in the rate of climb.

Leaving the elevators free, raise the flap and note the direction and rate of change in the pitch attitude.

Re-establish the aircraft in the climb with flap down. First, ensure the speed is not less than the recommended flap down climbing speed then raise the flap whilst adjusting the attitude to achieve the normal climb speed. Re-trim.

Note. Use of the correct flap raising procedure will achieve minimum climb rate reduction during flap retraction.

Student practice.

PRE-FLIGHT BRIEFING

CLIMBING
Demonstration 3.

Aim — *The Cruise Climb*
To teach you how to achieve an economical climb to altitude during navigation flights.

What — A constant climb at a selected airspeed to give additional forward speed for only a small reduction in the rate of climb.

Airmanship — Lookout, weather, ATC and controlled airspace considerations, including the correct use of altimeter settings.

How — *Climbing (en-route) Range*
During the normal climb:
Note the specific rate of climb.
Increase the airspeed to the selected cruise climb speed.
Note the small reduction in climb rate for the increased climb speed.
If applicable to aircraft type:
Select 75% power and use mixture control during the climb according to the manufacturer's recommendations.

Above 5000 feet and regardless of power used the operation of mixture control will become necessary.

Above 5000 feet airspeed reduction 5 knots per 5000 feet.

Application to en-route climbing during navigation flights.

Student practice.

CLIMBING
Demonstration 4.

Aim — *The Maximum Angle of Climb*
To teach you the method of achieving the maximum angle of climb.

What — A climbing procedure which gives maximum gain of height relative to distance travelled.

Airmanship — Lookout and ATC considerations including the application of aircraft performance.

How — *Climbing at the Maximum Angle*
Determine the maximum angle of climb speed for the particular aircraft type.

Select maximum power and adopt the climbing attitude for the best angle of climb speed. Re-trim.

The nose attitude will be higher than for the normal maximum rate of climb.
The rate of climb will be slightly less but the gain in height for the distance travelled will be greater.

When extended climbs of this nature are carried out, the engine temperature and pressure gauges must be monitored more frequently.

Application to obstruction clearance after the take-off.

Student practice.

Climbing

Flight Demonstrations

INTRODUCTION

The contents of the total climbing exercise may be divided into specific demonstration groups as follows:

1. Climb Entry, Maintaining the Climb and Levelling Off.
2. Levelling Off at Selected Altitudes.
   Climbing with Flaps Down and Returning to the Normal (clean) Climb.
3. The Cruise Climb.
   Use of Mixture Control During the Climb and Change of Climbing Speed with Increase of Altitude.
4. The Maximum Angle of Climb.

The initial demonstration and practice of climbing will be concerned with the basic climb entry, maintaining the climb and levelling off. It would be advisable to leave levelling off at pre-determined altitudes until the next flight lesson.

The demonstration and practice of climbing with flaps down is in preparation for the 'go round again situation' during the approach and landing.

The introduction of cruise climbing and use of mixture control can be conveniently left until the navigation stage.

The use of the best angle of climb is normally applicable to the obstruction climb out technique following take-off, and the demonstration and practice of this procedure will fall naturally into the consolidation period of circuits after first solo or during that stage when Forced Landings With Power are being taught.

Airmanship items will be introduced and developed at appropriate times during all demonstrations.

DEMONSTRATION 1. CLIMB ENTRY, MAINTAINING THE CLIMB AND LEVELLING OFF

Flight Lesson	*Demonstration Sequence*
Climbing flight	
Entering the climb	Select a reference feature to one side of the nose. Lookout, clear area ahead, above and to either side. Select climbing power whilst maintaining lateral level, direction and balance. Raise the nose to the climbing attitude. Maintain this attitude until the airspeed settles to a constant figure. Adjust the attitude as necessary to achieve the correct climbing speed. Re-trim as required.
Maintaining the climb	All three controls are used in the normal sense to maintain the correct pitch attitude with the wings level and direction and balance constant. Cross refer from the natural horizon and nose position to the ASI in order to maintain the attitude for the correct climbing speed. Check engine temperature and pressure at frequent intervals. Maintain a constant lookout and during longer climbs change heading to clear the blind spot beneath the aircraft nose.
Levelling off	Select the pitch attitude for level flight at normal cruising power. When the airspeed approaches the cruising speed select cruising power, maintaining the wings level and direction and balance constant. Cross refer between the aircraft attitude in pitch and the altimeter to ensure that level flight is being achieved. Re-adjust the pitch attitude as necessary. Re-trim as required.

Student practice: Short climbs should normally be practised at this
    stage in order that the student may have plenty of practice at
    entering the climb and levelling off.

DEMONSTRATION 2.   LEVELLING OFF AT SELECTED ALTITUDES

Flight Lesson	Demonstration Sequence
Achieving specific altitudes From the climb	Just before the pre-selected altitude is reached commence gentle levelling off action. Maintain a frequent cross reference between the altimeter and the nose attitude in pitch. When the correct altitude and attitude are achieved, reduce to cruise power. Small adjustments to pitch attitude will be necessary as cruise power is selected. Re-trim as required.

Student practice: The student should now practise levelling off at pre-selected altitudes during this and subsequent flights.

	CLIMBING WITH FLAP DOWN AND RETURNING TO THE NORMAL CLIMB
The effect of flap during the climb During the normal climb select partial flap (in smooth flight conditions)	Note rate of climb at normal climbing airspeed. Whilst lowering the flaps maintain the normal climbing speed. Re-trim and note the reduced rate of climb. Reduce the airspeed to the recommended climbing speed with flap down. Re-trim and note the slight improvement in the rate of climb.
Raise the flap	As the flaps are raised, temporarily leave the controls free and note the direction and rate of change in the pitch attitude.
Resume the normal climb. Lower the flap and adopt the correct attitude, airspeed and	Check the airspeed is not less than the correct flap down climbing speed.

| trim condition for climbing with flap down | Raise the flaps whilst adjusting the aircraft attitude to achieve the normal climbing speed and re-trim. |
| | Note: If the flaps are raised in conjunction with the correct attitude and airspeed control procedure, only a momentary reduction in rate of climb will be incurred. |

Student practice: The student should now practise lowering different amounts of flap, and adopting the flaps down climbing speed, followed by raising the flaps in stages and returning to the normal climbing speed.

DEMONSTRATION 3. THE CRUISE CLIMB

Flight Lesson	*Demonstration Sequence*
Climbing (en route) range	
Adopt the normal climbing airspeed	Note rate of climb at normal climbing airspeed. Increase the airspeed to that required for a cruise climb. Re-trim. Note the small reduction in rate of climb compared to the larger gain in forward speed. When not more than 75% power is used during this technique the mixture control can often be used below 5000 feet (dependent upon the manufacturer's recommendations). Above 5000 feet the use of mixture control will normally be required regardless of climbing power in use. Above 5000 feet the airspeed should be reduced according to the climb performance tables shown in the Flight/ Owner's Manual. Application to the en-route climb during navigation flights.

Student practice: As applicable during navigation flights.

DEMONSTRATION 4.   THE MAXIMUM ANGLE OF CLIMB

Flight Lesson	Demonstration Sequence
Maximum height gained in relation to distance covered At a relatively low altitude	Select the maximum power and adopt the attitude for the best angle of climb speed. Re-trim. Note the slightly higher nose attitude. Note the maximum angle of climb speed results in a slight reduction in the rate of climb. When extended climbs of this nature are used, monitor the engine temperature and pressure gauges more frequently.
Student practice: The student should now practise climbing at the maximum angle of climb speed and familiarise himself with the higher nose attitude.	

MAXIMUM GLIDE

• SPEED 70 MPH (IAS)
• PROPELLER WINDMILLING
• FLAPS UP • ZERO WIND

HEIGHT ABOVE TERRAIN (FEET)

12,000
10,000
8000
6000
4000
2000
0

0   5   10   15   20

GROUND DISTANCE (STATUTE MILES)

Descending

Instructor's Guide

As with climbing the main effort from the student during the initial practice of this exercise will occur during the entry to and levelling off from the descent. Therefore in order to better utilise training time most of the student's early practice of descending should be directed to the performance of short period glides and powered descents.

The student will need to have mastered the task of gliding and descending with power reasonably accurately before being introduced to the consolidated circuit, approach and landing lessons. However as with climbing there will be sufficient time between his introduction to descending and the commencement of detailed approach and landing instruction to spread the various descending demonstrations over several hours and the instructor should plan his training task with this in mind.

The practice of descending should be combined with climbing to ensure maximum utilisation of the student's dual training time. Before each flight where a particular type of descent is to be demonstrated and practised the instructor should review its practical use during the pre-flight briefing and ensure the student understands the purpose of the procedure to be followed in order to achieve the performance required.

AIRMANSHIP

Ensure from the beginning that the student is meticulous with his procedure for selecting a safe descent area. Once an aircraft is in a descent there is the double danger of having other aircraft climbing up in the blind spot beneath the nose of the descending aircraft and also the possibility of the descending aircraft arriving on top of another which is in level flight. Therefore prolonged descents must incorporate heading changes to ensure the pilot can continually check that the area below remains clear of other aircraft.

Statistics reveal that about 50% of the air miss situations which occur in the vicinity of airfields involve dual flights. This highlights the added workload during instructional flights and the need for greater awareness when descending in the vicinity of airfields as well as when flying in the circuit pattern.

Another emphasis item is the appreciation of the altimeter setting, and when descending into the lower levels preparatory to joining a circuit the student must develop an awareness of what datum he has set upon his altimeter. Finally when gliding is being carried out get the student to develop the good practice of opening up to half throttle for a few seconds at a time every 500 feet to maintain a reasonably warm engine and clear plugs.

BEFORE THE EXERCISE

The Long Briefing should cover the following:

> Objectives.
> Forces.
> Glide Descent – Angle – Airspeed – Rate of Descent.
> Effect of Flap.
> Effect of Wind.
> Effect of Weight.
> Engine Considerations.
> Power Assisted Descent – Power/Airspeed – Rate of Descent.
> The Cruise Descent.
> The Sideslip.
> Airmanship.
> Common Errors.

The short Pre-Flight Briefing should be based upon the practical aspects of that part of the Long Briefing in relation to the Air Exercise to be covered. Ensure during this period that the student understands how to use the Flight/Owner's Manual to obtain the relevant gliding speed and gliding distance figures. The power settings appropriate to particular airspeeds and rates of descent can be established by trial and error during the demonstration and practice of the powered descent.

DURING THE AIR DEMONSTRATION

As with the earlier exercises emphasise that Attitude Flight is the primary object and in the case of the glide or powered descent, the attitude is more clearly seen due to the better view of the natural horizon with the nose in a lower position. Point out that the nose position during the descent with flap up is only slightly lower than when in straight and level flight.

When establishing the glide ensure the student clearly sees the additional amount of elevator trim control movement required. Emphasis on this point during your first demonstration will be of benefit to his initial practise at trimming the aircraft when in the gliding attitude.

EFFECT OF FLAP
The student will already be aware of the effect on the aircraft attitude during lowering and raising of flap but he should be reminded of the pitch and trim change which will take place and the effect of flap operation on the airspeed. The entry to the climb from the descent should be practised from both gliding and powered descents as this is a useful introductory exercise to the going round again procedure.

THE POWERED DESCENT
Following the initial demonstration of this exercise the student should be given the opportunity to practise descending at different airspeeds and rates of descent. Probably the most commonly used descent rate is 500 feet per minute with an airspeed about 10 – 15% higher than the gliding speed, this would therefore be a good base to start teaching from, and during this part of the exercise he should especially note the approximate power setting required on the particular aircraft to achieve this condition.

For a different purpose and as a preparatory exercise to the approach and landing it will be beneficial to introduce the use of a ground feature reasonably well ahead for the student to practise maintaining a constant descent angle at a given airspeed. This will involve power and attitude adjustments similar to those required during the powered approach.

SIDESLIPPING
Although the practical requirement to use a sideslip is rare in the case of aircraft fitted with flaps, it should nevertheless be covered for two reasons. Firstly, the flap system may become unserviceable during flight, and secondly there is the possibility of having to use a gentle sideslip to keep smoke away from the cabin area in the event of an engine fire occurring, such action sometimes being recommended in the appropriate Flight/Owner's Manual. Students should not be permitted to carry out steep sideslips to ground level due to the high descent rate and degree of judgement required to recover and complete a safe landing from a very low height. Also on some aircraft gross amounts of bank and rudder, coupled with too low an airspeed, could lead to a 'flick manoeuvre' as a result of a stall in the crossed controls situation.

COMMON ERRORS
• Many accidents have been attributed to a lack of attention to the

maintenance of a correct airspeed during the approach to landing, and practice at maintaining a constant descent angle at a constant airspeed is very good training prior to the introduction to the circuit, approach and landing.

• Failure to clear the descent area prior to commencing a descent is quite a common fault. The instructor should prevent the descent being commenced until the area has been cleared rather than reminding the student of his failure to do so after the descent has been started.

• The student will usually have a little trouble in trimming the aircraft with reasonable accuracy during his early practice at gliding. The basis of this fault lies in the greater amount of trim movement required as a result of the lower airspeed and the strong nose down moment when power is reduced to idling. The instructor should give a clear indication of the approximate amount of trim movement required in the glide during his initial demonstration.

• It will be too early at this stage for the student to develop an accurate appreciation of the aircraft capability in relation to gliding distance and the development of this type of judgement should be left until glide approaches are introduced.

Descending

Long Briefing

OBJECTIVES

Primarily the purpose of this exercise is to teach the student how to initiate normal glide entry, maintain the glide and level off. Later the exercise will include the effect of flap on the glide and how to establish a powered descent at different airspeeds and descent rates. The effect of using flap during the powered descent will also be covered and the procedure for entering the climb with flap down will be practised. Finally the student will be taught how to enter, maintain and recover from a sideslip.

INTRODUCTION

There are two practical ways of descending the aircraft, one is to close the throttle completely and glide, the other is to partially close the throttle and carry out a power assisted descent. In a glide descent the pilot flies the aircraft at the appropriate gliding speed and accepts whatever rate of descent this produces, but in the powered descent the pilot can select an airspeed and rate of descent compatible with his requirements.

THE FORCES

A simple presentation of the forces of Lift, Drag and Weight in the glide is shown in fig. 8-1.

From this illustration is can be seen that in the glide the Weight of the aircraft is acted against by both Lift and Drag and the resultant

Fig. 8-1

of the Lift and Drag forces balances the weight. Weight still acts perpendicular to the horizontal and Lift at 90° to the relative airflow (path of flight). The angle between the Lift line and the total resultant of Lift and Drag is equal to the angle between the flight path and the horizontal.

In examining the forces acting on an aircraft in the glide the relationship which was covered during the long briefing for climbing still exists i.e.

$$SIN \ \gamma \ = \ \frac{T - D}{W}$$

However during a glide the thrust, T, is reduced to zero and the summation is simplified as follows:

$$SIN \ \gamma \ = \ \frac{D}{W}$$

Where D = drag
      W = weight
      γ = flight path inclination
          (angle of glide in degrees)

This relationship shows that the minimum angle of glide is obtained by flying the aircraft in a condition which incurs minimum total drag and since the aircraft lift is essentially equal to the weight the minimum angle of glide will be achieved when the aircraft is flown at the maximum Lift/Drag ratio.

In light aircraft without use of flaps the angle of glide is relatively small and the ratio of glide distance to altitude is equal to the aircraft's Lift/Drag ratio. Due to the fuselage and other parasite drag effects this will be less than the Lift/Drag ratio of the wing and a typical figure would be about 10:1.

In a steady glide at a constant rate of descent the forces are in equilibrium. The weight is now acting forward relative to the aircraft flight path and a component of weight therefore substitutes for engine thrust as shown in fig. 8-2. The steeper the angle of glide the greater this component of weight becomes and the speed is correspondingly increased.

GLIDE DESCENT – ANGLE – AIRSPEED – RATE OF DESCENT

The Glide Descent
Gliding performance is of greater importance in the case of the single engined aircraft, particularly when engine failure or malfunction

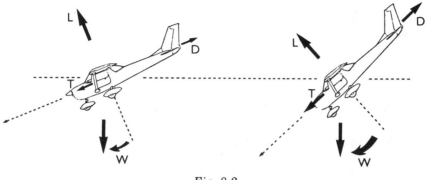

Fig. 8-2

occurs. Two separate performance aspects are involved, and these are the minimum glide angle and the minimum rate of descent.

Minimum Glide Angle.

When this is adopted it will produce the greatest proportion of glide distance to height loss and will result in the maximum range glide or in other words the minimum loss of altitude for a specific glide distance.

The airspeed for the range glide is normally shown in Flight/ Owner's Manuals together with a table or graph showing the gliding distance from various heights in conditions of zero wind.

The gliding performance can be appreciated from fig. 8-3 which shows the rate of descent versus airspeed. A straight line drawn from the point of origin tangential to the drag curve locates a point A which produces the maximum proportion of speed to rate of descent. Since the rate of descent is proportional to the drag curve, point A represents the aerodynamic condition of maximum lift/drag ratio and corresponds to a particular airspeed.

The best gliding speed for range will not normally be coincident with that for level flight. This is because the normal level flight range speed is the best compromise between aerodynamic and engine considerations and during a glide the engine considerations will not apply. This can be appreciated by bearing in mind the effect of the slipstream passing over the inboard wing sections when in normal level flight. The extra lift created from this additional airflow energy although small, will not be present in a glide. Further to this and during the glide there is the added parasite drag from the windmilling propeller.

Due to the shape of the drag curve small deviations from the best lift/drag ratio speed will not cause a significant change in the glide

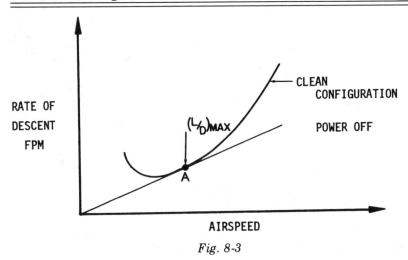

Fig. 8-3

angle. Flight at airspeeds greatly above or below the speed which coincides with the best lift/drag ratio will however result in a shorter distance travelled, therefore any attempt to stretch the glide by changing the speed will result in a shorter gliding distance, as illustrated in fig. 8-4. For example, any reduction of airspeed below that which gives the best lift/drag ratio will reduce the rate of descent but the reduction in descent rate will not be proportional to the reduction in airspeed and as a result the range of the glide will be reduced.

Fig. 8-4

Any increase of airspeed above the best range glide speed will also result in a reduction of distance travelled for height lost and the greater the increase in speed the lesser will be the distance travelled. A rough proportional indication of the effect of increasing or decreasing speed relative to the reduction in distance travelled is shown in fig. 8-4.

Minimum Rate of Descent
During climbing flight when the power available is greater than

the power required for level flight the excess power will permit a rate of climb. This climb rate will depend upon the amount of excess power available. Similarly when the power available is less than the power required for level flight, the deficiency of power available will produce a rate of descent.

The minimum rate of descent without any power available will occur at the angle of attack and airspeed which together produce a condition of the minimum power required. Figure 8-5 shows this relationship to the minimum angle of descent, (range glide).

Fig. 8-5

A simple rule of thumb to obtain the minimum rate of descent airspeed is to use 75% of the airspeed required for minimum angle of descent.

Although the practical use of a minimum rate of descent glide is limited, it could clearly be of value if it is required to extend airborne time while attempting to correct an engine malfunction. The minimum rate of descent glide will normally only be of value provided the reduction in distance travelled does not detract from the safety of planning for an arrival over a suitable area to carry out a forced landing. It would however be of some advantage when over the sea and out of range of land, or over mountainous areas where time airborne may be of more importance than distance.

Flight at the minimum sink speed will in the case of a light aircraft reduce the normal rate of descent by between 25% and 35%, the exact amount depending upon aerodynamic design features. If the aircraft normally loses 600 f.p.m. during a range glide then the time taken to reach the ground from 6000 feet will be 10 minutes. However adopting a minimum rate of descent glide will result in a rate of descent between some 400 to 450 f.p.m. depending upon the aircraft type. This will increase the descent time to between 13 and 15 minutes, a factor which in certain circumstances may have important benefits.

Entering and Maintaining the Glide

Once the Airmanship considerations of lookout have been completed, the aircraft is placed in the glide by the following method:

Glide Entry

Power	When applicable the carburettor air should be selected to Hot, and after a short pause the throttle should be closed smoothly whilst keeping the wings level, the heading constant and the aircraft in balance.
Attitude	The aircraft should be held in the level flight attitude until the airspeed approaches the correct gliding speed. At this stage the nose should be lowered to the approximate gliding attitude and held in this position.
	At a reduced power setting and particularly with the throttle closed completely as when in the glide, the tailplane surfaces will become less effective, this together with the inherent nose down action due to the Lift/Weight couple will cause a positive nose down action to occur whenever power is reduced, and a coarser movement of the controls will be required to hold the nose in the level attitude.
Trim	Whilst waiting for the airspeed to settle to a constant figure the trimmer should be adjusted to remove the fairly high load on the control column. When the speed has settled, further attitude adjustment will normally be required to achieve the exact gliding speed, following this attitude adjustment the aircraft can be finally and accurately trimmed.

Note that the nose attitude in the glide will be only slightly lower than when the aircraft is in cruising flight and that the correct glide attitude with the wings level, the heading constant and the aircraft in balance is maintained by the use of elevators, ailerons and rudder in a similar manner as when in straight and level flight.

The aircraft is returned to level flight by the following method:

Levelling Off

Power   Return carburettor air to Cold (if applicable). Select cruising power, keeping the wings level, the heading constant and the aircraft in balance.

Attitude   At the same time as cruising power is selected the nose should be positioned for the level flight attitude.

Trim   Initially trim out the fairly strong pressure on the control column and cross refer between the aircraft attitude in pitch and the altimeter. If a constant altitude is not being maintained, the nose attitude will have to be re-adjusted acordingly. Following such adjustments the aircraft can be finally and accurately trimmed.

Levelling Of at a Pre-selected Altitude

A lead figure of 10% of the rate of descent can be used in the same manner as when levelling off at pre-selected altitudes during climbing. During transition from the descent to level flight at a specified altitude the main effort will be in co-ordinating the rate at which the throttle is opened together with the fairly strong forward pressure on the control column which is needed to prevent the nose rising above the level flight attitude.

EFFECT OF FLAP

 The minimum glide angle is achieved by flying at a speed which corresponds to the angle of attack which gives the best Lift/Drag ratio. If any additional parasite drag is caused by changing the aircraft configuration, for example by lowering conventional flap or landing gear, then the Lift/Drag ratio will be effectively reduced. Therefore it is important to maintain a clean aircraft configuration and fly with the flaps and landing gear retracted when the best range glide is required.

The effect on the Lift/Drag ratio of lowering flap or landing gear is shown in fig. 8-6.

Descending with Flaps Down

When flaps are lowered during a descent, the usual change in pitch attitude will occur and for a given airspeed the descent rate will be greater. If however the descent speed is reduced slightly the greater rate of descent will diminish. Figure 8-6 shows that the maximum Lift/Drag ratio with flap down occurs at a slightly lower airspeed than with flap up. A practical application of using a slightly lower airspeed in a descent with flap down can occur during an approach to land when flaps are used to increase the descent angle, giving the pilot a better view along the approach path to the landing runway. If

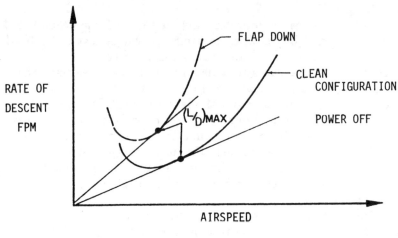

RATE OF
DESCENT
FPM

FLAP DOWN

CLEAN
CONFIGURATION

(L/D)MAX

POWER OFF

AIRSPEED

Fig. 8-6

the airspeed is reduced slightly during normal landing approaches the greater rate of descent will also be reduced without significantly affecting the view along the descent path, and this will enable the flare out prior to touchdown to be made more easily.

EFFECT OF WIND
Wind will have the same effect on gliding performance in relation to distance travelled as it does during normal cruising flight. That is to say, a headwind will reduce the gliding range and a tailwind will increase it (see fig. 8-7).

WIND

DISTANCE

Fig. 8-7

In principle this means that it would be advantageous to decrease the gliding speed when a tailwind exists and increase the gliding speed when flying into a headwind. These actions should increase the proportion of ground distance covered to the altitude lost. However from a practical viewpoint there will be little advantage gained unless starting from a reasonably high altitude or operating in a very strong headwind or tailwind. Further, such changes in the gliding speed will not be very effective unless the wind strength is at least some 25% of the normal range glide speed.

EFFECT OF WEIGHT
Provided an aircraft is flown at the angle of attack which gives the best Lift/Drag ratio the actual weight will not affect its gliding range. The best gliding speed will however be affected in that the heavier the aircraft the greater must be its speed along the flight path.

The effect of weight upon the gliding performance is shown in fig. 8-8, and from this it can be seen that additional weight will in effect cause the aircraft to move faster down the descent path which in turn will increase the lift for a constant angle of attack.

From this it will be seen that the best L/D ratio can be maintained regardless of aircraft weight.

Fig. 8-8

To sum up therefore, the aircraft forces will remain in equilibrium and the effect of an increase in weight will be for the aircraft (in still air) to arrive at the ground sooner but the actual distance covered will be unchanged.

In practical terms a 10% increase in all-up weight will require a 5% increase in glide speed to maintain the angle of attack at the best Lift/Drag ratio. Gliding speeds quoted in aircraft manuals are normally based upon the aircraft's all-up weight. However with light single-engined aircraft the variation in weight carried is fairly small, further to this, small deviaitons from the best Lift/Drag ratio will not significantly effect the glide performance and therefore in the practical sense a single value of glide speed can normally be specified and used.

ENGINE CONSIDERATIONS
When the use of carburettor heat is appropriate it is advisable to select 'Hot Air' prior to closing the throttle. There are several reasons for this and three important ones are outlined below:

1. If the throttle is closed first any carburettor icing which may have started to occur will not be noticed and although Hot Air may be selected immediately following the closing of the throttle, there will be no indication available (such as a drop in RPM) to show that the hot air system is working properly.
2. Due to natural human reactions there will always be the possibility of a pilot reaching out and selecting the wrong lever, knob or switch. In the event that the mixture lever is inadvertently operated instead of the Hot Air lever or control the engine will stop immediately and the mistake will be clearly evident. However if this action takes place after the throttle has been closed it is highly possible that the mistake will go unnoticed until the throttle is re-opened again. This is due to the fact that at normal gliding speeds the propeller will continue to windmill even though the engine is not receiving any fuel.
3. The purpose of selecting Hot Air in a reduced or no power condition is largely an insurance action because in this power condition the visual and aural indications of carburettor ice forming are not discernible. It is also possible that pre-occupation or distraction may cause the pilot to forget to select Hot Air. Therefore from a psychological viewpoint it is better to make the selection of Hot Air the primary action.

During gliding the engine should be opened up at intervals for a variety of reasons as follows:

1. Although aero engines are designed to withstand extremes of heat or cold, it is incorrect operating practice to allow large variations of temperature to occur. Such temperature changes increase the onset of fatigue to both the moving and fixed parts.
2. Prolonged cooling of the engine results in the oil becoming very cold, a condition which reduces its capability to lubricate effectively.
3. When the throttle of a cold engine is suddenly opened a condition of imperfect vaporisation can easily occur which will result in uneven firing, power loss and sometimes a complete engine stoppage.
4. During the glide or operation at low power settings the warning symptoms of carburettor icing, e.g. RPM reduction followed by rough running are not easily identifiable. This same situation may apply to certain aircraft fitted with constant speed propellers, as with these aircraft the first warning of carburettor icing comes from a small reduction in manifold pressure. This small reduction of manifold pressure may be concealed in a descent because with lowering altitude the atmospheric pressure rises, and as a result the manifold pressure will also rise, and this could

conceal any warning that carburettor icing is occurring.

5. When Hot Air has been selected, there is normally no way of ensuring that the carburettor hot air source is continuing to function. Further, the supply of hot air is obtained from the heat exchanger or similar system which is warmed by the exhaust gases. The heat content of these exhaust gases gradually reduces when the engine is not under power.

6. Although modern aero engines are not prone to oiling up of the plugs, all aero engines can suffer from plug fouling as a result of the carbon deposits produced from the burning of fuel. Whilst this is avoided during ground operations by maintaining approximately 1200 RPM (a figure which ensures a sufficient burning temperature) to keep the plugs clean, when an aircraft is gliding the cooling airflow over the engine is considerable and therefore cooler burning occurs leading to a high possibility of plug fouling.

The action of opening the throttle to the half-way position for a few seconds at periodic intervals during the descent, will ensure that the engine and oil supply are kept reasonably warm and that imperfect vaporisation does not occur. Also the problems associated with failure to recognise or prevent carburettor icing and plug fouling will be avoided. When cooling gills or engine oil shutters are fitted, attention should be paid to their operation in conjunction with the cylinder head temperature gauge. Most aircraft manuals recommend optimum, minimum and maximum temperatures and indications to this effect are suitably marked on the cylinder head temperature gauge.

THE POWER ASSISTED DESCENT

The powered descent is basically used when a particular rate of descent at a selected airspeed is required. In this flight condition the airspeed is controlled by the elevators and the rate of descent by the throttle. The forces acting on the aircraft will be similar to those during the glide but the component of weight which acts forward along the flight path is supplemented by the amount of engine thrust selected. This additional thrust would result in the aircraft increasing its airspeed along the original flight path, but if the elevators are used to maintain the airspeed at the original figure the flight path will be shallower and the descent rate less.

In a powered descent at a constant airspeed the addition of power will require the nose to be raised slightly in order to maintain the speed and a reduction of power will require that the nose be lowered slightly to maintain the speed.

Entering and Maintaining the Powered Descent
First decide upon the rate of descent and airspeed to be used.

Airmanship considerations as for gliding will still apply and once these have been met the aircraft is placed in a powered descent by the following method:

Select Hot Air (if applicable). Power should then be reduced and the attitude adjusted to give the selected airspeed. Trim out the residual control pressure, and when the airspeed and attitude are established note the VSI reading.

If the descent rate is insufficient, reduce the power slightly and lower the nose attitude to maintain the speed. Re-trim and re-check the VSI to see if the correct rate of descent is now being achieved. Continued adjustments to power, attitude and trim should be made until the aircraft is finally descending at the correct rate of descent. If the descent rate is too great, increase the power slightly and raise the nose attitude to maintain the correct speed. Re-trim and re-check the VSI to see if the correct rate of descent is now being achieved. Continued adjustments to power, attitude and trim should be made until the aircraft is finally descending at the correct rate of descent.

THE CRUISE DESCENT

The considerations involved in the cruise descent are the same as for the cruise climb and the benefits of this method of descending are normally related to the closing stages of a navigation flight.

The basic cruise descent is carried out with the aircraft in the clean configuration at cruising speed. A reduced power is set to give a gradual rate of descent. This type of descent can normally be made towards the end of a cross country flight when the aircraft has been cruising at medium to high altitudes.

The pilot should plan the descent bearing in mind the 'Safety Altitude' during the period of the let down and the required descent rate in relation to the distance to go to reach the area of the destination airfield. A good general rate of descent would be 500 feet per minute and if for example the aircraft had been cruising at 5000 feet and it was intended to let down to 2000 feet by the time the destination airfield is reached the descent should be commenced 6 minutes before the estimated time of arrival.

THE SIDESLIP

This is a manoeuvre in which the aircraft is placed in a banked attitude and the natural tendency for the aircraft to turn and the nose to drop is prevented by the use of opposite rudder. The nose position in pitch is controlled by the elevators and in this way the heading can be maintained and the rate of descent increased without increasing the airspeed. This will result in an increased angle of descent because the aircraft will be descending partially sideways, exposing more surface area to the oncoming air and thus increasing the drag. This effectively reduces the Lift/Drag ratio in a similar manner as would be accomplished by the lowering of flap.

The operational use of this manoeuvre is to lose height rapidly if misjudgment of the approach path occurs and the aircraft is too high in the later stages of the approach to land. Its operational importance has however been minimised due to the advent of flaps. Nevertheless, it is an exercise which will still have operational value should the flap system fail during flight.

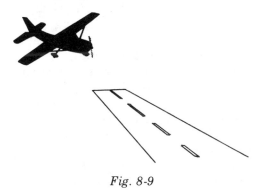

Fig. 8-9

Sideslipping is an unnatural condition and both the lateral and directional stability characteristics of the aircraft will oppose it. Ailerons are used to maintain the selected bank angle and rudder is used to maintain a constant heading. The elevators are used in their normal sense to control the airspeed. The greater the angle of bank used the greater will be the increase in descent rate. However the degree of sideslip along a constant heading (known as the Forward Slip) will be limited by the amount of rudder available.

Fig. 8-10

Because of the location of pitot tubes and static vents in relation to the sideways flow of air during a sideslip some aircraft pitot/static systems will produce erroneous indications of airspeed, and the pilot must establish whether this applies to the aircraft he is currently flying.

The method of entering and recovering from a forward slip
From the straight glide lower one wing and use opposite rudder to yaw and hold the nose to one side of the intended descent path. Sufficient rudder is used to ensure the original ground track is being maintained. At the same time the aircraft attitude will need to be adjusted in pitch to maintain the correct descent airspeed.

Recovery is accomplished by levelling the wings and at the same time centralising the rudder and re-adjusting the pitch attitude to maintain the speed.

Sideslipping should be used with caution when near the ground as the descent rate will normally be high and time will be needed to effect a recovery to the normal glide. Bearing in mind the possible effects of wind gradient near the ground added caution is necessary when strong or gusty winds are prevailing.

Sideslipping with flaps down may be restricted on certain types of aircraft. This restriction will usually apply to aircraft which have powerful flaps and if a sideslip is initiated with the flaps down a very high rate of descent can occur. Further to this the lowering of flaps usually reduces the effectiveness of the elevators and rudder both of which need to be adequately responsive to effect a crisp recovery from the sideslip condition. This is particularly important when the aircraft is near the ground and the aircraft c.g. is well forward. When a restriction is placed upon sideslipping with flap down this information will be shown in the Flight/Owner's Manual and/or placarded in the cockpit.

USE OF INSTRUMENTS TO ACHIEVE PRECISION FLIGHT

In descending as with climbing, the tendency to monitor the airspeed without maintaining the attitude must be avoided. Transient disturbances in the air cause short period variations in airspeed, and if the pilot continuously reacts to this type of airspeed fluctuation precision flight will become very difficult.

When in the correct descending attitude the position of the index aircraft on the attitude indicator instrument must be carefully noted in relation to the artificial horizon line. When normal airspeed changes occur during a descent the attitude of the index aircraft must be adjusted accordingly and held in a constant position so that the airspeed can settle to its new constant figure.

Finally, remember to keep reference to the instruments as brief as possible in order to maintain a high standard of lookout throughout the descent period.

AIRMANSHIP

Prior to and during the descent the necessity for a good lookout retains its high degree of importance. Bear in mind that although a lower nose attitude is held during a descent providing a better view of the ground and horizon features than when climbing or flying straight and level, the area of the pilot's visibility in relation to the flight path is virtually the same. However unlike climbing it is generally more difficult to spot aircraft lower down against the background of the earth's surface and greater care must therefore be exercised.

Lookout is not just a word to be remembered. It includes many things, for example, it is a positive action which must become instinctive and as such will require personal effort and practice to

Blind Spots Extend To Infinity

achieve, it also means the development of scanning techniques which will enable the pilot to direct his lookout into the right area at the right time. The knowledge of where to primarily direct one's lookout at a particular time will come from experience but it will also be assisted by information received by listening out and noting the content of R/T transmissions, which will often relate to the height/ altitude and position of other aircraft.

All aircraft have inherent design features which restrict vision and these blind spots extend to infinity. Pilots must therefore adapt their lookout techniques to overcome this problem whenever possible.

Pilots must lookout in all directions within their field of view and periodically scan the entire viewing field. One effective technique is for the pilot to divide his visible region into separate blocks and then scan the entire region by a method in which he pauses for a lookout of one or two seconds in each block. The visual field should also be increased by head and body movements and when this is insufficient the aircraft heading should be temporarily changed.

Descending is probably most commonly employed in the vicinity of an airfield and bearing in mind that statistics reveal that 80% or so of all mid-air collisions occur within the traffic pattern area, the importance of lookout increases even more whenever the aircraft is operating adjacent to or within this area.

PRE-FLIGHT BRIEFING

DESCENDING
Demonstration 1.

Aim

To teach you how to attain and maintain the glide and how to return the aircraft to level flight.

What

It is a condition of flight which involves a descent without power, at a constant airspeed and heading with the aircraft in balance. Glide descents have a practical application to the development of airspeed control, co-ordination and judgement of the aircraft's gliding capability in the event of engine failure.

Airmanship

The considerations of lookout in relation to a clear area below and to either side of the intended descent path.

How

Glide Entry

Lookout, clear the area to one side and below. Turn into the cleared area.

Mixture – if used return to Rich. Carburettor Heat – select (if applicable).

Power. Close the throttle and maintain the level flight attitude. Keep the wings level and direction and balance constant.

Attitude. When approaching the correct gliding speed, lower the nose and adopt the approximate gliding attitude.

Trim. Trim out the control pressures. A large trim change in pitch will be felt. Maintain the attitude until the airspeed remains constant. Re-adjust the pitch attitude as necessary to achieve the correct gliding speed.
Re-trim.

Student practice.

Maintaining the Glide

Lookout maintained.
Use elevators, ailerons and rudder to maintain the correct gliding speed, with the wings level and the direction and balance constant.

Cross refer between the nose attitude and the ASI to maintain the correct gliding speed.

Engine considerations – Avoid low engine temperature by momentary application of half power for a few seconds at a time. Repeat this action at every 500 feet loss of height during the glide.

Maintain a constant lookout and during long descents change the heading at intervals to clear the blind spot beneath the nose.

Student practice.

Levelling Off

Maintaining the lookout, select carburettor air to Cold (if applicable).

Power. Apply cruising power whilst keeping the wings level and the direction and balance constant. A strong nose-up moment will be experienced as the power is increased.

Attitude. Adjust the pitch attitude for level flight.

Trim. Initially trim to relieve major pressures on the controls. Cross refer between the pitch attitude and the altimeter to ensure that level flight is being achieved. Re-adjust the pitch attitude as necessary to maintain level flight.
Re-trim.
Student practice.

PRE-FLIGHT BRIEFING

DESCENDING
Demonstration 2.

Aim

To teach you:

(a) To level off at a pre-selected altitude.
(b) To establish a descent with the flap down.
(c) The method of climb entry from a descent with flap down.

What

(a) A transition from the descent to level flight at a precise and pre-determined altitude.
(b) A condition of flight in which the aircraft descends with flap lowered.
(c) A phase of flight during which the aircraft is taken from a descent and placed into a climb, followed by the flaps being retracted and the aircraft established in a normal (clean) climb.

Airmanship

The operational aspects of (a) and (b) are related to the circuit pattern as well as other phases of flight, and in the case of (c) to a situation where an aircraft has to be taken round again during or immediately following an approach or landing. The eventual airmanship considerations will therefore relate to the continuance of lookout and will also include ATC liaison and an awareness of the position of other aircraft in the circuit.

How

Levelling Off at a Pre-selected Altitude

From the glide:

As the selected altitude is approached open the throttle to cruise power, co-ordinating the change in pitch attitude to stop the descent at the required altitude.

Trim out the major control pressures. Maintain a frequent cross reference between the nose attitude in pitch and the altimeter and make small pitch adjustments as necessary to maintain the selected altitude.

Re-trim.

Student practice.

Establishing a Descent with Flap Down

During the descent:

Note rate of descent and lower partial flap. Maintain normal descent speed and re-trim. After the flap is lowered note the lower nose attitude and increased rate of descent.

Reduce the speed slightly and note the reduction in the rate of descent. Maintain speed, lower full flap and re-trim. Note the lower nose attitude and higher rate of descent.

Raise the flap in stages and adjust the nose attitude to regain the normal descent. Re-trim.

Student practice.

Entering the Climb from a Descent with Flap Down

From a descent with flap down:

Apply full power and adjust the attitude for the appropriate flap down climbing speed. If applicable ensure Cold air is selected. Trim out the major elevator control force.

When the correct airspeed is reached raise the flaps (in stages if appropriate) and re-adjust the attitude to achieve the normal (clean) climbing speed and re-trim.

Note: when full flap has been used it is advisable to raise the flap in stages.

Student practice.

PRE-FLIGHT BRIEFING

DESCENDING
Demonstration 3.

Aim
To teach you how to attain and maintain a controlled descent at a constant rate and/or angle.

What
The powered descent is a standard method of descending when a particular rate and/or angle of descent is required. It consists of selecting a descent rate or angle and achieving and maintaining it by the use of power and the primary flying controls.

Airmanship
Normal airmanship points applicable to descents will apply throughout the use of this procedure.

The Powered Descent

How
Establish a clear area below the aircraft. Mixture, selected to Rich (if used). Use carburettor heat as applicable. Determine the airspeed required and the rate or angle of descent to be achieved.

Select the estimated power required for the air-speed and rate of descent (or angle). Adjust the attitude to achieve the desired speed and re-trim. When the airspeed is achieved cross refer to the VSI. If the descent rate is insufficient, reduce the power slightly and lower the nose to maintain the speed. If the descent rate is too great increase the power and raise the nose to maintain the speed. Finally re-trim as required.

To return to level flight, anticipate the required altitude, increase the power and adjust the pitch attitude for level flight. Re-trim. During navigation flights the descent with power is applicable to the cruise descent.

Student practice.

DESCENDING
Demonstration 4.

Aim
To teach you how to lose height without increasing airspeed in the event that flap is not available.

What
A condition of flight in which the aircraft is flown out of balance during a glide descent. This results in an increase of descent rate which is limited by the effectiveness of the rudder and the need to maintain a particular heading.

Airmanship
Is mostly confined to being aware of other aircraft and the need to return to the normal descent at a safe height prior to touchdown.

Sideslipping

How
Adopt a moderate bank angle whilst using opposite rudder to maintain the heading and simultaneously adjust the nose attitude to maintain the speed.

Note the increased rate of descent.

Increase the bank angle using more rudder to keep the heading constant and adjust the pitch attitude to maintain the airspeed.

Continued increase in bank will lead to a condition where more rudder will be needed to maintain the heading. The maximum rate of descent in a forward slip will be reached when full rudder is necessary to maintain the heading. Any further increase of bank will cause the heading to change in the direction of bank.

To recover, use all three controls simultaneously to level the wings and maintain airspeed and heading constant.

Student practice.

Descending

Flight Demonstrations

INTRODUCTION

The contents of the total descending exercise may be conveniently divided into specific demonstration groups as follows:

1. Glide Entry, Maintaining the Glide and Levelling Off.
2. Levelling Off at Selected Altitudes.
   Descending with Flaps Down.
   Entering the Climb from the Descent with Flaps Down.
3. The Powered Descent.
   The Cruise Descent.
4. Sideslipping.

The initial demonstration and practice of descending will be concerned with the glide entry, maintaining the glide and levelling off. It would be advisable to leave levelling off at selected altitudes until the next flight lesson.

The demonstration and practice of descending with flap down is in preparation for approaches to land and should be practised with various degrees of flap lowered.

The powered descent is the normal technique used for landing approaches and practising this type of descent at altitude will afford the student an introduction to them.

The cruise descent is simply a pre-planned powered descent at a particular airspeed and rate of descent. It is normally employed during the final stages of a navigation flight when it is often more convenient to adopt a gradual descent towards the airfield of intended landing whilst maintaining the cruising speed.

Sideslipping is a method of losing height during an approach to land when the aircraft is too high and a greater rate of descent is required but an increase of airspeed is not acceptable. Its value as an operational exercise in an aircraft fitted with flaps is somewhat debatable as the use of flap is more simple and effectively gives all the benefits of a sideslip without any necessity for unbalanced flight. Nevertheless provided it is practised at frequent intervals it would be of value should the flap system fail.

Airmanship items will be introduced and developed at appropriate times during all the demonstrations.

DEMONSTRATION 1. GLIDE ENTRY, MAINTAINING THE GLIDE AND LEVELLING OFF

Flight Lesson	*Demonstration Sequence*
Gliding flight Entering the glide	Establish a clear area to one side and below the aircraft. Turn into the direction of the cleared area. Mixture (if used) return to RICH. Carburettor air, select HOT (if applicable). Close the throttle whilst maintaining the level flight attitude. Maintain lateral level, direction and balance, and as the airspeed approaches the correct gliding speed lower the nose and adopt the approximate gliding attitude. Trim. Maintain the attitude until the airspeed settles to a constant figure. Re-adjust the pitch attitude as necessary to achieve the correct gliding speed. Re-trim.
Maintaining the glide	All three controls are used in the normal sense to maintain the correct pitch attitude with the wings level and the heading and balance constant. Cross refer to the ASI and maintain the attitude for the correct gliding speed. Oil temperature should be checked at frequent intervals, avoid low oil temperature by use of cooling gills/shutters (when fitted) and by momentary application of half power (held for a few seconds) every 500 feet to keep the engine warm, and the plugs clear. Maintain a careful lookout and during prolonged glides change the heading at intervals to clear the blind spot beneath the nose.
Levelling off	Maintaining the lookout select carburettor air to cold (if applicable).

	Apply cruising power and adjust the attitude in pitch to achieve level flight for the power selected, whilst maintaining the wings level and the direction and balance constant.
	Trim out the control pressures and cross refer between the aircraft attitude in pitch and the altimeter to ensure level flight is being achieved.
	Re-adjust the pitch attitude as necessary and re-trim.

Student practice.   Short glides should normally be practised at this stage in order to give the student plenty of practice at entering the glide and levelling off.

DEMONSTRATION 2.   LEVELLING OFF AT SELECTED ALTITUDES

Flight Lesson	*Demonstration Sequence*
Achieving a specific altitude	
From the glide	Anticipate the altitude required, as in climbing.
	Just before the pre-determined altitude is reached open the throttle to cruising power.
	Maintain a frequent cross reference between the nose attitude in pitch and the altimeter.
	Initially trim out the control pressures.
	When the correct altitude, attitude and power are achieved re-trim.

Student practice.   The student should now practise levelling off at pre-selected altitudes.

	DESCENDING WITH FLAP DOWN
The effect of flap during the glide	
During the normal glide select partial flap.	Note the rate of descent at the normal gliding speed.
	Whilst lowering the flaps maintain the normal gliding speed.

	Re-trim and note the lower nose attitude, and increased rate of descent. Reduce speed (as applicable to type). Note the rate of descent will now be slightly decreased.
Lower full flap	Whilst lowering further flap maintain the speed used for partial flap. Re-trim and note the lower nose attitude and increased rate of descent.
Raise the flap	Raise the flap in stages and adjust the nose attitude to regain the normal glide. Re-trim.

Student practice: The student should now practise:
  (a) Lowering various amounts of flap whilst adjusting the attitude to maintain the correct flap down gliding speed.
  (b) Raising the flap in stages and adusting the nose attitude to regain the normal gliding speed.

ENTERING THE CLIMB FROM THE DESCENT WITH FLAP DOWN

Preparatory exercise (conducted at altitude) for the missed approach and go around procedure	
From the descent with flap lowered	Apply full power, and adjust the attitude for the flap down climbing speed. Ensure COLD air selected (if applicable). Note: Moderately strong control column forces will need to be overcome, due to residual nose-up trim from the preceding descent. Re-trim. At a safe height raise flap and adjust the attitude to achieve the normal climbing speed. Re-trim.
	Note: When full flap has been selected it is normally advisable to reduce maximum drag flap by stages immediately after a safe airspeed has been obtained.

Student practice: The student should now practise controlling the aircraft whilst entering the climb from the descent and returning to the normal clean climb.

DEMONSTRATION 3.   THE POWERED DESCENT

Flight Lesson	Demonstration Sequence
Effect of power and airspeed during the descent Select a specific airspeed and rate of descent	Establish a clear area to one side and below the aircraft into which a descent can be made. Mixture (if used) return to RICH. Carburettor air select HOT (if applicable). Select the estimated power required for the chosen airspeed and selected rate of descent. Adjust the pitch attitude to give the airspeed required. Re-trim. Cross refer to the VSI. If the descent rate is too great, increase the power (as required) and raise the nose attitude to maintain the speed. Re-trim. If the descent rate is too small, reduce the power (as required) and lower the nose attitude to maintain the speed. Re-trim. In a prolonged powered descent, heading changes are needed to clear the area below the aircraft.
Returning to level flight	To return to level flight, anticipate the desired altitude. Increase the power as required and re-adjust the pitch attitude. Re-trim.
Student practice: The student should now practise descending at selected airspeeds and rates of descent, and also levelling off at selected altitudes.	
Application to the final stages of a navigation flight	**THE CRUISE DESCENT** Select a descent rate which will bring the aircraft down to the height required overhead or within a short distance of the destination airfield. Ensure the area along the intended descent path is clear. Mixture (if used) return to RICH. Carburettor air select HOT (if applicable). Reduce power as required and lower the nose to maintain the cruising airspeed.

Re-trim.
Adjust the power as necessary to
achieve the selected rate of descent.
Maintain the cruise speed and re-trim.

Student practice: The student should receive instruction and practice
in this procedure during the navigation stage of his training.

DEMONSTRATION 4.   SIDESLIPPING

Flight Lesson	*Demonstration Sequence*
Effect of sideslipping during the glide	
From the normal glide	Adopt a moderate bank whilst using opposite rudder to maintain a constant heading. Adjust the nost attitude to maintain the correct gliding speed. Note the increased rate of descent. Increase the bank angle and use more opposite rudder to maintain the heading. As the bank is increased more rudder will be necessary to maintain the heading, this will govern the amount of forward slip which can be obtained. Note the higher rate of descent.
	Note: On certain aircraft, angle of bank and rudder application must not be excessive, as coupled with an inadvertent and very low airspeed these 'crossed controls' could lead to a flick manoeuvre.
Recovery to the normal glide	To recover to the normal glide all three of the primary controls are used together. Roll the wings level, centralise the rudder and adjust the nose attitude to maintain the correct gliding speed.

Student practice: The student should now be given the opportunity to
practise varying amounts of sideslip.

Turning

Instructor's Guide

Medium turns are the commencing point for instruction in manoeuvring the aircraft and in a sense their practice represents the culmination of the development of the basic co-ordination exercises. They will also extend the student's workload in relation to lookout and orientation.

The co-ordination and timing of control movements to achieve and maintain the required attitude in pitch and bank whilst maintaining a balanced flight condition will require much practice. Once the student has grasped the fundamental control movements in relation to the applied pressures on the controls he should be given the opportunity to correct his own errors without too much direction from the instructor. Over-instructing and constant telling by the instructor will do little to develop the student's ability to analyse his own faults and take corrective action. To sum up, allow him to make his own mistakes and only step in with advice or further instruction if he is unable to appreciate or correct them.

When turning, the student has to continually assess the attitude of the aircraft in bank and pitch and the quicker he can develop the ability to hold a constant bank angle the quicker his progress in smooth control co-ordination will become. During a turn the assessment of aircraft attitude in relation to outside references becomes a little more difficult and an increased frequency of instrument scan will also be needed. These two factors will produce a significant increase in the student's workload. It would therefore be advisable to introduce an 'observation turn' at the beginning of the exercise, during which the student should not handle the controls but relax and have his attention directed to the bank attitude and the position of the aircraft's nose in pitch in relation to the natural horizon.

During this turn further observations can include reference to the altimeter to ensure the altitude is being held constant, the balance indicator to ensure that balanced flight is being achieved, the ASI to ensure the student clearly sees the slight loss of airspeed when turning at a medium bank angle in level flight and finally he can be shown the back pressure required on the control column to maintain a constant altitude.

AIRMANSHIP

One of the instructor's major problems in relation to airmanship during turning is to ensure the development of an instinctive lookout by the student prior to and during the turn. One successful method of developing an instinctive lookout prior to turn entry is to prevent the student entering any turn unless the lookout procedure has been completed. Provided this action is always taken whenever failure to lookout occurs the student will very quickly develop the instinctive lookout which is required.

Towards the end of the initial turning exercise the instructor should brief the student to roll out onto a selected outside reference feature. This will assist him to maintain his lookout during the turn as well as being a useful exercise in preparation for the later practice of rolling out onto selected headings by reference to the heading indicator.

At this stage of training the student should be introduced to handling minor emergency situations and at least one of these procedures should be practised on this and following flights. Such emergencies should include the procedures to be followed in the event of systems failure, e.g. alternator, radio, flaps etc.

After a series of practice turns, wind effect may cause the aircraft to be drifted a long way downwind and efforts should be made to avoid this. Once the student is making reasonable efforts at turning he must be briefed to take stock of his location after each turn, and this action will also assist in developing his sense of orientation.

BEFORE THE EXERCISE

The Long Briefing should cover the following:

Objectives.
The Forces.
Use of Controls.
Use of Power.
Maintenance of Attitude and Balance.
Medium Level Turns.
Climbing and Descending Turns.
The Slipping Turn.
Turning onto Selected Headings – Use of the Heading Indicator and the Magnetic Compass.
Airmanship.
Common Errors.

The short Pre-Flight Briefing should be based upon the practical aspects of that part of the Long Briefing in relation to the Air Exercise to be covered.

DURING THE AIR DEMONSTRATION

Stress from the beginning that ailerons are used to control the bank angle, elevators are used to control the pitch attitude i.e. altitude or airspeed, and the rudder is used to control the aircraft in balance. However, movement of any one control will cause the need for movement of the other two if the correct flight condition is to be maintained.

MEDIUM LEVEL TURNS

Emphasis should be placed upon the use of such aircraft features as the engine cowling or the cockpit coaming to relate the angle of bank and pitch attitude to the natural horizon but cross reference to the instruments must be developed if a reasonable standard of accuracy is to be achieved.

Turns to both left and right should be covered and practised during the first demonstration, but where side-by-side seating is involved the instructor should not expect the student to practise a turn to the right unless he has first been shown the apparent change of nose attitude in pitch relative to a turn to the left, because to the student the nose position in pitch will appear lower in a turn to the right than in a turn to the left.

RATE AND RADIUS OF TURN

The air demonstrations showing the difference between rate of turn and radius of turn are best left until advanced turns are taught.

SLIPSTREAM EFFECT RELATIVE TO DIRECTION OF TURN

Except in the gliding turn, rudder application will vary depending upon the direction of turn in relation to the power and airspeed being used. This is due to the slipstream effect coupled with the direction of propeller rotation. This effect of power not only applies to the use of rudder, but because of further effects, it will also influence the bank angle.

Therefore, whenever rudder pressure is a continued requirement during a turn it will also affect the angle of bank, and at times it may be necessary to use the ailerons to counteract an overbanking or underbanking tendency. To give the student specific instructions in each case will often serve to confuse him and it would be better to simply teach him to control the angle of bank with the ailerons and the balance with the rudder.

CLIMBING TURNS – RATE OF CLIMB
A valuable demonstration during climbing turns is to maintain the correct climbing speed and increase the bank angle to approximately 40° to show the effect of increasing bank in relation to the rate of climb.

DESCENDING TURNS
During an approach to land the need for accurately controlled descending turns (with and without flap down) will assume a greater importance than when carried out at altitude. The student's performance of these turns must therefore be measured on this basis and until they can be performed with reasonable accuracy the student should not be introduced to consolidated circuit training.

THE SLIPPING TURN
The instructor should ensure the student knows the purpose of this manoeuvre and is aware of any ASI errors which may occur during its execution. Airspeed control is more vital than the degree of sideslip attained.

COMMON ERRORS
• Many accidents which occur during the approach to land and shortly after take-off do so as a result of inadequate speed control or marked unbalance at low speeds. Considerable emphasis must be placed upon the necessity to maintain correct speeds and balance during these phases of flight. Turning practice at higher altitudes gives the student the opportunity to develop accuracy in relation to both speed and balance.
• At the beginning of his dual instruction in turning, the student will often attempt to lean over into the direction of turn rather than sitting normally and riding with the aircraft. It is important that this does not become a habit, or delay in the development of his sense of co-ordination can easily result.
•Many of the individual errors which occur during turning do so because of a lack of co-ordination of control movements. Make it quite clear during the initial demonstration that movement of one control to achieve a particular condition automatically affects the action of the other controls. Therefore no control can be used singly when entering the turn or rolling back to straight and level flight. This also applies when making any adjustments during the turn.
• One common fault is the excessive use of rudder, and it is very important to point out that rudder is in the main required during the entry and roll out period. Once in the turn little or sometimes no rudder pressure is required. During climbing turns the student sometimes becomes confused over the use of rudder in relation to

balance due to the influence of slipstream over the vertical tailplane. For example, when the propeller rotation is clockwise the slipstream effect will often create a need to hold right rudder pressure during a climbing turn to the left. The best way of resolving this apparent inconsistency in the use of rudder is to emphasise to the student that rudder is used to keep the ball in the middle and the aircraft in balance.

• As with the straight climbing exercise the student will normally have more difficulty in maintaining the correct speed during climbing turns due to his limited reference to the natural horizon. Only practice and quickening of his instrument scan will enable him to overcome this difficulty.

• Descending turns with flap down will also often create the same difficulty in airspeed maintenance due to the significantly lower position of the aircraft nose relative to the natural horizon. This difficulty will normally be overcome through practice and a repeated reference to the ASI.

• The problem of lookout is intensified during turning, but the efficiency of the student's lookout must eventually be good enough to ensure the safety of his own and other aircraft. This efficiency of lookout is directly related to his workload, i.e. when the workload is high his lookout will usually deteriorate. The instructor should therefore train the student to cope with the problems of lookout in the inevitable situations of increased workload.

• One method would be to ask the student to perform several tasks at the same time, for example, turning to a selected heading while entering a descent and perhaps using the magnetic compass only. A request of this sort will often cause the student to omit lookout due to his preoccupation with the number of simultaneous actions asked of him. Under these circumstances, if the lookout is forgotten the instructor should place a firm hand on the control column and prevent the turn from being initiated until an adequate lookout has been completed. Training of this kind will give better results than merely reminding the student of his error after he has commenced a turn entry.

1 HORIZONTAL COMPONENT OF LIFT

2 TOTAL LIFT VECTOR

3 VERTICAL COMPONENT OF LIFT

Turning

Long Briefing

OBJECTIVES

The primary purpose of this exercise is to teach the student how to carry out a controlled and co-ordinated manoeuvre to effect a change in the aircraft heading. Initially he will be given an understanding of the principles and then taught how to achieve a medium banked turn whilst holding a constant altitude and maintaining the aircraft in balanced flight.

This will be followed by the demonstration and practice of moderately banked climbing and medium banked descending turns. During this exercise the student will also be taught how to turn the aircraft onto specific headings through the use of the gyro heading indicator.

INTRODUCTION

Many of the misconceptions which occur in relation to manoeuvring performance and pilot control techniques are the direct or indirect result of misunderstanding of the aerodynamic forces and their varying effects upon the aircraft during manoeuvres.

As stated previously the weight of the aircraft always acts straight down relative to the horizontal but the direction of the forces produced by Lift, Thrust and Drag will be controlled by the direction of the aircraft flight path. The horizontal flight path of an aircraft can be changed by simple application of rudder but this will produce an action similar to that applied to a car when taking a corner at speed. It will be uncomfortable and due to the aircraft's inherent stability it would be an extremely inefficient flight condition and one with a limited practical application.

THE FORCES

An aircraft in flight, like any other moving object, requires a sideways force to make it turn. In normal turning flight this is produced by banking the aircraft and tilting the lift force.

This effectively produces two components of lift at right angles to each other. One acting into the direction of turn and supplying a turning force and the other acting upwards against the aircraft weight.

The horizontal lift component is the sideways force which causes the aircraft to turn (centripetal force). The equal and opposite reaction to this sideways force is centrifugal force. Figure 9-1 shows the relationship of the forces on an aircraft during normal banked turning flight.

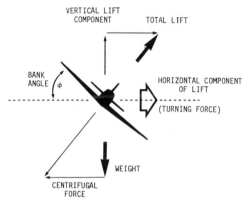

Fig. 9-1

When an aircraft is in turning flight it is not in a state of static equilibrium because there exists a condition of acceleration into the turn. In a steady co-ordinated turn during level flight the vertical component of lift must be equal to the weight of the aircraft so that there will be no acceleration in a vertical direction. This introduces an important term in relationship with manoeuvring flight, i.e. Load Factor. The load factor is the proportion between lift and weight and is determined by:

$$n = \frac{L}{W}$$

$$n = \frac{1}{\cos \phi}$$

where n = load factor (or G)
cos = cosine of the bank angle, ϕ (phi)

This summation can be shown graphically by the following diagram which shows the relationship of lift, weight, angle of bank and load factor.

Assuming the aircraft depicted in fig. 9-2 (A) has an all-up weight of 1000 lbs and ignoring any down load which may be required on the

Fig. 9-2

tailplane for a condition of level flight to exist then it will require 1000 lbs of lift to maintain a constant height. At (B) the same aircraft is in a normal medium turn at a 30° bank angle, and the lift force will now be inclined to the vertical. It can be seen that the vertical component of lift will no longer be sufficient to balance the weight and the aircraft will descend. If the total lift is now increased so that the vertical component of lift is restored to 1000 lbs as at (C) the aircraft can once again maintain a constant height. The situation at (D) shows that the more the lift line is tilted the more total lift will have to be produced to bring the vertical component of lift back to the original value. It will also be seen that a 60° angle of bank will necessitate a doubling of the total lift to achieve the original vertical lift force.

During a level turn the additional lift can be obtained by the pilot increasing the airspeed or the angle of attack. The most practical choice is to alter the angle of attack by application of back pressure on the control column during the entry and throughout the maintenance of the turn.

Bearing these factors in mind it can be seen that in the case of a steady co-ordinated turn the vertical component of lift must equal the weight of the aircraft so that there will be no acceleration in the vertical direction. Therefore the following relationship exists between the bank angle and the forces acting upon the aircraft:

$$n = \frac{L}{W}$$

$$n = \frac{1}{\cos \phi}$$

$$n = \sec \phi$$

where n = load factor or G
L = lift, lbs
W = weight, lbs
ϕ = bank angle, degrees (phi)

This summation confirms that for a steady co-ordinated turn at a constant height a specific value of load factor will be incurred, the value of which will depend upon the angle of bank, e.g. a bank angle of 60° will result in a load factor of 2. Apart from the significance of the wing having to supply more lift than the weight to maintain the aircraft at a constant height, the resulting increase in load factor will cause an increase in the stalling speed. The principles and practical effects of this are dealt with during the Long Briefing on Stalling.

Turning Performance
The performance of an aircraft in a steady turn is measured in terms of turning rate and radius. This can be seen by the following equations which are based upon the horizontal component of lift being equal to the centrifugal force during the turn.

Turn Rate: Turn Radius:

$$\text{R.o.t.} = \frac{1{,}091 \tan \phi}{V} \qquad\qquad r = \frac{V^2}{11.26 \tan \phi}$$

where R.o.t. = rate of turn in degrees per second.
ϕ = bank angle in degrees.
V = velocity in kts (TAS)

where r = turn radius in feet
V = velocity in kts (TAS).
ϕ = bank angle, degrees.

The above relationships define the rate of turn and the turn radius as functions of the two variables, bank angle and velocity. Therefore when an aircraft is in a correctly balanced turn at a constant angle of bank and airspeed the turn rate and turn radius are fixed and are not dependent upon the aircraft type or its weight. The different values of turn rate and turn radius are illustrated in the graph at fig. 9-3. Although the conditions shown are for the case of a correct turn at constant height they can also be used in relation to climbing or descending flight when the angles of climb or descent are fairly small.

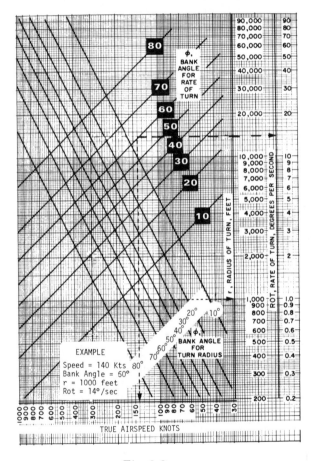

Fig. 9-3

The rate of turn at any given airspeed depends upon the amount of sideways force causing the turn, in other words the amount of the horizontal lift component. In a correctly executed turn the horizontal lift component varies directly in proportion to the degree of bank. Thus, the rate of turn at a given airspeed increases as the angle of bank increases. Reference to fig. 9-3 shows that at 140 knots a 60° angle of bank would produce a rate of turn of 14 degrees per second and a turning radius of 1000 feet. At the same airspeed a 20° angle of bank would give a rate of turn of about 3 degrees per second and a turn radius of 4800 feet. This particular rate of turn of 3 degrees per second is known as a 'Standard Rate' or 'Rate One' turn and it is commonly employed during flight. A simple rule of thumb for estimating the correct bank of a rate one turn is by using 10% of the IAS and adding 7 for knots or 5 for m.p.h., e.g. 100 knots = 10 + 7 = 7° of bank for a rate one turn.

Finally it can be seen by reference to the radius of turn figures in fig. 9-3 that for a given angle of bank the radius of turn will be least at the lowest airspeed at which the aircraft can be flown. The operational use of turns of small radius would normally be confined to a situation of manoeuvring around an airfield during very poor visibility, however as the minimum turn radius is achieved at the lowest speed for a given bank angle considerable care should be taken to avoid flying too close to the stalling speed. This is an important consideration because the stalling speed increases with increase of bank angle.

USE OF CONTROLS
Application of bank is achieved by using the ailerons to roll the aircraft to the desired bank angle. The rate at which the aircraft rolls is controlled by the amount of aileron deflection and the steepness of the bank is controlled by the length of time the ailerons are deflected. When the required angle of bank is reached the ailerons are returned to the neutral position and thereafter used to monitor the bank angle.

It will be appreciated from the knowledge gained during the exercise 'Effect of Controls' that whenever an aircraft is banked there will initially be an adverse yaw, i.e. a yaw in the direction opposite to the applied bank. Yaw is prevented by the use of rudder and therefore whenever a turn is initiated the simultaneous use of aileron and rudder will be required to keep the aircraft in a condition of balanced flight. The rudder in this case will be used into the direction of the turn, that is, if a left turn is required the control column will be moved to the left and at the same time sufficient pressure must be applied to the left rudder pedal to maintain the aircraft in a balanced condition.

Once the aircraft is in a banking attitude there will be a tendency for it to slip sideways and also to drop the nose. Figure 9-4 (a) shows the initial effect of tilting the lift line in relation to weight. It can be seen that if the amount of lift remains as it was in the straight and level flight situation there will be insufficient vertical lift to balance the weight and the aircraft will commence sinking. The force produced from the resultant of lift and weight will also affect the situation and pull the aircraft sideways and downwards resulting in a sideslip.

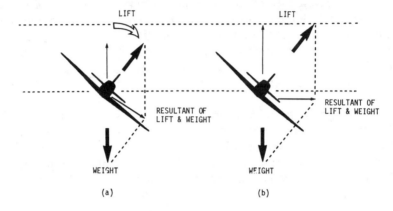

Fig. 9-4

This sideslipping tendency can be counteracted by applying back pressure to the control column which will increase the angle of attack and produce more lift. This action will in turn compensate for the effect of tilting the lift line as the aircraft is rolled into a banked attitude and is seen in fig. 9-4 (b). The use of the elevators during the entry and throughout the turn will need to be sufficient to produce the increased angle of attack to provide the added lift which is needed for level flight to be maintained.

The rudder is used throughout the sequence of turning as a balance control to correct for any slip or skid and is applied as necessary into the direction of indicated unbalance. During a turn the indications of small unbalance can only be checked by reference to the balance indicator and if the ball is to the left of centre, then left or further left rudder is required to bring the aircraft back into a balanced condition. If the ball is to the right of centre then right rudder or more right rudder will be required. This simple fact applies regardless of the direction of turn.

To return the aircraft back into straight and level flight, the ailerons should be used to roll the wings level and rudder used to prevent any adverse yaw. This means that rolling out from a left turn the control column will have to be moved to the right whilst simultaneously applying sufficient right rudder to prevent yaw. During this period the back pressure on the control column should be released in co-ordination with the other control movements to ensure that the aircraft does not gain altitude as the total lift line becomes in line with the weight.

USE OF POWER

It has already been stated that in order to maintain a constant altitude during a turn it will be necessary to increase the total lift force by increasing the angle of attack. However an increased angle of attack will lead to an increase in the induced drag and if power is not increased to overcome this, a reduction in airspeed will occur. This would normally be an adverse situation as reduction in airspeed will lead to a reduction in lift which in turn will require a further increase in the angle of attack and this cycle of events will continue until there is insufficient airspeed for flight.

However at moderate angles of bank (up to 35°) the amount of additional lift needed is small, therefore the increase in angle of attack and additional drag is also small. For shallow and medium banked turns there is no practical advantage in adding power to counteract this slight increase in drag, as it only causes a small reduction in airspeed. At steeper angles of bank the larger increase in lift required to maintain altitude produces a substantial increase of induced drag and an increase of power will be essential to prevent large airspeed loss and the cycle of events described above to occur.

Figure 9-5 shows the general effect of turning flight in relation to the power required curve.

Fig. 9-5

In effect the increase of power required in a turn is similar to the increase of power required due to increased all-up weight in straight and level flight. The following figures give a more specific indication of the increased drag and consequent increase in power required as a result of turning at 30, 45, and 60 degrees of bank respectively:

BANK ANGLE	% INCREASE IN INDUCED DRAG
30	33.3
45	100.0
60	300.0

Because induced drag is greatest at lower airspeeds it is particularly important to avoid steeper turns during the period immediately after take-off or during the approach to land phase.

MAINTENANCE OF ATTITUDE AND BALANCE

After a turn has been established there will be several factors which
will prevent the aircraft from automatically maintaining the selected
angle of bank and therefore the bank angle will need to be checked
for re-adjustment throughout the turn. The adverse yaw created
during the rolling action as the turn is entered will cease and
academically it could be said that during the turn the need to use
rudder will disappear. However due to the probable need for re-
adjustment of the bank attitude the use of rudder will in practice
continue but in a diminished amount. The necessity for re-adjustment
of bank will also affect the use of the elevators in that whenever the
bank is altered an adjustment of elevator control pressure will be
required if the altitude is to remain constant.

Whereas the primary use of rudder during turn entry is to prevent
adverse yaw as a result of induced roll, it must be appreciated that
yaw is also created by the propeller slipstream and whilst power is
being used this slipstream effect will always be present. Because of
this a certain amount of rudder pressure will normally be required
throughout the turn. The actual amount and direction of rudder
pressure required will be affected by the direction of propeller
rotation, airspeed and amount of power in use. This can lead to a
situation where if in straight and level flight right rudder pressure is
needed to maintain balance then upon entering a left turn the
balance may have to be maintained by relaxing some of the right
rudder pressure, this could therefore lead to a condition where in a
turn to the left some right rudder pressure is still having to be
applied in order to maintain balanced flight.

Whenever rudder is used its further effect will cause a rolling
action and if rudder pressure is needed to balance the aircraft
throughout the turn then this will cause an overbanking or
underbanking tendency dependent upon the direction of the rudder
pressure in relation to the direction of turn. Although during a turn
the outer wing will be travelling faster than the inner wing and
producing more lift the overbanking tendency from this source is very
weak. This is due to the very small percentage increase in lift on the
outer wing having a lesser effect than the further effect of the rudder.
This can usually be clearly seen during climbing turns when the
slipstream influence is strong due to the high power and relatively
lower airspeed being used.

MEDIUM LEVEL TURNS

For instruction purposes, turns are divided into three classes; gentle, medium and steep. Medium turns are chosen for initial instruction because they are the easiest to perform and when carried out from level flight they allow the student to develop a feel for balance and the effect of control pressures more easily than when climbing or descending. Cross reference to the natural horizon, altimeter and balance indicator will be needed for the maintenance of constant bank, altitude and balance. Later on this cross reference will include the heading indicator in order to roll out onto specific headings.

Entry and Maintaining Level Turns

Having first ensured that the area all round the aircraft is clear, use the ailerons to roll on bank in the required direction and at the same time apply sufficient rudder pressure into the direction of turn to maintain balanced flight. The use of elevator will be required to counteract the tendency for the nose to drop as a combined result of using the ailerons and rudder to achieve bank. The nose will have to be positioned slightly higher than in straight and level flight to increase the angle of attack and so provide the added lift required to maintain a constant altitude. Because a turn is a transitional manoeuvre the elevator trim is not used to relieve this back pressure.

Once the desired angle of bank (approximately 30°) is reached the ailerons should be neutralised and then used as required to maintain a constant bank angle. During the turn the lateral attitude (in this case the bank angle) must be maintained by the use of the ailerons and the pitch attitude controlled by the use of the elevators. The altimeter will need to be monitored in order to make small readjustments to the pitch attitude for the maintenance of constant altitude.

 Whereas the bank angle and approximate pitch attitude can be assessed by visual reference to the natural horizon the maintenance of balance throughout the turn can only be checked by reference to the balance indicator. If the ball is out to the right, right rudder will be required and if the ball is out to the left, left rudder will be required and this interpretation will apply regardless of the direction of turn.

During the turn entry and throughout the turn a good lookout must be maintained and this lookout should not only cover the direction into which the aircraft is turning but to either side, ahead, above and below.

Resuming Level Flight

The return to straight and level flight should be achieved by rolling the wings level by the use of the ailerons and at the same time using the rudder to maintain the balance. When rolling out from a left turn, right rudder will be required and when rolling out from a right turn, left rudder will be required, i.e. rudder pressure will always be required in the same direction as the control column is moved (or in the case of a wheel the direction in which it is turned). Whilst the wings are returning to the laterally level position it will be necessary to reduce the back pressure on the control column or the nose will rise leading to a gain in altitude.

Faults in the Turn

The basic faults which can occur during the turn are:

Incorrect bank.
Incorrect pitch attitude.
Incorrect balance.

These faults can occur individually or collectively but for clarity they are covered individually in the following paragraphs.

If during a turn altitude is gained or lost the first check should be to assess the bank angle. If the correct back pressure on the control column has been applied and maintained and the bank angle has been allowed to increase then altitude will be lost. The correction in this case would be to re-adjust the bank angle to its correct value whilst the back pressure is held constant. However to return to the original altitude it will be necessary to temporarily increase the back pressure.

If the correct back pressure for the required angle of bank is held and the bank angle is allowed to decrease then altitude will be gained. If this occurs the bank angle should be re-adjusted to its original value but it will also be necessary to temporarily reduce the back pressure in order to return to the original altitude.

If in either of the preceeding cases the bank angle is being maintained correctly then the change in altitude is usually due to an incorrect back pressure on the control column. In this case the nose attitude will first need temporary re-adjustment to lower or raise the nose and return to the original height. Following this a further re-adjustment of back pressure will be necessary to maintain the correct pitch attitude for the required bank angle.

The use of rudder will also affect the application of ailerons and elevators. For example when rudder is applied during a turn its further effect is to increase the rate of roll during the entry. If rudder is still required after the turn is established then its further effect will be to increase the bank and create a tendency for the nose to lower.

From the foregoing it can be seen that during a turn the use of ailerons, elevators and rudder are closely related and movement of one will affect the use of the others. A general guide to the sequence of correcting faults in a turn will be to first check and make any necessary corrections to the bank angle, re-adjust the back pressure and finally check and ensure the aircraft is in balance.

Turning Direction
In aircraft equipped with side-by-side seating the pilot will obtain a different view of the aircraft attitude in relation to outside reference features when in a turn to the left to that which he sees when turning right. The reason for this being that when side-by-side seating is used the pilot sitting to the left of the aircraft centre line when turning left will be lower in relation to the centre line, and when turning right he will be higher. This results in a different line of view relative to the aircraft structure, e.g. the engine cowling and the natural horizon. Figure 9-6 illustrates this difference as seen from the left seat when turning left and when turning right. With practice this difference in the pilot's line of view will be appreciated and accurate turns achieved in either direction.

TURNING LEFT   TURNING RIGHT

Fig. 9-6

CLIMBING AND DESCENDING TURNS
The principles which apply to level turns are also true of climbing and descending turns but with one exception; instead of using the elevators to maintain a constant altitude they are used to maintain a constant airspeed.

The Climbing Turn
During a climbing turn the pilot is concerned with both rate of climb and rate of turn. In a level turn the greater the angle of bank the greater will be the power required to overcome drag. If during a climb the aircraft is also put into a turn there would be less power available for climb performance and the rate of climb will be less than in a straight climb. Because of this effect of bank on climb performance it is normal practice to limit the bank angle during the execution of climbing turns.

The climbing turn is entered in the same way as for a level turn but the bank is limited to 20° and the nose attitude adjusted in pitch to maintain the correct climbing speed. Bearing in mind that when an aircraft is in a banked attitude the nose will tend to drop it will not normally be necessary to apply forward pressure to the control column to maintain the climbing speed but rather to use a slight back pressure once in the turn to prevent the nose dropping below the attitude in pitch which will give the correct climbing speed.

It is during a climbing turn that the higher power and lower airspeed associated with climbing flight will produce the maximum yaw effect from the propeller slipstream. If during the straight climb an amount of right rudder pressure is necessary to maintain balance then it is possible upon entering a climbing turn to the left for right rudder pressure still to be needed, though to a smaller extent. Under the same conditions a climbing turn to the right will continue to require a positive right rudder pressure throughout the turn. This needs to be appreciated in order to avoid confusion over the use of the controls during climbing turns. Finally it will be necessary to make frequent cross reference to the ASI and balance indicator to ensure that the turn is being performed correctly.

The Descending Turn

Descending turns can be carried out either from a glide or a powered descent. In both these situations the effect of propeller slipstream is minimal and the use of rudder is more straightforward. During gliding the application of bank will incur an increased rate of descent if the same airspeed is maintained, and in most circumstances this is considered as acceptable, however when it is desired to maintain the same rate of descent then power must be introduced and the glide converted into a powered descent.

The descending turn is entered in the same way as for a level turn and because the performance criteria experienced in the climbing turn does not apply a 30° angle of bank is normally used. During the descending turn the nose will need to be slightly lower to maintain the correct descent speed but as with climbing once the banked attitude is adopted the nose will tend to drop of its own accord and in effect a very slight back pressure on the control column will be necessary to maintain the correct descent airspeed.

Descending turns with partial flap lowered are part of the training syllabus and these are practised as a forerunner to the initial approach to land procedure. They should be practised at various airspeeds and during calm air conditions are normally accomplished at a slightly lower speed than the normal descending speed.

During all turns the stalling speed of the aircraft is increased, i.e. the aircraft will stall at a higher speed. However the increase of stalling speed at moderate bank angles is very small, for example, at a bank angle of 30° the stalling speed is increased by 7%. Normal climbing and descending airspeeds are usually about 70% to 80% in excess of the basic stall speed for training aircraft and therefore there is no need to increase the airspeed for safety reasons during climbing or descending turns.

SLIPPING TURNS

As with the basic sideslip the requirement for slipping turns has diminished with the advent of aircraft equipped with flaps, they nevertheless form a useful exercise in the development of flying skill and are incorporated in the Private Pilot Licence Syllabus.

The object in the slipping turn is to lose height more quickly during a turn without increasing the airspeed. It is accomplished by applying rudder in the opposite direction to the turn whilst using the ailerons to maintain the bank angle. This will produce a condition similar to the normal sideslip in which the drag and descent rate is increased but the aircraft heading continues to change. For any given angle of bank the rate of heading change will be reduced during a slipping turn in comparison with a normal turn and if the original rate of turn is required then the angle of bank will have to be increased.

During the slipping turn a nose down tendency will occur and back pressure on the control column will be required to prevent an increase of airspeed. As with the normal sideslip the slipping turn is an unnatural flight condition and errors in the ASI reading will be present due to the sideways airflow component over the pitot tube, static port or combined pressure head.

The normal application of a slipping turn would be during the turn onto final approach for a landing when due to misjudgement the aircraft is too close to the landing area with an excess of height and no flap available.

The use of slipping turns with flap down is not normally recommended for the same reasons given during the Long Briefing on Descending.

TURNING ONTO SELECTED HEADINGS

 Before the aircraft can be turned accurately onto selected headings the gyro heading indicator must be checked to see that it is still correctly synchronised with the magnetic compass.

Turns onto selected headings are normally made in the shortest direction towards the required heading. When an angle of bank of 30° is being used the roll out should be commenced some 10° before the new heading is reached and when lesser angles of bank are used this anticipation factor should be less. The control co-ordination and timing should be such that the wings become level as the aircraft arrives on the new heading.

USE OF INSTRUMENTS TO ACHIEVE PRECISION FLIGHT

During turning flight the aircraft attitude in relation to bank angle, pitch and balance can change more rapidly than with the previous manoeuvre. Therefore the pilot will need to speed up his rate of scan over the appropriate instruments and make more frequent cross reference between the bank and pitch attitude in relation to the natural horizon and the indications of the aircraft instruments.

The bank indications shown on the attitude indicator are clearly and accurately depicted by the index marks and this is a very useful aid in the achievement and maintenance of accurate bank angles. Figure 9-7 shows the standard presentation on the face of the modern attitude indicator. The index marks at the top of the instrument (a) show bank angles of 10°, 20° and 30° respectively. The diagonal lines below the artificial horizon line (b) normally indicate angles of 20° and 40° or angles of 15° or 30°.

Fig. 9-7

The balance indicator will become more important in relation to instrument cross reference, as it is the only reference during turning flight whereby accurate balance can be achieved. When carrying out climbing or descending turns at a specific rate the VSI will also assume greater importance during the scan of the instruments.

Because instrument cross reference requires a greater frequency of scan during turning flight the basic requirement of maintaining an adequate lookout can easily become neglected and this must be kept in mind throughout the development of the precision flight stage.

AIRMANSHIP

Apart from being an exercise in the co-ordination of the three primary controls, turning will also require co-ordination in lookout allied to aircraft handling. Lookout is not merely a matter of maintaining a 'roving eye in the sky' it has to be controlled in such a manner that it becomes an efficient facet of pilot ability. It is unfortunately a basic fact that a pilot cannot achieve a 100% lookout due to the physical barriers which exist in relation to his head movements and the obstructions which present themselves in terms of cockpit and aircraft design, i.e. the pilot's seating position and his area of view relative to the position and size of items which are part of the aircraft structure.

Apart form the constraints mentioned above there is also the question of cockpit workload which will create diversions from lookout in order to read instruments, charts, check lists and navigation log sheets and to this must also be added the need to operate switches, levers, fuel cocks etc. Bearing these various factors in mind it soon becomes clear that a pilot must be trained to look into the right area at the right time and the ability to do this instinctively will need more than the building up of flying experience. It can in fact only be achieved through the application of self discipline and good training.

The correct procedure prior to commencing a turn is to carefully look all round the aircraft, above, below and at the same level. This lookout sequence should however first start in the direction opposite to the direction of intended turn. This is to ensure that any aircraft which may shortly be passing directly behind the turning aircraft is not missed during the lookout phase immediately prior to the turn. Figure 9-8 illustrates the reason for this sequence.

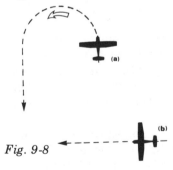

Fig. 9-8

Assuming the pilot of the aircraft at (a) intends to turn left then to look left and behind as a first action would not reveal the aircraft at (b) and by the time the pilot has looked out to the right and behind, the airraft at (b) will have moved to the 6 o'clock position and may now be out of viewing range. In these circumstances the aircraft at (b) will not be seen until a hazardous situation is created.

Although there are many opinions expressed in relation to the problems of lookout in high or low wing aircraft and also those fitted with bubble canopies, an appraisal of the basic facts will soon make any pilot realise that the wing will always cause a large blind area to be permanently present regardless of where it is placed. Further to this the placing of a wing in the low or high position will quite often make little difference because of the many other associated factors relating to obstructions created by aircraft and cockpit design, e.g. the seating position and the vertical position of the pilot's eyes relative to cockpit coamings, windscreen surrounds, horizontal and vertical distances from the wings etc.

The vision in a low wing aircraft is obscured below the aircraft and on either side and with the high wing aircraft vision is obscured above to either side. It is a simple fact that an aircraft must climb up as many times as it descends and therefore in this respect the balance between the high wing and the low wing is equal. During a descent a high wing aircraft offers a much better visibility range whereas in the climb a low wing may have the advantage provided it is equipped with clear vision panels in the cockpit roof.

During turning the low wing aircraft offers the pilot a better view into the direction of turn, but when side by side seating is used this better visibility will only apply when turning to the side on which the pilot is seated, because when turning the opposite way the cockpit roof will cover the area into the direction of turn unless clear vision panels are suitably arranged in the roof.

Aircraft which are designed with bubble canopies would therefore appear to offer the best all round view at the same level and above the aircraft, but again the area which is hidden by the wing will still remain a large blind area to the pilot. Two disadvantages with bubble canopies concern cockpit temperatures and reflections. The cockpits of aircraft fitted with this type of canopy can become rather warm and the pilot has to guard against any relaxing of his alertness, a disadvantage which is often added to by the number of reflections from the cockpit instruments and switches etc, which appear in the perspex canopy during a turn in conditions of strong light or sunshine.

To sum up these problems, no designer can arrange to give the pilot a 100% range of visibility from the cockpit and therefore the pilot must learn to adapt his implementation of lookout to fit the particular type of aircraft which he is using and by so doing achieve the best lookout possible throughout the varying circumstances of flight.

★ LOOK before you turn
   Afterwards may be
       TOO LATE *****

PRE-FLIGHT BRIEFING

MEDIUM LEVEL TURNS
Demonstration 1.

Aim   To teach you how to enter and maintain a medium (30°) banked level turn and how to return the aircraft to straight and level flight.

What   It is a manoeuvre in which the aircraft changes heading at a uniform rate whilst the height and balance are maintained. Turning flight is a fundamental manoeuvre used to change an aircraft heading and as a training exercise it provides practice in control co-ordination and the use of changing control pressures to achieve smooth and balanced flight.

Airmanship   The vital necessity of a thorough lookout prior to and during the turn, also the need to maintain a sense of orientation and a knowledge of the aircraft position relative to known landmarks.

How   Initially an observation turn. Prior to this turn note the airspeed, altitude and method of lookout. During the turn note the bank angle, the pitch attitude relative to the natural horizon and also that constant altitude and balance is maintained. A slight back pressure is required on the control column and the airspeed is slightly reduced.

Turn Entry

Lookout, all round, above, below and behind.
Co-ordinated use of:
  Ailerons to achieve a bank of 30°.
  Rudder to maintain balance – cross reference to balance indicator.
  Elevators to adjust pitch attitude to give a constant altitude – cross reference to the altimeter.

Maintaining the Turn

Maintain the lookout, particularly into the direction of turn.
Bank – adjusted and maintained by the use of ailerons.
Balance – adjusted and maintained by the use of rudder.
Pitch Attitude – adjusted and held constant by use of elevators.
Student Practice.

Recovery to Straight and Level Flight

Whilst still maintaining a careful lookout,
Co-ordinated use of:
  Ailerons to roll the wings level.
  Rudder to maintain balance – cross reference to balance indicator.
  Elevators to re-adjust the pitch attitude to maintain a constant altitude.

Turning in the opposite direction:
Lookout method – Turn entry, maintenance and recovery as before. With side by side seating, note the changed view of the nose relative to the natural horizon. Constant altitude is maintained.

Student Practice.

PRE-FLIGHT BRIEFING
TURNING
Demonstration 2.

Climbing Turns

Aim
To teach you how to enter and maintain a climbing turn and how to return to the straight climb.

What
A climbing manoeuvre during which the aircraft changes heading whilst using 20° of bank at the correct climbing speed in balanced flight.

Airmanship
The need for lookout prior to turn entry and during the turn. The requirements for orientation, remaining clear of cloud, controlled airspace and when applicable adhering to the regulations pertaining to airfield traffic patterns.

How
Entry from climbing flight:
Lookout. Entry as for a medium level turn. Bank angle limited to 20°.
Elevators used to maintain climbing speed, cross reference to ASI.
Note slightly lower nose attitude in pitch than for the normal straight climb.
Greater influence of slipstream in relation to control of balance.
Decreased rate of climb, cross refer to VSI.

Recovery: As from a medium level turn re-adjusting the pitch attitude to maintain the correct climbing speed.

Student practice.

Effect of increasing bank:
Enter a climbing turn and increase the bank angle to approximately 40° and note the reduction in the rate of climb.

Student practice.

Descending Turns

Aim
To teach you how to enter and maintain a descending turn and how to return to the straight descent.

What
A descending manoeuvre during which the aircraft changes heading whilst using 30° of bank at the correct descending speed in balanced flight.

Airmanship
The need for lookout prior to turn entry and during the turn. The requirements for orientation, remaining clear of cloud, controlled airspace and when applicable adhering to the regulations pertaining to airfield traffic patterns.

How
Entry from gliding flight:
Lookout. Entry as for a medium level turn. Bank angle maintained at 30°.
Elevators used to maintain the descent speed, cross reference to ASI.
Note slightly lower nose attitude in pitch than for the normal straight descent.
Increased rate of descent, cross refer to VSI.

Recovery: As from a medium level turn re-adjusting the pitch attitude to maintain the descent speed.

Student practice.

Effect of increasing bank:
Enter a gliding turn and increase the bank angle to approximately 40° and note the increase in descent rate.

Student practice.

Effect of flap:
Turn entry from gliding flight with flap lowered.
Note increase in descent rate.
Original descent rate can only be maintained by the application of power.

Student practice.

PRE-FLIGHT BRIEFING

TURNING
Demonstration 3.

Slipping Turns

Aim
To teach you how to accomplish a controlled sideslip during a turn.

What
A method of losing height without increasing airspeed during a descending turn.

Airmanship
Normal lookout considerations will apply including positioning the aircraft in relation to other traffic in the circuit pattern.

How
During a gliding turn:
Apply rudder opposite to the direction of turn and use the ailerons to maintain the required bank angle.

Adjust pitch attitude with the elevators to maintain the correct airspeed.

Importance of using a moderate amount of slip and maintaining a safe airspeed.

Recovery:
Apply rudder pressure into the direction of turn to regain balanced flight whilst using the ailerons to maintain the required bank angle.

Adjust pitch attitude with the elevators to maintain the correct airspeed.

Student practice.

TURNING
Demonstration 4.

Turning onto Selected Headings

Aim
To teach you how to roll out of a turn onto a specific heading using the heading indicator for precise reference.

What
A manoeuvre during which the aircraft is turned (normally the shorter way) onto a precise heading.

Airmanship
Normal lookout considerations will apply.

How
Select a specific heading to turn onto and plan the turn direction to be the shorter way.
Lookout.   Normal turn entry.
When using a medium angle of bank commence the roll out 10° before reaching the selected heading.

Co-ordinate and complete the roll out as the selected heading is reached.

For bank angles of less than 30° a smaller anticipation will be needed.

Note: Frequent cross reference to the heading indicator will be required during the final stages of the turn.

When straight flight has been resumed further cross reference to the heading indicator will be required to ensure the selected heading is maintained.

Student practice.

Turning

Flight Demonstrations

INTRODUCTION

The contents of this turning exercise may be divided into specific demonstration groups as follows:

1. The Medium Level Turn.
2. Climbing and Descending Turns.
3. The Slipping Turn.
   Turns onto Selected Headings.

The initial demonstration and practice of turning will be concerned with the turn entry, maintaining the turn and returning to straight and level flight. Turning onto selected headings incorporating the use of the heading indicator should be left until the student can perform medium, climbing and descending turns with reasonable accuracy. It would nevertheless be of value to introduce rolling out in relation to a reference feature as soon as the student can cope with this additional task.

Climbing and descending turns can form part of one air lesson and thereby utilise the student's time to greater effect in the same way that the exercises of climbing and descending were combined.

The slipping turn should where possible have been taught prior to the introduction of consolidated circuits, approaches and landings.

Airmanship items will be introduced and developed at appropriate times during all demonstrations.

DEMONSTRATION 1.   THE MEDIUM LEVEL TURN

Flight Lesson	Demonstration Sequence
Turning flight From straight and level flight.	The observation turn. Note the airspeed and altitude. Note the lookout method prior to entry.

	Once in the turn: Note the bank angle and pitch attitude relative to the aircraft features (coaming cowling and windscreen frame) and the natural horizon. A constant altitude and balance is maintained and the airspeed is slightly lower. Finally, if the control column is released the nose will drop below the horizon.
The turn entry	Lookout to either side above, below and behind the aircraft. Bank in the required direction and use sufficient rudder to maintain balance. Adjust the pitch attitude to maintain a constant altitude. When a 30° bank is reached neutralise the ailerons and re-adjust rudder pedal pressure to maintain balance.
During the turn	Maintain the lookout. The ailerons are used to adjust and maintain the bank angle. The rudder is used to maintain balance. The elevators are used to maintain a constant altitude. Continued cross reference of the instruments is required to maintain altitude and balance.
Returning to straight and level flight	Roll the aircraft back to the laterally level attitude and at the same time use rudder to maintain the balance and the elevators to re-adjust the pitch attitude.

Student practice: The student should now be allowed to practise the turn entry, maintaining the turn and recovering to straight and level flight. If the aircraft is equipped with side-by-side seating his practice turns should be confined to the direction used during the demonstration.

When aircraft with side-by-side seating are used the turn should also be demonstrated in the opposite direction.	
From straight and level flight.	Lookout to either side above, below and behind the aircraft. Entry and maintenance of the turn is the same as before. Note the changed position of the nose in

pitch as seen by the pilot relative to the natural horizon.

Student practice: The student should now take over control and practise maintaining this turn and recovering to straight and level flight followed by repetition as required.

DEMONSTRATION 2. CLIMBING AND DESCENDING TURNS

Flight Lesson	Demonstration Sequence
The climbing turn	
From the straight climb	Note the rate of climb. Lookout all round and particularly up into the area of the intended turn. Use all three controls in the same way as for entering a level turn. Limit the bank angle to 20° and maintain the correct climbing speed.
During the turn	All the controls are used in the normal manner to maintain the aircraft at the correct bank angle, airspeed and in balance. Note the slightly lower nose attitude and the reduced rate of climb.
Returning to the straight climb	Use all three controls in the same way as recovering from a level turn, re-adjusting the pitch attitude to maintain the correct climbing speed.
Demonstrate reduction in the rate of climb with increase of bank angle	Lookout and enter a normal climbing turn. Note the rate of climb at 20° of bank. Maintain the climbing speed and increase the bank to approximately 40° and note the positive reduction in the climb rate.

Student practice: The student should now practise climbing turns in both directions.

The descending turn	
From the straight glide	Note the rate of descent. Lookout all round and particularly down into the area of the intended turn. Use all three controls in the same way

	as for entering a level turn. Limit the bank angle to 30° and maintain the correct gliding speed.
During the turn	All the controls are used in the normal manner to maintain the aircraft at the correct bank angle, airspeed and in balance. Note the slightly lower nose attitude and the increased rate of descent.
Returning to the straight glide	Use all three controls in the same way as when recovering from a level turn, re-adjusting the pitch attitude to maintain the correct gliding speed.
Demonstrate the increase in rate of descent with increase of bank angle	Lookout and enter a normal gliding turn. Note the rate of descent at 30° of bank. Maintain the gliding speed and increase the bank angle to approximately 40° and note the positive increase in the descent rate.

Student practice: The student should now practise gliding turns in both directions.

Demonstrate the effect of flap and use of power during descending turns	From the straight glide, lower flap and adjust the attitude to obtain the flap down gliding speed. Enter a gliding turn. Note the rate of descent. Power can be used to maintain the original or any selected rate of descent. The greater the angle of bank used the greater will be the power required to maintain a particular descent rate.

Student practice: The student should now practice descending turns with flap lowered both in the glide and powered descent. Point out the application of this exercise to the base leg and final approach turns.

DEMONSTRATION 3.   THE SLIPPING TURN

Flight Lesson	*Demonstration Sequence*
Sideslipping during a descending turn	Note the rate of descent. Apply rudder opposite to the direction of turn and use ailerons to maintain the required bank angle. The elevators are used throughout to control the airspeed.

	Note the increased rate and angle of descent.
Application to turning onto finals when flap is not available.	Emphasise the need to maintain a safe airspeed.

Student practice: The student should now practise moderately banked slipping turns.

DEMONSTRATION 4. TURNING ONTO SELECTED HEADINGS

Flight Lesson	Demonstration Sequence
Turns incorporating the use of the heading indicator.	Select a specific heading and decide the way to turn for the heading selected. Lookout, followed by normal turn entry. When using a 30° bank angle commence the roll out 10° before reaching the selected heading. When a lesser bank angle is used the anticipation in degrees should be correspondingly less. Frequent cross reference to the heading indicator is required during the final stages of the turn.

Student practice: The student should now be given the task of rolling out of turns onto specific headings from level, climbing and descending turns.

Slow Flight

(Awareness of Flight at Very Low Airspeeds)
Instructor's Guide

Slow flight is a valuable training exercise both in relation to the development of decision making ability and handling skills when the aircraft is flown at very low airspeed. If we consider for a moment the time spent in taking a light aircraft from an operational speed of say, 70 knots down to the stalling speed and back again in the manner used during training stall entries and recoveries, it normally amounts to between 6 and 8 seconds. If the student does 20 stalls in his training then he will have spent between 2 and $2\frac{1}{2}$ minutes handling the aircraft in the speed region where stalls can easily occur. This is hardly acceptable as being sufficient time for him to develop judgement, awareness and ability to handle the aircraft safely in the inadvertent stall/spin situation.

On the other hand a student who has practised slow flight at V_{S1} and $V_{S0} + 10$ knots and $+5$ knots for only 10 minutes will have had 5 times more opportunity to develop the necessary skill to control the aircraft safely whilst taking positive action to return to a safer airspeed. It should however be understood that slow flight is not an operational procedure and it is not taught for this purpose. It is included in the syllabus primarily to extend the student's handling ability and to develop a stronger sense of awareness of an impending stall situation. The benefits of practising 'slow flight' are many, but probably the most important one is in relation to the prevention of inadvertent spins, in that it gives the student the opportunity to obtain practice at keeping the aircraft in balance at low speeds when the effect of power is at its greatest in creating yaw. Remember, an aircraft will not normally spin unless it is yawing during the stall.

Whereas students have plenty of opportunity to develop the ability to maintain balance during cruising, climbing and descending flight at normal operational airspeeds – they have very little chance of practising the maintenance of balance at very low airspeeds and it is at low airspeeds that stalls/spins occur.

To emphasise this point it can be said that even extreme unbalance at normal cruising, climbing or descending airspeeds will not in itself be dangerous – uncomfortable, inefficient and wasteful of fuel, yes, but not necessarily dangerous. However at very low speeds it can be disastrous. So students must be given the opportunity of learning how to control yaw at speeds approaching the stall. The few seconds spent during normal stall practice are not sufficient for this purpose.

In conclusion it could be correct to say that training in spin prevention begins with training in the exercise of 'slow flight'. There is no doubt as to the importance of this practice and the opportunities to do it during a 40 hour course are plentiful.

If students are taught to safely control the aircraft whilst maintaining pre-selected altitudes and headings at low airspeeds whilst keeping the aircraft in balance, they will have obtained a greater insurance against entering an inadvertent stall/spin than by practising many actual recoveries from developed stalls.

AIRMANSHIP

During the exercise the aircraft will be flown with a high nose attitude therefore Lookout assumes great importance, and it will be advisable to ensure that there are no other aircraft in the area before commencing the demonstration and practice. It is also essential that a high standard of lookout is maintained throughout the period of practice.

The aircraft will be flown at low airspeed for varying periods of time and the cooling effect of airflow in relation to the engine will thus often be reduced, so a careful watch on engine temperatures and pressures should be maintained, particularly when climbing at low airspeed.

BEFORE THE EXERCISE

The Long Briefing should cover the following:

Objectives
Aircraft Handling Characteristics During Slow Flight
   Aspects of Control and Performance
Setting up Slow Flight –
   at V_{S1} and V_{S0} + 10 knots
   at V_{S1} and V_{S0} + 5 knots
Straight and Level Flight
Level Turns
Climbing and Descending
Climbing and Descending Turns
Distractions During Flight at Slow Speed
Use of Full Power when in the Landing Configuration
   Overshooting – Going Round Again – Pitch Characteristics for
    the specific Aircraft Type.
Airmanship
Common Errors

This exercise is a natural introduction to stall training and whilst most modern aircraft have stall warning devices such as horns or lights it has been found that these alone do not prevent inadvertent stalls from occurring. The present-day stall warning devices leave much to be desired as a positive means of alerting the pilot to the impending stall situation, in that lights are almost totally ineffective when visual flight is being carried out because the pilot's main attention is outside the cockpit. A further weakness is that most stall warning lights are situated next to the airspeed indicator and if the pilot was looking in this direction he would, on most occasions, already have noticed his airspeed was too low. The effectiveness of a horn warning decreases substantially whenever the pilot is pre-occupied with operational contingencies and a number of pilots who have been involved in an inadvertent stall situation have stated that they did not hear the horn at all or that they did not remember hearing it.

It is obvious that greater safety and pilot competency will be achieved by more practice at handling an aircraft in the slow speed region thus allowing the senses of vision, hearing and feel to become more attuned at recognising the early stall symptoms.

DURING THE AIR DEMONSTRATION

The method of setting up slow flight should not be hurried as during this period the control responses are changing and becoming less effective. Time is needed to cope with the changing control pressures as the speed is reduced and the slight variations in power which will be required particularly if there is some atmospheric turbulence.

The demonstration of rapid airspeed reduction when entering a level turn is very important, and during this demonstration the instructor should fly the aircraft whilst the student notes how quickly and by what amount the airspeed decreases.

A vital part of the training in slow flight concerns the additional difficulty of maintaining the aircraft in a state of balance when flying at low speeds, and this point must be emphasised by the instructor.

COMMON ERRORS

The student will normally tend to concentrate on the airspeed which in one sense is beneficial, but as the object of the total exercise is complete control over airspeed, altitude, heading and balance he must learn to scan the various instruments whilst also maintaining a careful lookout. In this respect it should be pointed out that once the correct power setting has been achieved, the maintenance of a constant altitude will also result in a constant airspeed, unless the aircraft is allowed to become unbalanced or updraughts/downdraughts are present.

Balance, particularly when the aircraft is being flown at high power and low airspeed will create a much larger problem than when the aircraft is being flown at normal operational speeds, and it may be necessary in the early stages for the instructor to fly the aircraft in relation to pitch and lateral level and leave the student the single task of maintaining balance by use of the rudder.

NOTE: Slow flight, all forms of stalls and recovery from spins at the incipient stage are those exercises included in the mandatory two hours of stall/spin awareness and avoidance training which is now part of the private pilot licence course.

Low end
of white =
Vso

Low end
of green =
Vsɪ

Slow Flight

Long Briefing

OBJECTIVES

The purpose of Slow Flight being incorporated in the Private Pilot Syllabus is to ensure the student obtains the opportunity to develop the ability to safely handle the aircraft at very low airspeeds.

Slow Flight is not an operational exercise, its primary objective being to strengthen the student's sense of awareness via sensory perceptions that the aircraft is being flow in a speed region close to the stall. This sense of awareness is gained by spending a reasonable amount of time in handling the aircraft at airspeeds below those used in normal operations, thus developing the sense of vision, hearing and feel to the extent that he is able to intuitively recognise an impending stall situation.

Practice in flying at these low speeds will also give the student training in the maintenance of balanced flight when operating at airspeeds lower than those commonly used for normal manoeuvres. For example, on those occasions immediately after take-off or during the few seconds the aircraft spends in the landing flare, or on those occasions where the airspeed has inadvertently been allowed to decrease to a low figure. In relation to the latter it should be appreciated that whilst there is ample opportunity during training to practise the maintenance of balance when operating at cruising, climbing and descending airspeeds, the time which is spent at very low speeds, i.e. during take-offs and landings and when entering and recovering from practice stalls and incipient stage spins is extremely brief. Yet it is at these very low airspeeds, particularly when power is being used, that the aircraft is most prone to enter an unbalanced condition, with the result that a wing could drop very rapidly and entry to a spin may occur. This latter effect will be most marked when the centre of gravity is in an aft position, though still within limits, a condition which is quite common when passengers are carried and pilot distractions are more likely to occur.

If a student can safely control an aircraft whilst flying at pre-selected low airspeeds, altitudes and headings, with the aircraft in balance then the following objectives will have been achieved:

- The ability to recognise the early symptoms which indicate the aircraft is close to a stall.
- The ability to safely control the aircraft whilst taking the corrective action to regain a normal operational airspeed.

INTRODUCTION

Because a pilot must be able to operate his aircraft in complete safety over a wide range of circumstances and conditions it is difficult to decide on a relative order of importance of the exercises, Slow Flight, Stalling and Recovery, and Recovery from a Spin at the Incipient Stage. However in view of the absolute requirement to be able to recognise the early symptoms of an inadvertent stall situation, the practice of Slow Flight is extremely important and should be conducted at regular intervals throughout the course of training.

The flight exercises, Slow Flight, Stalling and Recovery and the Recovery from Spins at the Incipient Stage collectively form that part of the syllabus known as Stall/Spin Awareness and Avoidance training. Two hours of this must be included in the course for the issue of a Private Pilot's Licence.

THE FORCES AND AIRCRAFT CHARACTERISTICS IN SLOW FLIGHT

Slow flight can be defined as flight in the speed range from below the endurance speed to just above the stalling speed. The amount of lift, and the control of an aircraft in flight depend upon the maintenance of a minimum airspeed. This speed will vary with the all-up weight, imposition of loads due to manoeuvre, aircraft configuration and density altitude. The closer the actual speed to this minimum speed the greater the angle of attack and the less effective are the flying controls. The minimum speed below which it is impossible to maintain controlled flight is called the stalling speed.

Figure 10-1 shows that as the angle of attack increases, the centre of pressure moves forward.

Fig. 10-1

This movement brings the c.p. and c.g. closer together and weakens the normal nose down tendency brought about by the L/W couple. At the same time the elevators which depend upon the speed of the airflow for their effectiveness will become less responsive as the airspeed reduces with increasing angle of attack.

The ailerons and rudder will also begin to lose their effectiveness as the airspeed decreases and coarse movements of all controls will become necessary to control the aircraft about the three axes. If however the power is increased in a propeller driven aircraft the elevators and rudder will become a little more effective due to the higher speed of the air within the slipstream cylinder. At the low airspeeds associated with slow flight the slipstream effect in producing yaw is very strong and positive use of rudder must be made to maintain the aircraft in balanced flight. At low speeds and high power settings the larger amount of rudder deflection needed to maintain this balance will produce sufficient further effect to require a positive application of aileron to hold the wings in a laterally level attitude. This will result in the aircraft having to be flown in a 'crossed controls' condition in order to achieve balanced flight with the wings level.

Fig. 10-2

An important feature in slow flight training is the development of the ability to estimate the margin of safety above the stalling speed by the diminishing response of the aircraft to movement of the flying controls. The student pilot must develop this awareness in order to fly safely at the lower speeds involved during take-off and landing.

SETTING UP SLOW FLIGHT
Slow flight should be introduced initially from straight and level flight at V_{S1} + 10 knots, i.e. 10 knots higher than that indicated at the bottom of the green arc on the airspeed indicator. In later practice this speed should be reduced to V_{S1} + 5 knots. To set up slow flight the power should be gradually reduced and the nose attitude raised to maintain a constant altitude. The lateral level, heading and balance must be maintained as the airspeed reduces to the selected figure.

The speeds of V_{S1} + 10 knots and 5 knots will be sufficient to permit manoeuvring flight, whilst being close enough to the stalling speed for the reduced effectiveness of the controls to be clearly felt. In this situation the aircraft will be flying at the lower end of the 'power curves' as shown in fig. 10-3 and in this region the aircraft will have minimal climb performance.

Fig. 10-3

In these circumstances any attempt to regain lost altitude by raising the nose will result in a rapid increase of induced drag and without an increase in power the airspeed will fall. No altitude will be gained and continued raising of the nose will only result in altitude being lost and eventually the aircraft will reach the stall. Therefore any attempt to regain altitude when operating at very low airspeed demands an increase of power as the nose is raised.

Following practice of slow flight in the straight and level condition the aircraft should be placed in a medium level turn (without increase in power) and the student shown how rapidly the airspeed lowers when the altitude is being maintained. This decrease in airspeed is significantly greater and more rapid than the speed reduction which occurs when medium level turns are being carried out at normal cruising speed. Thus it is most important to increase the power whenever turning during slow flight at constant altitude.

Straight climbs and descents should then be practised, followed by climbing and descending turns. During climbs conducted in slow flight the climb performance will be poor due to the increased induced drag and as seen from the characteristic shape of the horsepower required and horsepower available curves the aircraft will be operating in an area where a small margin of power available exists (fig. 10-3).

Descents at slow speed should be practised with and without power. In the power-on condition the desired rate of descent can be achieved at the selected airspeed by reducing the power and re-adjusting the nose attitude to a lower position in the same manner as for a descent during normal flight.

Once the student has had reasonable practice in straight and level flight, climbing and descending, and climbing and descending turns at V_{S1} + 10 knots these manoeuvres should be practised with the flaps lowered at V_{S0} + 10 knots. When a sufficient degree of competence has been demonstrated in all the manoeuvres covered in the preceding paragraphs the student should receive practice at regular intervals of flying the aircraft in these four basic manoeuvres at V_{S1} and V_{S0} + 5 knots.

During the consolidation period when the student is practising slow flight the instructor will demonstrate the effects of unbalance during climbing and descending turns. This demonstration will be one in which the aircraft is brought very close to the stall during the turn and the characteristic reaction of the particular aircraft noted.

DISTRACTION DURING FLIGHT AT SLOW SPEED
Analysis of past accidents which involved stalling or spinning as a causal factor reveals that in many cases the pilot was being subjected to distractions of one sort or another. In consequence, slow flight training will include occasions when the instructor will deliberately induce 'pilot distractions' during the practise of this exercise.

USE OF FULL POWER IN THE LANDING CONFIGURATION
During approach and landing circumstances may occur which will require the pilot to initiate 'overshoot' or 'go round again' procedure. An important aspect of this situation is that when the aircraft is trimmed for the approach and landing with flaps lowered, the application of full power may cause a very strong change in pitch. A similar change may also occur when the flaps are raised in the initial climb-away phase. Both will require an adjustment of the trim control to counteract the strong control pressures. It is therefore essential for safety reasons that the student is given experience in controlling the aircraft under these conditions before actually implementing the 'go round again' procedure from an actual approach and landing. This will initially be demonstrated and practised at a safe altitude and the control forces and pitch changes noted for the particular training aircraft.

PRE-FLIGHT BRIEFING
SLOW FLIGHT
Demonstration 1.

V_i V_{end}

Aim
To acquaint you with the handling characteristics and control feel at low airspeeds and also to give you practice in controlling the aircraft at these lower speeds.

What
Controlled flight at V_{S1} + 10 knots and with flaps lowered at V_{S0} + 10 knots.

Airmanship
The maintenance of a safe height above the surface and normal lookout requirements, also due to the lower airspeed being used the oil temperature must be monitored more frequently.

How
Level Flight
Estimate the power required for flight at V_{S1} + 10 kts.
Reduce power, adopt attitude and trim.
Re-adjust attitude and power as required.
Maintain altitude, heading and balance.
Altitude loss is corrected by use of elevators and increase of power.

Student practice.

Climbing
Nominate a rate of climb and from level slow flight at V_{S1} + 10 kts gradually increase power whilst maintaining airspeed, heading and balance.
Stabilise power setting when nominated rate of climb is achieved. Re-trim.

Return to level slow flight at V_{S1} + 10 kts.

Student practice.

Turning Flight
Maintenance of lookout.
From slow flight at V_{S1} + 10 kts enter a medium level turn without increasing power.

Note how quickly the airspeed lowers when altitude is maintained in the turn. Return to straight flight.
Lookout and re-enter the medium turn whilst increasing power in order to maintain airspeed and altitude.
Note the amount of power required to maintain airspeed and altitude.

Student practice. Turning in both directions.

Descending
Nominate a rate of descent, lookout and gradually reduce power whilst maintaining heading, balance and V_{S1} + 10 kts. Stabilise power setting when nominated rate of descent is achieved. Re-trim.

Return to level slow flight.

Student practice.

The student should now practise level flight, level turns, straight climbs and descents and climbing and descending turns with flap down at V_{S0} + 10 knots.

PRE-FLIGHT BRIEFING

SLOW FLIGHT
Demonstration 2.

Aim

To acquaint you with the aircraft's handling characteristics in the range, V_{S1} + 5 knots and V_{S0} + 5 knots, to the minimum airspeed(s) at which the aircraft can be controlled.

What

Controlled flight at V_{S1} + 5 knots and lower, and with the flaps down at V_{S0} + 5 knots and lower.

Airmanship

The maintenance of a safe height above the surface and normal lookout requirements, also due to the lower air-speeds being used the oil temperature must be monitored more frequently.

How

Level Flight

Set the estimated power required for level slow flight at V_{S1} + 5 kts. Adjust the attitude for the correct airspeed whilst maintaining heading and balance. Re-trim.

Climbing

Nominate a rate of climb and from level slow flight at V_{S1} + 5 kts. Increase power whilst maintaining airspeed, heading and balance. Re-trim.

Return to level slow flight at V_{S1} + 5 kts.

Student practice.

Turning Flight

Lookout and from slow flight at V_{S1} + 5 kts enter a medium level turn without increasing power. Note how quickly the airspeed lowers when altitude is maintained in the turn. Return to straight slow flight.

Lookout and re-enter the medium level turn whilst increasing power to maintain airspeed and altitude.

Student practice.

Descending

Nominate a rate of descent and from level slow flight at V_{S1} + 5 kts reduce power to achieve the correct rate of descent. Re-trim. Return to level slow flight.

Student practice.

The student should now practise level flight, level turns, straight climbs and descents and climbing and descending turns with flap down at V_{S0} + 5 knots.

During climbing the importance of monitoring the oil temperature and pressure will assume increased importance.

At the end of this period the symptoms of the stall can be demonstrated together with the fact that only a small forward movement of the control column is necessary to return the aircraft to a condition of controlled slow flight.

Slow Flight

Flight Demonstrations

INTRODUCTION

The contents of the total slow flight exercise may be divided into specific demonstration groups as follows:

1. Demonstration and Practice of Slow Flight at V_{S1} + 10 knots in Straight and Level Flight, Level Turns, Straight Climbs and Descents and in Climbing and Descending Turns. These manoeuvres should also be practised (with flaps down) at V_{S0} + 10 knots.

2. Demonstration and Practice of Slow Flight at V_{S1} + 5 knots in Straight and Level Flight, Level Turns, Straight Climbs and Descents and in Climbing and Descending Turns. These manoeuvres should also be practised (with flaps down) at V_{S0} + 5 knots. During these manoeuvres the instructor will introduce pilot distractions.

3. Demonstration and Practice in controlling the aircraft during the application of full power when the aircraft is trimmed for the approach configuration and when flaps are raised in the climb.

   NOTE: This exercise is part of Descending, but is mentioned again under Slow Flight as a reminder if not already demonstrated during the Descending exercise.

Slow Flight is a good preparatory exercise to stalling and assists the student to develop control feel and knowledge of the rate and amount of control movement which is needed when flying in the lower airspeed range.

Airmanship items including the need for a constant lookout and an increased rate of monitoring the engine temperature and pressure gauges will be introduced at the appropriate times during the demonstrations and practice.

DEMONSTRATION 1.   SLOW FLIGHT

Flight Lesson	Demonstration Sequence
Controlled flight at low airspeed	
From straight and level flight	Maintain a lookout whilst reducing power and maintaining altitude, heading and balance. Re-trim in stages and when V_{S1} + 10 knots is established, adjust power as necessary to maintain airspeed and altitude. Note the change in pitch attitude and reduced response from the flying controls. Altitude loss is corrected by use of the elevators together with increasing the power. Student practice.
Climbing flight	From controlled straight and level flight V_{S1} + 10 knots. Nominate a particular climb rate. Lookout. Gradually increase power whilst maintaining speed, heading and balance. Stabilise the power setting when the selected rate of climb has been achieved.
Turning flight	From level slow flight at V_{S1} + 10 knots, lookout and enter a medium level turn without increasing power. Note loss of speed when altitude is maintained. Re-enter a medium banked turn, increasing power and maintaining constant speed and altitude. Note the higher pitch attitude and the need to use elevators and power to correct any altitude loss. Student practice.
Descending flight	From controlled straight and level flight at V_{S1} + 10 knots. Nominate a rate of descent. Lookout and check a clear area along the descent path. Gradually decrease power whilst maintaining speed, heading and balance. Stabilise the power setting when the selected rate of descent has been achieved.

Return to straight and level slow flight
by maintaining speed and increasing
power until the descent rate is zero.
Heading and balance should be
maintained throughout.
Student practice.

Student practice: Following the completion of the slow flight demonstration and practice as described above, the student should be given
the opportunity of practising slow flight at V_{S0} + 10 knots with the
flaps lowered. Manoeuvres should include straight and level, level
turns, straight climbs and descents, and climbing and descending
turns.

During this period the instructor will introduce pilot distractions.

DEMONSTRATION 2.   SLOW FLIGHT

Flight Lesson	Demonstration Sequence
Controlled flight at low airspeed	
From straight and level flight	Maintain a lookout whilst reducing power and maintaining altitude, heading and balance. Re-trim in stages and when V_{S1} + 5 knots is established, adjust power as necessary to maintain airspeed and altitude. Student practice.
Climbing flight	From controlled straight and level flight at V_{S1} + 5 knots, nominate a specific rate of climb. Lookout and gradually increase power whilst maintaining airspeed, heading and balance. Stabilise the power setting.
Turning flight	From level slow flight at V_{S1} + 5 knots, lookout and enter a medium level turn without increasing power. Note how quickly the airspeed lowers when altitude is maintained in the turn. Return to straight slow flight. Lookout and re-enter a medium turn whilst increasing power to maintain airspeed and altitude. Student practice.
Descending flight	From controlled straight and level flight at V_{S1} + 5 knots, nominate a rate of descent. Lookout and select a clear area along the descent path. Gradually decrease power whilst maintaining airspeed, heading and balance.

Stabilise the power setting when the selected rate of descent has been achieved. Re-trim.
Student practice.

Student practice: The student should now practice level flight, level turns, straight climbs and descents and climbing and descending turns with flap down at V_{S0} + 5 knots.

Note 1.At the end of this period the symptoms of the stall can be demonstrated. Only a small forward movement of the control column is necessary to return the aircraft to a condition of controlled slow flight.

Note 2. If a demonstration of the effects of applying full power when the aircraft is trimmed with flaps down in the landing configuration has not yet been carried out, then it must be demonstrated at this stage.

Stalling

Instructor's Guide

The stalling exercise covers a flight condition during which the aircraft is operating at high angles of attack. Such other factors as airspeed, load factor, configuration, weight, c.g. position and turbulence all individually or collectively affect the aircraft stalling characteristics, and where it is possible their effects must be demonstrated to the student.

Following the introduction to the aircraft characteristics during slow flight the stalling exercise can be commenced. The instructor should ensure that during this introductory stage the stalls demonstrated are of a reasonably gentle nature. Such features as a marked high nose attitude and rapid nose or wing drop should be avoided at this stage as they can often inhibit learning due to a student's psychological or physical discomfort, or to his fear of the unknown.

It will take time to demonstrate and practise all the facets of stalling and recovery from various flight situations, power settings and configurations, therefore care is necessary to itemise the total exercise into specific phases and to make your teaching progressive. Once stalling has been introduced ensure the student gets short periods of stall practice on as many flights as possible.

AIRMANSHIP

All the items of airmanship which have been introduced to the student during previous exercises will apply. However due to the nature of this exercise it is recommended that added emphasis be given to the requirements of safe operating practices, and immediately before commencing the stalling exercise certain safety checks should be made. These will concern height, security of loose articles, engine and ancillary systems, lookout and location. The order in which these checks are carried out will possibly vary between different instructors and aircraft types.

Although the example shown in the Long Briefing uses the mnemonic HASELL there are other sequences which can be used to achieve the same purpose, and dependent upon the aircraft type or immediate situation variations of the actual order in which safety checks are carried out may be necessary.

For example, aircraft configuration is listed under 'airframe considerations', but if a high-wing aircraft is being used the lowering of flap at this point will restrict the area in which the final lookout is conducted and it would therefore be more sensible in this case to lower flap after the clearing turn and immediately prior to entering the stall. The few seconds taken in lowering the required flap will not invalidate the clearing turn provided that care has been used to ensure that the surrounding airspace within a sufficient distance from the aircraft is clear of other air traffic.

In relation to clearing turns undertaken to ensure the area around and below the aircraft is clear, it is important to stress that the object is 'to ensure the area is clear' and not just to carry out a 360° turn. Clearing turns may be of varying amounts of heading change and in different directions or combinations of direction depending upon the circumstances at the time.

Finally although there is no legal requirement for ensuring the recovery takes place above 3000 feet above ground level, it is an established safety practice and should be adhered to. If one compares 3000 feet of height with the length of a 3000 feet runway it can be graphically appreciated just how little 3000 feet of height really is in the practical sense.

BEFORE THE EXERCISE
The Long Briefing should cover the following:

Objectives
Characteristics of the Stall
The Effectiveness of the Controls at the Stall
Factors Affecting the Stalling Speed
    Effect of Flaps/Slats/Slots
    Effect of Power/Weight and C of G/Load Factor
The Effects of Unbalance at the Stall
The Symptoms of the Stall
Stall Recognition and Recovery
Stalling and Recovery
    With Power On
    With Flaps Down
Maximum Power Climb (straight and turning flight) to the Point of Stall with Uncompensated Yaw.
* Stalling and Recovery during manoeuvres involving more than 1g (accelerated stalls, including secondary stalls and recoveries).

* *Consideration must be given to any manoeuvre limitations as detailed in the Aircraft Manual including weight and balance restrictions.*

Recovering from Incipient Stalls in the Landing and other configurations and conditions.
Recoveries at the Incipient Stage during Change of Configuration
Airmanship
Common Errors

The short Pre-Flight Briefing should be based upon the practical aspects of that part of the Long Briefing in relation to the Air Exercise to be covered. Ensure the student understands how to use the Flight/Owner's Manual in order to work out the Indicated Stalling Speeds, and to what extent these vary with change of weight, configuration and angle of bank. Further to this he must also understand the meanings of RAS/CAS in relation to IAS.

Despite the fact that all pilots receive training in stalls and are tested for proficiency in recognition and recovery, stalling accidents continue to occur. However, it must be appreciated that there is a marked contrast between a student's reaction to stalls practised during training and those which occur in other flight phases, possibly under more critical conditions such as in the event of an engine failure. This is particularly true during landing or take-off when the elements of surprise, very low altitude, identification of trouble, etc. all call for a high degree of speed of action and proficiency if an accident involving serious injury is to be avoided.

Stall training, for obvious reasons, is conducted at higher altitudes where most of the pilot's conscious attention can be directed towards the performance of the stall recovery, and no real sense of urgency or pilot workload exists. In this safe training situation there is ample opportunity for him to detect stall characteristics, to co-ordinate and control the performance of the aircraft, and to make an almost immediate recovery at the appropriate moment.

If a pilot enters an inadvertent stall at a relatively low height then statistics show he will almost inevitably have an accident, regardless of how quickly he can recover from a premeditated training stall in the ideal condition of several thousand feet above the ground. Remember therefore, that the objective of this exercise is to ensure as far as is possible that the student will never inadvertently enter a stall situation, and to this end considerable emphasis and practice must be given to teaching the recovery at the incipient stage.

In deciding how best to obtain value from the practice of recovery at the incipient stage one must consider that most light aircraft of today have such items as stall warning lights, horns, buzzers or similar alerting devices. However, light aircraft still figure substantially in the current stalling accident statistics. The question of failure of these stall warning systems when such accidents occur is not necessarily a reasonable assumption and it must often mean therefore that these accidents occur in spite of such warning devices.

In reviewing this it is clear that cockpit workload and mental concentration is fairly high during the approach to landing, going round again and during the period immediately after take-off. This workload is greater for the inexperienced or 'out of practice' pilot and if the workload becomes very high in any of these flight phases then the senses will often fail to pick up the warnings given by lights, horns, etc. This points to the fact that there is insufficient value in teaching incipient stall recoveries at the stage where aural and visual stall warnings operate.

The ability to develop a deeper instinct to 'trigger off' the sense of awareness of an impending stall is not an easy task, but it could be fostered and developed more quickly during stall training by bringing the aircraft to within a few miles an hour of the stalling speed for the particular flight condition and configuration. and then effecting a recovery. These incipient stall situations should be carried out in all normal configurations and power settings until the student is instinctively recovering safely before the actual stall takes place.

DURING THE AIR DEMONSTRATION

Probably the most uncommon inadvertent stalls occur from the level flight condition with power off, flap up and a load factor of 1. It is therefore extremely important to ensure that the student obtains consistent practice at stalling in different attitudes, power settings and aircraft configurations. Nevertheless good teaching principles necessitate the introduction of stalling in a logical sequence, i.e. one which starts by the introduction of simple stalls and progresses in a natural way to the more complex situations.

Due to the different stall characteristics between aircraft of different types and the reactions of the same type of aircraft with differing c.g. locations, the instructor may face certain practical difficulties in showing the full range of these variations. In such instances the student must be given adequate ground instruction to ensure he has a sound understanding of the different situations and aircraft stall characteristics which he may meet in his future flying.

As the student becomes more proficient the workload should be increased during entries to the stall. This can be achieved by giving him tasks which are unrelated to stalling and which divert his attention. This will prepare him for the typical situations in which most inadvertent stalls occur.

Finally be especially alert to the student's physical reactions during this exercise and do not hesitate to change your planning of the intended flight lesson when necessary. If symptoms of airsickness occur the flight should be cut short and the aircraft returned to the airfield as quickly as possible. Many students have been unnecessarily put off flying because their instructor failed to recognise symptoms of airsickness in time. Remember that if a student is actually airsick it will be a strong deterrent to his future motivation and progress.

COMMON ERRORS
During both slow flight and the approach to the stall the changing effectiveness of the rudder as the speed decreases will normally cause the student difficulty in maintaining a balanced flight condition. This will be particularly evident during slow flight or when stall entries are made with a power setting higher than for the normal cruise. If the student continues to have difficulty in maintaining balance during the early stages of power on stalling practice then one way of improving his performance is to make him temporarily responsible for the use of rudder to maintain balance whilst the instructor handles the elevators, ailerons and power up to the stall.

A very common fault is the use of aileron when a wing drops at the stall. This use of ailerons to level the wings is the natural result of his previous training and will be completely instinctive. It is nevertheless a habit which must be prevented when the aircraft has stalled. It can only be overcome by constant practice and a demonstration of the lack of aileron effectiveness at the stall will assist towards achieving the desired result.

During the standard recovery the student will usually have a little difficulty in timing the rate of control column and throttle movement. Again only through practice will he eventually achieve the correct co-ordination between the two.

A common fault which can lead to a secondary stall is moving the control column backwards too quickly or too far immediately after the initial recovery. This produces a particularly dangerous condition, as at this stage full power will have been applied and a secondary stall under these conditions will often lead to a rapid and violent wing drop.

The stall with flap down can produce a marked change in the effectiveness of the elevators, and the student must be made aware of the additional and positive forward movement of the control column needed to effect a satisfactory recovery.

When practising stalls from turning flight the student will initially find some difficulty in maintaining a moderate bank angle. If the bank is allowed to steepen the tendency for the nose to drop will often prevent the continued reduction in airspeed and although the aircraft can be stalled at higher speeds it will require a greater control force. At this stage the intention is to teach entries and recoveries from the stall at moderate bank angles and therefore the instructor must emphasise the need for positive use of aileron to maintain the bank angle during the approach to the stall.

During approaches to the stall in the turn a student will often fail to keep moving the control column back until the positive stall occurs. Failure to maintain a continuous backward movement will often result in the speed lowering to such an extent that the elevators will be unable to provide sufficient effect in pitch for the stalling angle to be reached, and the aircraft will continue in a tight turn with the control column fully back.

On certain aircraft and particularly those with an aft c.g. the action of a wing dropping at the stall during a turn can be very rapid and the student may initially be too slow in his use of the controls to effect a recovery before a steeply banked nose down attitude is reached. Under these circumstances the use of power must be delayed until the recovery is completed and the nose raised towards the level attitude.

● A recent review of the accidents to aircraft with weights below 2300 kg revealed that . . .
Nearly one third of all fatalities were caused due to inadvertent stall/spin occurrences. Such accidents are rarely caused by a temporary lapse in flight safety, instead they are usually the end result of incorrect flight practices or procedures which may have even begun on the ground prior to flight.

Such instances include failure to ensure that a sufficient take-off run/distance is available relative to the type of ground surface and wind condition at the time.

A lack of navigation planning which has often led to pilots penetrating weather conditions beyond their capabilities, with a resulting loss of control.

Incorrect weight and balance calculations resulting in an overweight aircraft and/or one with the c.g. outside the permitted limits.

Engine failure due to fuel mismanagement which has resulted in an attempted forced landing, and during which the aircraft has stalled during the final approach.

These and many other similar instances have led to an eventual stall/spin accident and with such facts in mind all instructors must strive to develop a keen sense of awareness in their students to make them appreciate that practising 'set piece' stalls and recoveries in itself will not prevent the occurrence of inadvertent stalls.

Stalling

Long Briefing

STALL SPEEDS – MPH CAS			
Gross Weight 1600 lbs.	ANGLE OF BANK		
CONDITION		40°	60°
Flaps UP			
Flaps 20°			
Flaps 40°	48	54	
POWER OFF — AFT CG			

OBJECTIVES

The purpose of this exercise is to develop the student's ability to instinctively recognise an impending stall situation, and by thorough training prevent him from ever entering an inadvertent stall. The exercise should commence with a demonstration of the stall symptoms followed by the full stall and correct recovery method. Whilst it is appreciated that the student must eventually be able to recover from a stall with a minimum loss of altitude this can only be achieved as a result of practice; thus in the early stages the emphasis must be upon a positive recovery.

Entries to the stall must be practised with various power settings, aircraft configurations and attitudes, such as straight and level, climbing, descending and turning flight. Finally the main emphasis will be on recovering from a stall at the incipient stage.

INTRODUCTION

Stall training inevitably involves entering and recovering from developed stalls, but it must be appreciated that the final objective must be to achieve a state of competence in which the pilot will be most unlikely to enter an inadvertent stall.

Because many of the stalling incidents and accidents occur due to some form of pilot distraction, the instructor will introduce situations of this type at suitable times during the student's practice.

CHARACTERISTICS OF THE STALL

Lift obtained from a wing depends amongst other factors upon the smoothness of the airflow passing around it. As the angle of attack is increased the lift increases, until at a certain angle the boundary layer separates. At this stage the smooth streamline flow breaks down and becomes turbulent resulting in a large loss of lift and increase in drag. During this 'stalled flight' condition height will be lost and the aircraft nose normally drops.

Lift is defined as the net force developed at 90° to the relative airflow. It is an aerodynamic force which is generated by the pressure distribution on the wing and can be described by the following equation:

$$L = C_L qS$$
$$\text{Where } L = \text{lift (lbs)}$$
$$C_L = \text{lift coefficient}$$
$$q = \text{dynamic pressure (p.s.f.)}$$
$$= \tfrac{1}{2}\rho V^2$$
$$S = \text{wing surface area (sq.ft)}$$

The lift coefficient which is used in this equation is the ratio of the lift pressure and the dynamic pressure and is related to the shape of the wing and the angle of attack.

The aerodynamic characteristics of the wing can be shown by the curve of lift coefficient versus angle of attack. A typical curve is illustrated in fig. 10-4 for a specific aircraft in the clean and flap down configuration.

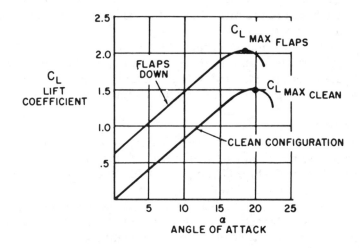

Fig. 10-4

It can be seen that the lift coefficient increases with angle of attack until a certain angle is reached (20° in the illustration). Any further increase in the angle of attack produces a stall condition and the lift coefficient then decreases. Since the maximum lift coefficient will correspond to the minimum speed of flight any controlled flight below this speed is impossible. The indications of the stall can therefore be related to a particular speed known as the 'stalling speed.'

It should be appreciated that apart from the use of flap, a particular aircraft will stall at the same angle of attack regardless of dynamic pressure, weight, load factor, etc. The stalling speed however will be affected by weight, load factor flap and other factors.

In level unaccelerated flight, the lift is just equal to the weight (thrust effects ignored) and at the stall the lift coefficient is maximum; therefore by transposing the basic lift equation and solving for velocity, the stalling speed can be found. The following summation illustrates the effect upon the stalling speed of weight and wing area (wing loading) maximum lift coefficient ($C_{L_{max}}$) and altitude:

$$V_S = \text{stalling speed} = \sqrt{\frac{2W}{\rho C_{L_{max}} S}}$$

Where V_S = stall speed (TAS)
  W = all-up weight (lbs)
  ρ = density
  S = wing area (sq. ft)

The actual stalling characteristics of an aircraft, including the stalling angle and airspeed will be affected by many factors such as:

1. The shape of the wing section (the thickness chord ratio and position of maximum thickness).
2. The planform of the wing including the aspect ratio.
3. The position of the horizontal tailplane.
4. The incorporation of wing washout, slats and slots.
5. The configuration, i.e. flap position.
6. The power being used at the stall.
7. Wing loading, (all-up weight) and the c.g. location.
8. The load factor.
9. The effectiveness of the controls at the stall.

THE EFFECTIVENESS OF THE CONTROLS AT THE STALL
The horizontal tailplane will normally remain in an unstalled condition when the mainplanes reach their critical angle. This is due to several factors which include the different wing section used for the tailplane i.e. a symmetrical shape, the lower angle of incidence at which it is set, the lower aspect ratio and the effect of the downwash direction from the mainplanes.

The effectiveness of the tailplane controls (elevators, stabilator and rudder) is dependent upon their surface area, aspect ratio, wing section, distance from the c.g. and c.p., and also their position in relation to the effect of downwash and slipstream. The pilot will vary the effect of these factors during normal flight operations by changing the angle of attack, airspeed, power setting and flap position.

Elevator Effectiveness

Although the design factors are not within the control of the pilot it is interesting to note that in relation to tailplane characteristics many modern aircraft have been designed with a limited upward travel of the elevators. This design feature is built in to reduce the possibility of an inadvertent stall if the controls are misused at low airspeeds. When such a feature is incorporated it can limit the forward position of the c.g. in which case a stabilator can be used instead of conventional elevators.

Claims made that particular aircraft are stallproof should be accepted with certain reservations, because regardless of limited up elevator or stabilator movement the effectiveness of the controls also depends upon airspeed, and at higher speeds the pitch controls are quite capable of bringing an aircraft to the stalling angle of attack (dynamic stall). Of interest in this respect is the fact that when modern light aircraft are gradually brought to the stalling angle there comes a time when the airspeed has been reduced sufficiently to prevent the limited effectiveness of the controls bringing the mainplanes to the critical angle, and as a result no positive drop of the nose will occur. The degree and suddenness of the nose dropping at the stall is dependent upon the rate at which the stalling angle is approached, in that a rapid (dynamic) entry will cause the wings to pass without pause through the stalling angle of attack, which will create a very positive stall due to the greater loss of lift which in turn produces the positive pitch-down action.

Fig. 10-5

Approaching a stall slowly can therefore produce a quasi stall followed by the aircraft entering a stalled condition in a level attitude and during which height is rapidly lost. Figure 10-5 shows the change of airflow direction which creates a technically stalled condition of flight in which the elevators are still strong enough to maintain the aircraft in a fairly level attitude and prevent the nose dropping. If this situation occurs the pilot must not be deceived by the aircraft attitude as it is in a condition of stalled flight from which normal recovery action must be taken before safe flight can be resumed.

Aileron Effectiveness

As stated earlier, during the approach to the stall all three flying controls begin to lose their effectiveness and the aircraft is slower to respond to control movements. However at the stall most modern light aircraft and indeed some older ones have a degree of aileron effectiveness, the amount of which is dependent upon certain design features. In order to obtain certification all modern light aircraft have to demonstrate aileron capability to control roll at the stall, and as a result in certain conditions it will be possible to hold the wings level or even raise a dropped wing by the use of aileron at the stall.

The action of using aileron following a wing drop at the stall is nevertheless a hazard because this aileron capability can only be relied upon should the stall occur with flaps up and power off. If the stall occurs with flap down and/or power on, the use of ailerons will have little or no effect and may even induce a worsening wing drop situation due to the increased mean effective angle of attack on the dropping wing. The dropping wing automatically increases its angle of attack (see fig. 10-6(a)) and together with the lowering of aileron in an attempt to raise the wing (see fig. 10-6(b)) will combine to increase the mean angle of attack still further. This will lead to a more developed stall of the dropped wing, possibly causing autorotation to occur particularly if the aircraft is being flown with an aft c.g.

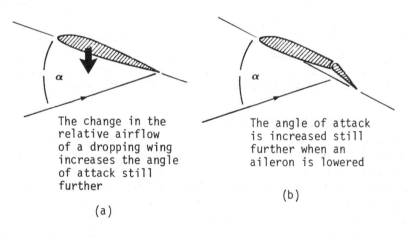

The change in the relative airflow of a dropping wing increases the angle of attack still further

(a)

The angle of attack is increased still further when an aileron is lowered

(b)

Fig. 10-6

The usual flight phases where flap and/or power are being used with a low airspeed occur near the ground during the approach to land, and the 'go round again' situation, or immediately after take-off. In all these cases the height needed for stall recovery is at a premium. It is for this reason that although during the practice of stalling all three controls are permitted to be used in the normal sense during the approach to the stall, the use of ailerons must be excluded from the stall recovery action. Any rolling tendency leading to yaw during the stall must be counteracted by the use of rudder. Rudder should not however be used to roll the wings level, and as will be seen later the amount of rudder needed to roll the wings level could cause a spin to develop.

Rudder Effectiveness

The rudder is affected by change of airspeed in the same way as the elevators and ailerons and when the mainplanes are at a high angle of attack the flow separation of the fuselage boundary layer in the vicinity of the tailplane will also reduce the effectiveness of the vertical stabiliser. However this latter effect is normally quite small on light aircraft of conventional design.

Regardless of how low the airspeed becomes during flight the rudder will remain unstalled because its angle of attack is related to the vertical plane. Therefore, although it will have less effect at low airspeeds it will continue to function throughout the stall. Because of this it is a valuable means of counteracting any development of yaw and further wing dropping at the stall. Care should be taken to avoid using larger rudder movement than is necessary because if excess rudder is used it can create a yaw and possible autorotation in the opposite direction to the original yaw. Autorotation is covered more fully during the Long Briefing on spinning but at this stage it can be described as a condition of flight during which the aircraft has a tendency to continually rotate about the longitudinal axis due to a marked variation of lift between the left and right wings.

FACTORS AFFECTING THE STALLING SPEED

The speed at which the stall occurs can vary, but as the angle of attack of the wings cannot be observed, speed is the only means of guidance as to when the stall will occur. The speed will vary dependent upon the particular aircraft type and its condition of flight, and provided this is understood there need be no confusion. The basic stalling speed of an aircraft means the speed at which the aircraft will stall from level flight with the throttle closed, flaps up and the control column being moved gently back until the stall occurs.

For any particular aircraft the stalling speed will vary according to its all-up weight, the manoeuvre being performed (load factor effect), the amount of power being used and the position of the flaps. These factors are summarised as follows:

● The Flaps – With the flaps lowered, the lift coefficient of the wings is increased. Therefore the speed required to maintain sufficient lift for level flight is less than when the flaps are up. Thus the stalling speed is correspondingly reduced.

The incorporation of slats or slots on the aircraft wings can produce a similar effect to the stalling speed.

● The Power – When an aircraft has power on, the stalling speed will be lower. This is because the thrust will be inclined upwards and so contribute to lift. In addition, in propeller driven aircraft the slipstream gives a faster airflow over the wings and helps to prevent the airflow becoming turbulent, as well as providing more lift. The slipstream will also modify the angle of attack of the centre section of the wing.

● The Weight – If extra weight is carried, greater lift will be needed to maintain the aircraft in level flight. Therefore, at all angles of attack including the stalling angle, more airspeed will be needed to provide the greater lift. In other words the stalling speed will be higher.

The location of the centre of gravity will also have an effect on the aircraft's stalling speed due to changes in the aerodynamic download on the tailplane.

● The Load Factor – In a turn the lift must be increased in order to maintain level flight, therefore the load factor and the stalling speed will be higher. Sudden accelerations in pitch will also increase the load factor and this is most noticeable when pulling out of a dive. During this manoeuvre the inertia of the aircraft prevents it from immediately following the new flight path suggested by the new attitude, and the angle of attack is thus momentarily increased. This type of manoeuvre can raise the stalling speed by a considerable amount.

The Effects of Flap
When trailing edge flaps are lowered there will be an increase in the maximum lift coefficient and a change in the angle of attack at which the maximum lift coefficient is achieved. Typical figures being:

Configuration	$C_{L_{max}}$	Angle for $C_{L_{max}}$
Flaps up	1.5	20°
Flaps down	2.0	18.5°

As a result of this the stalling speed will be reduced by a certain value in relation to the increase in $C_{L_{max}}$ because an increased lift coefficient will require a lesser angle of attack for any given amount of lift, or stated another way the same lift can be obtained with a lesser airspeed at a given angle of attack, for example:

Increase in $C_{L_{max}}$	Reduction in Stall Speed
2%	1%
10%	5%
50%	18%

The amount of reduction in stalling speed will depend among other factors upon the particular aircraft, the all-up weight and the amount of flap used.

The use of flap will also affect the symptoms leading up to the stall and also the lateral stability and responsiveness of the flying controls. Lowering flap will normally have a small adverse effect on lateral stability and as a result upon aileron effectiveness. Whilst this has no practical significance when the aircraft is flown at normal speeds it can have considerable importance in the region of the stall.

Figure 10-7 shows the lateral lift envelope over the wing together with the lateral centres of pressure. The position of these lateral centres of pressure will affect the lateral stability of the aircraft and the closer they become to the fuselage the weaker becomes the stability. Partial span trailing edge flaps have a detrimental effect because their use moves the lateral centres of pressure inboard reducing the effective moment arm $\bar{\gamma}$.

Fig. 10-7

Therefore although the values of the lift change will be the same about each wing, the rolling moment introduced by dihedral is decreased. The greater the effectiveness of the flaps in producing an increase in lift coefficient the greater will be the change in lateral lift distribution and the more detrimental will be the effect upon the aircraft lateral stability.

When a reduced lateral stability exists, a wing which drops will tend to drop faster and further, and the ailerons will have to be more effective to counteract this motion. However as aileron response is affected by airspeed and the airspeed at the stall is lower when flaps are down, the aileron power is less, and larger deflection angles will be necessary. Under these circumstances the lowered aileron will probably create a sufficient increase in the mean angle of attack of the downgoing wing to stall it still further, causing autorotation to occur.

Because of these effects the ailerons should never be used during the early stages of the stall recovery. Further to this effect of a lower stalling speed when flaps are down, there will also be a change in the downwash path over the tailplane which will make both the elevators and rudder less responsive. Therefore a larger and more positive movement of the elevators and rudder will be necessary to unstall the aircraft early to prevent a large yaw occurring in the event of a wing dropping.

The Incorporation of Wing Washout, Slats or Slots

An important design consideration is the need to prevent the outer section of the wing from stalling first. If the outer section is first to stall then a sharp wing drop can occur leading to autorotation.

In order to reduce the tendency for a wing to drop at the stall the designer can incorporate one or more basic design features such as washout, leading edge spoilers (stall strips), wing slats or slots. As stated earlier the actual stalling angle of a wing will depend upon the shape of the wing section and the aspect ratio. The lower the aspect ratio the higher will be the stalling angle, for example delta wing sections (low aspect ratio) can have stalling angles of over 30°. However most of the current light training aircraft such as the Beagle Pup, Cessna 150/172, Cherokee 140, Robin series and others have a stalling angle of 20°.

On a rectangular wing the airflow separation at the stall usually starts at the root and moves outwards with a further increase in angle of attack. This produces a satisfactory stalling chracteristic since only small rolling moments take place, and during power off flight in the clean configuration with a load factor of 1, the effectiveness of the ailerons is retained at the stall. However when the use of a rectangular wing conflicts with other design philosophies or requirements then two different types of wing section having different stalling angles can be combined. The part of the wing with the higher stalling angle is used for the outboard section, and this will result in the inboard section of the wing stalling first and also permit aileron effectiveness (control in roll) to be present at the stall.

Another method is to incorporate washout, which is a design feature providing a twisting of the wing section along its span to produce a smaller angle of incidence at the outboard sections, so that the wing root reaches the stalling angle earlier than the wing tips. Washout angles are normally of the value of 1° to 3°.

angle of
washout

Fig. 10-8

On some aircraft, design requirements favour the use of leading edge spoilers, these are often called anti-spin or stall strips. They are attached to the leading edges of the inboard wing sections and at high angles of attack disrupt the smooth flow of air and cause the inboard sections to stall before the wing tips.

leading edge
spoiler

Fig. 10-9

A further design feature which can reduce the tendency for a wing to drop at the stall is the incorporation of slats or slots. Slats are moveable surfaces which can be manually or automatically operated at low speed. Slots perform the same function but are built in as an integral part of the wing. When slats or slots are fitted along the leading edge section of the wing they will increase the stalling angle of attack of that section of the wing directly behind them and therefore when incorporated along the outboard wing sections they will assist in reducing the stalling speed and also in delaying any tendency for a wing to drop at the stall. Due to the lower stalling speeds achieved when slats or slots are used the controls will be slightly less effective at the stall and will need to be used more positively during stall recovery.

slat

Fig. 10-10

The Power being used at the Stall

An entry to the stall with power on will produce a lower stalling speed and effectively change the stall characteristics. At high angles of attack the direction of the thrust line has a significant vertical component as shown in fig. 10-11(a). This vertical component of thrust will produce a small increment to the total lift produced by the wing and will therefore reduce the stalling speed by a small amount.

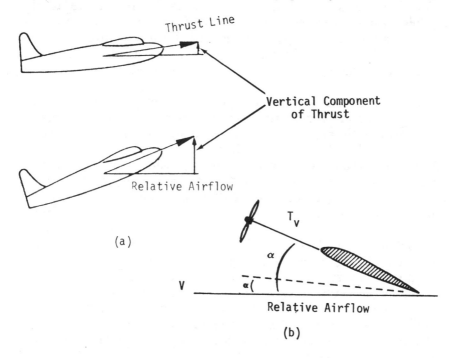

Fig. 10-11

The angle of attack of the inboard wing sections will also be modified by the airflow within the slipstream cylinder. In fig. 10-11 (b) V represents the normal airflow and T_v the airflow produced by the propeller thrust.

The resultant of these two airflows is indicated by the dotted line. Since the thrust available with a propeller driven aircraft increases with decrease of speed it is seen that the resultant airflow line will move closer towards the thrust line T_v as power is increased and forward speed decreased.

Therefore the greatest effect of T_v on the normal airflow direction will occur at the stall. When these conditions apply the angle of attack of the wing sections within the slipstream diameter will be decreased and the outboard wing sections may stall first, a condition which is more severe if the flaps are down. This change in the angle of attack can be quite significant and as a result may overcome the effect of washout or other design features which have been incorporated to prevent the wing tips stalling first.

A further effect of slipstream is the additional energy derived from the increased velocity of airflow over the wing sections behind the propeller. This added energy will produce more lift from the mainplanes and also lead to an increased effectiveness of the tailplane and associated elevator and rudder controls. The ailerons, being outside the slipstream influence will be less effective at the lower stalling speed and control in roll may no longer be possible, and if used under these conditions may produce an adverse yaw leading to autorotation.

A final and adverse effect of slipstream can occur when an aircraft yaws at the stall. Figure 10-12 shows that due to yaw the propeller slipstream is not aligned to the longitudinal axis and as the dynamic pressure in the slipstream is higher than in the free stream, the lift from the starboard wing in this case is greater than from the port wing. However the resultant effect of the slipstream influence is difficult to predict, as the angle of attack and amount of lift variation to each wing will change due to yaw, sideslip angle and slipstream path. The interaction of these effects could be such that if an aircraft is temporarily held at the stall, an oscillatory motion of alternate wing dropping may occur. This explanation may seem academic but it could have a very practical implication. If the control column is not moved forward sufficiently to unstall the aircraft, and rudder used to oppose the yaw, the application of rudder could coincide with the moment when the wing drops in the direction of the rudder applied. This action by the pilot may induce a flick or similar manoeuvre leading to a spin entry.

Fig. 10-12

To sum up, if an aircraft is stalled with power on the elevators and rudder will be more effective, but a rapid wing drop may occur which is normally aggravated if the flaps are down. Prompt recovery action will therefore be necessary to prevent the aircraft rolling into an acute bank angle at a time when height is being lost.

Wing Loading, All-up Weight and C.G. Location

During level flight the total weight of the aircraft must be balanced by the total lift produced. The lift varies with the angle of attack and airspeed and at any angle of attack a certain airspeed will achieve the required amount of lift. Figure 10-13 shows the same aircraft at different weights but identical angles of attack.

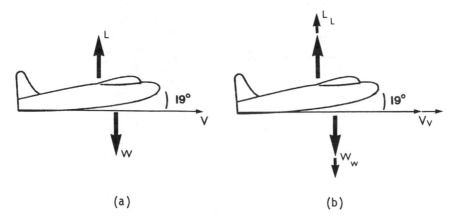

(a) (b)

Fig. 10-13

In order to supply the added lift to balance the added weight at (b) the aircraft will have to fly faster. Assuming the critical angle of attack (stalling angle) is 20° and the actual angle of attack in the illustration is 19° it can be seen that the heavier aircraft will stall at a higher speed.

Many specific conditions of flight are achieved at certain fixed angles of attack and lift coefficients. The effect of weight as a percentage of an airspeed for any specific lift coefficient and angle of attack is identical. It can for example be seen from fig. 10-14 that a 10% increase of weight increases the basic stalling speed by 5%. Taking the case of a small aircraft whose permitted all-up weight is 1150 kg. (2540 lbs) and assuming a figure of 810 kg. (1780 lbs) for the basic weight and variable load, then the disposable load will be 340 kg. (750 lbs). 340 kg. expressed as a percentage of 1150 kg. is approximately 30%. Reference to fig. 10-14 shows that a 30% increase in weight will produce an increase in the stalling speed of approximately 15%. Assuming a basic stall speed of 50 m.p.h. at 810 kg. then the stall speed at 1150 kg. will be 57.5 m.p.h. During flight under normal circumstances an increased stalling speed of this order will entail no hazard but during take-off or landing this will become significant to the safety of the aircraft and the lift-off and approach speeds adjusted accordingly.

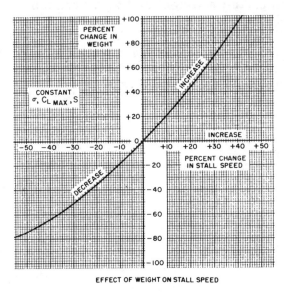

EFFECT OF WEIGHT ON STALL SPEED

Fig. 10-14

Location of the C.G.

When an aircraft is in level flight with the normal arrangement of couples due to Lift and Weight, Thrust and Drag as illustrated in fig. 6-3 there will normally be a download on the tailplane. This download will be greater with a forward c.g. and smaller with an aft c.g. Figure 10-15 shows a comparison of the lift required to balance the total weight. At (a) it is assumed that no download is present but at (b) the download required to counteract the nose-down pitch moment produced by the L/W couple must be counteracted by additional lift from the mainplane. This means that for any angle of attack extra speed will be required to balance the physical weight of the aircraft and any required force of aerodynamic download. At the stalling angle the airspeed will be higher by an amount proportional to the amount of download (negative lift on the tailplane).

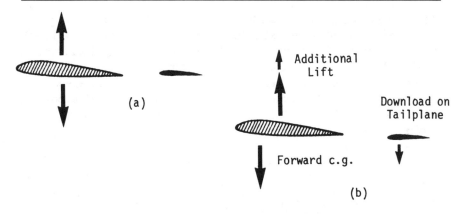

Fig. 10-15

Forward movement of the c.g. will increase the strength of the nose-down couple between lift and weight and as a result increase the amount of download required on the tailplane. In effect this increase of download is similar to an increase of weight and therefore a forward c.g. will lead to an increase of stalling speed and an aft c.g. to a reduction of stalling speed. However as the permitted range of the c.g. position is fairly small the amount of change to the stalling speed is also fairly small. If the c.g. limits are exceeded the change in stalling speed will become significant.

The Effect of Load Factor
During turning flight and manoeuvres the effect on stall speed is similar to the effect of weight. A steady level turn requires the vertical component of lift to be equal to the weight of the aircraft and the horizontal component of lift to be equal to the centripetal force. Therefore in a steady turn the aircraft has to develop more lift than its weight. The relationship between bank angle and load factor has been covered during the Long Briefing on medium turns and can be expressed as follows:

$$n = \frac{L}{W}$$

$$= \frac{1}{\cos \phi}$$

where n = load factor ('G')

cos φ = cosine of the bank angle.

At a given speed at constant height the angle of attack must be increased to produce the extra lift necessary to support the aircraft, therefore the stalling speed will be higher in a turn and this increase of stalling speed will become greater with increase of bank angle. Figure 10-16 shows the percentage increase of stalling speed in a steady level turn and because it applies to a steady turn at a constant maximum coefficient of lift, it will be valid for any aircraft at any speed.

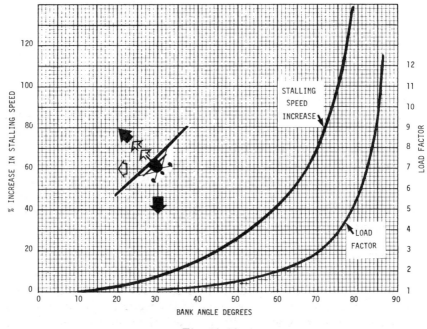

Fig. 10-16

The important information gained from this illustration is that whereas no significant change occurs to the stalling speed at moderate angles of bank such as up to 30°, the increase of load factor at 45° and above causes marked increases in stalling speeds. This clearly shows the need to avoid steep bank angles or sharp pull-ups at low speeds when the aircraft is near the ground, such as immediately after take-off or during the approach to landing phase.

THE EFFECT OF UNBALANCE AT THE STALL
When a condition of unbalance is occurring at the stall the aircraft will have a natural tendency to drop a wing and enter the incipient stage of a spin. The rate at which a wing will drop in these circumstances will depend upon the aerodynamic characteristics of a

particular aircraft. Most modern training aircraft, when operating in the utility category, have a centre of gravity which is fairly well forward, and this often results in a wing dropping at a sluggish rate. Nevertheless the same aircraft can have a very marked rate of wing drop when the centre of gravity is in an aft position, such as when passengers are carried in the rear seats.

THE SYMPTOMS OF THE STALL

The air exercise of stalling will commence by an introduction to the stall with the power off and the flaps up. This short period will be used to show the student the change in aircraft attitude during the stall and to acquaint him with the physical sensations which will be felt during the practice of stalls. Following this, the symptoms of the stall should be demonstrated by slowly approaching the stall condition. These symptoms will be as follows:

● A lowering of the airspeed, when the throttle is closed and the aircraft held in the approximately level attitude.

● A reduced response from all three controls as the airspeed becomes lower.

● If a stall warning device is fitted (aural warning or flashing light) this will commence to operate some 5 to 10 kts before the stall is reached.

● A buffet may sometimes be felt over the elevators as the smooth airflow breaks away and becomes turbulent over the inboard wing sections. Note: This may not occur with all aircraft when in the clean configuration with power off, but is usually present to some degree when a stall occurs with flap down and power on.

● The final symptom occurs at the stall itself and is a condition where height is lost and/or the nose drops even though the control column is held well back or even fully back.

STALL RECOGNITION AND RECOVERY

To recover from a stall it is necessary to reduce the angle of attack until it is below the angle at which the stall occurred. This reduction in the angle of attack can be made by moving the control column forward and applying power. These actions will change the flight path of the aircraft and therefore the relative airflow which will now meet the aircraft at an angle less than the stalling angle of attack.

The object of the air lessons is to teach the student to recognise the approach to the stall and eventually to be capable of recovery with a minimum loss of height. Recovery is normally made by moving the control column forward and at the same time increasing the power. The student must appreciate that even at full power the forward acceleration of the aircraft from a stalled condition is relatively slow and it will be difficult to increase speed, regain control and maintain height simultaneously. Therefore a small lag in regaining airspeed has to be accepted.

It is possible to increase airspeed and regain control rapidly by moving the control column a long way forward putting the aircraft into a dive, but this would involve a large loss of height. Two important aspects of stall training will therefore concern:

● The recognition of the stall symptoms and the taking of early recovery action before the full stall occurs, and the recovery from a stalled condition during which the minimum amount of height is lost.

This latter aspect means moving the control column sufficiently far forward to unstall the wings whilst at the same time applying full power. In cases where a stall occurs with a large power setting already in use, there may be no great advantage in further increase of power during the recovery.

The minimum amount of height lost will be determined by the amount of forward control column movement and the rate and amount of power applied. However it is important to strike the right balance between the desire to achieve a minimum height loss recovery and the achievement of a positive recovery, because if the control column is not moved forward sufficiently an adverse condition can occur leading to a marked wing drop and possible autorotation.

In the case of a stall in which a wing drops, the correct recovery action is to incorporate sufficient rudder application, integrated with the normal recovery actions already described. With modern aircraft the positive stall in the clean configuration normally occurs with the nose fairly high in relation to the natural horizon and in this attitude the ability to detect yaw at an early stage is reduced. In these circumstances the yaw can be more easily recognised through the direction of the dropping wing.

The previous paragraph must not be interpreted as meaning that stalls will only occur when the aircraft is in a high nose attitude. It must be understood that the attitude of an aircraft relative to the horizon bears no fixed relationship to the stalling angle of attack. An aircraft can in fact stall in any attitude relative to the horizon because it is the direction of relative airflow which determines the angle of attack for any condition of flight. For example, if the throttle is closed and the aircraft held in the level flight attitude it will commence to sink and the airflow will come up from below. This can produce a critical angle of attack even though the aircraft is in the level flight attitude. Similarly the aircraft can be made to stall in a climb, descent or a turn, in fact at any time the wings are being presented at too large an angle to the relative airflow.

Recovery Without Power

This is the first stall recovery demonstration and it will be made by the use of the elevators alone. The stall will be entered from a power off condition with the flaps up. At the stall the control column must be moved sufficiently forward to unstall the aircraft and at the same time the ailerons must be kept in the neutral position and rudder applied if needed to prevent yaw.

The purpose of providing practice at stall entry and recovery in this manner is twofold:

It permits the student to see clearly that forward movement of the control column is the basic recovery action and one which is completely effective.

It provides for a fairly gentle type of stall and one in which only a small amount of yaw normally occurs. Therefore the complication of integrating positive rudder pressure will not normally be necessary.

Once the student has grasped the procedure involved and can effect positive recoveries using this method the instructor will point out the loss of height incurred and the procedure whereby stall recovery is effected by the combined use of elevators and power will be introduced.

Recovery With Power

Although a recovery from the stall by the use of elevators alone is completely effective it does nevertheless involve an unnecessary loss of height. Therefore a better method is to smoothly apply full power at the same time as the control column is moved forward. Apart from reducing the height lost the use of power will also increase the effectiveness of the elevators and rudder.

This second part of the stall recovery demonstration will commence with the stall entry being made with the throttle closed and the flaps up. At the stall the control column should be moved forward, the throttle fully but smoothly opened and any yaw controlled by the use of rudder. Two basic differences will occur during this recovery:

The control column will not need to be moved so far forward as with the power off recovery but a strong nose up movement in pitch due to the application of power will have to be counteracted.

The use of power will also induce yaw, and a more positive use of rudder will be needed to maintain balance.

The initial practice of this method of recovery will be concerned more with reducing the height loss rather than attempting to recover with a minimum loss of height. Later and as practice continues with recoveries from stalls in various flight situations the emphasis will gradually be transferred to effecting recoveries with the smallest possible loss of height.

Recovery when a Wing Drops

If a wing drops at the stall it will stop going down at the same moment as the aircraft is unstalled. Following this the ailerons and rudder can be used in co-ordination to return the wings to the laterally level condition. When stall recovery is promptly and correctly effected the aircraft will only be stalled for a matter of two or three seconds, therefore there is no great need to react violently to the yaw caused by the dropping wing. However when entry to the stall is made with power on or flap down it will be necessary to take prompt and positive recovery action as delay can cause the aircraft to roll into steep angles at a time when height is being lost quite rapidly.

At first difficulty will be experienced in holding the ailerons neutral when a wing drops at the stall. This is a natural action following many hours of correct and instinctive use of ailerons to control the lateral level of the aircraft. Nevertheless the automatic reaction to use ailerons at the stall must be suppressed. The basic reason for this is that by the end of his training a pilot must have learned an automatic and instinctive recovery action to the stall, regardless of where and under what flight conditions it occurs.

Aircraft which are inadvertently stalled at height rarely appear in accident statistics. This is because height is available for a recovery to be effected even though it may take a little time. It should be appreciated that most stalling accidents occur when the aircraft is near the ground at the time of the inadvertent stall. Under these circumstances the aircraft is most likely to be on the approach to a landing, going round again or climbing out following a take-off, when the speed will be low and the aircraft in a condition where it is under power and possibly with flap down.

Referring back to the aileron effectiveness at the stall it is under these circumstances that the ailerons could fail to produce the expected effect, or worse, they could adversely affect the stall characteristics. The consequences of using aileron in this case are obvious and it is only training which will ensure that a pilot avoids using aileron and effects a prompt and efficient recovery from this situation.

STALL ENTRY WITH POWER ON

A moderate power setting should be used during the introduction to power-on stalls. Later, and as proficiency increases, higher power settings can be used. The stall entry and standard recovery action remains unchanged but the student should note the higher nose attitude and the probable tendency for a wing to drop rapidly. During power-on stalls the slipstream effect at low speed produces a fairly critical condition of unbalance which is not easily corrected, and even a momentary yaw at the stall will result in a wing dropping.

Power-on stalls should be practised from level, climbing, descending and turning flight. The entry to the stall should normally be fairly gradual and made without rapid control movements or sudden control pressures. In this way the student will be able more accurately to determine the exact point of stall and to effect prompt recovery. As the student's proficiency increases, dynamic stall entries can be practised to cover those flight conditions when sudden manoeuvres are likely to be carried out. (Normally covered in Advanced Turns.)

The following characteristics will be noted during stall entries with power on:

A higher nose attitude at the stall.

A more positive tendency for a wing to drop.

A lower stalling speed.

If prompt recovery action is taken a smaller height loss will be incurred.

Note: In some aircraft the air speed indicator may suffer larger than normal errors at the lower speed associated with the power-on stall and it may not be possible to note accurately the difference between the power off and the power on stalling speeds.

STALL ENTRY WITH FLAP DOWN

Entry to and recovery from the stall with the flaps down and power off is an important part of the stalling exercise. This configuration is most commonly used during the approach to land where height will be critical should an inadvertent stall occur.

The two main differences to be noted during this stall entry will be the increased rate at which the airspeed lowers and the reduced effectiveness of the controls due to a lower stalling speed. For reasons stated earlier the lateral stability of the aircraft decreases with the flaps lowered and the controls begin to lose their effectiveness earlier, though they will still be sufficiently effective to control the aircraft in the normal way to that point where the stall occurs.

The standard stall recovery should be used, but forward control column movement and any rudder action used to counteract yaw will need to be larger and more positive than when recovering from a stall in the clean condition. Full power must be introduced promptly to avoid a large height loss, but continued forward movement of the control column may be necessary to counteract the pitch up moment which could lead to the occurrence of a secondary stall.

The stall entry will first be taught from a level attitude with power off and in this flight condition it may be difficult to produce a positive stall during which the nose pitches down. This is due to the reduced effectiveness of the elevators at the lower airspeed and the changed direction of the downwash from the mainplanes. In these circumstances it will be necessary to make a dynamic stall entry (a faster rate of entry) so as to obtain a clearer indication of the stall during the initial practice. Thereafter slower rates of entry can be made and recovery effected at that time when the control column reaches the fully aft position. Even though no pronounced drop of the nose has occurred the descent rate of the aircraft will be such that at the time when the control column reaches the aft position the aircraft will be in a technically stalled condition.

The following characteristics will be noted during stalls with the flaps down:

A lower nose attitude at the stall.
A slightly increased tendency for a wing to drop.
A lower stalling speed.
A quicker recovery can be effected but coarser movements of the controls will be required.

UNCOMPENSATED YAW AT HIGH POWER
The tendency to drop a wing is directly related to an unbalanced condition and this demonstration is included in the syllabus in order to show a student how power affects the balance of an aircraft when it is flying at a low airspeed. Should an aircraft be flown in an unbalanced condition at low speed the tendency to enter the incipient stage of a spin can be very strong and the purpose of showing this effect at a high power setting is to reinforce this knowledge and ensure that the student is fully aware of the consequences.

STALLS AT HIGHER SPEEDS
The type of stalls referred to under this heading are basically manoeuvre stalls, e.g. from turns or pull-ups and these are more appropriately covered in the air exercise Advanced Turning. Nevertheless aircraft can be induced to stall during normal turning flight at shallow and moderate bank angles, therefore stalling in the turn must be introduced and practised prior to the first solo flight.

The method of practising a stall and recovery during a turn is to set a low cruising power and enter a normal medium turn. Allow the natural decrease of speed to occur and then gently raise the nose to decrease the speed still further (a slight increase in bank may be used to assist the speed to decrease). At this stage, and whilst maintaining the bank angle, ease the control column back in one continuous movement until the aircraft stalls. This backward movement of the control column should be positive but not violent.

During a turn a wing will normally drop at the point of stall and this becomes the most easily recognised stall feature. An immediate unstalling of the wings will be achieved by a positive forward movement of the control column. The elevators, ailerons and rudder are then used in the normal way to complete the recovery and return the aircraft to straight and level flight.

SECONDARY STALLS

Throughout the practise of stalls the student must learn to appreciate the danger of an insufficient forward movement of the control column during the recovery or moving the control column back too quickly before recovery is properly effected. Either of these actions might occur because of the desire to achieve a minimum height loss recovery, and the result in either case will be a secondary stall. In this situation the power will have been fully applied and the rearward position of the control column coupled with the pitch-up moment due to power will lead to a very sharp stall condition from which the aircraft may yaw and roll rapidly into a state of autorotation leading to a spin, or at best considerable height may be lost before further recovery action can be applied.

STALLING IN THE APPROACH CONFIGURATION

This section of the stalling exercise consists of entering the stall with flap down and power on. It essentially simulates the normal approach-to-land condition and the purpose of introducing it as a training exercise is mainly to ensure the student learns to appreciate the necessary amount and rate of control movement to achieve a rapid recovery. The characteristics at the stall in this flight condition will be a combination of those already experienced during the individual power-on and flap-down stalls and recoveries.

It is in this particular condition that a wing may drop very rapidly and if it occurred near the ground a strong degree of self discipline would be needed to avoid using the ailerons and in moving the control column sufficiently far forward to effect a prompt recovery. Stalls in the approach configuration should be practised from straight and turning descents, with and without power and with various amounts of flap selected.

STALL AWARENESS AND AVOIDANCE, RECOVERY AT THE INCIPIENT STAGE

The definition 'Incipient Stall' relates to that flight condition just preceding the actual stall. Although a pilot can be trained to recover from a stall and lose a minimum of height in the process, such a recovery will be of no value if the height available at the time is insufficient for recovery to be completed before the aircraft reaches the ground. Such a situation could occur during the final stages of an approach to landing, during the 'go round again' situation, or immediately after the take-off.

Therefore the student's objective during stalling practice is to develop the instinctive ability to recognise the approach of a stall and return the aircraft to a safe flight condition before a stall actually occurs. This action will require the co-ordinated use of the flying controls and unless the aircraft is already in a descent, this recovery when successfully accomplished will involve no loss of height.

The method of practising this exercise will be to set the aircraft up in slow flight at a particular configuration and power setting. The speed should then be reduced to a stage where any further backward movement of the control column would cause a stall to develop. At this point recovery should be initiated by gentle forward pressure on the control column and the smooth application of power. These recoveries are practised from level, climbing, descending and turning flight with different configurations and power settings.

An extension to the practice of stall recovery and one which aids the development of a pilot's ability to maintain control at low speeds, is to approach the stall and recover at the incipient stage whilst flap is being lowered or raised. This generally adds to the workload during the recognition and recovery stages, and therefore provides additional training. Such stall situations should include the approach to the stall in various flight attitudes and with different power settings.

AIRMANSHIP

Prior to and during the practice of the stalling exercise the application of airmanship will assume a greater degree of importance. During stalling periods the aircraft will be frequently losing height, and the heading is unlikely to remain constant. Following each stall a climbing turn will normally be employed to regain altitude, and to ensure the area below and to either side remains clear of other aircraft. Throughout the exercise the student will have to direct his attention to several factors of aircraft handling and instrument indications. He will also need to review frequently the orientation of the aircraft in relation to cloud, ground reference features, and possibly controlled airspace.

These airmanship items are many and varied, and their implementation by a systematic procedure and a simple mnemonic is necessary. Although there are several such mnemonics in use, the word HASELL has been selected in this case to amplify one procedure. This particular procedure incorporates all the relevant airmanship items as follows:

H Height, sufficient for entry to and recovery from the stall above 3000 feet above ground level. An allowance must be made when the area QNH is used.

A Airframe, as required for the particular stalling practice, e.g. flaps up or down, landing gear position and brakes off (if applicable).

S Security, loose articles stowed, e.g. maps, kneeboards, fire extinguisher secure etc. Harness tight and heading indicator caged (if applicable).

E En-route checks and engine considerations. The time spent during individual stall training periods normally occupies from 10 to 20 minutes and it will therefore be necessary to carry out the following checks at intervals – ammeter and suction gauge readings, fuel state and where applicable fuel pressure readings, engine oil temperature and pressure observations and mixture control position etc.

On completion of the stalling exercise the heading indicator should be re-synchronised with the magnetic compass.

L Location, the student must ensure that stalls are not carried out over large towns, or in the close vicinity of active airfields or controlled airspace.

L Lookout, a careful lookout must be made before each stall entry and it will be necessary to turn the aircraft to ensure the area all round and below is clear of other air traffic.

Note: When clearing the area it is not essential to carry out continuous turns through 360 degrees. It is however vital to ensure the area in the immediate vicinity and below the aircraft remains clear of other aircraft. To this end, and bearing in mind the need to stay clear of towns, airfields etc, any combination of turn direction and length of turn may be employed.

PRE-FLIGHT BRIEFING

STALLING
Demonstration 1.

Aim
To familiarise you with the symptoms and characteristics of the basic stall and to teach you the standard recovery.

What
A condition of flight in which the aircraft is flown to an angle of attack at which a large loss of lift occurs. In this stalled condition the nose may pitch down and (regardless of pitch attitude) height will be lost.

Airmanship
The vital checks and drills which must be completed prior to the practise of stalling can be remembered by the use of a mnemonic (HASELL or alternative) which must cover Height above the surface, Airframe, Security, En-route and Engine Checks, Location and Lookout.

How
The Symptoms – When the safety checks have been completed, select HOT air (if applicable) close the throttle and maintain a level attitude in pitch. NOTE: The lowering airspeed, less responsive controls, stall warning indications (aural, light or buffet). Finally, even though the control column is held back a loss of height occurs and the nose may drop.

Recovery using the Elevators
Safety Checks – Completed.
Maintaining lateral level and balance enter the stall.

Recovery: Holding the ailerons neutral move the control column forward to unstall the wings (note the nose attitude).

After the recovery is completed return to the level flight condition.

Student practice.

Repeat the recovery demonstration and note the stalling speed and height loss.

In order to reduce the height loss the use of power will be necessary.

Recovery using Elevators and Power
Safety Checks – Completed.
Maintaining lateral level and balance enter the stall.

Recovery: Holding the ailerons neutral move the control column forward to unstall the wings. At the same time smoothly apply full power and correct yaw by the use of rudder.
Return to the level flight condition.

Student practice.

Repeat the recovery demonstration and note the reduced height loss.

Student practice – as required.

The Standard Recovery
Safety Checks – Completed.
The procedure in event of a wing dropping at the moment of stall.

Note: If necessary a small amount of power can be used on entry to make this demonstration more effective.

If balance is not maintained during the entry, a wing may drop at the stall.

Recovery: Holding the ailerons neutral move the control column forward and apply full power. At the same time use rudder to prevent further yaw.

When the aircraft unstalls use all controls in the normal way to return to level flight.

Student practice.

PRE-FLIGHT BRIEFING

STALLING
Demonstration 2.

Aim   To introduce you to the stalling characteristics when power is on and/or flap is down. This period will also be used to extend your practice of stall recoveries.

What   An extension of the stalling exercise which will include recoveries from stalls entered with various power and flap settings. Recoveries will be practised from the positive stall.

Airmanship   All normal airmanship considerations will apply and the relevant safety checks will be completed prior to each stall.

How   *The Power-On Entry and Recovery(a)*
Safety Checks. Set power required and enter the stall.
External observations:
     Higher nose attitude at the stall.
     Greater tendency for a wing to drop.
Standard recovery.
Safety checks. Set power required and enter the stall.
Further observations:
     Lower stalling speed. With prompt recovery the wing
     drop is controlled and the height loss is small.
Standard recovery.   Student practice.

The Flap-Down Entry and Recovery (b)
Safety Checks. Select flap required. Enter a power-off stall.
External observations:
     Lower nose attitude at the stall.
     A wing drop may be more pronounced than for a clean
     stall.
Standard recovery. (Avoid exceeding the flap limiting
speed.)
Safety Checks. Enter the stall with flap down and power
off.
Further observations:
     From the level attitude the airspeed reduces more
     quickly.
Stall speed lower. Control movements larger to effect a
standard recovery.   **Student practice.**

The Entry with Power On and Flap Down(c)
Safety Checks. Set power and flap required.
Application to the landing configuration.

Stall entry and standard recovery.

A larger movement of the controls is required to effect a
prompt recovery.

Student practice.   From straight descents.

Effect of Unbalance at the Stall (Demonstration Only)
The instructor will demonstrate the effects of entering a
stalled condition whilst climbing power is being used and
the resultant yaw is allowed to develop without any
compensation.

PRE-FLIGHT BRIEFING

STALLING
Demonstration 3.

Aim
To teach you an understanding of stalls during turning flight and the correct recovery method. To revise and consolidate previous stalling practice.

What
A demonstration of inadvertent stall entry during turning flight.

Airmanship
All normal airmanship considerations will apply and the relevant safety checks will be completed prior to each stall.

How
Stall Entry and Recovery from Turning Flight
From normal cruising flight select a reduced power setting. Note the airspeed obtained in level flight. Gradually raise the nose until both altitude and speed have settled to constant figures. Note it is possible to fly at two airspeeds for this power setting.
Return the aircraft to normal level flight.

Select a low cruise power and enter a medium level turn. Raise the nose slightly and allow the speed to settle to a lower figure, then ease the control column backwards in one continuous movement until the aircraft stalls.

Note: A strong control pressure is not needed if the stall entry is made from flight at low airspeed.

Recovery: Control column forward, then use rudder and aileron to re-adjust attitude and return the aircraft to straight and level flight.

Student practice.

Secondary Stalls and Recoveries
The instructor will demonstrate the effect of applying power during the stall recovery whilst the control column is held back, or not moved sufficiently far forward.

Note the aircraft characteristics as it enters a secondary stall condition. From this the importance of moving the control column sufficiently far forward can be seen. The same situation will occur if the control column is moved back from the forward recovery position too quickly during the recovery.

Student practice.

The student should now practice recovering from stalls during turns entered from level, climbing and descending flight.

PRE-FLIGHT BRIEFING

STALLING
Demonstration 4.

Aim   To teach the student how to recover at the incipient stage of a stall.

What   An extension of the stalling exercise in which the aircraft is brought very close to the stall condition, but recovery is effected just prior to the positive stall occurring.

Airmanship   All normal airmanship considerations will apply and the safety checks completed prior to the exercise.

How   *Recovery at the incipient stage*
Safety Checks. Adopt the level slow flight attitude. Complete a final lookout and commence an entry to the stall.

Just prior to the stall, effect a recovery to normal flight. Recovery: Ease the control column forward, apply full power and use ailerons and rudder in the normal way to maintain a condition of balanced flight.

Height loss is insignificant or nil if prompt and effective recovery action is taken at the incipient stage.

Student practice. Recoveries will be practised from entries made during:
- Level flight
- Climbing flight   } with various power and flap settings.
- Descending flight

Stall Recovery at the Incipient Stage During Turns
Recovery at the Incipient Stage:
Repeat stall entry as above but use recovery action at the incipient stage and continue with the turn or regain straight and level flight.

Student practice.

Various Stall Entries with Recoveries at the Incipient Stage
The relevant safety checks must be completed prior to each stall entry.
The student should practise entries and recoveries from the following stall entry conditions:

- Level
- Climbing   } Aircraft clean,
- Descending   without power.
- Turning

- Level
- Climbing   } Aircraft clean,
- Descending   with power.
- Turning

Further entries and recoveries should be practised in the conditions listed above and with various stages of flap lowered.

Recoveries at the Incipient Stage:
Stall entries, with recoveries made at the incipient stage should also be practised in all the above flight conditions.

Stalling

Flight Demonstrations

INTRODUCTION

The contents of the total stalling exercise may be divided into specific demonstration groups as follows:

1. Symptoms and the Stall.
    Recovery by use of the Elevators.
    Recovery by using Elevators and Power.
    Recovery when a Wing Drops at the Stall (The Standard Recovery).
2. Entry to and Recovery from the Power On Stall.
    Entry to and Recovery from the Stall with Flap Down.
    Entry and Recovery from the Stall with Power On and Flap down.
    Effect of Unbalance at the Point of Stall when Climbing Power is being used, (straight and turning flight).
3. Entry to and Recovery from Stalls during Turning Flight (accelerated stalls)
    Secondary Stalls and Recoveries.
4. Recognition and Recovery at the Incipient Stage of the Stall in the Landing and other Configurations.
    Recovery from the Stall at the Incipient Stage during change in Aircraft Configuration.

Before demonstration 1 the student should have been shown one or two introductory stalls during preceding flights. These are intended to show the attitude change during the stall, the physical sensations of a stall, and the fact that a recovery from the stall is not complicated or difficult to achieve.

Demonstration 1 should ideally cover the content of the basic stalling exercise up to the practice of the Standard Recovery, and where possible the student should have been introduced to all the demonstrations included in 1 to 4 prior to his First Solo flight.

Airmanship items including the additional 'Safety Checks' will be introduced and developed at the appropriate time during each demonstration.

DEMONSTRATION 1.   THE STALL ENTRY AND STANDARD RECOVERY

Flight Lesson	Demonstration Sequence
The symptoms, the stall and the recovery	
The symptoms from level flight	When the safety checks are completed select HOT air (if applicable). Close the throttle and maintain the aircraft in a level attitude in pitch. Note the following symptoms: Speed lowering whilst in the level flight attitude. Controls becoming less responsive. Stall warner (sound or light) as applicable). Continue to move the control column back and note the buffet (if applicable). The nose drops even though the control column is held back. The wing drops at the stall (as applicable). Recovery effected.
Stall recovery using elevators	Safety checks completed. Enter the stall with power off. During the approach to the stall use all three controls to maintain pitch attitude, wings level and the aircraft in balance. At the stall, hold the ailerons neutral, move the control column forward and prevent yaw with the rudder. At this stage note the nose attitude and the increasing airspeed. The recovery has been effected. Raise the nose, increase the power and return to level flight. Student practice at entering the stall with power off and recovering by use of the elevators.
The stall recovery using the elevators and noting the height loss.	Safety checks completed. Enter the stall as before and note the stalling speed and the altitude at the stall. Recover by the use of elevators. When normal level flight is regained, note the altitude loss incurred. This height loss would not be acceptable if a stall occurs at low altitude.

The stall recovery using elevators and power	Safety checks completed. Enter the stall as before and note the altitude at the stall. At the stall, recover by holding the ailerons neutral, moving the control column forward and smoothly applying full power. At the same time the rudder is used to prevent yaw. When level flight is regained note the reduced height loss. Student practice at entering the stall and recovering by the use of elevators and power.
The procedure for stall recovery when a wing drops at the stall	Safety checks completed. Enter the stall in the normal way. Note: If the aircraft has shown no tendency to drop a wing during previous stall entries with power off, it will be advisable to use some power (1200 – 1500 RPM) during this entry.
The standard recovery	Recovery. With the ailerons held neutral, move the control column forward, smoothly applying full power and use positive rudder application to prevent further yaw. When the aircraft unstalls: Use ailerons and rudder in the normal way to level the wings and regain balance. Return to the level flight attitude.

Student practice: The student should now complete a short session of practice at recovering from stalls using the standard recovery. Throughout the rest of the exercise of stalling and as the student becomes more proficient at recovery, the emphasis on minimum loss of height during recoveries should assume greater importance.

DEMONSTRATION 2.   STALL ENTRIES/ RECOVERIES WITH DIFFERENT POWER SETTINGS AND CONFIGURATIONS

Flight Lesson	*Demonstration Sequence*
Stall entry and recovery during flight with power on and with flap down	
Power on entry and recovery	Safety checks completed. Set the required power and enter the normal stall. Delay the recovery so that the degree and effect of a wing dropping can be clearly seen.
	External observations: High nose attitude. A more pronounced tendency for a wing to drop. Standard recovery. Set the required power, complete a final lookout and again enter the normal stall. Effect a prompt recovery.
	Further observations: Stall warner operates at a lower speed. Lower stalling speed. Less height is lost during the recovery. If prompt use is made of elevators, power and rudder, a quicker recovery can be achieved and the wing drop controlled. Student practice.
Flap down entry and recovery	Safety checks completed. Lower the flap and enter a power off stall.
	External observations: Lower nose attitude. A wing drop will sometimes be more pronounced. Standard recovery. Complete a final lookout and again enter a power-off stall with flap down.
	Further observations: From the level attitude the airspeed will decrease more quickly. Stall warner operates at a lower speed. Lower stalling speed.

	Standard recovery. A larger movement of the controls will be required to effect a prompt and positive recovery. Prompt and correct use of the elevators, ailerons and rudder will achieve a quick recovery from the stall, and any tendency for a wing to drop can be controlled. Student practice.
Stall entry and recovery with power on and flap	Application to a stall during the approach to land. Complete the safety checks and assume a simulated approach configuration with power on and landing flap lowered. At the stall use the standard recovery. In addition, if a wing drops, positive rudder application will be required to control the yaw. Student practice.
Demonstration of the effects of unbalance at the point of stall when high power is being used	At this stage the instructor will demonstrate how lack of balance at the point of stall causes a marked wing drop when high power is being used. The effects will be shown during a straight climb and a climbing turn.

Student practice: The student should now complete his practice for this flight by entering stalls in various configurations and power settings from level, climbing and descending flight.

DEMONSTRATION 3.   ENTRY TO THE STALL DURING TURNING FLIGHT

Flight Lesson	Demonstration Sequence
Demonstration of two speeds for one power setting in level flight	
Select a low cruise power	Note the power setting and airspeed obtained whilst maintaining the correct pitch attitude in level flight. Gradually raise the nose until the speed settles at a lower figure and the height remains constant. Note that at this lower airspeed the aircraft is in an incorrect nose high attitude for the selected power. During straight and level flight this attitude is clearly recognised as the wrong one.

	During turning flight, and particularly with flaps down, the incorrect pitch attitude is not so easily identified. No student practice – observation only.
Entry to a stall during a turn	Complete the safety checks and enter a medium level turn with a low cruise power selected. When the normal reduction of airspeed has occurred, gently raise the nose and allow the speed to stabilise at a lower figure. Move the control column back smoothly and continuously until the stall occurs.
	Note: The control pressures are relatively light when the stall is entered from a low speed condition. A positive wing drop normally occurs at the stall during a turn. For recovery, move the control column forward and use aileron and rudder to adjust the lateral attitude and return the aircraft to level flight. Student practice.
	Secondary stalls
Recoveries from secondary stalls during level and turning flight	The instructor will demonstrate the aircraft characteristics when the control column is held back and full power is applied at the point of stall. This demonstration is made to emphasise the need to move the control column sufficiently far forward during stall recovery action.

Student practice: The student should now practise stall entries and recoveries during medium level turns.

DEMONSTRATION 4. STALL RECOVERY AT THE INCIPIENT STAGE

Flight Lesson	*Demonstration Sequence*
Recognition and recovery from a stall at the incipient stage in different configurations and attitudes	Complete the safety checks and adopt the slow flight condition for the required attitude, configuration and power setting. Complete the final lookout and commence an approach to the stall. Just prior to stall entry recover by moving the control column forward and applying full power smoothly.

	Use aileron and rudder throughout to maintain balanced flight. Note: Height loss is nil or insignificant.
Incipient stage recovery in the landing configuration	Complete the safety checks. Enter a descent with power on and landing flap selected. Bring the aircraft to the incipient stage of a stall and recover. Student practice at recovering from the incipient stage of a stall in straight and turning flight in the landing configuration.
Incipient stage recoveries in different configurations and attitudes	Complete the safety checks. Student practice at recovering from incipient stage stalls during straight, climbing and descending flight and level, climbing, and descending turns, with and without power on and flaps lowered.
Incipient stage recoveries during changing configurations	Complete the safety checks. Student practice at recovering from incipient stage stalls whilst the aircraft configuration is being changed.

Student practice: The instructor should direct the student to approach the stall in various situations and recover at the incipient stage. This will give the student the opportunity to recognise and recover promptly and safely, from any combination of the stall situations previously demonstrated.

Spinning

Instructor's Guide

Training in the recovery from developed spins is no longer a mandatory requirement in the Private Pilot course. Nevertheless, instructors may demonstrate and give their students practice in recoveries from developed spins should they wish. However it is essential that the aircraft being used is certificated for this purpose and any restrictions or limitations shown in the Flight/Owner's Manual/Pilot's Operating Handbook are complied with.

Whether or not developed spins are practised an instructor must appreciate that if an inadvertent spin should occur during flight in the circuit or any other occasion when the aircraft is at a relatively low altitude, there will be little chance of effecting recovery action before the aircraft reaches the ground. It is therefore extremely important that the major part of a student's training in this exercise is directed towards his ability to recover at the incipient stage. For this reason the recovery at the incipient stage is dealt with in the first part of the Flight Demonstration section of this manual.

In this respect it is also essential to differentiate between the aerodynamic definition of an incipient spin and the definition implied in the type of flight training which leads to stall/spin awareness and avoidance. The aerodynamic definition is that stage between the onset of the developed stall and the aircraft entering the developed stage of a spin. During this period the aircraft may rotate through 360 degrees several times and obviously this would be most hazardous when the aircraft is at a low altitude. Therefore in training a pilot to recover at the incipient stage it will be necessary for recovery action to be effective before the aircraft reaches a 90-degree banked attitude.

With this in mind it can also be seen that if recovery action is taken too early much of the value in training a pilot to recover at the incipient stage of a spin will be lost, as the aircraft will not have reached an attitude much beyond that which occurs when a wing drops at the stall. It is therefore recommended that following a stall the wing be allowed to drop to at least an angle of 45 degrees and not more than 60 degrees before recovery action is taken (fig. 11-5).

If the intention is to proceed to recoveries at the developed stage of a spin instructors should appreciate that most students approach this exercise with some apprehension and it will often tax an instructor's ability to set up a relaxed atmosphere in the cockpit, prior to and during this form of training. It will therefore be of considerable help to play down the physical sensations through the use of a little humour at the introductory stage, and any spins performed at this time should be of short duration only.

Initially the instructor's main task will be to gradually instil confidence in the student in relation to the integrity of the aircraft and the student's own capabilities. This is best achieved by first explaining that there is no mystery about spinning, and secondly demonstrating that once the direction of spin has been determined the recovery action is straightforward and effective. However, this second point should not ignore the explanation that many aircraft are not cleared for this manoeuvre and with those that are, difficulties will be experienced if the aft c.g. limits are exceeded by incorrect loading.

AIRMANSHIP

The mnemonic used to cover the safety checks prior to spinning must be applied meticulously and any omissions from these checks considered unacceptable. Considerable emphasis must be placed upon remaining clear of other air traffic during the spin manoeuvre. This safety action will only be achieved by turning the aircraft to check that the area to either side and down into the intended spin path is clear and will remain clear during the period of the spin. Clearing turns should be conducted at not more than 30° to 40° of bank, otherwise the student's attention will be directed more to the control of the aircraft than in searching the area for other aircraft.

For the purpose of training in developed spins and recoveries, a one- or two-turn spin will normally provide the necessary experience. All of the characteristic motions and control functions will be involved during short period spins and when the stable spin cannot be achieved a longer spin will often only result in a high airspeed during the recovery. This latter effect will lead to an unnecessary loss of height and result in a time-consuming climb back to a safe height with a consequent reduction in the effectiveness of training time.

The action of entering, sustaining and recovering from a spin will usually involve a relatively large loss of height, and even when spins are of short duration some 500 to 700 feet can be lost before the aircraft is once again under the positive control of the pilot. This fact must be stressed prior to any spin practice and the student made fully aware of the difference in altitude values of QNH and flight levels in relation to height above the ground in the immediate vicinity of the aircraft.

Disorientation in relation to the geographic position of the aircraft can easily occur during spinning practice and an essential item of the safety checks will be to ensure the student re-assesses his aircraft location prior to each spin entry.

Physiological effects are most pronounced during and immediately after stable spins and when the spin stops they can often cause a sensation of spinning in the opposite direction. The importance of these effects should not be underestimated by the instructor as they can be strong enough to cause the student temporary difficulty in returning the aircraft to a normal flight attitude.

It is also important to remember that the Air Navigation Order specifically requires the wearing of a harness during spinning practice. Instructors must therefore ensure this requirement is met at all times when deliberate spinning is being carried out. It should also be appreciated that the inertia reel type harness will not always restrain the upper torso during spinning or recovery, and whereas on modern training aircraft there is little load factor change during the spin, a vigorous recovery could induce body movement which an inertia reel type harness may be unable to restrain. The student must therefore be briefed for this possibility.

NOTE: A single lap strap does not constitute a harness, but a lap strap together with either one or two diagonal shoulder straps will meet the legal requirements.

Finally, and regardless of whether developed spin recoveries are to be practised or not the instructor must ensure that the student receives a detailed briefing on the cause and aerodynamics of the aircraft's spinning characteristics including the items listed below.

BEFORE THE EXERCISE
The Long Briefing should cover the following:

Objectives.
Causes, Stages, Autorotation, and Characteristics of the Spin.
The Spin Entry.
Recognition and Identification of Spin Direction.
The Spin Recovery.
  Use of Controls.
  Effect of Power/Flaps. (Flap restrictions applicable to type.)
Effect of Centre of Gravity on Spinning Characteristics.
Spinning from Various Flight Attitudes.
Recovery at the Incipient stage.
  From various attitudes and configurations.
Airmanship – Safety Checks.
Common Errors.

The short Pre-Flight briefing should be based upon the practical aspects of that part of the Long Briefing which relates to the Air Exercise to be covered. In the event that developed spins are to be practised, ensure that the student understands it is the pilot's responsibility to establish that:

The aircraft being used is cleared for deliberate spinning.
Whether there is a limitation on the number of turns that can be carried out during the spin.
The weight and balance is within the prescribed limits for the manoeuvre.
The aircraft is fitted with a safety harness and that it is worn correctly.

An important feature is that the position of the c.g. can produce marked changes in both the spin and spin recovery characteristics. A forward c.g. normally makes spin entry more difficult to achieve, but modern aircraft are usually only cleared for spinning when the c.g. is forward and the all-up weight is restricted, i.e. in the Utility Category.

However, if the c.g. is further aft and the maximum all-up weight is used, i.e. the Normal Category, the spin characteristics could undergo a marked change. The aircraft will enter a spin more easily and require a more positive forward pressure on the control column to effect recovery. It could also take longer for the applied recovery action to take effect. This feature can only be brought to the student's attention through the medium of a ground briefing, as aircraft are not normally cleared for spinning when operated in the normal category. It should therefore be stressed during training, that on modern aircraft the rather gentle forward pressure and small amount of elevator used following application of opposite rudder during practice spin recovery, will need to be more positive should an inadvertent spin occur when the aircraft is flown with the baggage area and/or passenger seats filled.

DURING THE AIR DEMONSTRATION
In order to avoid any misunderstanding as to when spin recovery action should be initiated the simple phrase 'Recover Now' should always be used, particularly when the developed spin is being practised.

RECOVERY AT THE INCIPIENT STAGE
The recognition of the conditions immediately preceding a spin and taking prompt effective action to prevent the development of a spin are the performance standards which the student must eventually attain.

In most cases the stages of spin development can be recognised sufficiently early for effective action to be taken, but in certain flight attitudes with more than low power, the incipient stage entry can be sudden and vigorous. The student must therefore be taught to effect a positive recovery at the incipient stage under these conditions for his training to be fully effective.

During recoveries at the incipient stage the use of power in effecting a return to level flight with a minimum loss of height must be applied dependent upon the nose attitude relative to the horizon. When the nose is well down below the horizon during the recovery stage the throttle should be closed and power should not be applied until the nose is raised; whereas when the aircraft's nose is relatively close to or above the horizon during the recovery stage, full power should be used immediately control of the aircraft is regained.

SPIN ENTRY CHARACTERISTICS

Many training aircraft are often reluctant to enter a positive or incipient stage spin. This is largely due to a limited up elevator movement and a forward c.g. In these circumstances the student will be unable to appreciate the importance of spin training, and may conclude that inadvertent spin entries are very difficult to achieve and so are unlikely to occur. In this event, his motivation in learning and developing skill at spin recovery will be substantially reduced. However under certain aircraft conditions e.g. aft c.g., high power and low airspeed, many modern and seemingly docile training and touring aircraft can exhibit emphatic spin qualities. It is therefore important for the student to acquire a healthy respect for anti-spin training and appreciate its value.

LEVELLING THE WINGS FOLLOWING RECOVERY

It is important that the wings are levelled following recoveries from developed spins and before easing out of the dive. Failure to do this from a steep spin attitude could easily result in the development of a spiral dive. The student will need reminding that he must look upwards immediately the spin stops to focus on the natural horizon which will enable him to level the wings more quickly and easily.

PROLONGED SPINNING

When a particular aircraft type is capable and also certificated to carry out prolonged spins the student may be given the opportunity to practise these in the later stages of his spin training. However, he must be warned of any changed recovery characteristics, such as the temporary speeding up in rate of roll, steepening of the pitch attitude, or a delay in the eventual recovery. When such characteristics occur it will also be important to stress that the standard recovery action must not only be applied, but must be sustained until recovery is effected.

DISORIENTATION

An important factor in recovery from developed spins is the positive recognition of the direction of spin by reference to the turn indicator, but care must be taken not to induce disorientation by asking the student to note instrument aspects during the early stages. Such a request can easily lead to vertigo, air sickness and confusion due to the conflicting information received in his brain from such different sensors as the eyes, body muscles and the balance mechanism of the ears. This can be aggravated by a condition known as 'coriolis stimulation', in that if head movements which direct the eyes from outside references to the instrument readings are made whilst the aircraft is rolling and yawing, a stimulation of the balance mechanism in the ears in two planes at the same time will occur. This can produce a spontaneous stimulation of the balance mechanism in a third plane causing completely confusing messages to be transmitted to the brain.

To avoid the possibility of this spatial disorientation it would be more sensible to introduce reference to instrument indications after the student has attempted several developed spins and recoveries from a known spin direction.

SPIN ENTRIES FROM TURNS

During the spin entry from the turn the spin may not always occur in the direction of the turn and the student should be taught to be prepared for the aircraft to enter an incipient or developed spin from either direction.

COMMON ERRORS

The largest number of fatal accidents occur due to inadvertent stalls and spins and although during training stalling and spinning teaching is given to the student, the accident records suggest the possibility that such training is not always sufficiently effective.

Most stall/spin accidents occur during the flight phase when the aircraft is near the ground at low speed and in conditions where cockpit workload is high. The most common cause of inadvertent spinning is normally due to the direct or indirect misuse of the controls when the aircraft is at or close to the stall. Therefore it is necessary during training for the student to demonstrate his capability to handle situations when the aircraft is close to a stall or spin situation and he is in conditions of increased workload. Errors of any sort must be eliminated and every effort must be made to teach the student an automatic and instinctive recovery action for any situation where the stall is not recognised early enough and the incipient spin occurs.

Many students forget to throttle back when spinning from a manoeuvre with power on. If the aircraft manual permits, a comparative demonstration should be given to show the greater loss of height during the final recovery dive when power is left on, but care should be taken not to exceed the V_{ne} or limiting RPM.

The position of the controls can be deceptive when identifying an unintentional spin. Most students expect the rudder to be fully applied and the control column right back. It should be pointed out that identification of the spin by the position of the controls is unreliable, and that the spin should be identified by:

- The stages leading up to the spin, i.e. stall, yaw, nose down movement and spiral descent, some of which are not easily apparent under certain circumstances.
- The attitude of the aircraft and the sensation of autorotation.
- A high rate of descent without a continuous increase in airspeed.

Application of rudder is often hesitant in the early stages but this is usually rectified after practice, however violent application of rudder should be discouraged.

A student will sometimes forget or delay the action of centralising the rudder immediately following the termination of the spin rotation. This is normally due to tenseness leading to a lack of timing of control movements in relation to the particular stage of the spin recovery. This error will usually disappear with further practice.

The student will usually have some difficulty in judging the rate and amount of forward control column movement during the initial stage of recovery. It must be stressed that this movement should be made in a positive – but not a violent manner and it should continue until that moment when autorotation stops. Continued forward movement after this stage will lead to a very steep diving attitude and the V_{ne} could be exceeded. He will however need careful briefing to ensure he appreciates that with a well-developed spin a significantly stronger forward pressure and a larger forward movement of the control column will be required, and it will also take longer for autorotation to stop.

When practising spins or incipient stage recoveries from turning flight a very common fault is to allow the bank to steepen continuously, and this leads to a condition where the aircraft nose gets lower and the airspeed increases. A spin entry from this condition becomes progressively more difficult and the benefits of the exercise are lost. Explain that during approaches to the stall during turns it will normally be both necessary and correct to move the control column in the opposite direction from the turn in order to keep the bank relatively constant.

Spinning

Long Briefing

OBJECTIVES

The objective of spin training is to teach the student how to recognise the development of a spin situation at the incipient stage and to instinctively effect an early recovery. Nevertheless because the possibility of inadvertently entering a developed spin cannot be ruled out, some instructors may also teach their students the recovery at the developed stage of a spin.

INTRODUCTION

Whether or not developed spins and recoveries are taught, the required training in Spin Awareness and Avoidance is confined to demonstration and practice of recovering from a spin during the incipient stage. If developed spins are included in the student's training it will be necessary to ensure that the aircraft being used for this purpose is cleared to carry out deliberate spins and any restrictions or limitations complied with.

Although most training aircraft are cleared for spins the Flight/ Owner's Manual should always be checked to ensure that spinning is permitted and any specific limitations should also be noted. Aircraft which are cleared for spinning and which are certificated in both the Normal and Utility Category, will be prohibited from deliberate spins when operating in the Normal Category, and a fairly common limitation is that spinning is usually prohibited with flap down.

It should also be understood that although a particular make and type of aircraft may normally be cleared for deliberate spinning it is not necessarily true that every aircraft of the same type is also cleared. For example within the life of a particular aircraft certain modifications may be incorporated which may give rise to restrictions being imposed in relation to certain operations or manoeuvres. These restrictions may be placarded in the cockpit or alternatively shown on the Certificate of Airworthiness.

A further point to be remembered is that the Air Navigation Order requires the aircraft to be fitted with a safety harness before it can be used for spinning manoeuvres. Lap straps are insufficient but on certain aircraft specifically cleared by the CAA a combination of a lap strap and one diagonal safety strap is considered to constitute a harness for this purpose.

Understandably many students approach this exercise with some apprehension but this is mainly the result of a psychological uneasiness in relation to the unknown, rather than any expectancy of physical discomfort.

With practice however apprehension will normally disappear.

CAUSES, STAGES, AUTOROTATION AND CHARACTERISTICS OF THE SPIN

A spin is a condition of stalled flight in which the aircraft describes a spiral descent. During a spin the aircraft will be simultaneously rolling, yawing and pitching until recovery is initiated by the pilot.

Causes of a Spin

If an aircraft is either inadvertently or deliberately brought to the stall it is a characteristic of many aircraft that one wing will drop. There are several reasons which may produce this condition but usually the primary reason is the development of yaw when the aircraft is close to, or at the stalling angle of attack. To understand how this yaw occurs it must be appreciated that no pilot can consistently fly an aircraft in a condition of perfect balance; the best he can do is to continually regain fine balance by reference to the balance indicator.

When an aircraft is brought up to or near a stalled condition, there will be an associated airspeed change leading to a constantly changing rate of response to the control pressures made by the pilot while at the same time the aircraft will be approaching a critical condition of lateral stability. From this it can be seen that the most difficult time to maintain a constant condition of balanced flight will be when the airspeed is continuously reducing and the control pressures which are required to maintain balance are constantly varying.

Figure 11-1 shows a typical situation during which the aircraft is brought close to the stall and initially yaw is absent (the stalling angle is assumed to be 20°). At (a) the wings have reached an 18° angle of attack. At (b) a yaw to the left has occurred which will temporarily change the airflow speed about each wing and the slight differential of lift between the two wings causes the right wing to rise and the left wing to drop. This small rolling action leads to a change in the angle of attack affecting each wing. The lowering wing obtains a higher angle of attack while that of the rising wing decreases. The lowering wing now reaches the stalling angle and drops more quickly which will in turn lead to a higher angle of attack and a more stalled condition.

(a)   (b)

YAW

REDUCED V
= REDUCED L
= WING DROP

INCREASED V
= INCREASED L
= WING RISE

α
= 18°

L

R

α 20°

L

-L

α 16°

R

+L

DROPPING WING
BECOMES STALLED
OR MORE STALLED

RISING WING
BECOMES LESS
STALLED

Leads to AUTOROTATION

and SPIN ENTRY

LATERAL BALANCE
CRITICAL

Fig. 11-1

Figure 11-2 illustrates the aerodynamic characteristics in relation to the C_L and C_D curves versus the angle of attack for a typical light aircraft during the autorotative stage.

The downgoing wing being more stalled will produce more drag causing the aircraft to yaw in the direction of the downgoing wing. Due to the upgoing wing being less stalled it will always have more

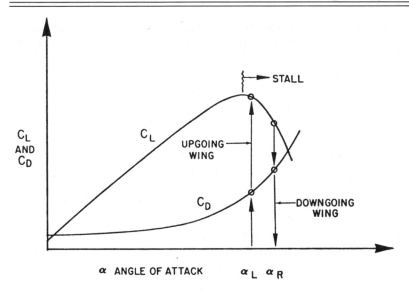

Fig. 11-2

lift than the downgoing wing and this condition will be self perpetuating.

The various design techniques used to reduce the tendency towards tip stalling have been covered during the Long Briefing on Stalling and two factors were mentioned which could reduce or even defeat the designer's efforts. These were the influence of power, and the effects of flap, and when either is being used at the stall a strong tendency towards a rapid wing drop may exist.

A third factor which may have a significant influence on the tendency for a wing to drop at the stall is variation in rigging. Minor asymmetric rigging of the angle of incidence between the left and right wings on certain aircraft is sometimes used to cure a wing low tendency in flight, and this will result in a small difference between the angle of attack of the two wings.

Stages of the Spin

The circumstances which can cause a spin will be (1) any condition of flight at or near the stall, and (2) the development of yaw. The aircraft may assume some unusual attitude but unless yaw is present it will not spin. An aircraft will not spin directly from any state of normal cruising flight. In practice, it will be found that to spin carelessness in the handling of the controls near the stall is necessary. It must be borne in mind that a single speed of entry is not significant, as a stall can occur at various speeds dependent upon configuration, weight, position of the c.g. and the load factor imposed.

The aircraft does not go directly from the stall into the spin: there is a transition period, the duration of which varies with different types of aircraft. When a wing drops at the stall, the aircraft nose begins to yaw towards the lower wing, and as the angle of bank steepens, it may drop sharply. If no preventive action is taken at this stage, the aircraft will enter a state of autorotation and pitch downwards. A change of loading will be felt and this is the development period of the spin condition.

During the spin the aircraft assumes a nose-down attitude and autorotation is continuous. Often some vibration or buffeting is experienced, and the airspeed remains at a low figure. The aircraft is out of control and its attitude and behaviour may to a certain extent be considered as stabilised. Some aircraft will tend to pitch regularly whilst spinning, and when this happens the rate of rotation usually decreases as the nose comes up and increases as the nose sinks.

Autorotation

The mechanics of autorotation have been briefly introduced in the previous paragraphs but the following gives a more detailed explanation.

Immediately a wing drops there will be a change in the direction of the relative airflow, which now becomes a resultant of two velocities, the forward speed of the aircraft and the downward or upward speed of the wing. This causes the down-going wing to become further stalled while the up-going wing undergoes a partial recovery. As a result of this inequality in the lift of the wings the aircraft starts an automatic rolling action about its longitudinal axis called 'Auto-rotation'.

The rate of this autorotation varies with different aircraft and with different circumstances in the same aircraft. Sometimes it takes the form of a positive flick in which the aircraft may even become inverted, and in other cases, e.g. with a forward c.g. the nose will tend to drop more quickly as the wing goes down, and this action may reduce the angle of attack sufficiently to unstall the wing, preventing autorotation from occurring. In this latter case the aircraft may only assume a moderate angle of bank, which will develop into a spiral descent if no corrective action is taken.

It can be generally stated that at angles of attack beyond the stall any damping in roll is negative and a rolling motion produces a moment in the direction of roll. This absence of damping in roll will assist to sustain the occurrence of autorotation.

The autorotative rolling and yawing moments of an aircraft at high angles of attack are the major pro-spin moments of a conventional aircraft and tend to accelerate the aircraft into the spin until other equal and opposite moments provided by aerodynamic damping or inertia forces limit the rate of rotation and yaw.

The Characteristics of a Spin

A spin is a condition of flight in which the aircraft is experiencing rolling, yawing, pitching and sideslipping. It will be losing height rapidly and descending along a vertical path about the spin axis, the helix of which is fairly small and can be less than the span of the wings. An important characteristic is that during a spin the predominant tendency is to continue the autorotation and the aircraft generally has a spinning motion which is primarily rolling, with moderate yaw and a degree of sideslip. If an aircraft has a large amount of directional stability it will be a favourable influence on the spin characteristics as it will minimise the displacement due to yaw and make it easier to effect a recovery.

The development and the characteristics of a spin will depend upon the aircraft design and the distribution of its mass, as well as the operation of the control surfaces. The aircraft will usually rotate several times before it settles down into the state of spinning steadily and the pitch angle it takes up may be steep or flat. The latter characteristic is mainly affected by the position of the c.g., which is an important factor in modern light aircraft.

The actual motions of the aircraft throughout the entry to and during a spin are of a complex nature. Once the aircraft has settled into a spin the forces and moments acting upon it will be in equilibrium and this balance of forces and moments will determine the values of angle of attack, sideslip, turn radius, rate of descent and other factors.

During the steady spin the aircraft will be in a condition where the rate of yaw and roll will settle down to a constant value and the rate of descent will also become constant. Some aircraft through design features or the position of the c.g. may be unable to achieve a true spin and as a result the forces and moments will not balance out. In this case an oscillatory spin motion will occur which could more accurately be described as an autorotative spiral.

During a settled spin it is the balance of the moments which will determine the final state of equilibrium and which will have a large influence upon the recovery characteristics. The actual balance of the forces is of less importance but in view of their effect upon the rate of descent and considerations relating to the position of the c.g. they must be discussed here. The three primary forces are, the resultant of the aerodynamic forces, the centrifugal forces, and the weight. The approximate interelation of these forces is shown in fig. 11-3.

The position and direction of weight is easily established as acting directly downward through the c.g., and throughout the spin the

TOTAL RESULTANT
of the
AERODYNAMIC FORCES

DRAG

LIFT

CENTRIFUGAL
FORCE

SPIN
AXIS

WEIGHT

TOTAL RESULTANT
of the
CENTRIFUGAL and
WEIGHT FORCES

Fig. 11-3

aircraft will be descending, therefore the overall relative airflow will be coming from below. In consequence the drag will be acting against the weight and when the aerodynamic resistance equals the rate of descent then drag will be balancing weight, i.e. in a steady spin the rate of descent will settle to a constant value.

Lift acting at 90° to the relative airflow will now be approximately horizontal and the centrifugal force brought about by the aircraft rotation in the spin will oppose the lift. The conditions for equilibrium will be met when Drag = Weight and Lift = Centrifugal Force.

Figure 11-4 shows the resultant of the aerodynamic forces, the effect of up-elevator and the direction of the centrifugal forces in relation to the c.g.

A = Aerodynamic Force (Resultant of Lift and Drag).
B = Aerodynamic Effect of 'Up Elevator'.
C,D are the Centrifugal Forces.

The aerodynamic resultant of L and D acting behind the c.g. produces a nose-down moment and the up elevator force tends to oppose this. The centrifugal forces acting on the fore and aft masses of the aircraft will produce a nose-up moment. It can be seen that the closer the c.g. is to the aerodynamic force the flatter the spin will become. This is more clearly visualised if one considers the effect of having the c.g. aft of the aerodynamic force in which case both the aerodynamic force and the centrifugal forces will be acting together to flatten the spin.

A about the C.G. = a nose down moment

B dampens the nose down moment

The couple between C and D = a nose up moment

Fig. 11-4

As the spin flattens the angle of attack increases and the resulting increase of drag will decrease the rate of descent. The centrifugal forces will also have a stronger effect in the horizontal plane which will lead to an increase in the rate of rotation and a decrease in the spin radius.

There are other factors involved in the determination of spin characteristics such as the effect of wing span and sweep, the length of the fuselage and the distribution of weight in the wings. These factors have a bearing upon whether the use of ailerons will assist or impede spin entry or recovery. Such factors are complex and outside the scope of this manual, but it can generally be stated that in relation to many small conventional aircraft the use of ailerons during the spin recovery will have an adverse effect. Note: If ailerons are to be used in spin recovery the manufacturer's flight manual will usually say so.

RECOGNITION OF THE INCIPIENT SPIN
The incipient stage of the spin is that period after the entry and before the spin has progressed to the developed stage. From a training viewpoint the incipient stage is best described as that period before the wings first roll past the vertical, and as such it is similar to the

Fig. 11-5

situation of a positive 'wing drop' at the stall. Figure 11-5 shows this period.

THE RECOVERY AT THE INCIPIENT STAGE

The incipient stage of a spin is that period following a stall when a positive wing drop is being experienced. At this point the wing will be adopting a steeply banked attitude and the most important action will be to effect stall recovery by making a positive forward movement of the control column. At the same time, and because yaw will be taking place, the rudder should be used to prevent further yaw occurring. Provided the forward movement of the control column is sufficient the wing will stop its rolling movement and following this the airspeed will be increasing; therefore a natural follow-up action will be to use all three controls to return the aircraft to a normal flight attitude.

To sum up, the recovery actions should be:

● Control column forward to unstall the wings.
● Rudder to prevent further yaw.
● Co-ordinated use of the elevators, ailerons and rudder is then made to return the aircraft to the level flight attitude.

Recovery at the Incipient Stage from Various Attitudes
When sufficient competence at recovering from an incipient spin entered from the level flight attitude has been obtained, the student will consolidate this ability by entering incipient stage spins from various attitudes. These entries will be accomplished from level turns, straight climbs and descents and climbing and descending turns. The amount of power being used and the degree of unbalance will normally have an affect upon the rate at which a wing will drop; therefore a quicker reaction will be needed to stop the tendency for a developed spin to occur whenever climbing power is being used.

SPIN RECOVERY AT THE DEVELOPED STAGE
Spin entry normally occurs when the aircraft is at or near the stall and a strong yawing moment occurs due to deliberate or inadvertent misuse of the controls. In training the entry is achieved by bringing the aircraft close to the stall and then applying full rudder to create the yaw whilst moving the control column fully back. Although these actions are virtually simultaneous it is usually more effective to lead with the rudder because near the stall, control surface effectiveness is significantly reduced. If the control column is moved back first the rudder responsiveness will be less and it may not be possible to induce sufficient yaw to achieve spin entry.

At the spin entry the wings should normally be held level and use of aileron to lower a wing in the direction of spin entry should be avoided because lowering a wing in this manner will tend to reduce the amount of yaw being obtained from the use of rudder.

An entry to the spin can be made from many flight attitudes, e.g. level, climbing descending etc., but many modern light training aircraft, due to their forward c.g., reduced rudder area, and limited up-elevator movement, often give difficulties in producing clean and positive spin entries from a power-off condition. With power on, spin entries are easier and more positive and do not require as much control force as entries with power off. Therefore spin entries may more easily be achieved by using 1400 to 1500 RPM during the entry stage as this will provide greater rudder and elevator effectiveness. However it will be necessary to establish whether power-on entries to deliberate spins are permitted for the particular aircraft before using this method.

Recognition and Identification of Spin Direction
During the deliberate spin entered as a training exercise the direction of spin will automatically be known, but in an inadvertent spin the direction will have to be established before correct recovery action can be taken. During the training spins the direction of the rotation of the aircraft can be seen with reference to the ground.

However if an inadvertent spin should occur, visual reference of this sort could be inconclusive in determining the spin direction, and a more precise method will become necessary.

This can be achieved by reference to the turn indicator. As the direction of spin is determined by the direction of yaw, the turn indicator will indicate a turn in the same direction as the yaw. Therefore during a spin to the left the turn indicator will show a turn to the left, and when spinning to the right a right turn will be indicated by the turn indicator.

Fig. 11-6

The degree of turn indicated during the spin is not necessarily the maximum, and dependent upon the stage of spin could be less than that shown whilst executing turns during taxying. The balance portion of the instrument, whether it is a ball or needle type of presentation will not be of any value in determining spin direction and the same applies to the attitude and heading indicators either of which could have toppled or in any event be confusing to interpret. To sum up therefore, these last three instrument indications cannot be used with sufficient accuracy to determine the direction in which an aircraft is spinning.

The Spin Recovery
In order to recover from a spin the controls must be used in a correct sequence. This sequence and the degree of control movement will need to be modified depending upon whether the spin is at the incipient, oscillatory or settled stage. Recovery at the incipient stage has been covered in this briefing but the following applies to the use of the controls during the settled and oscillatory spins.

Use of Controls during the Developed Spin
The rudder is the primary yaw control and therefore will be the most effective anti-spin control during the recovery. During a settled spin the moments on the aircraft are in balance and the initial application

of full opposite rudder will temporarily unbalance these moments. Following this the elevators are used to unstall the aircraft and stop the autorotation. Due to the motion of the aircraft during a spin the vertical tailplane will have an area which is partially shielded by the horizontal tailplane, and when the elevators are moved down during the recovery stage this shielded area on some aircraft is increased, thus reducing the anti-spin yawing moment obtained from the use of rudder.

In order to benefit from a temporary unbalance of the spin moments and to minimise rudder shielding, a short pause should be made after applying anti spin rudder and before moving the control column forward to unstall the aircraft. This is known as the standard spin recovery.

In recent years, certain foreign manufactured aircraft whose spin recovery characteristics are different to those built and certificated in accordance with the British Civil Airworthiness Requirements, have been introduced into the UK.

The Flight Manuals or equivalent documents of these aircraft therefore outline spin recovery procedures which are different from that which has historically become known as the 'Standard Spin Recovery'.

Pilots must therefore check the Aircraft Manual for the particular aircraft type to ensure that they are aware of the recommended spin recovery technique for the aircraft they are currently flying.

To summarise the Standard Recovery action, the controls must be used in a firm and positive manner and in the following sequence:

Standard Spin Recovery:
- Throttle closed.
- Ailerons held neutral.
- Full rudder applied – opposite to spin direction.
    Pause – momentarily.

Ease the control column forward – continue this action until the spin stops.
- When the spin stops – immediately centralise the rudder and level the wings by the use of ailerons.
- When the wings are levelled – ease the aircraft out of the dive.

Use of Controls during the Oscillatory Stage

Most aircraft will pass through the oscillatory type spin before settling into the stable spin condition. During the oscillatory stage the aircraft will appear to be spinning with varying rates of rotation and nose positions relative to the horizon. At this stage the normal Standard Spin Recovery should be used unless otherwise directed by the Flight/Owner's Manual or Pilot's Operating Handbook.

Use of Controls during the Autorotative Spiral

It has already been stated that due to design philosophy or a forward position of the c.g. an aircraft may not achieve a condition of settled spin. This autorotative spiral will be recognised by the airspeed increasing during the autorotation stage. When this occurs the action of applying full rudder deflection could possibly be made at speeds higher than the manoeuvring speed in which case the limiting loads on the aircraft would be exceeded. The reasons for not using full and abrupt application of the controls at speeds higher than the manoeuvring speed are discussed more fully during the Long Briefing on Advanced Turning, but at this stage it can be stated that caution must be used when applying full rudder during an autorotative spiral.

A recovery from this condition will in any event require a lesser amount of rudder to be applied than for a standard spin recovery, and a smaller forward movement of the control column will be advisable, because a large forward movement in this situation could easily lead to the aircraft exceeding the V_{ne} during the following dive.

NOTE: If there is any doubt as to whether the aircraft is in an autorotative spiral or a spin then it will be advisable to use the normal spin recovery for the particular aircraft type.

INSTRUMENT INDICATIONS

A spin will cause the toppling limits of most air driven gyro instruments to be exceeded, but the turn indicator and the pressure-operated instruments will remain operative. It follows, therefore, that when spinning in instrument weather conditions all recovery actions must be made with the assistance of the limited panel only. During the spin, the turn indicator will register a fairly high rate of turn in the direction of the spin, the balance indicator will usually show a

Fig. 11-7

skid in the opposite direction but it may take up any position depending upon the forces involved. The airspeed indicator will remain at a low figure, and the altimeter and the vertical speed indicator will both show a high rate of descent.

The loading caused by acceleration in pitch causes the turn indicator to exaggerate any small yawing movement during the recovery from the dive when the spin stops. Therefore when the spin stops and the turn needle swings back towards the neutral mark it will usually overshoot this mark and indicate a yaw in the opposite direction until the back pressure is eased from the control column. It is most important that the pilot should appreciate this transient error when recovering from a spin during instrument weather conditions.

EFFECT OF POWER/FLAPS

The effect of spinning with power on and/or flap down will change the spin characteristics. This change will vary between different aircraft and also aircraft of the same type with different c.g. locations. In either event it can generally be stated that the effect of power or flap will be to impede the recovery.

Effect of Power

The effect of power during the stall has already been covered and it was seen that power application had a de-stabilising tendency on the aircraft. A reason for this occurring during the spin can be understood by referring to the asymmetric lift about the wings created by the slipstream path being misaligned with the horizontal axis during a yaw, causing more lift on the outer wing.

During the spin the aircraft will yaw into the spin direction and any additional lift experienced by the outer wing will cause the rate of roll to increase. Further to this the slipstream angle will also serve to decrease the angle of attack which may also increase the rate at which the upgoing wing rises, leading to an increase in the rate of rotation. Because of the generally accepted adverse effects of power during a spin, the throttle should be closed fully at the start of the recovery procedure.

Effect of Flaps

In most aircraft intentional spinning with the flaps down is prohibited. The basic reason for this is their adverse affect upon control responsiveness and the possibility of exceeding the flap limiting speed during the recovery. With flap down, the airflow over the tail section is disturbed and deflected to a greater degree and therefore the responsiveness of the rudder and elevators is reduced. During the spin recovery the effectiveness of the controls has a vital bearing upon the ability to recover promptly.

Therefore whenever an inadvertent spin occurs the pilot must remember to include an added check to ensure the flaps are up. If they are in the lowered position they must be raised immediately, if possible prior to the recovery action being commenced.

EFFECT OF THE CENTRE OF GRAVITY ON SPINNING CHARACTERISTICS

The spinning characteristics of any particular aircraft will vary with the position of the c.g. even though its position is within the permitted limits for the aircraft concerned. The effect of a forward position of the c.g. is to cause a steeper spin with a faster rate of descent. However, recovery action is easier as the spin is far less stable. An extreme forward position of the c.g. may in some cases prevent a spin being achieved altogether, in which case the aircraft will remain in a steep, and usually tight spiral descent during which the airspeed increases.

The effect of an aft c.g. is to make the spin flatter, in which case the rate of descent is less, the spin is more stable and recovery is more difficult. This is reflected in the need for a stronger and sustained push force on the control column when carrying out recovery action under these conditions. If the c.g. is aft of the permitted limits a serious situation can occur in that the aircraft may not be capable of recovering from a settled spin condition.

NOTE: Under circumstances of an aft c.g. the push force on the control column will need to be stronger and the forward movement must be maintained until the spin stops. Nevertheless, certain differences in spin recovery procedure exist between different aircraft, and the recommendations made in the particular Flight/Owner's Manual or Pilot's Operating Handbook must be taken into account.

SPINNING FROM VARIOUS FLIGHT ATTITUDES

A spin can occur from any flight attitude and with any power setting or aircraft configuration. Therefore although the introduction to spin training will commence from the level flight attitude with little or no power it will later be necessary to practise recoveries from spins entered from various flight attitudes with and without power. Due to the normal prohibition of deliberate spin entries with the flaps down, these entries will all be carried out in the clean configuration. The amount of power used during spin entries may also need to be restricted due to the high gyroscopic loads involved and/or Flight Manual Limitations.

NOTE: Prior to practice spinning it must be established that the aircraft type is cleared for deliberate spinning and that it is not being operated in the Normal Category.

Spin Entry and Recovery from Level Flight

When the safety checks have been completed the usual method of spin entry from the level flight attitude will be to reduce the power to a low setting and raise the nose slightly to reduce the airspeed. Maintain the aircraft in balance with the wings level and continue moving the control column back until the aircraft is near or at the stall.

At this stage whilst holding the wings level, apply full rudder smoothly and positively towards the required spin direction and move the control column fully back. The aircraft will now yaw and roll into the direction of applied rudder, autorotation will occur and the spin will develop. The controls will have to be maintained in the direction they have been applied and the control column will need to be held fully back. Maintain a visual reference outside the cockpit during the first few practice spins and thereafter the habit of checking the turn indicator should be added to confirm the spin direction.

Some aircraft, notably those with a forward c.g., are reluctant to enter a spin unless the conditions are right and the timing of the control movements is correct. In this respect it should be appreciated that the ailerons should be used to hold the wings level up to the moment of rudder application, and any movement of the control column in the direction of spin, i.e. towards the lowering wing must be avoided or the applied yaw will be reduced.

Following the spin entry the Standard Recovery action (if applicable to type) should be put into effect.

Ailerons neutral

At or near the stall,
hold the wings level
and apply full rudder
in required spin dir-
ection while moving
the control column
fully back.

ENTRY

INCIPIENT

STEADY

RECOVERY

Check... Throttle
closed and ailerons
neutral.

Apply full opposite
rudder, PAUSE... move
the control column
forward until the spin
stops.

When the spin stops.....
Centralise the rudder,
roll the wings level and
ease gently out of the dive.

Fig. 11-8

Spin Entry and Recovery from Other Flight Attitudes

Spin entries should (when permitted on the aircraft type) be practised
from other normal flight attitudes such as climbing, descending and
turning. When possible, entries should also be made from climbing
and descending turns. The entry from any of these attitudes is similar
to that used during the level flight condition but a few variations will
apply. For example, whenever a cruising or higher power setting is
being used it will not normally be necessary to make such large or
positive control movements as when power is low or at idle.

This illustrates the fact that although the controls must be used
fully and positively during power off flight, it is relatively easier to
enter an inadvertent spin when normal power is being used.
Therefore during entries made from straight climbing flight or
climbing turns, the speed should be reduced gradually and sufficient
rudder applied whilst the control column is moved back until the spin

entry takes place. During descending flight when power is off or at a low setting a more positive movement of the controls will be needed to effect a clean spin entry, and this will also apply to descending turns.

The spin entry from a medium level turn is achieved by setting a low cruise power for slow flight, then entering the turn whilst maintaining height. The aircraft should be held in the turn until the normal speed reduction associated with this manoeuvre is reached. At this point the control column should be moved back in one continuous movement whilst applying rudder until the spin entry occurs.

Note 1. It will however be important to ensure that the particular aircraft is permitted to enter spins with power on.

Note 2. The spin entry and recovery from steeper turns is covered in the Long Briefing on Advanced Turning.

The Standard Recovery is used regardless of the flight attitude at entry, but the cautionary advice given under the use of controls during recovery from the autorotative spiral will still apply if this flight condition occurs instead of the true spin.

If, owing to careless handling, an aircraft enters a spin from an inverted attitude, in most cases the resultant spin will be quite normal. If the aircraft is on the point of stall with the control column nearly fully forward and a positive yaw occurs the aircraft may go into an inverted spin. In this situation the characteristics are similar to a normal spin, except that the pilot is on the outside of the spin and the small change in loading is reversed. Recovery is made by applying full opposite rudder and then moving the control column back until the spinning stops. The rudder must then be centralised and the aircraft rolled back into level flight.

AIRMANSHIP

The basic airmanship items are the same as those which apply during the practice of stalling, but because a greater loss of height will be involved the entry to a spin must be commenced at a greater height. During spinning the loss of height will be rapid and the aircraft will probably lose some 500 feet for each turn of the spin. Because of this, the minimum height to enter a practice spin should be 4000 feet above ground level.

Once the aircraft has been put into a spin it will remain outside the control of the pilot until recovery action has been taken. Therefore during the spin the pilot will not be able to take avoiding action in relation to other aircraft. As a result it is of paramount importance that the area traversed by the aircraft during this manoeuvre remains clear of other air traffic. This situation can only be achieved by completing a very thorough lookout before each spin entry.

Following each spin recovery it will be advisable to re-check the aircraft location in relation to known landmarks, as a student can easily become disorientated in respect of the aircraft position following several spin practices.

Finally it is the pilot's responsibility to ensure that the aircraft is cleared for intentional spins, that the weight and balance is within the required limits, and that a harness is worn during all periods of spin training. A lap strap is insufficient to meet either the requirements of the Air Navigation Order or the implementation of flight safety.

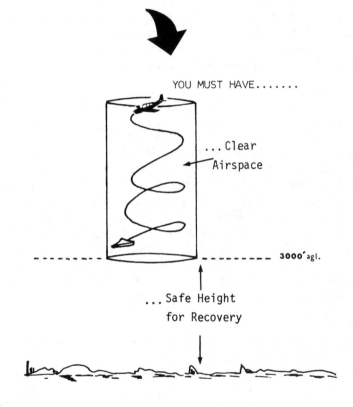

YOU MUST HAVE.......

...Clear Airspace

3000´agl.

...Safe Height for Recovery

PRE-FLIGHT BRIEFING

SPINNING

Demonstration 1. (Spin Awareness and Avoidance)

Aim
To teach you to recognise the approach to a spin condition and to effect a recovery at the Incipient Stage.

What
Demonstration and practice at recovering to the normal flight attitude just before a spin occurs.

Airmanship
The normal airmanship considerations will apply and the relevant Safety Checks completed at appropriate times.

How
Recovery at the Incipient Stage
From level flight:
Safety Checks – completed.
Set up straight and level 'Slow Flight'.
Gradually apply back pressure to the control column without maintaining balance, i.e. allow a yaw to occur. In this unbalanced condition a wing will normally drop as the aircraft stalls.

Note: If a wing is reluctant to drop, it will be necessary to move the control column backwards more rapidly during the approach to the stall, use a little more power or apply rudder to create a more unbalanced condition.

Delay stall recovery until the wing drops between 45 and 60 degrees. For training purposes this flight situation can be considered as the incipient stage of the spin and a prompt recovery must now be effected.

Recovery:
Control column forward and sufficient rudder to prevent further yaw.
Power as required.
Level the wings and at the same time regain balanced flight.
Return to normal straight and level flight.

Student practice.

Note: The emphasis is on a prompt and effective recovery. However if the nose has dropped well below the horizon before recovery can be effected, the power should not be increased until the initial stage of the recovery is complete and the aircraft nose is being raised towards the horizon. This is to avoid unnecessary height loss.

Recoveries at the Incipient Stage from Various Flight Attitudes and Manoeuvres.

Safety Checks completed. Set up incipient spin entries from:

The straight descent.
The straight climb.
Level turns.
Climbing and Descending turns.
Entries are normally easier if they are initiated from conditions of 'Slow Flight'.

Student practice.

11-27

PRE-FLIGHT BRIEFING

SPINNING
Demonstration 2.

Aim To teach you the methods of spin entry, to accustom you to the sensations of spinning and to teach you the correct method of recovery.

What A spin entry from level flight followed by demonstration and practice of the Standard Recovery.*

Airmanship The vital necessity to complete the Safety Checks, maintain orientation in relation to ground features and Controlled Airspace, and to ensure that a safe height above the surface is available before each spin entry.

How *The Developed Spin and Recovery*

Spin entry
From level flight.
Complete the Safety Checks.

Spin Entry:
Reduce power.
Maintain altitude and allow the speed to reduce.
Just prior to the stall apply full rudder and move the control column fully back.

The aircraft will now enter the spin.

Maintaining the Spin
Maintain application of full rudder and hold the control column fully back.

Confirm direction of spin.

To be introduced at a suitable stage:

Instrument Reference:
Turn indicator for confirmation of spin direction.
Airspeed low (or as applicable for type).
Altimeter and vertical speed indicator will show a high rate of descent.

Spin Recovery
Throttle closed.
Ailerons held neutral.

When spin direction is confirmed:
Apply full opposite rudder.
Pause. . . . . .
Ease the control column forward until the spin stops.
Centralise the rudder.
Look up for horizon reference and level the wings.

Ease gently out of the dive and regain lost height.

Student practice.

* The Flight/Owner's Manual/Pilot's Operating Handbook, must be checked to ensure whether spin entries with 'power on' are permitted and whether any differences from the Standard Spin Recovery apply.

The Incipient Spin

(Spin Awareness and Avoidance)
Flight Demonstration

INTRODUCTION

The demonstrations and practice at recovering from a spin during its incipient stage will be introduced after you have become reasonably proficient at recoveries from developed and incipient stalls.

These demonstrations and practice will intially be carried out from straight and level 'Slow Flight'. Following which you will be given practice at recovering during the early stage of spin development from climbing and descending flight. The exercise will be completed after you have demonstrated competence at recovering safely from incipient spins entered during level, climbing and descending turns.

The contents of this exercise can therefore be divided into the following specific demonstration groups:

1. Recovery from incipient spins entered from straight and level, climbing and descending flight.
2. Recovery from incipient spins entered during level, climbing and descending turns.

Airmanship items and considerations will be introduced and developed at appropriate moments during the demonstrations.

DEMONSTRATION 1. RECOVERY AT THE INCIPIENT STAGE OF A SPIN

Flight Lesson	*Demonstration Sequence*
The early recovery	
From level flight	Safety Checks (as applicable) completed. Reduce power and set up straight and level 'Slow Flight'. Without maintaining a balanced flight condition gradually apply back pressure to the control column until the

Note:
At this stage avoid
rapid / large rudder   →
application or entry
to a spin may occur

aircraft stalls and a marked wing
drop occurs.
Note: If a wing is reluctant to drop at
the stall it will be necessary to repeat
the entry and:
  (a)   Move the control column back
        more rapidly, or
  (b)   Use a little more power during
        the stall entry, or
  (c)   Apply rudder to create a more
        unbalanced condition at the
        point of stall, or
  (d)   Use all of the above actions.
Delay stall recovery until the wing has
dropped to between 45 and 60 degrees.
Recovery:
  Promptly move the control column
  forward a sufficient amount to stop
  the stall and use rudder to prevent
  further yaw.
  Increase power as required and
  level the wings whilst regaining
  balanced flight.
Return to normal straight and level
flight.
Note: If the nose drops well below the
horizon during the entry to the incipient spin it will be advisable to delay
any increase of power during the
recovery.
Student practice.

From the straight descent

Safety Checks (as applicable)
completed.
Reduce power and set up descending
slow flight.
Repeat the incipient spin entry and
recovery as for straight and level
flight.
Note: The entry to an incipient spin
from a descent may result in a greater
nose-down attitude and care should be
used when increasing power during the
recovery or unnecessary height loss
may occur.
Student practice.

*From the straight climb

Safety Checks (as applicable)
completed.
Set up slow flight in a straight climb.
Repeat the incipient spin entry and
recovery as for straight and level flight.
Note: Due to the higher power setting
in the climb a greater degree of yaw
will occur in unbalanced flight and the

	wing drop will tend to be more rapid. Student practice.
*From level turns	Safety Checks (as applicable) completed. Set up slow flight in a medium turn. Repeat the incipient spin entry and recovery as before. Note: Whether the left or right wing drops during a stall will depend upon a number of factors. If during a turn the outer wing drops then the aircraft will roll out of the turn. However if the inner wing drops the bank will increase rapidly and there will be less time to recover before the wings pass the vertical, thus a more prompt recovery action will be needed. Student practice.
*From climbing and descending turns	The above exercise should now be repeated from turns during climbs and descents. Student practice.

Student practice: The student should practice this exercise until he is competent at recovering promptly and effectively from incipient spins entered from all normal flight conditions and manoeuvres.

*Important Note: Depending on the flight characteristics of the aircraft it may not be advisable to practice incipient stage spins with a high power setting in those aircraft which are not cleared for deliberate spin entries.

The Developed Spin

Flight Demonstrations

INTRODUCTION

This is only an optional exercise in the Private Pilot's Course; it is however a mandatory part of the Assistant Instructor Course.

Following the practice of recovering from spins at the incipient stage the contents of the developed spin exercise may be divided into specific demonstration groups as follows:

1. Spins from Level Flight and Standard Recovery.
2. Spins from Descending Flight.
3. Spins from Turning Flight.

Airmanship items will be introduced and developed at appropriate moments during the demonstrations. When spin entries with 'power on' are not permitted in the particular aircraft type, entries should be conducted with power off.

DEMONSTRATION 1.   THE DEVELOPED SPIN AND RECOVERY

Flight Lesson	Demonstration Sequence
The entry and standard recovery From level flight	Note: Power should only be used if the Aircraft Manual permits spin entries with power ON. Safety Checks completed. **Maintain altitude and allow speed to reduce.** Just before the stall occurs apply full rudder in the required direction and move the control column fully back.

* Refer to the particular Aircraft Manual to ensure whether any differences from the Standard Spin Recovery apply.	The aircraft will now enter a spin.
	* To recover:
	    Close the throttle.
	    Hold the ailerons neutral.
	    Confirm direction of spin.
	    Apply full opposite rudder – Pause.

Ease the control column forward until the spin stops.
Centralise the rudder and level the wings.
Ease gently out of the dive.

Student practice: At this stage the student should be given the opportunity to practise the spin entry and basic recovery actions.

From level flight	Safety Checks completed.
Spin entries in the opposite direction can now be introduced including the use of the turn indicator or turn co-ordinator to confirm direction of spin	Spin entry and standard recovery. Note the altitude of entry. Use of the turn indicator to confirm direction of spin. Note airspeed and rate of descent.
* Refer to the particular Aircraft Manual to ensure whether any differences from the Standard Spin Recovery apply.	* To recover: Close the throttle. Hold the ailerons neutral. Confirm direction of spin from the 'turn indicator'. Apply full opposite rudder – Pause. Ease the control column forward until the spin stops. Centralise the rudder and level the wings. Ease gently out of the dive. Note the altitude immediately following the recovery and before the level attitude is regained.

Student practice: The student should now practise spin recoveries in opposite directions using the turn indicator or turn co-ordinator to confirm the spin direction.

Note: The actual stage to bring in reference to the airspeed and rate of descent during a spin will depend upon the student's ability to cope with the added instrument references.

DEMONSTRATION 2.   SPINS FROM DESCENDING FLIGHT

Flight Lesson	*Demonstration Sequence*
The entry and standard recovery	Note: Power should only be used if the Aircraft Manual permits spin entries with power ON.
From descending flight	Safety Checks completed. Set up Slow Flight during a powered descent. Final lookout, reduce power.

* Refer to the particular Aircraft Manual to ensure whether any differences from the Standard Spin Recovery apply.	Spin entry: Apply rudder in the direction required and move the control column back until the aircraft enters a spin. * Spin recovery: Throttle closed. Ensure flap is selected Up and confirm spin direction. Standard recovery.

Student practice: The student should now practise spin entries and recoveries in both directions from descending flight.

DEMONSTRATION 3.   SPINS FROM TURNING FLIGHT

Flight Lesson	Demonstration Sequence
The entry and standard recovery	Note: This demonstration should only be conducted if the Aircraft Manual permits spin entries with power ON.
From a level turn	Safety Checks completed. Set up Slow Flight and commence a medium turn. Final lookout.
* Refer to the particular Aircraft Manual to ensure whether any differences from the Standard Spin Recovery apply.	Spin entry: Apply a progressively increasing amount of rudder whilst moving the control column backwards continuously until the spin occurs. * Spin recovery: Throttle closed. Confirm spin direction. Standard recovery.

Student practice: The student should now practise spin entry and recovery from left and right turns.

From a descending turn	Safety Checks completed. Set up Slow Flight during a descending turn with power. Final lookout.
* Refer to the particular Aircraft Manual to ensure whether any differences from the Standard Spin	Spin entry: Apply rudder in the direction required and at the same time move the control column progressively backwards until the spin occurs.

Recovery apply.

* Spin recovery:
Throttle closed.
Confirm spin direction.
Standard recovery.

Student practice: The student should now practise spin entry and recovery from left and right descending turns.

Take-off and Climb to Downwind Position

Instructor's Guide

TAKE - OFF DISTANCE									FLAPS RETRACTED — HARD SURFACE RUNWAY

GROSS WEIGHT LBS.	IAS 50 FT. MPH	HEAD WIND KNOTS	AT SEA LEVEL & 58°F.		AT 2500 FT. & 50°F.		AT 5000 FT. & 41°F		AT 75°C FT
			GROUND RUN	TOTAL TO CLEAR 50 FT. OBS.	GROUND RUN	TOTAL TO CLEAR 50 FT. OBS.	GROUND RUN	TOTAL TO CLEAR 50 FT. OBS.	GROUND RUN
1600	70	0	735	1305	910	1660	1115	2065	1360
		10	500	1035	630	1250	780	1510	970
		20	305	730	395	890	500	1000	640

NOTES: 1. Increase the distances 10% for each 35°F. increase in temperature above standard for particular altitude.
2. For operation on a dry, grass runway, increase distances (both "ground run" and "total to clear 50 ft. obstacle") by 7% of the "total to clear 50 ft. obstacle" figure.

MAXIMUM RATE - OF - CLIMB DATA								

GROSS WEIGHT LBS.	AT SEA LEVEL & 58°F			AT 5000 FT. & 41°F.			AT 10000 FT. & 23°F	
	IAS, MPH	RATE OF CLIMB FT./MIN.	FUEL USED, GAL.	IAS, MPH	RATE OF CLIMB FT./MIN.	FUEL USED FROM S. L., GAL.	IAS, MPH	RATE OF CLIMB FT./MIN.
1600	78	570	0.4	75	470	1.6	72	260

NOTES: 1. Flaps retracted, full throttle, mixture leaned to smooth operation above 5000 ft.
2. Fuel used includes warm-up and take-off allowance.
3. For hot weather, decrease rate of climb 15 ft./min. for each 10°F above standard day temperature for particular altitude.

The take-off is the commencing point for every flight and certain basic conditions will always apply. However due to the various effects of wind, weight, temperature, altitude and nature of the ground surface the techniques employed will vary with the prevailing conditions. These different techniques will all need to be covered during the student's training.

Although the advent of the nosewheel landing gear has removed some of the earlier problems such as a susceptibility to losing directional control during the ground run, aircraft continue to have accidents during this phase of flight. This may indicate that some of the take-off factors are not properly covered during periods of instruction.

In addition to the development of co-ordination and timing in relation to speed and control movements, the student will need a thorough understanding of the aircraft performance capabilities in relation to the take-off run and distance which is available. This will necessitate practical calculations with reference to the Flight/Owner's Manual and the available airfield data.

AIRMANSHIP

A meticulous approach to all drills and checks is needed and the use of check lists whilst on the ground should be encouraged. The latter is an important aid to the pilot who may only fly some 5 hours per year after acquiring his Private Pilot's Licence.

The use of check lists should be avoided in the circuit as this could detract from the student's lookout at a time when the risk of an airborne collision is highest. Statistics reveal that the largest number of mid-air collisions occur in the vicinity of airfields, therefore the maintenance of vigilance throughout the circuit must have absolute priority.

When an electric fuel pump is fitted its purpose is to maintain a supply of fuel to the engine if the mechanical pump should fail. If a failure of this nature occurs the engine will draw most, if not all, the fuel from the lines before the engine stops. It will take time for the electric pump to re-prime these lines, an action which is necessary to allow the engine to start again after the pump is switched on. Due to this delay the electric pump should be left in the 'ON' position until the aircraft has reached a safe height, at least 1000 feet above ground level, and whenever circuits are being practised it should be left on throughout. This will also avoid the possibility of the student mistakenly altering the sequence of 'on/off' switching of the pump, leading to a situation where the pump is switched 'ON' after take-off and 'OFF' prior to landing.

In relation to the data promulgated in the UK Air Pilot and applicable to specific airfields, the definitions of take-off run available and take-off distance available are respectively:

*Take-off Run Available (*TORA)*:* is defined as the length of the runway which is available and suitable for the ground run of an aeroplane taking-off.

Take-off Distance Available (TODA): is defined as the length of the declared take-off run plus the length of the clearway available.

Emergency Distance (ED): is defined as the length of the declared take-off run plus the length of the stopway available.

Stopway: an area at the end of the take-off run available, prepared and designated as a suitable area in which an aircraft can be stopped in the case of a discontinued take-off.

The available take-off run and distance must be adequate for a safe take-off to be conducted. It is not enough to assume that because the take-off is being conducted from an established airfield it automatically means that a sufficient take-off run or distance will be available for any light aircraft in any conditions.

The various factors which affect the length of the take-off run and distance may sometimes be such that a safe take-off cannot be achieved. Therefore, when any doubt exists, for example, under conditions of little wind or when a tailwind exists, or when the surface is soft due to prolonged rain and particularly when two or more of the factors affecting take-off are involved, the Flight/Owner's Manual must be consulted, together with the published take-off data in respect of the particular airfield to ensure that the pilot complies with the regulations detailed in the Air Navigation Order and abides by the principles of flight safety.

BEFORE THE EXERCISE
The Long Briefing should cover the following:

Objectives.

Handling – The factors affecting the length of the take-off run and initial climb.

The correct Lift Off Speed, use of Elevators, Rudder and Power.

Effect of Wind (including the crosswind component).

Effect of Flaps (including the decision to use).

Effect of Ground Surface and Gradient upon the Take-off run.

Effects of Weight, Altitude and Temperature upon Take-off and Climb Performance.

Pre Take-off Checks.

Air Traffic Control Procedures before Take-off.

Drills during and after Take-off.

Short/Soft Field Take-off Considerations.

Tailwheel Considerations (as applicable).

Emergencies:

    Abandoned Take-off.

    Engine Failure after Take-off.

Airmanship.

Common Errors.

The short Pre-Flight Briefing should be based upon the practical aspects of that part of the Long Briefing in relation to the Air Exercise to be covered. In order to promote flight safety after the student leaves the training environment ensure that at some time prior to completing the course the student can interpret the information given in the UK Air Pilot (and similar documents) relating to airfield take-off data and the tables or graphs shown in the Flight/Owner's Manual regarding take-off performance.

As a general rule the student should be introduced to the take-off and allowed to follow through on the controls during take-offs after he has had instruction and practice of taxying. Preparation for take-off practice can most easily be achieved by the method of following through and also ensuring that the student is given ample opportunity to practise taxying. This latter will improve the student's control of speed and direction at low speed which is a forerunner to handling the throttle and rudder at the higher speeds involved during take-offs. Providing the student receives preparation and correct introduction, the take-off should not prove difficult, particularly on nosewheel aircraft.

In those cases where the operating environment or Flight/Owner's Manual normally require the use of flap for take-off the student must also at some stage be given training in flapless take-offs.

DURING THE AIR DEMONSTRATION
Ensure the student appreciates that the pilot is responsible for the

safety of the aircraft, and although the instructions he receives from an Air Traffic Controller are normally necessary to provide positive control for the separation of aircraft it does not mean that such instructions should be obeyed in an automatic manner.

During the student's initial attempts at taking off he will usually require some assistance from the instructor in order that a reasonable degree of safety is maintained. It is therefore a good technique to make him responsible for only part of the procedure whilst the instructor does the rest, for example, checking the RPM, engine temperature and pressure and co-ordinating the required back pressure on the control column to ensure the lift off is made at the correct speed. After a few take-offs the student will be able to assume complete responsibility. Care should nevertheless be exercised to avoid giving more assistance than necessary or it will inhibit the natural development of the student's ability to perform this exercise.

Events happen quickly after the throttle has been opened and the instructor will need to speak clearly and avoid cramming all the points the student needs to know into any one take-off. He will also have to ensure that he speaks loudly enough to be heard above the noise of the engine.

The correct pitch attitude to adopt immediately after take-off and during that period when the airspeed is increasing to the best rate of climb speed must be clearly indicated to the student when the initial demonstrations are given.

CROSSWIND TAKE-OFF

Little value will be obtained from demonstrating crosswind take-offs in conditions where the crosswind component has little effect. Nevertheless the student must have a reasonable amount of practice under crosswind conditions and it may sometimes be necessary for the instructor to obtain ATC clearance to use a take-off direction which will provide the required conditions.

SHORT TAKE-OFF

Ensure the student understands the points made in the Long Briefing relating to the considerations involved when using this method, and on no account teach it as an abstract handling exercise. The student should be made to assess from the figures given in relation to the airfield data and the Flight/Owner's Manual whether such a method will achieve its purpose.

SOFT FIELD TAKE-OFF

This exercise should not be taught when using hard surfaced runways as there is a possibility of the tailplane stern post striking the ground during the take-off roll. An impact of this sort could easily cause damage to the aircraft. On soft ground this problem will not normally arise, however if this technique is employed on rough ground which is hard added care should be exercised to avoid a too high nose attitude during the take-off roll.

EFFECT OF ALTITUDE AND TEMPERATURE
When training is being conducted from relatively low level airfields the effect of Density Altitude can be demonstrated by using less than full power during the take off run and initial climb out. For example, restricting the power used to 90% would approximate a take-off from an airfield 2000 feet above sea level at a temperature of 38° C. However due to the additional TAS required when taking off from this altitude the power should be further restricted to 80% to give a closer approximation of density altitude effects upon aircraft performance. When demonstrating this effect care should be used to ensure a sufficient take-off run and that an obstacle free climb out path is available.

EMERGENCIES
Provided it is safe to do so on the particular training aircraft being used it will be of value during dual instruction to open a door or window during the take-off roll or immediately afterwards. This type of demonstration will take the student through the 'unknown to the known' and prove to him that should this minor emergency arise there will be no danger and that the aircraft will continue to fly normally.

A vital part of good instruction is to DO as well as to TELL, and therefore the abandoned take-off procedure should be physically practised at least once during the student's training.

When demonstrating Engine Failure after Take-off, do so from a height which will permit sufficient time for the demonstration and related explanation of the procedure to be adequately covered. A minimum height of 400 feet will normally be necessary to cover the points which have to be made and allow time for the student to appreciate what has to be done under these circumstances.

The method used to simulate engine failure should be to 'close the throttle', other methods such as turning off the fuel or moving the mixture control to the 'idle cut off position' should be avoided in single-engined aircraft as this practice has often led to the occurrence of an accident.

However, using the throttle to simulate engine failure does lead to the omission of one important drill, that is, the closing of the throttle by the student if a real engine failure occurs. In such an event a temporary or intermittent firing of the engine may occur which could lead the student or inexperienced pilot into a state of indecision resulting in the pilot changing his mind. This could cause rejection of a suitable landing area in an attempt to climb away and carry out a circuit and hopefully near normal landing back on the airfield. In the past this action has sometimes led to disastrous results, and for this reason the action of 'closing the throttle' has become an important part of this simulated procedure.

The problem of throttle closing can however be overcome by briefing the student that whenever you partially close the throttle following a take-off he is to assume an engine failure has occurred, and that he should immediately adopt the correct procedure during which he is expected to close the throttle fully.

When Setting Up a Practice Situation:

Do take notice of other aircraft in the circuit and particularly those taking off behind you. It is also necessary to use some form of R/T call which will enable the ATC unit and other aircraft in the circuit to know what you are doing.

Do keep an eye on your student to ensure he does not get carried away with his practice and actually switch or turn anything OFF.

Do remember to make an R/T call signifying you are climbing away following your practice. This is to assist the air traffic controller and other aircraft in the circuit.

Do take care to re-position your aircraft back into the circuit in a manner which will avoid inconvenience to others and prevent hazardous situations from occurring.

COMMON ERRORS

The student's ability to display a high standard of airmanship will be lacking during the initial stage of practice in this exercise due mainly to the workload involved. Whereas this must be accepted in the early stages it will become unacceptable as his experience and competence to handle the aircraft increases.

• The necessity for the student to make firm and confident decisions during this exercise is paramount and it is only after the development of this attribute that the student can be considered as fit for Solo flight.

• At first a common error will be for the aircraft to take control of the student, e.g. lift off occurring at too high an airspeed, and although this is understandable during early practice the ability to control both the aircraft and the situation must be developed as quickly as possible. The time this takes will depend upon the student and the environment in which he is being trained, i.e. busy airfields with mixed air traffic, or quiet grass airfields which may not have ATC facilities.

• Failures to keep straight in the early stages may be due to not looking sufficiently far ahead when distant reference features are not available or to a tendency to over control, this latter should quickly disappear with practice.

• Over concentration is quite common with many students in the initial stages of any flight and the instructor must make a positive effort to get the student to relax.

• Sometimes a student will get the tail too high during the initial stage of take-off in tailwheel aircraft. The instructor must anticipate this error in order to prevent a dangerous situation from developing.

• Once airborne the student will often be unable to maintain a track in line with the runway centre line, this will only be overcome with practice. Although at first the heading indicator will not normally be utilised, this valuable aid to the maintenance of heading during the climb away can normally be introduced prior to First Solo.

• During the practice of Engine Failure after Take-off the two most common faults will usually be a reluctance to lower the aircraft nose sufficiently to maintain a safe speed for the existing conditions, and the lack of a quick decision in relation to the selection of a landing path. In this latter case the student must be encouraged to look either side of the aircraft nose rather than develop the habit of only looking out ahead and to the left, a common failing when side by side seating aircraft are used.

The psychological effects on a pilot when the engine fails shortly after take-off must be fully appreciated and discussed with all students. It is not sufficient to merely demonstrate and practise the correct procedures, the pilot must develop the necessary self discipline to avoid the strong tendency to turn back to the airfield when this situation occurs at low height.

Take-off and Climb to Downwind Position

Long Briefing

OBJECTIVES

The purpose of this exercise is to provide the student with a thorough understanding of the various factors concerned with the take-off and the development of ability to safely take the aircraft off the ground, establish a climb and fly to the downwind position of the circuit.

The development of ability to handle the aircraft during this phase of flight in a safe manner can only be achieved by a thorough knowledge of the considerations involved.

INTRODUCTION

The act of taking off is relatively simple, particularly in nosewheel aircraft. It can however present many hazards and an appreciation of the factors concerned together with the use of correct judgement and technique cannot be over emphasised.

HANDLING – FACTORS AFFECTING THE LENGTH OF TAKE-OFF RUN AND INITIAL CLIMB

There are many factors to be considered in relation to the aircraft performance during the take-off and initial climb. Performance in this flight phase starts with a condition of accelerated motion and finishes with the aircraft being established in the climb at the correct airspeed and at a safe height. The criteria for the take-off will depend upon the length of take-off run available, the height of obstructions in the immediate climbing path, and the effect of ground surface, wind, weight, and atmospheric density.

During the take-off the aircraft will have to be accelerated from a standstill to the lift off speed. Therefore the immediate factors affecting this aspect of performance will be:

1. The lift-off speed, which is normally derived from the stalling or minimum flying speed. In order to ensure a satisfactory degree of control immediately after the aircraft becomes airborne this speed is generally calculated as 1.15 times the stalling speed.
2. The acceleration experienced during the take-off run. The

acceleration of an aircraft varies directly with the unbalance of the Thrust and Drag forces in relation to the retarding effect of the surface (rolling friction), and inversely as the mass of the aircraft.
3. The take-off length will be a function of both the acceleration and the aircraft speed.

The relationship between acceleration and velocity is very complex to produce with mathematical accuracy, however to understand the principles involved during the take-off run a degree of simplicity can be accepted, and using basic physics a relationship of acceleration, velocity and distance for a uniformly accelerated motion can be defined by the following equation:

$$S = \frac{V^2}{2a}$$

Where S = acceleration distance in feet
       V = final velocity in feet per second, accelerating uniformly and starting at zero velocity
       a = acceleration, feet per second^2

This equation could therefore relate the take-off distance in terms of speed and acceleration. The distance will vary directly as the square of the velocity and inversely as the acceleration. For example, assuming an aircraft is accelerated uniformly from zero speed to a take-off speed of 50 kts with an acceleration of 6.434 feet per second^2 (or, 0.2g, since g = 32.17 ft per second^2) the take-off distance would be:

$$S = \frac{V}{2a} = \frac{84.5^2}{(2)\,(6.434)} = 558 \text{ feet}$$

If the factors affecting engine power and or thrust were such as to reduce the acceleration developed by 10%, the length of the take-off run would be increased by 11.1% or if due to increase of weight or reduction of air density the lift-off speed was increased by 10% the required take-off run would be increased by 21%.

These figures reveal that in order to take-off safely a correct allowance must be made for the effects of any power loss due to temperature or density and for any higher speeds necessary to provide added lift to balance additional weight, and for a higher TAS required for a given IAS as a result of high ambient temperature or lower density.

CORRECT LIFT-OFF SPEED, USE OF ELEVATORS, RUDDER AND POWER
The minimum take-off run and take-off distance will normally be of primary interest during the transition from the beginning of the take-off roll to the establishment of the normal climb. The take-off run is that distance the aircraft travels until it becomes airborne. The take-off distance is the distance taken for the aircraft to reach an arbitrary height of 50 feet. These figures for a particular aircraft in a standard set of conditions can be found by reference to the Flight/Owner's Manual. Both of these distances are related to the aircraft becoming airborne at the correct speed for the conditions under which it is operating at the time.

Varying conditions may make a difference in the handling technique used during the take-off run or initial climb out. These conditions include the aircraft weight, the type of surface being used e.g. a smooth hard surface, a rough field, a soft field or one where the grass is long or a sloping surface is involved, and the effects of strong gusty winds will also have to be considered.

The Use of Elevators

When taking off from relatively smooth and firm surfaces the purpose of the elevators during the take-off roll will initially be to adjust the aircraft attitude so that the thrust line is approximately parallel to the ground. This will ensure that the thrust is producing the maximum effect in the direction of desired motion and also that the aerodynamic drag is kept to a minimum. In the case of nosewheel aircraft a slight back pressure on the control column will be necessary early in the take-off to start transferring weight from the nosewheel, thus minimising the loads on it. Their second function will be to rotate the aircraft clear of the ground when the correct lift-off speed is reached. It can be appreciated from the considerations outlined on the previous pages that a knowledge of the correct lift-off speed is very important when operating from areas with restricted take-off lengths, but it is also important when operating from large airfields with long runways because take-off speeds in excess of those needed will lead to unnecessary loads on the landing gear.

To sum up, the misuse of elevators during the take-off can increase the length of the take-off run and also create a marginal flight condition. If the control column is moved back too early sufficient lift may be obtained from the increased angle of attack to allow the aircraft to become airborne, but in a condition close to the stall and with a speed too low for sustained flight. In such circumstances the pilot would not be able to control the aircraft in event of either engine malfunction or an inopportune gust of wind.

At the other extreme, if the pilot delays lift-off by moving the control column back too late or by holding the aircraft down too long, then

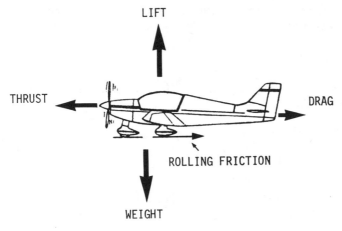

LIFT

THRUST

DRAG

ROLLING FRICTION

WEIGHT

Fig. 12-1

the take-off run will be unnecessarily increased to the extent where the landing gear would be taking excess strain and the climb-out path could be too low for safety. Therefore the ideal is that the aircraft becomes airborne in the shortest possible run consistent with safe operation and its ability to remain airborne and accelerate after lift-off.

Once the best rate of climb speed has been attained this should be held until the aircraft has reached a safe altitude. This altitude may vary with the terrain surrounding the airfield but should not in any event be less than 500 feet above ground. A combination of best rate of climb speed and maximum power will ensure that height is gained as quickly as possible to place the aircraft at such a height that in the event of engine failure a greater margin of safety will be available.

Use of Rudder
The rudder is used to maintain the aircraft direction throughout the take-off roll. With nosewheel aircraft the maintenance of heading is relatively simple due to the effectiveness of the nosewheel steering. At the stage where the nosewheel is lifted clear of the ground the higher speed will enable the rudder to be used more effectively. At the commencement of the take-off it will be necessary to align the aircraft with the runway centreline and straighten the nosewheel by rolling forward a few yards prior to the application of take-off power.

In the case of tailwheel aircraft the control of direction is more difficult and any tendency for the aircraft to change its direction during the early stages of the take-off roll must be corrected quickly and the application of rudder will need to be fairly coarse to be suficiently effective at low speeds. However as the speed rises the rudder will become more efficient and directional control will be easier to achieve.

Use of Power
When power is applied a condition of yaw will tend to occur. There are four elements which produce this yaw about the vertical axis of the aircraft. These are:

1. Torque Reaction
2. Effect of Slipstream
3. Gyroscopic Action of the Propeller
4. Asymmetric Blade Effect

Torque reaction involves Newton's Third Law of Motion which is that for every action there is an equal and opposite reaction. In relation to the application of power this simply means that as the propeller is revolving in one direction, an equal force is trying to rotate the aircraft in the opposite direction.

Fig. 12-2

During flight, this force is acting around the longitudinal axis of the aircraft but at normal flying speeds the effect is very slight in comparison with the lateral stability of the aircraft.

During the take-off roll the effect of torque causes more pressure to be experienced on one main landing wheel than the other and results in a yawing moment around the vertical axis. The direction of this yawing moment depends upon the direction of propeller rotation and as most light aircraft are equipped with propellers which rotate clockwise (as viewed from the pilot's seat) it is usually the left wheel which is pressed on the ground harder and so generally the effect of torque is to cause a yawing moment to the left. The magnitude of this moment is dependent upon the:

Amount of horsepower developed.
Size of the propeller and the RPM used.

Size of the aircraft.

Type of ground surface.

Although in small training aircraft the first three variables are relatively small they can become appreciable in the higher performance aircraft which a private pilot may fly after his training is completed.

Effect of Slipstream

The high-speed rotation of an aircraft propeller gives a spiral rotation to the slipstream. At high propeller speeds and low forward speed this corkscrew motion is tight and at its most effective in producing yaw. As the forward speed increases, the corkscrew elongates and becomes less effective.

Fig. 12-3

When the slipstream produces an angle of attack on the left side of the vertical fin, it causes a horizontal lift force and a moment around the vertical axis to the left. The tighter the slipstream spiral the larger will be the angle of attack and the greater the moment produced. The pilot will have to counteract this force through correct use of the rudder.

In addition to this the spiral path of the slipstream also causes a turning moment around the longitudal axis. As the spiral moves aft it strikes all tail surfaces (horizontal stabiliser and vertical fin) causing a rolling moment to the right. The tighter the spiral the stronger the rolling moment. The rolling moment caused by the spiral path of the slipstream is to the right, whilst the rolling moment caused by torque reaction is to the left; therefore in effect, one is counteracting the other. However it must be kept in mind that the effect of these forces vary and it is up to the pilot to apply a correcting action through the use of the rudder.

Gyroscopic Action of the Propeller

Before the gyroscopic effects of the propeller can be properly understood, it is necessary to recall the basic principles of a gyro. The practical applications of a gyro are based upon two fundamental properties, 'Rigidity in Space' and 'Precession'.

Fig. 12-4

Precession is the resultant action or deflection of a spinning rotor when a force is applied to its rim. As can be seen in fig. 12-4, the resulting force is 90° ahead of the point of application and in the direction of the gyro rotation. The rotating propeller of an aircraft makes a very good gyro and has the same properties. Any time a force is applied to deflect the propeller out of its plane of rotation, the resulting force acts at 90° in the direction of rotation and in the direction of application, causing a pitching moment, a yawing moment, or a combination of the two depending upon the point at which the force was applied.

This element of torque is most prominent when associated with tailwheel aircraft, and it occurs when the tail is being raised during the take-off run. This has the same effect as applying a force at the top of the propeller's plane of rotation as viewed from the cockpit. The magnitude of this moment depends on several variables; one of which is the abruptness with which the tail is raised (or amount of force applied). However, precession or gyroscopic action, occurs when a force is applied to the rim of a propeller's plane of rotation and the resultant force will be 90° from the point of application and along the direction of rotation. This will cause the aircraft to yaw left or right, depending on the direction of propeller rotation, and to pitch up or down, or to combine pitching or yawing.

From this it can be seen that as a result of gyroscopic action, it is necessary for the pilot to use elevator and rudder to prevent the occurrence of undesirable yawing effects whenever the pitch attitude is markedly changed or a yaw occurs during the take-off run.

Asymmetric Blade Effect
This is caused by the resultant of the velocity generated by the propeller blade in its plane of rotation and the speed of the aircraft

during the take-off. It will only be significant when the aircraft operates at high angles of attack such as the case of the tailwheel aircraft during the initial stages of the take-off or to nosewheel aircraft during the rotation on lift-off.

With the exception of the small rolling moment caused by the spiral path of the slipstream all the other elements which produce a yaw during take-off work in the same direction and when the propeller rotation is clockwise the effect will be to cause the aircraft to yaw to the left on take-off. Nevertheless it is not advisable to apply right rudder automatically during a take-off, because if a crosswind condition exists from the right the automatic use of right rudder will add to the tendency to yaw to the right from such a crosswind.

In summary, power must be applied gradually otherwise the aircraft may yaw sharply. Sudden and full power application should be avoided at the commencement of the take-off run. The greater the power used, the better the acceleration of the aircraft, the shorter the take-off run, and the sooner the aircraft will gain height. For these reasons, training aircraft will require the use of full power for a safe take-off.

EFFECT OF WIND

Of the various factors which affect the performance of the aircraft during take-off the effect of wind is by far the most significant in relation to the take-off run and distance.

The effect of a headwind is that it enables the aircraft to reach the take-off speed at a lower ground speed, whilst the effect of a tailwind requires the aircraft to attain a greater ground speed to achieve the take-off speed. The direct relationship in practical terms of the effect of a head or tail wind can better be appreciated by reference to fig. 12-5. From this it can be seen that a headwind which is 10% of the lift-off speed will reduce the ground distance travelled by approximately 20%. However a tailwind which is 10% of the lift-off speed will increase the distance travelled by approximately 20%.

Assuming a lift-off speed of 50 kts a tailwind of only 5 kts can therefore result in an increase of the take-off run by some 40% in comparison to taking off with a headwind of 5 kts.

The strength and direction also has a direct relation to the angle of climb in that a steeper angle is achieved into a headwind and a shallower angle of climb will occur if a tailwind condition exists. The angle of climb has a direct bearing upon the take-off distance (obstacle clearance) which can be achieved. A point which is not always appreciated is that when a zero wind exists at the surface a tailwind can often exist at a low altitude above the ground with a consequent deterioration in the climbing angle.

During strong, gusty winds the pilot should take-off at a slightly

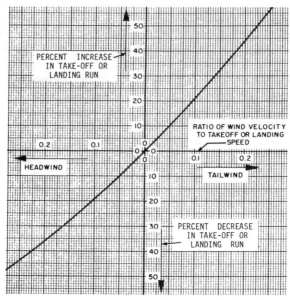

Fig. 12-5

higher speed than normal to ensure adequate control of the aircraft when encountering such gusts immediately after lift-off. While it is always preferable to take-off into wind there will be occasions when this is neither possible or practical, for example:

> When runways are used, the take-off direction is often out of line with the prevailing wind and the effects of a crosswind during and immediately after the take-off must be taken into account.

During the crosswind take-off there will exist a side force on the keel surface of the aircraft and as most of this keel surface is behind the c.g. the tendency will be for the aircraft to yaw into the direction from which the wind is coming. This has to be corrected for by the use of rudder during the take-off roll. Apart from the effect of the wind on the keel surface there will also be a tendency for the wing which is on the side from which the wind is coming to be lifted up as the speed increases throughout the take-off roll. This has to be counteracted by raising the aileron on that side to reduce the lift from the wing. When strong crosswind conditions prevail a large amount of aileron movement will initially be required, but as the aircraft accelerates to higher speeds and the ailerons become more effective, the amount of aileron movement must be reduced.

Due to the side force which exists during a crosswind take-off the aircraft will commence drifting sideways during and immediately after the lift-off. To appreciate this tendency during the final stage of the take-off run and just prior to lifting off it should be borne in mind that when the aircraft commences its take-off roll all the weight is being supported by the landing gear. As the speed increases this weight is gradually transferred to the wings and during this process the effect of the wind upon the side surface of the aircraft increases, and if sufficiently strong can cause the aircraft to commence drifting sideways whilst still on the gorund. This action could impose unacceptable stresses upon the landing gear and also give problems in the control of the aircraft.

It is particularly important on these occasions to use the correct lift off speed, this will give adequate insurance against the possibility of touching down again and one which will also ensure the sideways stress on the landing gear does not become severe. All aircraft have a limiting crosswind component and when this is exceeded during take-off the design tolerances relating to the landing gear sideways stress force will also be exceeded. This could lead to a weakening of the landing gear components and the danger of structural failure on that particular flight or on a subsequent one.

The limiting crosswind component will normally be placarded in the cockpit or found from the aircraft manual. If this figure is not available a safe and simple calculation can be made using 0.2 of the V_{S1} or if flap is used 0.2 of the V_{S0}. For example, if the V_{S1} is 50 kts then the maximum crosswind component can safely be assumed as 10 kts.

There are various methods used to assess the crosswind component when the wind velocity and the take-off direction are known. A simple rule of thumb is as follows:

Take-off 30° out of wind . . . crosswind component = ½ the wind strength.

45° out of wind . . . crosswind component = ¾ the wind strength.

60° out of wind . . . crosswind component = ⁹⁄₁₀ the wind strength.

90° out of wind . . . crosswind component = total wind speed.

Assuming a wind velocity of 330/20 kts and a take-off heading of 300° the above method will give the crosswind component as 10 kts.

The graph at fig. 12-6 shows the effect of a 20 knot wind which is 30° across the direction of the take-off path. A is the wind angle in relation to the take-off heading. B is the point on this angle which intersects the wind strength arc and following this down the graph reveals the strength of the crosswind component at C (10 kts). The headwind component under these conditions is shown at D (17 kts).

The tailwheel aircraft is particularly susceptible to the develop-

Fig. 12-6

Fig. 12-7

ment of a yaw during taxying and take-off, especially when a crosswind condition exists. This tendency is self sustaining and is due to the position of the c.g. in relation to the pivot point between the main wheels.

Figure 12-7 shows that when an aircraft yaws off heading during the ground roll the inertia will initially act straight ahead along the original direction of travel. In the case of a tailwheel aircraft, (a) the weight being behind the pivot point will act forward and so further increase the tendency to swing. The nosewheel aircraft (b) will however have its c.g. ahead of the pivot point and as a result the effect of inertia will tend to damp out the turning moment.

A common take-off technique in relation to tailwheel aircraft is to get the aircraft into the level attitude as soon as possible after the application of power and then apply slight back pressure on the control column so that it flies off the ground when it is ready. This does however lead to the possibility of becoming airborne prematurely and if this happens during a crosswind take-off the aircraft will usually touch down again. During the period when the wheels recontact the ground the aircraft will be drifting sideways and a sideways stress will be placed on the landing gear. Therefore the technique for crosswind take-offs in a tailwheel aircraft is to hold it down to a higher than normal speed before lift off and so reduce any possibility of sinking back to the ground immediately following take-off.

The advent of the nosewheel landing gear has made control of direction considerably easier than in the tailwheel type and the pilot can therefore monitor the ASI more closely and without the attendant problems of loss of directional control, and as a result the pilot is more easily able to lift off at an exact and correct speed.

Once the aircraft is safely airborne it will be necessary to make a shallow turn towards the prevailing wind direction to counteract the drift experienced during the climb out. This action will enable the aircraft to maintain a track over the ground which is coincident with the take-off heading.

An important factor in relation to a crosswind is that the headwind component for any given wind strength will be less. A rule of thumb calculation for this effect can be carried out by use of the following guide:

Take-off   30° out of wind . . . headwind component = $^9\!/_{10}$ the wind strength.

45° out of wind . . . headwind component = $^3\!/_4$ the wind strength.

60° out of wind . . . headwind component = $^1\!/_2$ the wind strength.

For example, reference to these figures or the graph at fig. 12-6 will show that a 30° crosswind of 20 kts will reduce the headwind component to 17 kts. This reduction in headwind component becomes very significant at larger crosswind angles and at 60° the original wind strength of 20 kts is halved.

EFFECT OF FLAPS

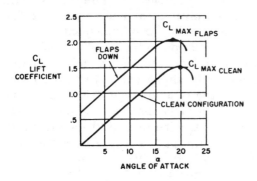

Fig. 12-8

The use of flaps during the take-off will lower the stalling speed for any condition of weight and in consequence the lift off speed will be lower. This generally reduces the length of the take-off run but may not give any reduction in take-off distance because application of flap usually causes a reduction in the rate of climb. Due to the variation between different aircraft in relation to the benefits obtained from the use of flap it will be necessary to consult the Flight/Owner's Manual or Pilot's Operating Handbook for type to see under what conditions the use of flap is recommended.

The decision on whether to use flap during take-off will therefore depend upon the manufacturer's recommendations and the prevailing circumstances. The use of flap when taking off from soft or rough surfaces will however be beneficial and this aspect is covered under the next heading.

EFFECT OF GROUND SURFACE AND GRADIENT UPON THE TAKE-OFF RUN

There may be occasions when an aircraft has to take-off from a surface which has been softened by a long rainy spell. In this event it would be an advantage to use flap and so obtain a lower lift-off speed. Soft surfaces significantly increase the rolling friction and the take-off run can as a result be appreciably increased.

When using soft ground the take-off run will be increased by some 10% but dependent upon the degree of softness this increase can be as high as 50% or more, particularly if the aircraft is operating at all-up weight.

On nosewheel aircraft one important factor when taking off in these circumstances is the need to raise the nosewheel, or at least get the weight off it as early as possible. When long grass or rough ground has to be negotiated during take-off the soft field considerations will also apply, and the take-off technique adjusted accordingly. In the case of rough ground a primary need will be to protect the landing gear and in particular the nosewheel. The use of flap will materially assist in this as a lower lift-off speed will be achieved. In

Fig. 12-9

the same way that drag increases by the square of the speed, so too will the increase of strain imposed upon the landing gear; therefore a small reduction in lift-off speed will result in a significant reduction to the shocks absorbed by the nose and main wheel structures.

Another factor in relation to the ground surface is the effect of runway gradient. The effect of a runway slope upon take-off distance is due to the component of weight along the inclined path of the aircraft. A slope of 1% would produce a force component along the aircraft path which is 1% of the all-up weight. A downslope would produce an accelerating force and an upslope would produce a retarding force. In the second case the retarding force adds to the drag and rolling friction to reduce the aircraft acceleration, and this has a marked effect upon small training aircraft which normally have relatively low thrust to weight ratios, i.e. $\dfrac{\text{HP available}}{\text{weight}}$.

As a rule of thumb a 2° upslope will increase the take-off run by some 20% and although the surface gradients found on normal airfields are small, their significance must become a primary consideration when operating at high weight and in light winds from airstrips or similar fields.

With small gradients the wind is the primary factor in deciding the take-off direction and it will be more beneficial to take-off into wind even though this means accepting an uphill gradient. However, when the gradient becomes large the existence of an up or downslope will become the primary consideration.

EFFECT OF WEIGHT, ALTITUDE AND TEMPERATURE
Referring back to fig. 10-10 it can be seen that an increase in the all-up weight of 10% will increase the stall speed by 5%, which means that the lift-off speed will be increased by 5%. However, increasing the weight has a threefold effect:

1.   Increased take-off speed.
2.   A greater mass to be accelerated.
3.   An increased retarding force.

Due to these three factors the net result of increasing the weight by 5% will be to increase the take-off run by at least 25% to 30% in those aircraft with relatively low thrust weight ratios.

The effect of pressure altitude and air temperature primarily defines 'Density Altitude' and this altitude can have a significant effect upon aircraft performance. An increase in density altitude will have a twofold effect upon the take-off run and rate of climb:

1.   An increased take-off speed (TAS) required.
2.   A reduction in engine power.

When an aircraft is taking off at an altitude above standard sea level it will still require the same dynamic pressure equivalent to become airborne at the lift coefficient coincident with lift-off. Therefore the aircraft will take off at the same equivalent airspeed (EAS) as at standard sea level, but due to the lower density the true airspeed (TAS) will be greater.

The effect of a high density altitude on the power developed from the engine is adverse, and less power will be available for take-off. A high density altitude means the air has a density associated with a high altitude in the standard atmosphere, i.e. a low density. Although the performance aspects of high density altitudes are normally absent when operating from relatively low airfields in temperate regions, a pilot will not necessarily be confined to operating in such areas and he should therefore have an appreciation of altitude and temperature effects upon the performance of an aircraft.

Density altitude is calculated from pressure altitude corrected for non standard temperature, and the approximate effects are as follows:

For every 1000 feet a.m.s.l. the take-off run is increased by 10%.
For every 10° C above standard (15° C) the take-off run is increased by 10%.

A high density altitude will also reduce the rate of climb and the climb angle will be noticeably flatter, with an obvious reduction in obstacle clearance capability immediately after take-off.

PRE TAKE-OFF CHECKS

Prior to every take-off a system of checking certain essential items must be strictly adhered to. Due to the increased complexity of modern light aircraft and the fact that most private pilots fly at infrequent intervals, the use of a check list is an insurance against forgetting any of these items.

The check list should be used correctly and followed carefully. The item must be read out and then the action accomplished. The tendency to recite checks without actually doing them, or doing some checks from memory and some from the check list must be guarded against at all times.

The exact checks and the order in which they are carried out will depend upon the particular aircraft, and to a certain extent the training organisation concerned. For this reason they are not tabulated in this manual. The basic purpose of these checks is to ensure a final review of the serviceability and correct settings of the essential systems and aircraft services required for the flight. The number of items included in this procedure will vary according to aircraft type and the operating environment, however they should not be expanded to more than is necessary, or the important items will be more easily missed or forgotten.

AIR TRAFFIC CONTROL PROCEDURES BEFORE TAKE-OFF

When an ATC facility exists at the airfield of departure it will be an important part of the take-off procedure to request departure clearance. Prior to this R/T transmission the pilot should ensure the approach and take-off path are clear of other aircraft. This action is a vital part of the airmanship considerations and will help to reinforce the essential habit of checking the runway and approach path when operating in conditions where no ATC facility is available.

DRILLS DURING AND AFTER TAKE-OFF

Although the power check prior to take-off (see page 2-9) includes checking the magnetos, oil temperature and pressure, it is an essential part of any take-off to re-check these readings during the take-off run after full power has been applied.

An engine or aircraft system which becomes unserviceable can do so without regard to the checks made previously by the pilot. By checking the RPM, oil temperatures, ASI, and where applicable the fuel pressure or fuel flow after full power has been applied the pilot is able to ascertain the exact serviceability state of these systems at the most vital moment of the flight.

Any noted indication of a system malfunction or positive lack of power at this stage will alert the pilot to close the throttle and abandon the take-off whilst the aircraft is still on the ground. This action will prevent the occurrence of an emergency situation which would otherwise occur at low height following the take-off.

Once safely established in flight the RPM, oil temperatures and pressure, and when applicable the fuel pressure or fuel flow, should be re-checked during the initial climb out. When flap has been used the retraction procedure can be phased in at this stage.

INTO WIND TAKE-OFF

Where possible the take-off is made into the direction of the prevailing wind for the following reasons:

1. It gives the shortest take-off run and the lowest ground speed at lift-off.
2. There will be no tendency for the aircraft to drift sideways, and therefore will ensure better directional control and less strain on the landing gear.
3. It gives a steeper climb angle which together with the shorter take-off run will provide a better clearance from obstacles in the aircraft climb path, and a lower landing speed and shorter stopping distance should the engine malfunction during or immediately after take-off.

For normal take-offs the aircraft must be positioned in the centre of the runway or take-off path in use and then taxied forward a short distance to enable the nose or tailwheel to be centred. When available a reference feature in the distance should be noted in order to assist in the maintenance of heading during the take-off roll. When a reference feature is not available the student should look well ahead of the aircraft, and when runways are used their sidelines converging into the distance will be of considerable assistance.

The student must ensure that his heels are resting on the floor and the balls of his feet are placed firmly on the rudder pedals; this will avoid the inadvertent application of brakes during the take-off roll. Even when the particular training aircraft is not equipped with toe brakes this action will still be applicable, as it will develop the habit of avoiding the use of brakes during normal take-offs on those aircraft fitted with toe brakes, which the pilot may fly at a later stage of his flying.

The throttle should be opened fully but smoothly and the aircraft direction controlled by the use of rudder. Abrupt opening of the throttle to the fully open position will give little, if any, benefit in reducing the length of the take-off run and is more likely to introduce a tendency for the aircraft to swing in the initial stages. When the power has been fully applied a small back pressure should be applied to the control column to ensure that the weight is gradually taken off the nosewheel as the speed increases. By the time the RPM, oil pressure, temperatures and ASI have been checked the aircraft will be approaching the lift-off speed. At this stage a positive application of back pressure will take the aircraft cleanly into the air and the nose should be held in a slightly lower pitch attitude than is used for the normal climb. This will enable the aircraft to attain the 'Take-Off Safety Speed' quickly.

Note: This take-off Safety Speed is sometimes quoted in aircraft manuals and is the speed derived from 1.2 the V_{S1} for the aircraft concerned. Its use is to ensure that adequate control is available in the event of a sudden engine failure immediately after take-off.

From the point of lift-off the ailerons and rudder will be used in the normal manner to achieve and maintain lateral level and balance. Within a few seconds after take-off the maximum rate of climb speed will be reached, and the pitch attitude can then be adjusted to maintain this airspeed until at a safe height above the ground (at least 500 feet).

TAILWHEEL CONSIDERATIONS
With a tailwheel type aircraft a slight forward pressure will need to be applied to the control column as full power is set. This is to raise the tail into the flying attitude and reduce the drag. The student must be very alert for any tendency of a swing to develop during this stage of the take-off and prompt and correct application of rudder will be necessary if the aircraft deviates even a small amount from the original heading.

As the speed increases, directional control will improve as the rudder becomes more effective, and during this increase of speed the forward pressure on the control column will normally have to be changed to a gentle back pressure, and as the lift-off speed is reached a small further amount of back pressure will lift the aircraft cleanly off the ground.

AFTER TAKE-OFF
The normal procedure for light aircraft is to continue climbing to a height of 500 feet a.g.l. and then commence a climbing turn to the crosswind leg which is at 90° to the take-off path. When the circuit height of 800 or 1000 feet is reaached the aircraft is established in level flight. When a rectangular circuit is being used, the heading on the crosswind leg must be adjusted to take into account the wind effect and so maintain the required track.

While flying the crosswind leg a careful lookout must be

CROSSWIND LEG

LEFT DOWNWIND LEG

maintained for other aircraft on the circuit, and particularly for those aircraft which may be rejoining in the downwind position or into the crosswind leg. When at a suitable distance out from the runway the aircraft should be turned onto the downward leg, and the R/T call made in the appropriate position. On this leg it will also be necessary to allow for any crosswind effect which may prevail at circuit height.

Fig. 12-10

The level and descending turns used in the circuit should normally be carried out at approximately 30° of bank rather than using rate one turns, which take longer to complete. The main reason for this is that regardless of whether high or low wing aircraft are used a large blind area will be present at the same level throughout the turn, e.g. the high wing will produce a blind area into the direction of turn, whilst a low wing aircraft will have a blind area beneath the raised wing, preventing the pilot in either case from seeing any aircraft which are converging at the same level. Reducing the length of time that these blind areas exist is therefore an advantage, provided the turns are not allowed to become too steep.

SAFEGUARDING THE NOSEWHEEL

On tricycle gear aircraft the nosewheel supports a significant part of the aircraft weight and is the weakest part of the landing gear structure. This must be borne in mind when using soft or rough surfaces, but even when smooth runways are used, due regard must be given to its protection during the take-off roll.

The correct safeguard procedure is to get the weight off the nosewheel as early as possible consistent with safe directional control. This technique will also reduce the possibility of the occurrence of 'Wheelbarrowing', a condition which can sometimes develop if the nosewheel is held down after the mainplanes have produced sufficient lift for flight, and consists of a porpoising action which not only produces unnecessary strain on the nose and main wheels but also leads to difficulties in controlling the aircraft.

CROSSWIND TAKE-OFF

When a small crosswind component prevails, the take-off technique will be almost the same as for an into wind take-off. A quicker reaction to any divergence of the aircraft heading into the direction of the prevailing wind will however be required.

When the crosswind component is larger, it will be necessary to vary the take-off technique to ensure adequate control throughout the take-off run. The take-off should be commenced in the normal way, but the aileron on the side from which the wind is coming must be raised, and in strong crosswinds the initial application of back pressure on the control column delayed. As the aircraft gathers speed during the take-off roll the ailerons will become more effective and should gradually be returned as necessary towards the neutral position to avoid the opposite wing from rising.

At the lift-off speed the aircraft must be taken cleanly off the ground by positive back pressure on the control column, whilst the wings are kept level. When safely established in the climb the aircraft should be turned partially into the direction of the wind to ensure a climb-out path along the extended centre line of the runway.

SHORT FIELD TAKE-OFF

The short field take-off is a procedure which is carried out when obstruction clearance on the take-off path is considered to be critical. The object in this type of take-off is to obtain the shortest take-off distance, and this means achieving the steepest angle of climb. The basic principle in achieving the best climbing angle is that for a given rate of climb any reduction in climbing speed will give an increase in the time the aircraft takes to cover a given forward distance. Provided the rate of climb is not decreased by this method, the aircraft will get to a greater height in a given distance.

In fig. 12-11 the aircraft climbing at 70 m.p.h. will take 26 seconds to travel 2640 feet ($\frac{1}{2}$ statute mile) and at a climb rate of 500 f.p.m. it will reach 214 feet in the 26 seconds. In fig. 12-12 the same aircraft climbing at 60 m.p.h. will take 30 seconds to travel the same distance and if it can maintain the original climb rate of 500 f.p.m. it will reach a height of 250 feet in the 30 seconds, thereby giving it an extra 35 feet of height in the same distance. The aircraft at fig. 12-12 will therefore have achieved a greater angle of climb. However, the

Fig. 12-11

Fig. 12-12

decision as to whether the lower airspeed (best angle of climb speed V_X) will be of sufficient benefit to ensure a safe take-off in an actual situation will probably be debatable for the following reasons:

● This type of take-off would usually be employed in restricted areas such as a small airstrip or farm field. The ability to relate the aircraft performance figures to the distance available would require accurate measurement of ground distance and obstacle height, neither of which may be available.

● The degree of surface roughness and gradient will also be difficult to assess, together with any exact figures of wind speed and direction.

● The effect of density altitude, though normally small (except at high elevation airfields) could well have a critical effect under such restricted take-off conditions.

This does not necessarily mean that the short take-off technique should be avoided as an operational procedure, but rather that its use should be confined to those conditions when it can be ensured the take-off distance will be sufficient but an added safety factor would be an advantage.

Short Take-Off Technique

This technique will normally relate to take-off distance, and having first established that the take-off can be safely conducted, the maximum advantage of a head headwind should be utilised where possible. For example, a headwind component of 15 kts would have more effect in reducing the take-off distance and increasing the climb angle than all the other factors of the short take-off technique.

The longest possible run should be utilised and the power applied against the brakes if a suitable braking surface exists. However, if loose stones cover the area at the commencement of the take-off run it will be inadvisable to apply high power against the brakes because of the risk of damage to the propeller from stones or gravel being sucked up by the airscrew blades.

The practical value of opening up to full power against the brakes lies more in the ability to check that full power is available, and that the oil pressure, temperatures (and when applicable the fuel flow or pressure) remain normal prior to the commencement of the take-off run. If at any stage the available power overcomes the braking action the brakes should be released immediately or valuable distance will be wasted. The lift-off should be made at the correct speed applicable to the aircraft weight, and the initial climbing speed (best angle of climb speed) should be as recommended in the Flight/Owner's Manual/Pilot's Operating Handbook.

The use of flaps for a short field take-off will often depend more upon the type of ground surface being used, i.e. the more the surface friction the greater will be the advantage of using flaps provided a lower lift-off speed can be utilised. However, once again the Flight/Owner's Manual/Pilot's Operating Handbook for the particular aircraft type will normally detail the conditions for the use of flaps.

Once the obstacle(s) have been cleared the flaps (if used) can be raised as the normal climbing speed is being assumed.

SOFT FIELD TAKE-OFF
The considerations applicable to soft-field take-offs have been covered under the Effect of Ground Surface, but the following paragraphs outline the technique for taking off from soft fields, including snow covered surfaces, long grass or rough ground.

Soft Field Take-Off Technique
The use of flap will normally give an advantage, and 10° to 20° can be usefully employed to obtain a lower lift-off speed. The exact amount of flap applicable to aircraft type will usually be specified in the Flight/Owner's Manual.

The aircraft may in the case of a very soft surface have to be kept moving and therefore a rolling start may be advisable. However the speed during this transition from taxying to take-off should be carefully controlled during the turn into the take-off direction.

As full power is applied the control column should initially be brought well back in the case of nosewheel aircraft. As the speed increases the elevators will become more effective and the control column will have to be gradually eased forward to avoid a too-high nose attitude. In this condition the weight will automatically be transferred from the wheels to the wings as the lift increases and the

Immediately After Lift Off

Immediately Following
Application of Power

Fig. 12-13

aircraft will become airborne at the lowest airspeed. Immediately
after the wheels leave the ground the nose attitude should be
carefully lowered so that the airspeed can increase quickly to the
climbing speed. At a safe height and airspeed the flaps can be
retracted and a normal climb assumed.

EMERGENCIES
When the aircraft is close to the ground the time factor to deal with
emergency situations may be extremely small, and it is only alertness
and training which will enable a pilot to handle this type of situation
safely.

Abandoned Take-Off
In the event that an engine misfires, runs roughly or does not develop
the normal power during the take-off roll there will normally be
ample time to close the throttle and abandon the take-off. It is for this
reason that such items as RPM, oil pressure, temperatures, and
where applicable fuel flow or pressure are included in the checks
carried out following the application of full power during the take-off
roll.

A further situation which could occur during the take-off run is for
a cabin door or window to open. In these circumstances it is advisable
to abandon the take-off provided sufficient distance is available. In
the event that a door or window opens after lift-off in a single-engined
aircraft, the most important action is to concentrate on flying the
aircraft. It is most unusual for open doors or windows to create
problems in the control of the aircraft and their effects are mostly
psychological, in that a loud noise level occurs and some buffeting
will often be felt over the tailplane surfaces. Therefore if a door or
window opens in flight a normal circuit and landing should be made
and the situation rectified once the aircraft is back on the ground.

Engine Failure After Take-off
An engine failure immediately after take-off and when the aircraft is
close to the ground is probably the most critical situation that could

confront a pilot. The major problem will be the time available to adopt and carry out a safe course of action. The time factor is not entirely dependent upon height, for example if the area immediately ahead consists of open countryside with large fields the decision on where to land will be reasonably straightforward, but if woods, obstacles or built up areas are across the climb-out path it will become more difficult to select a landing area quickly. The most vital action will be to lower the aircraft nose and maintain a safe gliding speed. Following this the exact method used to fit a particular situation will vary to a small extent but the best general advice is as follows:

● Look either side of the nose to find the best landing area and head towards it, turning no more than is necessary to avoid obstructions. Maintain a safe gliding speed throughout as with speed available the aircraft can be manoeuvred to avoid single obstacles.

● Keep in mind the wind direction and try to choose a landing path which is as nearly into wind as possible. The ground impact speed will be lessened if landing into a headwind. If the situation permits land with full flap down.

● One final point is that the throttle should be fully closed after the landing path has been selected. This is to ensure the pilot does not become diverted from his original decision in the event that the engine temporarily comes back into operation. However, in the case of time being available to complete some form of cockpit check for engine failure, the throttle should not be fully closed until this procedure has been completed, or it will not be known whether the failure check and possible rectification has been successful.

Landing in an open field regardless of whether it is short grass, growing crops or ploughed ground, will not normally cause injury to aircraft occupants provided they are strapped in securely and the landing is made under control. Any decision to carry out checks to ascertain the reason for power failure will depend upon the time available, but in view of the workload involved at this time they should not be attempted if the engine fails much below 800 feet a.g.l.

In addition to closing the throttle, and when time permits, the following actions should be carried out:

● Pull mixture control to 'Idle Cut Off' and turn Off the Fuel and Ignition.

● Unlock the door and turn Off the Master Switch. When electrically operated flaps are fitted the master switch should be turned off only after the final flap selection has been made.

AIRMANSHIP

The vital necessity for lookout during the whole of the circuit pattern is highlighted by the fact that most airborne collisions occur in the vicinity of airfields, when cockpit workload and other distractions can easily interfere with the maintenance of constant vigilance.

Lookout begins on the ground prior to take-off in that the approach path must be checked clear before moving into line for take off. Another important area for lookout occurs on the first crosswind leg where converging paths occur between aircraft climbing up and levelling off and those which may be joining on the downwind leg or have joined on the dead side of the circuit and are continuing their letdown during the crosswind leg.

Apart from normal airmanship considerations the take-off will always need to be conducted taking into account the take-off run and distance available and the performance capability of the aircraft in relation to the conditions at the time.

PRE-FLIGHT BRIEFING
THE NORMAL TAKE-OFF
Demonstration 1.

Aim
To teach you the procedures and control techniques necessary to take the aircraft safely off the ground and position it on the downwind leg.

What
The commencement of every flight during which the aircraft is controlled on the ground at high speed and safely flown into the air under various conditions of wind strength, aircraft weight, ground surface and gradient, airfield elevation and air temperature.

Airmanship
Considerations in relation to aircraft ground handling and positioning, performance calculations and pre take-off procedures. Lookout will be of vital importance throughout.

How

Before Take-off:
① Holding Point procedures, Airmanship considerations, Pre Take-off Checks, ATC liaison and Take-off Clearance.
② Line up with intended take-off path.
  Note: Wind strength and direction.
    Correct take-off path.
    Feet clear of brakes.
    Select feature for heading reference and roll forward to straighten nose/tailwheel.

During Take-off:
③ Open up smoothly to full power.
Use rudder to maintain direction. Apply slight back pressure on the control column.

> Tailwheel Aircraft: Apply slight forward pressure on control column to raise the tail.
> As the airspeed increases, change to a slight back pressure.
> Coarse use of rudder is initially required to maintain direction.

Note the RPM, oil pressure, temperature, fuel flow and ASI reading.

At the correct lift-off speed use positive but smooth back pressure on the control column to achieve a clean lift-off.

Student Practice.

After Take-off:
④ Note the initial pitch attitude. Maintain lateral level and heading.
When best rate of climb speed is attained re-adjust pitch attitude for the climb and re-trim.
⑤ Maintain lookout to either side and up into the climbing path. At . . . height carefully look out and turn onto the crosswind leg.
⑥ Allow for drift and at circuit height adopt level flight. Be alert for other aircraft and commence a medium turn onto the downwind leg.
⑦ Maintain track parallel with the take-off path.
R/T . . . . downwind call.

DOWNWIND

CROSSWIND

RUNWAY

PRE-FLIGHT BRIEFING
THE CROSSWIND TAKE-OFF
Demonstration 2.

Aim   To teach you the procedure and control technique necessary to take-off safely during crosswind conditions.

What   A take-off made in a direction which is not in line with the prevailing wind.

Airmanship   Considerations in relation to aircraft ground handling and positioning, performance calculations, pre take-off procedures and lookout.

How   *Before Take-off*:
   Note wind strength and direction.
   Calculate crosswind component and review the limiting crosswind component of the aircraft.

   Normal procedures and airmanship considerations. Pre take-off checks, ATC liaison and take-off clearance.
   Line up with the intended take-off path and select a reference feature.

During Take-off:
   Use rudder to maintain direction (differential braking may be necessary on tailwheel aircraft).
   Use ailerons to compensate crosswind effect.
   Anticipate weathercocking effect.
   Lift off cleanly at the correct speed.

After Take-off:
   Be alert to turbulence near the ground.
   Attain best rate of climb speed.
   When safely airborne turn sufficiently into wind to counteract drift.

   Bear in mind the effect of a headwind/tailwind component on the crosswind leg.
   Adjust the downwind heading to counteract drift.

   Student Practice.

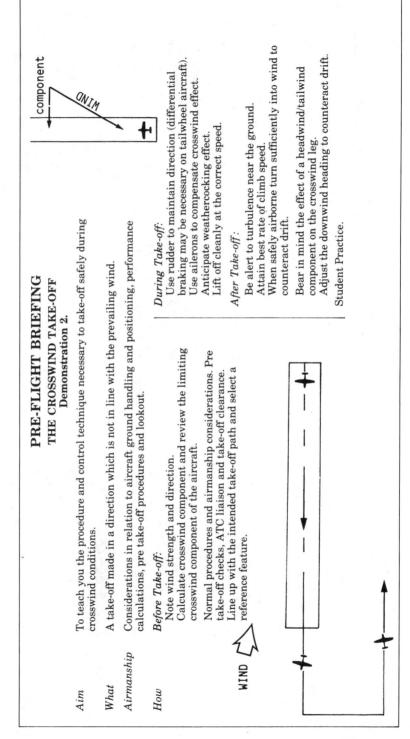

PRE-FLIGHT BRIEFING
EMERGENCIES DURING TAKE-OFF
Demonstration 3.

Aim
To teach you the procedures to adopt in the event of emergencies occurring during the take-off run or immediately after take-off.

What
Circumstances leading to a hazardous situation during or after take-off.

Airmanship
Normal airmanship considerations will apply but additionally there will be the need to maintain a safe minimum height during the practice of engine failure after take-off.

How
During the ground run if any of the following occur:

Significant loss of power.
Abnormal oil pressure or temperature.
Low fuel pressure/flow.
Vibration or engine rough running.
Nil ASI reading.
A door or window opens.

Procedure:

Close throttle fully.
Maintain directional control.
Apply brakes as required but take care to avoid skidding or the development of an uncontrollable swing.

Return to the parking area and report the unserviceability.

Student Practice.

> NOTE: These two emergencies will only be practised during dual flights.
> No solo practice.

Should an engine failure occur immediately after take-off the following procedure should be used:

Lower the aircraft nose and maintain a safe gliding speed. Warn the passengers and CLOSE the throttle.
Look either side of the nose and select the most suitable landing path compatible with obstructions and wind direction (turn no more than is necessary).
Maintain speed and manoeuvre as necessary to set up an approach path.

If workload permits transmit a 'Mayday' call.

Flap selection should be made according to height available and distance to go.
Check harnesses tight.

If time permits:
Mixture to 'Idle Cut Off'
Fuel and Ignition Off
Door unlocked
Master Switch Off (in the case of electrically operated flaps this last action should be made after final flap selection).

After touchdown leave the aircraft as quickly as possible.

Student Practice.

PRE-FLIGHT BRIEFING

THE SHORT FIELD TAKE-OFF
Demonstration 4.

Aim
To teach you the technique to be employed during a 'Short Field' take-off

What
The procedure to use when taking off from areas which have a restricted length in relation to take-off run or take-off distance.

Airmanship
Normal airmanship considerations will apply but additional caution must be used to ensure that the particular type of take-off can be made safely under the conditions which exist at the time.

How

Before Take-off:
Review aircraft manual and field data to ensure aircraft performance is sufficient to clear obstructions safely.
Review 'best angle of climb speed'. Pre take-off checks and if applicable ATC liaison.
Select best take-off direction in relation to wind, ground surface, gradient and obstacles.
Line up utilising full length of take-off path.
Use maximum power possible against brakes.
Check: RPM, oil pressure, temperatures, fuel pressure/flow.
If the readings are satisfactory release brakes.

During Take-off:
Control actions are as for a normal take-off.
Be prepared for an initial tendency to swing.
Lift off at the correct speed.

After Take-off:
Climb out at best angle of climb speed.
Ensure accurate control of airspeed and exercise particular care if gustiness prevails.
Vary climb path if compatible with improved headwind component and obstacle clearance.

Student Practice.

THE SOFT FIELD TAKE-OFF
Demonstration 5.

Aim
To teach you the technique to be employed during a 'Soft Field' take-off.

What
The take-off procedure to be used when surface conditions are soft, rough or covered with long grass. This also includes snow or slush.

How

Before Take-off:
Determine the best take-off path in relation to wind, surface conditions and gradient. Complete Pre take-off checks (including the appropriate flap setting and when applicable ATC liaison.
Note: When ground is very soft a continuous movement of the aircraft from the holding point to the take-off run may be of significant advantage.

During Take-off:
As maximum power is applied the control column is brought well back to allow the nose to rise.
With increase of speed a forward movement of the control column will be necessary to prevent the tail from touching the ground.
The aircraft will lift off at a low speed.

After Take-off:
Further forward movement of the control column will be needed to fly level with the ground and increase speed quickly.
When best angle or best rate of climb speed (as required) is achieved adopt the climb.
At a safe height and airspeed the flaps should be raised and the aircraft trimmed.

Student Practice.

Take-off and Climb to Downwind Position

Flight Demonstrations

INTRODUCTION

The contents of the take-off exercise can be conveniently divided into specific demonstration groups as follows:

1. The Normal Take-off.
2. The Crosswind Take-off.
3. Emergencies during the Take-off Phase.
    (a) Abandoned Take-off.
    (b) Engine Failure After Take-off.
4. The Short Field Take-off.
5. The Soft Field Take-off.

The contents of demonstration 1 will be gradually introduced over several flights so that a student is not faced with the entire contents for the first time during one take-off.

Circumstances such as a mandatory take-off direction in the form of a runway, or marked take-off path, may dictate the combining of demonstrations 1 and 2 from the beginning of the exercise.

The emergency situations in demonstration 3 will normally be dealt with separately, and each case introduced at a suitable stage of the student's training.

The short and soft field take-off procedure will normally form part of the student's consolidation training after first solo. However, the particular operating environment and prevailing circumstances may call for these to be practised earlier.

DEMONSTRATION 1.   THE NORMAL TAKE-OFF

Flight Lesson	Demonstration Sequence
Control on the ground at higher speeds and transition to flight	
At the holding point before the take-off	Pre take-off checks completed. Establish that take-off and final approach paths are clear. Make the R/T call (as applicable). Align the aircraft with the take-off direction. Confirm correct runway from heading indicator and check wind direction and strength.
During the take-off (nosewheel aircraft)	Select a reference feature (if available). Keep feet clear of brakes. Apply full throttle smoothly and keep straight by use of rudder. Apply slight back pressure on the control column. Note: RPM. Oil pressure and temperature within the green arc. (Fuel pressure/flow if applicable). ASI reading increasing. At the lift-off speed apply sufficient back pressure on the control column to ensure a clean lift-off.
During the take-off (tailwheel aircraft)	Select a reference feature (if available). Keep feet clear of brakes. Apply full throttle smoothly and keep straight by coarse use of rudder. Use forward pressure on the control column to raise the tail into the flying attitude. Note: Increasing effectiveness of rudder. Note: RPM. Oil pressure and temperature within limits. (Fuel pressure/flow if applicable.) ASI reading increasing. At the lift-off speed apply sufficient back pressure on the control column to ensure a clean lift-off.
After the take-off	Maintain lateral level with the ailerons and note the nose attitude in pitch. When best rate of climb speed is achieved re-adjust pitch attitude for the best rate of climb and re-trim. Adjust heading as required to maintain

the take-off track over the ground.
Maintain a lookout either side and
ahead into the climb path.
If flaps have been used these should be
raised at a safe speed and height.
At 500 feet or the specified height, lookout carefully and turn onto the crosswind leg.
Allow for drift and ensure the aircraft
tracks at 90° to the take-off direction.
Be alert for other aircraft, particularly
those which may be joining the circuit
pattern.
At circuit height, level off and adjust
power as required.
At a suitable distance out from the
take-off path, lookout carefully in all
directions and complete a medium turn
onto the downwind leg.
Once on the downwind leg, ensure the
aircraft is tracking parallel to the
take-off path and maintain the correct
height.

Student practice: The student's practice should be arranged so that
the responsibility for the complete sequence of airmanship and
control actions is gradually transferred to him.

DEMONSTRATION 2. THE CROSSWIND TAKE-OFF

Flight Lesson	Demonstration Sequence
Control on the ground at higher speeds and transition to flight during crosswind conditions	
At the holding point before the take-off	Normal airmanship considerations, pre take-off checks and ATC liaison. Note: Wind direction and review limiting crosswind component for type. Align the aircraft with the take-off direction and select a reference feature (if available). Considerations for use of differential braking (as applicable to type – tailwheel).
During the take-off	Apply full throttle smoothly and keep straight by use of rudder (differential

	braking may be necessary on specific tailwheel types). Raise windward aileron. Apply slight back pressure on the control column. Note: In strong crosswind conditions it may be advisable to avoid the use of back pressure during the initial stages of the take-off roll. Be alert for any tendency for the aircraft to yaw. Reduce aileron deflection as the speed increases. Lift off positively and cleanly at the correct speed and at the same time neutralise the ailerons.
After the take-off	Be aware of the possibility of additional turbulence near the ground. When the best rate of climb speed is attained, adopt the climb and when safely clear of the ground turn sufficiently into wind to counteract drift. Re-trim. Note the effect of a headwind or tailwind component (as applicable) on the crosswind leg. Allow for drift on the downwind leg.

Student practice: This procedure may have to be incorporated into the initial take-off demonstration and practice when dictated by the operating environment, but provided the student is not given responsibility for too many control actions in the early stage his progress should not be impeded.

DEMONSTRATION 3.   FLIGHT EMERGENCIES
DURING TAKE-OFF

Flight Lesson	Demonstration Sequence

Abandoning the take-off
During the take-off run
	The take-off should be abandoned if the checks during the take-off run reveal:
	  Significantly,
	    Low RPM
	    Low oil pressure
	    Low fuel pressure or flow
	    High oil temperature, or –

	Engine rough running, vibration, or a nil ASI reading. The take-off should also normally be abandoned if a door or window opens whilst the aircraft is still on the ground. However if this should occur at lift-off or just after, it will usually be preferable to continue the take-off.
Abandoned Take-off Procedure	Close the throttle fully. Maintain direction. Application of brakes may be necessary when using a restricted take-off path, in which case caution must be used to avoid skidding or the setting up of an uncontrollable swing. If obstructions exist ahead of the aircraft, avoiding action must be commenced early.
Engine failure after take-off This will normally be practised from a minimum height of 400 feet	Should the engine fail shortly after take-off the following procedure should be initiated: Lower the aircraft nose and maintain a safe gliding speed. CLOSE the throttle. Look either side and ahead of the nose and select the most suitable obstruction free area for use as a landing path. Bear in mind the wind direction. Turn the aircraft no more than is necessary to set up an approach path. Warn the passengers and make a Mayday call if time permits. MAINTAIN a safe gliding speed. Note: Failure checks should normally only be carried out when the time factor is sufficient. Flap selection should be made according to height available and distance to go. All harnesses checked tight. When time is available the following additional procedure should be included: Mixture to 'Idle Cut Off'. Fuel and Ignition – Off. Door unlocked. Master Switch – Off. (In the case of electrically operated flaps this last action should be made after final flap selection.)

Student practice: The student will only practise these emergencies during dual flights. The Engine Failure After Take-off procedure should be practised several times before first solo and at suitable intervals thereafter.

DEMONSTRATION 4.   THE SHORT FIELD TAKE-OFF

Flight Lesson	Demonstration Sequence
Achieving a short take-off run and maximum angle of climb	Having ensured that the aircraft is capable of safely clearing the obstructions on the take-off path the following procedure should be used:

Before take-off	Normal airmanship considerations, pre take-off checks, and when applicable ATC liaison.
	Determine the best take-off direction in relation to wind, surface condition, gradient and obstacle clearance.
	Select flap (if applicable).
	Align the aircraft with the selected take-off path utilising the maximum length.
	Open up to the maximum power possible against the brakes (if surface conditions permit). Tailwheel type – column hard back.
	Check: RPM
	    Oil pressure and temperatures.
	    Fuel pressure/flow (if applicable).
	If satisfactory release the brakes.

During the take-off	The control actions are as for a normal take-off, but be prepared for a swing in the early stages. Lift off at the correct speed compatible with the configuration in use.
After the take-off	When safely airborne adjust the attitude for the best angle of climb speed. Be prepared for a slight reduction in the acceleration as the aircraft leaves the area of ground effect. Alter climb path as necessary to obtain the maximum headwind effect and greater clearance over obstacles. After obstructions are cleared adopt best rate of climb attitude and if applicable raise the flaps. Re-trim.

Student practice: The student should be allowed to calculate the aircraft performance capability in relation to 'take-off run' and 'take-off distance' prior to the introduction of practice at this type of take-off.

DEMONSTRATION 5.   THE SOFT FIELD TAKE-OFF

Flight Lesson	*Demonstration Sequence*
Achieving the lift-off at minimum speed	
Before take-off	Normal airmanship considerations, pre take-off checks, and when applicable ATC liaison. Determine the best take-off path available in relation to wind, surface condition and gradient. Select the correct flap setting. Align the aircraft with the chosen take-off path utilising the maximum length. Note: It may sometimes be advisable not to stop the aircraft after lining up, but to employ a rolling start. This would obviate becoming stuck in very soft ground.
During the take-off	As maximum power is selected the control column is brought well back. As the speed increases the nose will rise automatically, and as the elevators become more effective the control column will have to be eased forward or too high a nose attitude will result. The aircraft will lift-off at a low speed.
After the take-off	Immediately after the take-off a further forward movement of the control column will be necessary to fly the aircraft parallel to the ground and obtain an increased airspeed. When the best angle or best rate of climb speed (as required) is achieved the appropriate attitude should be established. At a safe height and airspeed the flaps should be raised and the aircraft trimmed.

Student practice: It is advisable that the student practice is confined to grass areas only.

The Circuit, Approach and Landing

LANDING DISTANCE

GROSS WEIGHT LBS.	APPROACH SPEED, IAS, MPH	AT SEA LEVEL & 50°F.		AT 2500 FT. & 50°F.	
		GROUND ROLL	TOTAL TO CLEAR 50 FT. OBS.	GROUND ROLL	TOTAL TO CLEAR 50 FT. OBS.
1600	60	445	1075	470	1135

Decrease the distances shown by 10% or each 4 knots of headwind.
Increase the distance by 10% for each 60°F. temperature increase above standard.
For operation on a dry, grass runway, increase distances (both "ground roll" and "total to clear 50 ft. obstacle") by 20% of the "total to clear 50 ft. obstacle" figure.

FLAPS LOWERED TO 40° — POWER OFF
HARD SURFACE RUNWAY — ZERO WIND

Instructor's Guide

Before 'First Solo' the student must demonstrate competence at circuits, approaches and going round again. The major emphasis during the pre solo stage should be on safety rather than precision and on the ability to recognise:

- A bad approach.
- An incorrect 'Hold Off'.
- A mislanding situation.

In addition to recognising the above situations he must also demonstrate his ability to initiate and implement safely the necessary procedure for 'Going Round Again'.

Records show that more accidents occur during the landing phase than at any other time during flight. They further reveal that in most cases, rather than ignorance of what to do, the primary cause of such accidents was ignoring what should have been done. All instructors should therefore arrange that their students practise as many of the variable landing situations as possible and ensure they are capable of handling them by using the correct procedures.

Students must be taught to take into consideration such factors as wind, aircraft weight, nature and length of the available landing distance and landing run, the effect of obstructions, turbulence and vortices from other aircraft, before they can be considered sufficiently proficient for solo flight.

The approach and landing will probably be the most difficult exercise for the student to master, and also challenging for the instructor. However, with correct instruction and encouragement the average student will normally overcome the difficulties initially experienced.

One very important factor which often gets overlooked, particularly by junior instructors is the need to monitor the student's line of vision during the round out and hold off phase. There will always be a natural inclination to look directly ahead over the aircraft nose during this period, which causes particular difficulty if the student is short bodied, as the nose will cut off his forward perspective of the ground.

This usually prevents him from continuing to move the control column back throughout the period when he should be 'holding off', resulting in high speed arrivals and a tendency towards bouncy landings.

AIRMANSHIP

From the base leg onwards the student will tend to become more and more absorbed with the landing path and intended touchdown area. This is a particular distraction to normal lookout and it occurs at a time when collision risk is high. The instructor must watch for any deterioration of lookout by the student during this period.

 Check lists should not be used while flying in the circuit because of their obvious detraction from the maintenance of lookout. The pre landing checks should be limited to those items which are really applicable, and the tendency to introduce more checks than are necessary must be avoided.

Performance calculations in respect of landing distance and landing run should be applied in a practical manner and the student made to carry out such interpolations from the particular training aircraft manual and the published airfield data. Although when training is conducted from large airfields this procedure may appear to be a time wasting exercise it is only by habits instilled during training that a pilot can become conscientious and safe when the training environment is behind him. In the past a number of landing accidents have occurred because this type of calculation was omitted prior to landings on small grass airfields, particularly when the grass was wet and light wind conditions were prevailing.

BEFORE THE EXERCISE

The Long Briefing should cover the following:

Objectives.
The Downwind Leg, Base Leg, Approach Positioning and Drills.
Factors Affecting the Final Approach and Landing Run.
Effect of Weight.
Effect of Altitude and Temperature.
Effect of Wind.
Effect of Flap.
The Landing.
    Effect of Ground Surface and Gradient upon the Landing Run.
    Use of Elevators (Safeguarding the Nosewheel).
    Use of Brakes.
Types of Approach and Landing:
    Powered Approach and Landing.

Crosswind Approach and Landing.
Glide Approach and Landing.
Short Field Approach and Landing.
Soft Field Approach and Landing.
Flapless Approach and Landing.
Tailwheel Considerations.
Missed Approach.
Mislanding/Going Round Again.
Engine Handling.
Airmanship and Air Traffic Control Procedures.
Common Errors.

The short Pre-Flight Briefing should be based upon the practical aspects of that part of the Long Briefing in relation to the Air Exercise to be covered. In order to promote flight safety after the student leaves the training environment, ensure that at some time prior to completing the course the student can interpret the information given in the U.K. Air Pilot (and similar documents) relating to airfield landing data, and the tables or graphs shown in the Flight/Owner's Manual regarding landing distance and landing run.

The student should be gradually introduced to the circuit, approach and landing when returning from those flights during which the basic manoeuvres were taught. If this is done, the student will already have a grasp of what is involved before the consolidated practice of circuits and landings is undertaken.

DURING THE AIR DEMONSTRATION
Ensure the student appreciates that he must learn to take the initiative and make decisions for himself rather than wait for the instructor to do this for him. At first he will inevitably rely upon the instructor's assistance and advice but only when he is capable of making positive and correct decisions will he be competent to undertake his 'First Solo' flight.

THE POWERED APPROACH AND LANDING
In earlier days the glide approach and landing was the most important type of approach and landing the pilot had to learn, because the unreliability of early aero engines created many occasions of engine failure and from the commencement of circuit training the ability to judge gliding distance was essential. In latter days with reliable aero engines, mechanical failure has become a rarity, and today the powered approach and landing is the most common type used because it facilitates positioning and integration with other approaching traffic.

For initial demonstration and practice during training the powered approach offers the following basic advantages:

● It permits the length of the approach to be increased when necessary to enable the instructor to take more time over his demonstration points.

● The student will have longer to perceive and appreciate the points being made and more time to make corrections for the inevitable errors he will make in the early stages.

● The approach path is less steep, and the resulting roundout will be more shallow, an important facet during the early attempts at landing.

● It permits a more precise type of approach during which the aircraft can be controlled more easily into the pre-selected touchdown zone.

● Finally in these days of mixed aircraft being commonly flown in the same circuit pattern the most sensible common approach is the one with power. This prevents the many frustrating attempts at glide approaches from occurring, a situation which confuses the student during his initial attempts and slows down his rate of progress.

Nevertheless, when powered approaches are used to introduce the approach and landing, the practise of a few glide or partial glide approaches will be of benefit prior to first solo.

If, during the initial stages of landing practice, a touchdown area rather than a touchdown point is selected the student will find it easier to concentrate on his control of the aircraft during the landing phase. Accuracy in touching down at a pre-selected point is a necessary part of a student's training however, and specific touch-down points must be used as soon as possible compatible with the student's progress.

If the decision is to use full flap for the landing it will be advisable to lower the flap in two stages, for example, half flap should be lowered during the base leg and the final flap selection completed after the turn onto final approach. This will reduce the possibility of a marked decrease in airspeed which can occur when turning with full flap down.

In those training aircraft which are fitted with powerful flaps, the use of full flap settings for landings will be a distinct disadvantage to the student in his early landing practice. The full use of such flaps creates high descent rates, and extremely positive roundouts are required except in light winds. The use of full flap could therefore lead to accident inducing situations and should where possible be avoided until the student has acquired more experience. The need to introduce the use of full flap landings is however very important, and care should be taken to include this aspect of training at a suitable stage.

Whether full or half flap is used, instructors must ensure that students are given practice at going round again with full flap selected, in order that the reduced acceleration which impairs climb performance is appreciated. Together with this consideration all students must be given practice before being sent first solo, in changing the flap fuse in those aircraft which are equipped with electrically operated flap systems.

Whenever it is necessary to correct a powered approach by altering the power setting, it is always advisable to correct early so that a slight alteration will be sufficient. The student should be taught to aim for an approach that requires minimal power variations.

Give the student the opportunity to correct his own mistakes as soon as possible as he will never learn to take corrective action early enough if it is always done for him. However be ready to take control fully or partially if there is a possibility of the aircraft being damaged.

Due to the instructor often having to take control during the early stages of practising this exercise, be sure to avoid situations where the student is uncertain of whether he is flying the aircraft and making the decisions, or whether the instructor has assumed responsibility.

Control of the aircraft during the landing run is more effectively practised by completing full stop landings, but on the other hand a greater number of landings can be achieved by carrying out 'touch and go' landings. This latter is an acceptable method of training but instructors must ensure that an adequate number of full stop landings are practised, particularly when crosswinds are present, as this situation demands a greater degree of proficiency in aircraft handling during the landing roll. Due to the greater difficulties experienced during the landing run with tailwheel aircraft it is important that the number of 'touch and go' landings be restricted more than with nosewheel types.

Crosswind landings are more conducive to the occurrence of 'wheelbarrowing' and the instructor must ensure the student understands the corrective action to be taken in these circumstances.

THE GLIDE APPROACH AND LANDING

This is an exercise in judgement and is related more to the practise of 'Forced Landings' than with circuit training. The glide approach is an essential part of the student's training and must be tackled at the appropriate time, regardless of the difficulties which often arise at busy airfields with mixed types of circuit traffic.

FLAPLESS APPROACH AND LANDING

Although the operational use of this type of approach is related to strong crosswind conditions or flap failure, it is nevertheless another good exercise to aid in the development of judgement, whether in the glide or powered situation. Therefore this approach should be practised from time to time throughout the student's training.

THE SHORT FIELD LANDING

Ensure the student understands that the effect of a headwind will often reduce the landing length by a greater amount than the collective use of full flap and low approach speeds. Therefore, when strong winds exist it is of no advantage to select too low a speed for the final stages of the approach and is inadvisable as the effect of the attendant wind gradient may be far more hazardous than a short field length.

THE SOFT FIELD LANDING

This calls for judgement and good control in order to place the aircraft close to the ground and touch down at the lowest possible speed.

The technique of landing in the '3 point' attitude with the aircraft close to or at the stall is the correct method for tailwheel aircraft. The nosewheel aircraft however requires a change in technique not only because a tailwheel does not exist, but also because design geometry prevents a nosewheel aircraft getting to the stall when close to the ground in the landing situation without damage to the tail section or a possible heavy landing. This is due to the following reasons:

With the modern nosewheel training aircraft, stalling angles of attack of 20° are common and generally the angle the wings make with the horizontal when the tailcone touches the ground is only about 12°. Even allowing for the wing angle of incidence and the fact that the stalling angle is slightly reduced when flaps are lowered, the aircraft will not actually reach a stalled condition during landing, unless at the same time there exists a significant rate of sink. Full stall landings are therefore not a practical proposition to a student pilot, and any attempt at this type of landing on nosewheel aircraft could be conducive to a damaged tailcone or alternatively a heavy landing.

GOING ROUND AGAIN

The raising of flap on most light aircraft can be carried out with little, or no reduction in climb rate, provided they are raised at the correct airspeed. However in the hands of the inexperienced pilot the possibility of raising the flap at too low an airspeed is obvious, and this coupled with any marked trim changes could lead to a dangerous situation when the aircraft is near the ground. Because of this consideration a minimum height for raising flap should be about 200 feet a.g.l. A greater height than this would rarely produce a significant advantage due to the reduced climb rate whilst flap is lowered.

COMMON ERRORS
The student will be unable to display a high standard of airmanship during the initial stage of practising this exercise, due mainly to the workload involved. Whereas this must be accepted in the early stages, it will become unacceptable as his experience and competence to handle the aircraft increases.

• The necessity for the student to make firm and confident decisions during this exericse is paramount, and it is only after he has developed this capability that he can be considered for solo flight.

• A common error while practising approaches is to neglect to monitor the altimeter during the base leg after approach power has been initially selected. This often results in being too low or too high at the position for the final turn. Ensure the student understands from the beginning that the power selected at the key position is not a standard RPM, but will need to be varied according to the distance out from the touchdown area and the strength and direction of the wind. This latter item is particularly important during crosswind landings, when head or tailwind components will be experienced on the base leg.

• Failure to commence the turn onto final approach at the correct moment or not varying the bank angle as required to position on the extended centreline as the turn is completed are quite common errors. Because of the effect of delaying a settled approach path, these errors need to be overcome as soon as possible.

• A good landing is more likely to occur from a good approach. General difficulties and random errors during landings are often the result of inaccurate or badly executed approaches. Correct speeds and early use of power are very important. If the airspeed is allowed to wander more than a few knots the nose attitude will have changed, resulting in a misleading impression of the landing path position relative to the engine cowling and windscreen. This will often give the impression of being too high or too low when the descent path is actually correct or, alternatively masking a needed alteration of power.

• The student's failure to round out early enough, or rounding out and holding off too high can usually be corrected by the instructor approaching a little faster than normal, so that he can prolong the round out, holding off to allow the student more time to become accustomed to the appearance of the ground and the aircraft attitude up to the point of touchdown.

● Many students commence to hold off, but then discontinue the backward movement of the control column. This fault is often overcome by flying the aircraft slowly just above the ground, demonstrating that the elevators remain effective and that the control column should be moved as much as necessary to hold the main wheels off the ground to the point of touchdown.

● Vision – Most pilots over the age of 40 need spectacles to correct their vision for reading. Some will in addition need correction for distant vision and a number will need correction for vision at instrument panel range. The wearing of correct spectacles which are suitable for flying is therefore very important.

Where the only correction necessary is for reading, pilots should never use full-lens spectacles whilst flying, because the pilot's task requires frequent changes from near to distant vision and the latter will be blurred by reading glasses. The use of incorrect glasses for the task can often cause difficulty during landing and the instructor should ensure that where spectacles are being worn by a student they are of the correct type.

● Having landed successfully, a student may have difficulty in controlling direction during the landing run. This is often due to premature relaxing of his concentration, or diverting his attention to cockpit workload, R/T calls etc. Remember that habits once formed are difficult to overcome, and although the maintenance of direction immediately after landing may be relatively easy in gentle winds, or into wind landings, this will not be so during those occasions when a strong crosswind is prevailing. Any diversion from the maintenance of heading and aircraft control during the landing roll in this type of situation could become hazardous.

Therefore, the student should be taught a habit which will stand him in good stead for all circumstances, and in this case one which consists of handling R/T calls only after the aircraft has slowed right down, and carrying out the after-landing checks when the aircraft is stationary and clear of the landing path.

The Circuit, Approach and Landing

Long Briefing

OBJECTIVES

To teach the student a thorough understanding of the various factors concerned with developing the ability to maintain an accurate circuit pattern and to accomplish a safe approach and landing under varied conditions. The need to make positive decisions concerning the safe operation of the aircraft, e.g. when to initiate 'Go Round Again' procedure will be an integral part of the exercise.

INTRODUCTION

Statistics show that the largest number of aircraft accidents occur during the approach and landing phase despite the fact that this normally involves only a few minutes of each flight. Therefore it is clear that a thorough appreciation of the factors concerned will be vital to the implementation of the correct techniques, during which such existing conditions as wind, obstructions on the approach path, nature of ground surface, the aircraft weight, density altitude and the landing distance available must all be taken into account. It is therefore only from a review of these conditions that a pilot can decide upon the exact type of approach and landing to use.

In the initial stages of training the particular type of approach being used will depend largely upon laid down training practices rather than those related to specific weather, terrain and aircraft conditions. Nevertheless, such variables as wind and turbulence will form an integral part of the initial techniques employed. Eventually the student will be taught to assess each approach and landing situation and take into account not only the wind and weather conditions, but also those factors relating to landing distance, weight, effects of altitude and temperature, and the type and condition of the ground surface.

THE DOWNWIND LEG, BASE LEG, APPROACH POSITIONING AND DRILLS

In order to establish a common flow of air traffic movements around an airfield circuit a laid down pattern must be adhered to by all aircraft. This basic pattern constitutes a climb out and crosswind leg followed by a downwind leg, base leg and final approach. Figure 13-1 illustrates this basic pattern.

A left hand circuit is normally used but where this conflicts with the requirement for noise abatement over towns or for other reasons, a right hand pattern is flown. The airfield controlling authority or ATC decide the direction of the circuit pattern in relation to the particular runway in use. When no such control exists the pilot will have to decide which landing direction to use taking into account the existing conditions and safe operating practices.

The height to turn onto the crosswind leg following take-off, and the height established for the downwind leg will vary according to local operating practices, but the initial turn onto the crosswind leg is usually made at 500 to 600 feet a.g.l. and the downwind leg normally flown at 800 to 1000 feet a.g.l. The QFE is the datum normally used for circuit flying.

Fig. 13-1

Once on the crosswind leg the aircraft is flown to a position which is a suitable distance out from the active runway or landing path and then turned downwind. Apart from the initial climbing turn onto the crosswind leg all turns on the circuit are normally made at a 30° bank angle.

When R/T is being used the pilot should call 'Downwind' as soon as possible on the downwind leg and ATC will reply with information regarding clearance to the final approach and whether the aircraft is number one or two, etc. This action will also alert other listening aircraft in the circuit as to the approximte position of other air traffic. When R/T is not available the pilot should be prepared to receive light signals from the ground if that form of ground control is being used. The Pre Landing checks should, where possible, be completed approximately half-way along the downwind leg.

At a suitable distance from the touchdown area the aircraft should be turned onto the base leg and the approach will be prepared at some stage along this leg. The turn onto the final approach will have to be judged relative to the extended centre line of the runway to ensure that the aircraft is aligned with the landing path as early as possible on the final leg. Once established on the final approach the R/T call 'Finals' should be made and clearance to land obtained.

In some circumstances, e.g. if an aircraft is still on the runway ahead of the landing aircraft ATC will only give clearance to 'Continue' and a positive clearance to land must still be obtained and acknowledged or the missed approach procedure must be put into effect. This consists of the aircraft being taken round again without landing and being positioned on the crosswind leg for a further circuit. During the missed approach procedure it is advisable to change the aircraft flight path so that the climb is made parallel and to the right side of the landing and take-off path. This is to enable the pilot to see more clearly aircraft which may be climbing up from below.

FACTORS AFFECTING THE FINAL APPROACH AND LANDING RUN

The factors to be considered under this broad heading will be similar to those involved with the take-off. Such items as aircraft weight, altitude, temperature, wind, use of flaps and type of ground surface and gradient, together with their individual and collective effects upon an approach and landing will have to be understood, so that the pilot is sufficiently competent to operate his aircraft whatever differing conditions present themselves.

EFFECT OF WEIGHT

The effect of weight upon the stalling speed and aircraft performance has already been covered under the exercises of Stalling and Take-off. When related to the approach and landing this means that consideration must be given as to whether the approach speed should be increased if the all-up weight is increased, and by how much the landing run will be increased at the higher touch-down speed associated with the higher stalling speed.

Flight/Owner's Manuals/Pilot's Operating Handbooks base their recommended approach speeds upon the permitted all-up weight of the aircraft, and therefore even if the aircraft is operating at its maximum all-up weight there will not normally be any need to increase the approach speed on this account. However the effect of weight upon the landing run is significant, in that added weight means a higher touch-down speed (higher stalling speed), the actual figures are:

A 20% increase in weight will produce
a 10% increase in touch down speed.

To this must be added the greater energy to be dissipated during the landing roll. This energy increases with increased weights and touch-down speeds and a 20% increase in weight will result in approximately a 20% increase in the length of the landing run.

EFFECT OF ALTITUDE AND TEMPERATURE

Although altitude and temperature do not affect the landing distance as much as the take-off distance, it should be appreciated that their combined effects can produce a significant change to the length of the landing run under certain circumstances.

Engine performance is not a critical factor during a normal approach due to the reduced power settings required, but if a high density altitude exists the TAS at touch-down will be higher, and will consequently increase the length of the ground run. A rule of thumb to use when calculating whether a high density altitude will have a significant effect is to allow an additional 5% of the published landing distance for each 1000 feet of airfield elevation.

EFFECT OF WIND

As in the case of the take-off, the effect of wind upon landing performance is very significant, and because an aircraft will land at a particular touch-down speed regardless of wind strength, the main effect of wind is its ability to alter the ground speed during the landing and therefore affect the length of the landing run and distance. In relation to the terms 'Landing Distance' and 'Landing Run' as applicable to aircraft performance, the following definitions describe their meaning:

Landing Distance — The gross horizontal distance the aircraft will travel before it comes to a complete stop following a steady descent from an arbitrary 50 feet high datum above the surface.

Landing Run — The distance taken for the aircraft to come to a stop from the point of touch-down based upon the correct touch-down speed and a moderate use of brakes.

The effect of wind upon aircraft deceleration during the landing run is identical to its effect upon the take-off run, which can be seen by reference to fig. 12-5. A headwind which is 10% of the touch-down speed will reduce the landing run by approximately 20% and a tailwind which is 10% of the touch-down speed will increase the landing run by 20%. For example, the effect of a 5 kt tailwind on an aircraft which touches down at 50 kts and takes a 1000 feet landing run in conditions of zero wind will be to increase the landing run to 1200 feet.

The effect of a headwind upon the final approach path is to steepen the descent gradient for a given approach speed and a tailwind will be to make the approach path more shallow. This is due to the effect on ground speed relative to the air speed. When crosswind conditions exist, there will be a correspondingly reduced headwind or tailwind component during the approach and landing roll. This effect is identical to the effect of a crosswind factor on the take-off.

Wind Gradient
When the wind strength is moderate to strong the aircraft may encounter positive wind gradient effects as it nears the ground during the final stages of the approach to landing. Wind gradient (sometimes called 'Wind Shear') can have a significant effect upon an aircraft flight path and airspeed and is most likely to be met when the runway threshold is in the vicinity of buildings or trees, and also when the ground beneath the approach path is lower than the elevation of the runway.

Fig. 13-2

Under these conditions horizontal or vertical wind shear and gusts creating up and down draughts will be prevalent and the pilot must maintain an added state of awareness and be ready to counteract any sudden loss of airspeed or sinking by prompt and correct use of power and elevators. When these conditions occur the immediate action should be to increase power and lower the nose to maintain or slightly increase the approach speed.

When meeting wind gusts or wind shear the changing direction of airflow can often cause a rapid alteration in the angle of attack of the wings, and sudden changes of airspeed. The problem associated with this occurrence at the lower speeds used for approaches lies in the possibility of the aircraft getting close to the stall at a time when little or no power is being used. The aircraft can suddenly sink in an attitude where it is in a high drag condition. Therefore whenever strong winds are present it will be advisable to use less than full flap and approach at slightly higher airspeeds.

EFFECT OF FLAP

The primary purpose in using flaps during the landing approach is to change the aircraft attitude for a given approach speed. With flap down the nose position will be lower, thereby enabling the pilot to have a better view along the descent path to the intended touchdown area. Without the use of flap the modern streamlined aircraft would have a very flat approach attitude which would be an additional problem right up to touchdown.

The use of full flap is usually recommended for normal approaches and landings, but during the early stages of training or when strong gusty winds prevails, and particularly when strong crosswinds are present and powerful flaps are fitted, it may be advisable to restrict their operation to less than the fully down position. Flight/Owner's Manuals/Pilot's Operating Handbooks will usually contain advice as to when flap operation should be restricted.

Flaps decrease the stalling speed of an aircraft, and their use will give lower touchdown speeds. This latter may not be beneficial during strong crosswind conditions, as the slower the aircraft speed the greater will be the crosswind effect, and when added to the reduced rudder and elevator effectiveness associated with lowered flaps, will lead to reduced control during a vital stage of the landing. This aspect is covered later and in more detail under the Crosswind Approach and Landing.

THE LANDING

This phase of flight covers the period between the end of the final approach when the aircraft is 'flared' and held off, through the actual touch-down to the end of the landing run. The basic principle is to touch-down at the lowest speed compatible with the existing conditions and safe control of the aircraft. The actual handling methods used are detailed under 'Types of Approach and Landing', but at this stage the effect of the ground surface and gradient must be considered, together with the use of the elevators to safeguard the nosewheel, and the application of brakes.

EFFECT OF GROUND SURFACE AND GRADIENT UPON THE LANDING RUN

The length of the landing run will depend upon the wind strength and direction, the touch-down speed, the type of ground surface and whether it is flat or sloping. The effect of wind has already been covered, so the following paragraphs concern only the effect of ground surface and gradient upon the deceleration of the aircraft during the landing roll.

During the landing roll the aircraft will be dissipating the kinetic energy provided by the initial touch-down speed, therefore the effect of the initial touch-down speed has an important influence on the length of the landing run. The kinetic energy is a product of both speed and weight, but whereas at twice the weight there will be twice the energy to be lost, if the speed is doubled there will be four times the energy to be lost.

Having established the importance of having the correct touch-down speed, the next consideration is the effect of the ground texture, i.e. smooth concrete, long grass, soft ground etc. To consider this it must first be appreciated that two more factors will play an important part in the length of the landing run. The first is the aerodynamic braking effect of drag, and the second is the surface braking effect of ground friction. Figure 13-3 illustrates that at the point of touch-down only part of the aircraft weight is on the wheels, the remainder is supported by the residual lift which still exists for a short while after touch-down. As the aircraft slows down, more and more of the aircraft weight is placed on the wheels, and rolling friction increases. The use of the aircraft brakes will produce a third factor, braking friction but this is considered later in this briefing. To sum up, the minimum rolling friction will be experienced when the touch-down speed is high, a tailwind exists and the landing surface is smooth.

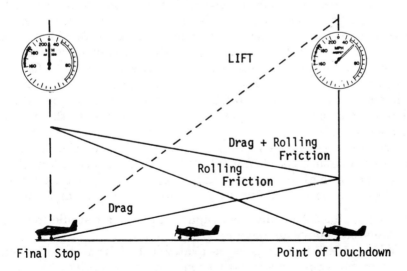

Fig. 13-3

The effect of gradient is similar to the take-off case, but the magnitude of its effect is not so great. Whilst runway slope must be taken into account, the degree of slope found at normal airfields will not have a large effect on landing distance, or landing run, and when this applies it is usually better to land into wind and accept a down slope.

USE OF ELEVATORS

It is important to keep the weight off the nosewheel during the early stages of the landing run and this is accomplished by maintaining a back pressure on the control column throughout the deceleration period. Care must be used if the landing speed is in excess of that normally recommended, as at higher speeds the elevators could be sufficiently effective to raise the nose after landing to an extent which could cause the aircraft stern post to strike the ground.

There may be occasions such as when landing in a strong crosswind where a slight forward pressure on the control column may be advisable after touch-down. This action will put more weight on the nosewheel and improve directional control. However if too much forward pressure is used a condition known as 'Wheelbarrowing' may take place, and whilst this condition is more likely to occur with low wing aircraft fitted with steerable nosewheels, it is a possibility with any nosewheel aircraft.

Wheelbarrowing may be described as an attitude or condition in a nosewheel aircraft that is encountered after initial touchdown during the landing phase while the nosewheel is more firmly in contact with the ground than the main wheels. This causes the nosewheel to support a greater than normal amount of aircraft weight, whilst providing the only means of steering. During a crosswind landing an aircraft in this situation tends to pivot rapidly about the nosewheel in a manoeuvre similar to a ground loop in a tailwheel aircraft. Other indications that wheelbarrowing is taking place can be wheel skipping accompanied by the loss of braking effect when the brakes are applied.

Normally wheelbarrowing may be encountered if the pilot is using an excess approach speed in a full flap configuration, in addition to touching down with little or no rotation or hold off. Corrective action will depend upon several factors but can be summed up as follows:

● When sufficient distance is available the aircraft should immediately be taken round again.
● When insufficient distance is available to initiate a 'go round again' procedure, the throttle should be checked fully closed and the control column moved gently to a slightly aft of neutral

position, which will lighten the load on the nosewheel and return steering and braking to normal.

USE OF BRAKES

The action of using the aircraft braking system is highly beneficial in reducing the length of the landing run on firm dry surfaces. However if the point of touch-down has been correctly planned and achieved, the use of braking during the early part of the landing run will normally be unnecessary, but if a late touch-down occurs the brakes may need to be applied to avoid the aircraft over-running the available landing area. When brakes are needed, they should be applied intermittently during that period when the speed is high and more prolonged application should be made as the aircraft slows down.

Fig. 13-4

When landings are being made on wet grass surfaces, the brakes will be almost ineffective at higher speeds and may have an adverse effect causing the aircraft to skid, leading to difficulties in directional control. In these circumstances the brakes will have to be used intermittently and cautiously, gradually extending the length of application as the aircraft loses speed. When landing on wet grass, the most important procedure will be to touch-down as early as possible compatible with safety and at the correct landing speed.

If the landing is being made on long grass, soft surface, slush or snow, the natural rolling friction will be high. Maintaining a relatively nose-high attitude in the early stage of the landing roll will provide aerodynamic braking action, and will be quite effective in keeping the weight off the nosewheel. Application of brakes during this period will have little effect.

Many light aircraft braking systems are operated hydraulically and should be exercised by their application during the pre-landing checks, if the brakes are found to be partially or wholly unservice-able, i.e. no resistance being felt when applied, then the pilot will be warned of this early, thus avoiding making the discovery during the landing roll when it may be too late.

For obvious reasons such a testing action is particularly important when a short landing is to be made or a strong crosswind prevails. What is perhaps not so obvious, is that if a short landing is planned, and one side of the braking system is unserviceable, the application of brakes immediately after touch-down could easily produce an uncontrollable swing. Also, if one brake is unserviceable and it is the one which is likely to be needed when landing in a strong crosswind, the pilot may be able to change his plan and use a runway where the crosswind effect will require the use of the serviceable brake.

CIRCUIT PROCEDURES, DOWNWIND AND BASE LEGS
Once on the downwind leg the height must be maintained and the datum for heading reference will be the landing path. The following items should be observed during this leg and fig. 13-5 shows a plan view of this part of the circuit:

Ensure the correct distance out from the runway is maintained, and that the aircraft continues to track parallel to the landing path. It sometimes occurs that the wind direction at circuit height is different to that at ground level resulting in drift experienced at height, although the landing path is into wind.

Ensure that the aircraft remains well clear of other air traffic and in this respect it may be necessary to alter heading slightly for a short period to maintain a safe separation. Remember to look all around the aircraft as often as possible throughout the whole of the circuit and avoid the tendency to concentrate the lookout ahead and into the direction of the landing path. The pre-landing checks

FINAL APPROACH

BASE LEG

DOWNWIND LEG

Fig. 13-5

should be carried out as soon as possible during this leg and they must be done meticulously, but not at the expense of lookout.

Due to the possibility of different types of aircraft, e.g. small and slow, or large and fast, using the same airfield it will often be difficult to turn onto the base leg at the ideal moment which is when the intended touch-down point lies at an angle of approximately 45° behind the wing. A good lookout all round should be made before the aircraft is turned onto the base leg.

During the base leg the crosswind effect will normally drift the aircraft further downwind, so a heading allowance must be made to prevent this. The aircraft nose should be positioned slightly into the direction of the prevailing wind to ensure the maintenance of a track line which is at 90° to the intended approach path.

TYPES OF APPROACH AND LANDING

The basic pre-requisite of a good approach is to maintain the aircraft at the right height, speed, attitude and position during its travel towards the runway or landing area. The use of power during an approach will assist considerably towards the accomplishment of this aim. Although the powered approach is the one most commonly used, there will be occasions when different types and variations of types of approach and landing will be employed.

The Powered Approach and Landing

This method is normally used for the initial demonstration and practice of the approach to landing. It commences from a point approximately a quarter to one third along the base leg, where the power is reduced, flap is selected and the airspeed adjusted to that chosen for the conditions, and the aircraft trimmed.

The power initially selected will be determined by the direction and strength of the wind relative to the landing path and the position of the aircraft in relation to the intended touchdown area. It is from this stage onwards that considerable care must be given to keeping the airspeed correct. The importance of accurate speed control lies first with safety, and secondly, if the speed is allowed to vary continuously it becomes more difficult to judge the approach path in relation to the intended touch-down area.

The rate of descent is controlled by the use of power and the airspeed maintained by the adjustment of the nose attitude in pitch. The rate of descent must be regulated to ensure that the aircraft is no lower than 500 feet a.g.l. as it enters the final turn onto the approach path. Assuming an into-wind landing is being made, the turn onto the final approach should be commenced just prior to intersecting the final approach path, and the bank angle varied to bring the aircraft onto the centre line of the approach path. The bank angle should not however exceed 30° and in the event that the aircraft overshoots the final approach path, the turn should not be steepened, but an adjustment to the aircraft heading can be made to bring the aircraft back onto the centre line after the final turn is almost completed. During this turn the airspeed must be monitored frequently. Once established on the approach path the position of the landing area and its perspective through the windscreen should be noted, and fig. 13-6 shows the different perspectives relating to the vertical position of the aircraft on the approach path.

RUNWAY
PERSPECTIVE

(a)   Correct Approach
Path

(b)   Too High

(c)   Too Low

Fig. 13-6

The student must keep his hand on the throttle during the whole of the approach except for those occasions when other controls e.g. trim etc. have to be operated. Provided reaction to errors in the approach angle is prompt, the amount of power variation and aircraft pitch adjustment will be quite small, and the student should appreciate that the sooner he can recognise the correct perspective for the correct angle of approach, the smaller his corrections will need to be.

During this final stage it is also important to remember that lateral level, heading and balance are achieved by the correct and combined use of the ailerons and rudder. Any tendency to use too much aileron and insufficient rudder will result in the aircraft becoming mis-aligned with the landing path.

The airspeed selected for the approach will depend upon the aircraft type, the use of flap, and the prevailing wind conditions, e.g. gustiness, turbulence, etc. Normally a range of speed is given in the Flight/

/Owner's Manual/Pilot's Operating Handbook, but a specific airspeed should be selected depending on the previously mentioned conditions. Bear in mind that the speeds quoted in aircraft manuals are usually for calm conditions.

Generally the greater the amount of flap used the lower should be the approach speed, but when strong winds or turbulence prevails, the airspeed should be increased for better control. The decision to increase the flap setting should be made shortly after completing the final turn and establishing the approach path. This permits the selection to be made, the airspeed adjusted as necessary and the aircraft trimmed whilst still at a reasonable height above the ground.

Some training aircraft are fitted with powerful flaps and the use of full flap during initial landing practice could be disadvantageous due to the strong trim changes, the steep nose-down attitude required to maintain the correct speed, and the very positive roundout immediately before touch-down. In such cases the use of half to two thirds flap will normally be used until the student has acquired more experience.

Ideally, when performing a powered approach the power should be left on until just prior to touch-down, and if the student judges the approach path correctly the final stages of the approach to touchdown will require a condition of a gradual decrease of power.

The actual height from which the flare commences will only be learnt during actual practice, however it will normally be about 20 feet above the ground, and at this stage the control column must be moved back to flare the aircraft, until it is flying parallel to and within a foot or so of the ground. At this point the hold-off commences, during which the throttle is closed fully and the control column moved continually back in an effort to keep the wheels just off the ground. With nosewheel aircraft the object is to land on the mainwheels in a slightly tail-down attitude to avoid the nosewheel taking unnecessary shocks and stress.

The ability to see clearly and to know where to look is an extremely important part of the landing phase. The student should direct his line of sight slightly to the left of the nose cowling and look about the same distance ahead as when driving a car at a speed equivalent to that being used for the landing.

In order to achieve the necessary depth perception during the round out at hold-off height, the student's vision will have to be focussed correctly. Speed blurs objects at close visual range, nearby objects seem to merge together whilst distant objects stand out clearly. The ability to choose the correct 'looking distance' ahead so that it is possible to keep the ground in the aircraft's immediate vicinity in focus is a primary requirement in landing the aircraft. Once this is established the student will be able to develop his judgement and the correct control movements.

As the airspeed lowers just prior to touch-down the distance at which it is possible to focus the vision comes nearer and the student's gaze should be adjusted accordingly.

The rate of backward movement of the control column should be adjusted to the aircraft sink rate. If the aircraft sinks slowly the control column should be moved back slowly, and if the aircraft sinks quickly the control column should be moved back quickly. Following the touch-down the control column should be held back slightly to keep the weight off the nosewheel until the speed has been reduced. Rudder will be required to maintain directional control and the brakes used only if necessary.

Whilst the aircraft is slowing down following the landing, speed can be deceptive, and it is important to ensure that a reasonably slow speed has been reached prior to any turns being made to take the aircraft clear of the landing area. Once the aircraft is clear of the landing area it should be brought to a stop, the throttle set to give 1200 RPM and the after landing checks completed.

CROSSWIND APPROACH AND LANDING
On those occasions when the landing path is not directly into wind, a crosswind circuit, approach and landing will have to be made. The effect of these crosswind conditions will concern each leg of the circuit from the climb-out to the final approach and landing.

During the climb-out it will be necessary to turn the aircraft slightly into the wind to offset drift and to enable a climb to be made in line with the extended centre line of the runway. Throughout the downwind leg it will be necessary again to turn the aircraft slightly to counteract the drift in order that a track parallel to the landing path can be achieved. Figure 13-7 illustrates this action.

Once on the base leg the effect of the partial head or tailwind component will increase or decrease the time taken to reach the point for the final turn. If the time to the final turn is increased, the reduction in power prior to the descent on the base leg will not be so great or the aircraft will lose too much height before the final turn due to the lower ground speed. Also it will be necessary to delay the commencement of the turn on to final approach until close to the extended centre line. If the time to the final turn is decreased, as

Fig. 13-7

when a tailwind component is experienced, the height loss will be more gradual and a lower power setting will be required to achieve the correct height of 500 feet a.g.l. on approaching the runway centre line. Also it will be necessary to commence the turn earlier, as the tailwind component will drift the aircraft across the centre line during the turn.

The heading on the final approach will have to be slightly into the direction the wind is coming from to ensure a straight track down the approach path and keep the aircraft on the landing path centre line. There are two methods of completing the final approach and landing when a crosswind is present.

One is to maintain the nose position off to the into wind side of the centre line, (fig. 13-8) and just prior to touch-down while keeping the wings level, application of rudder is made to set the aircraft straight aligning the longitudinal axis with the centre line of the landing path. Provided the controls are used correctly and the timing of these movements is accurate the aircraft will land correctly. If the rudder is applied too early the wind effect will overcome the aircraft inertia and a sideways motion will occur before touch-down. If the rudder is used too late the aircraft will travel sideways during the moment of touch-down and either of these situations will produce a sideways stress on the landing gear. Therefore the timing of the control movements will require the development of a reasonable degree of judgement.

Fig. 13-8

Fig. 13-9

The second method (fig. 13-9) is to lower the windward wing slightly and slip the aircraft into the wind just enough to maintain a straight path over the ground, co-incidental with the centre line of the landing path. This method will usually involve landing the aircraft on one wheel, and as the aircraft settles on to the ground the wings can be levelled and a normal landing run commenced. Particular care must be used in the second method to avoid the nosewheel touching the ground until both main wheels have settled, or a sudden change of direction may be induced upon touch-down.

GLIDE APPROACH AND LANDING

The primary function in teaching the glide approach is to develop the student's judgement for that stage of training when he will be practising forced landings without power.

Although a pilot can alter the steepness of his path of descent during the final approach into wind by the use of flaps, it is also a fundamental consideration of the gliding approach that his judgement should be implemented by manoeuvring the aircraft during the base leg when a rectangular pattern is being used. At this stage a small alteration in heading either towards or away from the airfield will make a large change in the distance the aircraft is away from the field when it turns onto the final approach. Therefore, in this way, undershooting or overshooting is primarily controlled when the aircraft is crosswind before the turn onto final approach.

Fig. 13-10

When a continuous moderate spiral descent is being used in the latter stages of the forced landing without power procedure, and ATC considerations permit, it will be possible to incorporate a continuous turn from the downwind leg onto the final approach, and the rate of turn can be modified to allow for any tendency to undershoot or overshoot.

The procedure for the rectangular circuit commences on the base leg when the student will have to decide the point to close the throttle completely. The approximate position for this action will be when the touchdown point is at 45° to the aircraft track. Ideally, once the throttle is closed, flaps should be selected and the aircraft trimmed. The use of flap should not however be automatic, first consider whether their use will cause a descent path which is too steep bearing in mind the aircraft position from the intended touchdown point.

From this stage onwards the student will have to constantly monitor his position in relation to his height and distance from the point of touchdown. If it is felt that the aircraft is losing height too quickly the aircraft should be turned towards the landing area by an amount which is considered to be compatible with the aircraft height and distance from the aiming point. Conversely, if the aircraft appears to be too high it should be turned away just sufficiently to correct this situation, or consideration given to an increase in the flap setting. Caution should however be exercised when selecting further flap as it is advisable to keep some flap in hand for use on the final approach should the aircraft be too high at this stage.

It should be noted that the roundout from a gliding approach will be greater due to the steeper descent without power and if full flaps are used this will need to be taken into account to ensure a safe landing.

SHORT FIELD APPROACH AND LANDING

A short landing means the techique used to land an aircraft in a confined space. Whether or not any given space can be considered as confined, depends upon the length of the landing run available, the presence of any obstructions on the approach and the strength and direction of the prevailing wind in relation to the intended landing path.

After the final turn into wind, speed is reduced progressively so that the lowest speed at which the aircraft can be controlled safely is reached as the aircraft arrives at the boundary of the field. As in the normal engine assisted approach, the engine is used to control the rate of descent and airspeed is controlled with the elevators. Full flap is lowered unless weather conditions e.g. strong winds or turbulence make this impractical.

The approach is carried out so that the aircraft crosses the field boundary at the lowest possible height consistent with obstacle clearance, to position it at hold-off height as near as possible to the landing path threshold. In the final stages of the approach it may be necessary to increase the power to arrest the rate of descent in order to prevent the aircraft landing heavily. Due to the low speed, the aircraft will experience minimum float before touch-down when the throttle is closed. The already short landing run may be further shortened by the judicious application of brakes.

A long, flat, low approach is to be avoided during this type of landing, but when the last portion of the approach is free from obstructions, the pilot can undershoot very slightly during the final stages, then increase power to position the aircraft for touchdown at the landing threshold.

SOFT FIELD APPROACH AND LANDING

When the landing surface is soft or rough or in the event that the landing is being made on long grass, the soft field approach and landing should be used. The approach is set up in the normal way, and the airspeed used for the short field landing will be appropriate. The touch-down should be made at the lowest possible ground speed, therefore a landing path which gives the strongest headwind component should be used, if possible with full flap applied.

The touch-down is required to be made on the main wheels, with the aircraft in a nose high attitude. This attitude will be coincident with the lowest touch-down speed and should be held as long as possible during the landing run. It is sometimes of benefit to leave a 'trickle' of power on during the initial stages of the landing roll, in order to improve the effectiveness of the elevators in holding the nosewheel clear of the ground until the aircraft has slowed down. This use of power will however depend upon the landing length available and when this is short the throttle should be fully closed throughout the landing roll.

When using the soft field technique with a tailwheel aircraft, the aim will be to have the tailwheel touch down just before or at the same time as the main wheels, and the control column should then be held fully back until the aircraft comes to a stop.

When landing in these conditions the application of brakes will normally be unnecessary but when they are applied for any reason, extreme care should be used to avoid placing a sudden load on the nosewheel or causing a sudden asymmetric skidding of the main wheels.

FLAPLESS APPROACH AND LANDING

The flapless approach is taught because there may be occasions when the use of flaps is not advisable, or not possible due to mechanical failure. During a flapless approach in light winds the path is extremely flat, and necessitates the final turn onto the approach path being made at a greater distance from the airfield. Therefore, judgment of the approach path is more difficult, particularly when making a glide approach. The lowest safe airspeed during the approach with flaps up is obtained with power on, so the flapless approach is normally taught as an engine assisted approach which must bring the aircraft over the boundary at the lowest height necessary to clear obstacles.

Because of the flat approach path the view forward is decreased and there is also very little change in attitude during landing. Due to the absence of drag from the flaps there will also be a longer float and landing run, therefore the touch-down should be made as near the runway threshold as possible. Although flapless approaches are more easily accomplished with the use of power, they can also be practised from the glide approach during training to assist in developing the student's judgement.

TAILWHEEL CONSIDERATIONS

Although the procedures used for the various types of approach will remain substantially the same, whether a nosewheel or tailwheel aircraft is used, there will be some variation in landing technique. With a tailwheel aircraft the technique following the flare varies in that during into wind landings, or on those occasions when only a small crosswind component exists, the aircraft is eventually brought into the '3 point' attitude, and ideally the main wheels and tailwheel are made to contact the ground at the same time. Basically the landing procedure will remain the same as for nosewheel aircraft, but the hold-off is continued for a slightly longer period in order to achieve the correct attitude. After touch-down the control column should be held well back.

| landing 3 points all flying speed lost | 'holding off' | levelling at 2 to 3 feet above ground | starting to 'level off' |

Fig. 13-11

Once on the ground the problem of directional control is made more difficult because of the weight being behind the pivot point which, as covered in the Long Briefing on Take-off, will cause any tendency to swing to be accentuated. A faster reaction to any divergence of heading will be necessary to maintain directional control and larger movements of the rudder will be required. A further point is that with the aircraft in the tail-down attitude, the view directly ahead is often poor, requiring particular alertness in detecting early the heading changes which may occur.

When strong, gusty winds prevail it will be advisable to use the

'Wheel Landing' technique. This type of landing differs from the 3-point landing in that the aircraft is landed on its main wheels with the tail held slightly lower than the normal level attitude. The touch-down will in consequence be made at a slightly higher airspeed and all the flying controls will be more effective during the initial stage of the landing roll. This effect will be of considerable assistance to the maintenance of directional control during strong crosswind conditions.

When employing the soft or short field landing techniques with tailwheel aircraft the control column must be held fully back throughout the landing run.

MISSED APPROACH

This procedure is used when it becomes necessary to discontinue the approach and climb back to the downwind position. Immediately the decision is made to abandon the approach descent, the throttle should be opened fully and a climb initiated. Forward pressure on the control column will be necessary to prevent the nose rising as the power is applied. This forward pressure will normally have to be quite firm as the effect of full power application when the aircraft is trimmed for a descent will cause a strong nose-up pitch change to occur. The flaps should be raised at the correct speed and once the climbing speed is obtained the aircraft should be re-trimmed. The requirement to conform to the circuit pattern will still exist and
the pilot must position the aircraft to carry out a normal crosswind and downwind leg. If the missed approach is initiated when the aircraft is still relatively high, circuit height will be reached during the climb straight ahead and the turn onto the crosswind leg should be delayed until the aircraft is in the normal position to commence this leg.

When runways or marked out take-off and landing paths are being used it will be advisable to turn the aircraft slightly during the climb to parallel the aircraft track along the right side of the landing path, this will ensure a safer situation in which the pilot will be able to see any aircraft which have just taken off and are climbing away. Before making this right turn, a careful lookout to the right must be made, to ensure no other overshooting aircraft is in the vicinity.

MISLANDING AND GOING ROUND AGAIN

Inevitably during training and also afterwards there will be occasions during the final stages of the approach or at any time throughout the landing phase when things do not work out as planned, for example, too early or too late a roundout, leading to a 'bounce' or floating too high above the runway. It is in these situations that the ability to make a positive decision to 'go round again' will be the hallmark of a proficient and safe pilot. To the student, and sometimes the more experienced pilot, the greatest difficulty will be in the taking of a quick and positive decision, but unless this ability is demonstrated during training the student will not be sent solo.

The basic procedure is to open the throttle fully, gain speed and establish the aircraft safely in the climb, and this action should be taken at any time the aircraft is wrongly positioned late on the final approach, or when positive doubt exists as to the accomplishment of a safe landing. In other words 'If in doubt there is no doubt' the throttle should be opened and the aircraft taken round again.

Remember that the wind or other circumstances can cause difficulties during the roundout and the touch-down phase. For example, whenever a student finds himself floating too high above the ground with lowering airspeed following the flare, or touching down too fast and becoming airborne again, the 'go round again' procedure should automatically be put into effect. This action will also be applicable to those situations when the aircraft has travelled too far along the landing path for a safe landing and a stop to be made.

When going round again, it is particularly important to obtain a safe speed before placing the aircraft into the climb, and this speed will depend upon such factors as the amount of flap being used, and when applicable the degree of turbulence being experienced at the time.

ENGINE HANDLING
Throughout any circuit, approach and landing, the engine will be operated at varying power settings, and the aim should be to operate the throttle smoothly at all times. This consideration is important, and when practising glide approaches it is particularly relevant when high power has to be used suddenly following a late recognition of an undershoot situation. In the event of a missed approach or 'go round again' action, the engine oil temperature and pressure, power output, and when applicable the fuel flow or pressure should be checked as soon as it is possible to do so safely.

The use of carburettor heat should be as recommended in the Flight/Owner's Manual/Pilot's Operating Handbook, and unless operating from high elevation airfields, the mixture control should be in the Full Rich position.

AIRMANSHIP AND ATC PROCEDURES
Aircraft proximity is close during the circuit, approach and landing,

and pilot workload will inevitably be increased during this phase. Therefore the airmanship considerations will be of the utmost importance. An extremely high standard of lookout and compliance with ATC procedures will need to be continuously maintained. The following airmanship points should be observed throughout the take-off, circuit, approach and landing:

Prior to taxying onto runways or take-off areas scan the approach path for possible landing traffic and manoeuvre the aircraft as necessary to provide a clear view of any aircraft approaching to land, landing or taking off. All checks and drills should be performed meticulously, and during those carried out whilst airborne a good lookout must be maintained.

When operating at ATC controlled airfields or where an RTF advisory facility exists, maintain two-way contact with the tower whilst in the circuit pattern. Make every effort to see and avoid any aircraft whose position has been signified by R/T and any other aircraft which may be in the vicinity unknown to the ATC unit or advisory service.

In many instances, the pilot's view of the surrounding airspace is restricted by the inherent design of the aircraft and its flight attitude. Compensate for blind spots by moving the head and body and where necessary manoeuvring the aircraft.

Fig. 13-12

Correct positioning and the maintenance of adequate spacing between aircraft is very important, and unless this is ensured dangerous situations can occur, particularly during the base leg and final approach.

When on base leg a very careful lookout must be maintained for aircraft which may be carrying out a long final approach. Blind spots between aircraft operating in this area are particularly hazardous as fig. 13-12 illustrates. Lookout must therefore be made to both sides of the flight path and above and below.

The final approach is the area where aircraft funnel into the landing path and during this period the workload on the pilot can easily reduce his standard of lookout. It is in this area that collision risk between aircraft is probably the highest, and this risk can only be reduced by constant vigilance.

A missed approach can be initiated at any time from the base leg onwards, and should always be carried out without hesitation when doubt exists as to the safe completion of the approach and landing. Getting too close to the aircraft ahead, or being inaccurately positioned on the approach path, or overhauling a landing aircraft too quickly for it to clear the landing path, are all examples necessitating missed approach procedure.

Some runways have sterile areas in the region of the physical threshold, this is to ensure that arriving aircraft do not approach too low over obstructions including roads and houses which are fairly close to the airfield boundary. The type of runway marking used to signify the existence of these areas is shown in fig. 13-13, and a landing aircraft must not touch down until it has passed over the line of V's or arrows.

Permanently Displaced
Landing Threshold

Temporarily Displaced
Landing Threshold

Fig. 13-13

PRE-FLIGHT BRIEFING
THE POWERED APPROACH AND LANDING
Demonstration 1.

Aim To teach you the procedure and control techniques necessary to land the aircraft safely from a powered approach.

What An approach during which power is used to regulate the descent path to a landing under varying conditions of wind, aircraft weight and airfield elevation.

Airmanship Performance calculations regarding landing run and distance, pre-landing checks, positioning in the circuit and the vital necessity of lookout, RTF procedures will be included as applicable.

How

Downwind Leg:

① R/T, Checks, Lookout, height and position relative to other aircraft and the landing path. Base leg position.

② *Base Leg:*
Lookout, medium level turn, allowance for drift. Position to reduce power.
> Select required power.
> Speed within flap range, select flap.
> Adjust attitude for correct speed.
> Re-trim.

Adjust power to regulate descent rate.
Maintain lookout either side and ahead.
At 500/600 a.g.l. turn on to final approach, maintaining speed and if necessary varying turn rate to position the aircraft on the approach path centreline.

The Landing:

④ Judge the height to flare out. Commence roundout and reduce power. Look ahead and slightly to one side. Move control column back compatible with the rate of sink. A foot or so above the ground close the throttle. Maintain wings level and direction. Continue hold-off and land on main wheels.

During the landing run keep the control column back, maintain direction with rudder and allow the speed to reduce. At a low speed the aircraft can be turned clear of the landing path/runway. Stop the aircraft and complete the after-landing checks.

Missed Approach:
Apply full power, attain correct climbing attitude and speed. If used, ensure carburettor 'Air' is returned to Cold and flaps are raised. Climb to the right of and parallel with the landing path. Above 500 feet and when in the correct position turn on to the crosswind leg.

DOWNWIND ① ②
BASE ③
FINAL ④ ⑤

③ *Final Approach:*
Note: Perspective and position of the runway through the windscreen. Use power to regulate descent and elevators to control the airspeed. Ailerons and rudder must be used together to maintain the approach path centreline. Select further flap as required.

④ *The Landing: (Tailwheel Aircraft)*
Reduce power during the initial roundout and look ahead and slightly to one side. Move control column back compatible with rate of sink. Close throttle, continue hold-off until the 3-point attitude is achieved at touchdown.

Student Practice.

⑤ *Going Round Again:*
Apply full power, keep straight and hold the wings level. Ensure carburettor 'Air' is returned to Cold. After lift-off attain a safe climbing speed. At a safe height and airspeed, raise flap, re-trim and adopt a normal climb.

13-33

PRE-FLIGHT BRIEFING
THE CROSSWIND APPROACH AND LANDING
Demonstration 2.

Aim To teach you the procedure(s) and control technique(s) necessary to land safely in crosswind conditions.

What A landing made in a direction out of line with the prevailing wind.

Airmanship Considerations in relation to crosswind limitations, landing performance calculations, lookout and ground handling.

How *Before Landing:*

Note wind strength and direction, review the aircraft limiting crosswind component. Decide flap setting to use.

Downwind Leg:
Allow for drift and remain parallel with landing direction.

Base Leg:
Allow for head/tailwind component increasing or decreasing power to arrive at 500/600 feet for final turn. The turn is commenced slightly earlier or later depending upon the wind component.

Final Approach (Crab Method):
Allow for drift by 'offsetting' the aircraft heading from the approach path centreline.

The Landing:
Just prior to touchdown, hold wings level and use rudder to align the aircraft heading with the runway centreline. After touchdown be prepared to prevent weathercocking action.

Student Practice.

Final Approach (Forward Slip Method):
Lower windward wing and use opposite rudder to maintain the approach path centreline.

The Landing:
In moderate crosswinds stop the slip a few feet above the ground and land normally.

In strong crosswinds land gently on the windward main wheel and then allow the aircraft to settle normally on both mainwheels. After landing be prepared to prevent weathercock action.

Wheel Landing (Tailwheel Aircraft):
Round out in the normal manner, adopting a slight tail-down attitude and gently fly the aircraft onto the ground, allowing the mainwheels to touch-down first.

After landing maintain a slight forward pressure on the control column.

Maintain a constant heading with rudder and allow the tail to settle gently onto the ground.

In crosswind conditions be prepared to prevent weathercock action when the tail is on the ground.

Student Practice.

Component

WIND

Crab Method

PRE-FLIGHT BRIEFING

THE GLIDE APPROACH AND LANDING
Demonstration 3.

Aim To teach you the judgement required to complete a successful approach and landing from a pre-determined position and without the use of power.

What An approach and landing made entirely without the use of power and which is practised in preparation for possible engine failure.

Airmanship All normal airmanship considerations will apply but additional caution must be used to ensure that the particular type of approach and landing can be made safely under the conditions which exist at the time.

How Downwind leg: Turn onto base leg earlier than for a powered approach.

Base Leg: Decide position to close throttle. Select carburettor heat (if applicable). Close the throttle, select required flap, attain the selected approach speed and re-trim.

Make small adjustments to heading to maintain the correct position compatible with aircraft height and position from the touchdown zone.

Final Approach: Vary the rate of the final approach turn as necessary, carefully monitoring the airspeed. On final approach small changes in heading or more flap can be used if the aircraft is too high.

NOTE: If during practice an undershoot situation occurs, open the throttle and re-position the aircraft on the correct glide path then continue with the glide.

The Landing: A steeper roundout will be required, therefore commence the roundout earlier than for a powered approach.

Hold off and touch down in the normal way.

Student Practice.

THE SHORT FIELD LANDING
Demonstration 4.

Aim To teach you the technique to be employed during the approach and landing into a short field.

What The procedure to use when landing in areas which have a restricted length in relation to landing run and distance.

How Before Landing: Review the aircraft manual and the available 'Field Data' to ensure the aircraft performance permits a landing to be made safely.

Base Leg: Complete this as for a powered approach but in light winds increase the length of the downwind leg.

Final Approach: At the appropriate height and position select full flap (if wind conditions permit) and adopt an airspeed lower than the normal powered approach speed.

NOTE: Exercise caution in strong wind conditions.

Regulate the descent rate with power and aim to land as close to the threshold or field boundary as is safely possible.

The Landing: A shallower roundout will be required.

When just above the touchdown point, close the throttle and anticipate a minimal float period. After landing hold the control column fully back and use the brakes as required.

Student Practice.

THE SOFT FIELD LANDING
Demonstration 5.

Aim
To teach you the technique to be employed during a soft field landing.

What
The landing technique to be used when surface conditions are soft, rough or covered with long grass (this also includes snow or slush).

Airmanship
Normal airmanship considerations will apply but additional caution must be used to ensure that the particular type of landing can be made safely under the conditions which exist at the time.

How
Before Landing: Determine the best landing path in relation to wind, surface conditions and gradient.

Base Leg: Complete this as for a powered approach but in light wind conditions increase the length of the downwind leg.

Final Approach: At the appropriate height and position select full flap (provided wind conditions permit) and adopt an airspeed lower than the normal approach speed.

NOTE: Exercise caution in strong wind conditions.

Regulate the descent rate with power and aim to position the aircraft close to the ground at the lowest speed compatible with safe control.

The Landing: Gradually close the throttle and allow the aircraft to settle on the ground with the nosewheel held up.

After the touchdown hold the control column fully back to keep the nosewheel clear of the ground as long as possible.

Student Practice.

THE FLAPLESS APPROACH AND LANDING
Demonstration 6.

Aim
To teach you the technique of approaching and landing without the use of flap.

What
A type of approach and landing which may have to be made when flap failure has occurred or very strong winds prevail.

How
Downwind Leg: Complete a longer than normal downwind leg to allow for the flatter and longer approach.

Base Leg: Reduce power earlier and use less power in order to offset the reduced rate of descent and higher approach speed without flap.

Final Approach: The flatter approach path will result in a restricted forward view in relation to the landing path.

Smaller power adjustments will be needed to regulate the descent rate.

With due regard to obstructions, aim to land as close as possible to the threshold of the landing area or runway.

The Landing: A shallower roundout will occur and the aircraft will float longer.

After landing the brakes are more likely to be required.

Student Practice.

The Circuit, Approach and Landing

Flight Demonstrations

INTRODUCTION

The contents of this exercise can be conveniently divided into specific demonstration groups as follows:

1. The Circuit, Powered Approach and Landing
   Missed Approach
   Mislanding/Going Round Again
2. The Crosswind Approach and Landing
3. The Glide Approach and Landing
4. The Short Field Landing
5. The Soft Field Landing
6. The Flapless Approach and Landing

The contents of demonstration 1 will be gradually introduced over several flights so that the student is not faced with the entire contents for the first time during one demonstration.

Circumstances such as mandatory landing direction in the form of a runway, or marked out landing path, may dictate the combining of demonstrations 1 and 2 from the beginning of the exercise.

The 'Mislanding' and 'Going Round Again' procedures will normally be integrated and introduced with the contents of demonstration 1.

The flapless, short field and soft field approaches and landings, and when applicable the wheel landing, will normally form part of a student's consolidation training after 'First Solo'. However the particular operating environment and prevailing circumstances may call for these to be introduced and practised at an earlier stage.

DEMONSTRATION 1.   THE CIRCUIT, POWERED APPROACH AND LANDING

Flight Lesson	Demonstration Sequence
The circuit procedure, and the basic approach and landing	
At the commencement of the downwind leg	Make the R/T call 'Downwind'. Complete the Pre-Landing Checks. Maintain lookout and check height and positioning in relation to the landing path and other aircraft. Note the position to turn onto base leg. A careful lookout followed by a medium turn onto the base leg.
Base leg	Make an allowance for the drift. Note the position to reduce power:
	Apply carburettor heat (if applicable to type. Select required RPM. Maintain level attitude until the speed is within the flap lowering range. Lower flap as required and adjust the attitude for the selected approach speed.
	Adjust power as necessary to control the rate of descent. Lookout either side. At 500/600 feet and just before the approach centre line is reached commence a turn onto the final approach. Vary the turn rate as required to position the aircraft on the centre line as the final approach is commenced.
Final approach	Note the perspective of the runway/landing path and its relative position through the aircraft windscreen. Ailerons and rudder must be used together to maintain the aircraft on the centre line. Adjust power to control the rate of descent and elevators to control the attitude for the correct airspeed. Select further flap if applicable and adjust attitude to achieve the correct speed.

The landing	At the appropriate height start the initial round-out whilst gradually reducing power. Look ahead and slightly to one side. Move the control column back in phase with the rate of sink. A foot or so above the ground close the throttle, maintain direction, wings level and 'hold off' to the point of touch-down.
The landing run	Keep the control column back and maintain direction with rudder. As the speed reduces use brakes (if required) to slow down sufficiently to turn clear of the runway or landing path. When clear of the runway/landing path complete the 'after-landing checks'.
The landing (Tailwheel)	At the appropriate height start the initial round-out whilst gradually reducing power. Look ahead and slghtly to one side. Move the control column back in phase with the rate of sink. Before ground contact is made close the throttle completely and whilst keeping the wings level and maintaining direction continue to move the control column back until the '3-point' attitude is achieved at touchdown.
Missed approach	If at any time during the final approach any doubt exists as to the achievement of a safe landing: Apply full power and attain the correct climbing speed and attitude. At a safe speed and height, raise the flap and turn slightly to the right side of the landing path. Ensure COLD AIR applied. Maintain a track parallel to the landing path and continue climbing to circuit height or turn onto the crosswind leg according to the locally established procedure (not below 500 feet).
Going round again from a mislanding or roller landing	Apply full power, keep straight and hold the wings level. Ensure COLD AIR selected.

| | After lift-off, attain a safe climbing speed. At a safe height and airspeed, raise flap, re-trim and adopt a normal climb. |

Student practice: The student will be introduced to the contents of this exercise gradually until able to safely accomplish all the procedures and control actions.

DEMONSTRATION 2.   THE CROSSWIND APPROACH AND LANDING

Flight Lesson	*Demonstration Sequence*
Achieving a safe approach and landing when a crosswind exists	
At the commencement of the downwind leg	All normal circuit procedures and air-manship considerations will apply. Adjust the aircraft heading to maintain a track parallel with the landing path. Make allowance for the aircraft heading when assessing the position to turn onto the base leg.
Base leg	An allowance must be made for the head or tailwind component (as applicable) and power adjusted to take this into account, i.e. greater or lesser time taken to reach the approach path. Select flap as required and adjust the attitude to attain the approach airspeed. When a headwind component exists, commence the final turn when closer to the final approach path, and be prepared to reduce the bank angle to arrive on the centreline and on the correct approach heading. When a tailwind component exists, commence the final turn earlier. If drifting across the centreline avoid steep bank angles but adjust the roll-out heading to intersect the approach path.

Final approach (Crab Method)	An allowance must be made for drift, and heading adjustments will normally be necessary during the descent.
The landing	Just prior to touch-down, yaw the aircraft to align it with the runway centre line whilst keeping the wings level. After touch-down be prepared for the effect of weathercocking and use rudder to maintain direction.
Final approach (Forward Slip Method)	Upon completion of the final turn and when on the centreline of the approach path, lower the windward wing and use rudder to maintain the descent track.
The landing	For moderate crosswinds the slip can be stopped during the landing flare and a normal landing carried out. When a strong crosswind is present it will be usual to land gently on the into wind main wheel. When both wheels are on the ground added caution will be necessary to keep the aircraft on a straight heading.
Wheel landing (Tailwheel aircraft) An approach and landing normally used when strong gusty winds or crosswinds occur	
Final approach	Normal procedures will apply but consideration should be given to the use of a slightly higher approach speed.
The landing	Round out in the normal manner. Adopt a slight tail-down attitude and allow the main wheels to touch down first. Apply a slight forward pressure on the control column after touch-down to keep the main wheels on the ground with the aircraft in the flying attitude. Maintain a constant heading with the rudder and allow the tail to settle gently onto the ground. Special care must be exercised to forestall any tendency to ground loop.

Student practice: The student should practise these types of landings as and when applicable at intervals throughout his training. The opportunity must be taken to ensure the student has reasonable practice of crosswind landings as early as possible during the course. They must have been demonstrated and practised prior to solo navigation.

DEMONSTRATION 3.   THE GLIDE APPROACH AND LANDING

Flight Lesson	Demonstration Sequence
An approach and landing made without the use of power and commenced from the base leg	
Downwind leg	All normal circuit procedures and airmanship considerations will apply. Turn onto base leg earlier than for a powered approach.
Base leg	When it is judged that the aircraft can be flown from circuit height to the touch-down area without use of power, select carburettor heat (if applicable to type) and close the throttle. Select flaps as required and adjust attitude to adopt the correct approach speed. Re-trim and make small adjustments of heading as necessary to maintain the correct position compatible with the height and position from the touch-down zone.
Final approach	Once on the final approach small changes in heading or use of additional flap can be used if the aircraft is too high. If the aircraft is undershooting open the throttle to re-position the aircraft on the glide path and then continue with the glide.
The landing	The descent path is steeper than that for a powered approach. Commence the flare a little earlier, then hold off to touch down in the normal way. Application to the forced landing procedure.

Student practice: This is an exercise to aid the development of judgement. It will have to be fitted into the student's landing practice as and when other traffic requirements allow.

DEMONSTRATION 4.   THE SHORT FIELD LANDING

Flight Lesson	Demonstration Sequence
The type of approach and landing used when the length of the landing area is restricted	
Downwind leg	All normal circuit procedures and airmanship considerations will apply. In moderate winds turn onto base leg at the normal position for a powered approach. In light wind conditions turn onto base leg slightly later than for a powered approach.
Base leg	Control actions and aircraft positioning are as for a normal powered approach.
Final approach	Once established on the final approach select full flap. Note in strong winds it may be advisable to use less than full flap. Adjust the attitude for the final approach speed, normally less than for the standard powered approach. Regulate rate of descent with power, and airspeed with the elevators. When no obstacles exist in the vicinity of the threshold, aim to undershoot very slightly. When obstacles do exist select a touch-down point further into the field.
The landing	Due to the higher nose attitude at the lower approach speed a lesser round-out is required. Maintain power on throughout the round-out and close the throttle just before or as the main wheels contact the ground.
	Note: If too high when over the selected touch-down point do not close the throttle in an attempt to land

> more quickly, instead convert to a normal powered approach landing or go round again.
>
> After landing use the brakes as required.

Student practice: The student should be introduced to the practice of this type of approach and landing before he commences solo navigation, or earlier if circumstances dictate.

DEMONSTRATION 5.   THE SOFT FIELD LANDING

Flight Lesson	Demonstration Sequence
The procedure used for landing on soft or rough surfaces	
Downwind leg	All normal circuit procedures and airmanship considerations will apply. In moderate winds turn onto the base leg at the normal position for a powered approach. In light wind conditions it is advisable to turn onto base leg slightly further downwind.
Base leg	Control actions and aircraft positioning are as for a normal powered approach.
Final approach	Once positioned on the final approach select full flap. Note in strong winds it may be advisable to use less than full flap. Adjust the attitude for the correct approach speed, normally less than for the standard powered approach. Regulate rate of descent with power, and airspeed with the elevators.
The landing	Aim to position the aircraft close to the ground at the lowest speed compatible with safe control. Gradually close the throttle and allow the aircraft to settle on the ground with the nose wheel held up. Maintain a firm back pressure moving the control column backwards to keep the nosewheel clear of the ground as long as possible.

When landing distance allows, a small amount of power may be left on during the initial stages of the landing roll to improve elevator control and thereby assist in keeping the nosewheel clear of the ground.

Student practice: The student should be introduced to this type of approach and landing before he commences solo navigation, or earlier if circumstances dictate.

DEMONSTRATION 6.   THE FLAPLESS APPROACH AND LANDING

Flight Lesson	Demonstration Sequence
An approach and landing made without the assistance of flap	
Downwind leg	All normal circuit procedures and airmanship considerations will apply. Commence the base leg later than for a normal powered approach. This allows for the flatter approach path.
Base leg	Reduce the power earlier, use less than normal power and select a higher approach speed.
Final approach	Note the decreased forward visibility angle due to the higher nose attitude and flatter approach path. Smaller power changes are necessary to adjust the descent path. Aim to touch down on the runway threshold.
The landing	Note the shallower roundout. A longer float period and landing run will occur. The need to use brakes is more likely to occur.
Application to flap failure or landing in strong crosswinds.	

Student practice: The student should practise this type of approach and landing at periodic intervals throughout his training.

Supplement No. 3

In today's environment of General Aviation, light aircraft regularly use airfields in conjunction with larger, more powerful, aircraft (including airliners).

This operational mixing of small and large aircraft does however bring with it added workloads to the pilots of small aircraft and the attendant hazards of encountering powerful 'Prop Wash' and 'Jet Blast' on the ground and 'Wake Turbulence' when airborne.

PROP WASH AND JET BLAST
All pilots of light aircraft must be constantly aware of the hazards involved when taxying in the vicinity of larger aircraft and remain at a safe distance from them. The illustrations in fig. 13-14 show the strength of the air velocity behind large airliners when 'Idle Thrust' 'Breakaway Thrust' (the power needed to commence taxying) and 'Take-Off Thrust' are being used.

The actual figures shown can only be approximate as the strength of the gale force winds will depend upon the all-up weight of the aircraft and the power developed by their engines.

The engine exhaust velocities produced by these aircraft during the take-off roll and the drifting of the turbulence created by the application of take-off power in relation to possible crosswind effects clearly show the necessity for small aircraft to hold well clear of the active runway during pre-take off procedures. What is not always so clear is the strength of these exhaust velocities in relation to the distance from the generating aircraft when Idle Power or Breakaway Thrust is being used.

Added caution is necessary when light aircraft approach or position at holding points prior to take-off and in such circumstances they must position well clear of larger aircraft particularly when those aircraft are parked parallel to the taxyway.

WAKE TURBULENCE
All aircraft generate horizontal vortices from the wings whilst in

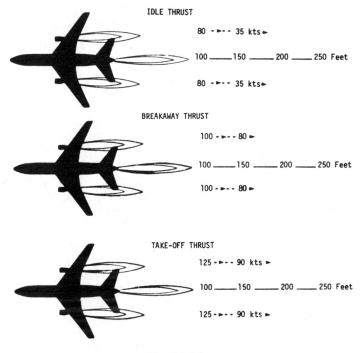

Fig. 13-14

flight and these can become very powerful at high angles of attack such as during lift-off or during the landing flare.

These vortices are caused by the overspill of air from under the wing into the area of low pressure above the wing, the greater the pressure differential between the underside of the wing and the upper surface the greater will be the vortex strength. Figure 13-15 shows the commencement of the vortex as air spills over the wing tip at (a). The airflow continues aft of the wing tip to produce two counter rotating cylindrical vortices as shown at (b) and (c). The tangential velocity of the air within these vortices can exceed 150 kts and any small aircraft coming within them would be uncontrollable.

The actual circulation of these two cylinders of air move outwards and downwards behind the generating aircraft, and remain active for several minutes. With this knowledge certain procedures can be used to avoid them.

Figure 13-16 shows the normal route taken by the vortices after being shed from the wing tips, therefore it can be seen that during flight it is safer to be slightly higher when passing behind or moving into the area previously occupied by a large aircraft. When a light aircraft takes off behind a heavier aircraft, and they are both taking off from the same runway position, a time interval of at least 2 to 3 minutes

(a)

(b)

(c)

Fig. 13-15

Sink Rate
400/500 F.P. Min.

Residual Chop
Remains

Max. Sink
800/900 Ft.

Breakup Starts

Fig. 13-16

Rotation

Wake Begins

Rotation Point

X

Fig. 13-17

should be allowed. The light aircraft should rotate and lift off before the point of the heavier aircraft's lift-off. An intersection take-off would therefore be inadvisable in these circumstances.

When landing after the arrival of a large aircraft, delay the final approach as long as practical and maintain a high approach path in order to stay above any vortex wake which may still be present. Plan the approach in order to land beyond the larger aircraft's point of touch-down. The recommended distance and time intervals are shown in the table at fig. 13-18 in relation to the larger aircraft's weight.

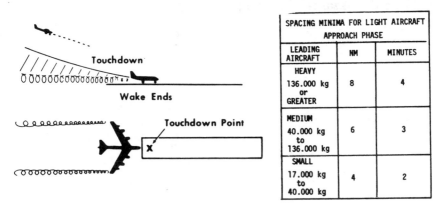

SPACING MINIMA FOR LIGHT AIRCRAFT APPROACH PHASE		
LEADING AIRCRAFT	NM	MINUTES
HEAVY 136.000 kg or GREATER	8	4
MEDIUM 40.000 kg to 136.000 kg	6	3
SMALL 17.000 kg to 40.000 kg	4	2

Fig. 13-18

During take-offs or landings there will sometimes be occasions when light crosswinds prevail and this can bring about a dangerous situation in that the upwind vortex (see fig. 13-19b) will tend to move outward and away from the runway but when the crosswind

Fig. 13-19

component is equal to the outward speed of travel of the vortex then the vortex core will remain stationary and persist in this region for some while.

All pilots must appreciate the dangers of vortex encounters and being able to visualise the path they are most likely to take in the existing conditions will help them to make correct and sensible decisions to minimise the hazards which might otherwise occur.

First Solo and Consolidation

Instructor's Guide

The first solo flight is a significant occasion in a student's training and its successful completion gives him confidence which is often reflected in a subsequent improvement in flying ability.

The recognition of the correct moment to send a student on his first solo is one of the main difficulties in basic instruction. If sent solo before he is fit, his confidence may be badly undermined by the flight and could result in an accident. On the other hand, postponing the first solo after the appropriate moment can often cause a deterioration in flying and retard progress. In any event, very low hours to first solo should be avoided as they are seldom a measure of extraordinary ability.

The main consideration is not finesse in flying, but overall competence and safety, and the ability to correct errors. The instructor must feel confident that his student will act promptly and correctly in an emergency, and his reactions should be noted when any circumstances in the nature of an emergency occur during dual flights. The following is a guide as to what constitutes an acceptable standard for first solo:

Take-off and Climb.

Swings should never be allowed to develop during the take-off run. The aircraft should be flown off at close to the correct lift off speed. The student should be able to maintain a good lookout whilst carrying out checks during the climb to the crosswind leg.

The Circuit.

This need not be precisely accurate in all respects, but each leg should be approximately the correct length and the correct heading. Variations of height which are suitably corrected are acceptable, provided the student does not have such large height errors that they cause substantial difficulty on the approach. Turns should be well controlled without any tendency towards steep bank angles.

14-1

The Approach.

A safe speed on base leg and final approach is essential, particularly during the turn and the latter stages of the approach to land. Power corrections and any decision to go round again should be made at an early stage.

The Landing.

Safety is the main consideration, and there must not be consistent faults such as holding off too high. A series of good landings does not indicate that a student is necessarily ready for solo, unless he has also demonstrated his ability to recognise a situation which calls for going round again, and has made the decision to do so without any assistance from the instructor.

AIRMANSHIP

A good lookout should be maintained without prompting from the instructor, and checks should be faultless. There should be no doubt about a student's ability to position his own aircraft correctly in relation to other circuit traffic, and choose a safe landing path when grass airfields are being used.

EMERGENCIES

Prior to First Solo the following emergencies should have been demonstrated and practised to the stage where the student is competent to handle them:

Abandoned Take-off.
Engine Failure After Take-off.
Brake Failure.
Action in Event of Fire:
  Engine.
  Cabin.
  Electrical.
Flap Failure.
Electrical Failure.
Radio Failure (when applicable).
Escape Drills.

It is advisable not to tell the student that you plan to send him on his 'First Solo' flight until a few minutes before you do so. This is to avoid apprehension or a tendency for him to try too hard, which may detract from his performance. The dual period which eventually precedes this first solo flight should not normally exceed 45 minutes, as the student expends a lot of nervous energy at this stage of training, and longer preceding dual flights could well lead to an unsuccessful first solo.

Only a short briefing is necessary, and this can be given while taxying to the holding point. The instructor should inform his student that whereas only one take-off, circuit and landing is the intention, he should not hesitate to go round again if the student thinks it advisable. Whenever possible a period of low traffic activity should be chosen, and periods which indicate the possibility of a runway change should be avoided.

During the natural pre-occupation with getting a student ready for an intended first solo, instructors must obviously take care to consider the weather conditions to be expected during the student's solo flight, also the aircraft fuel state, and the time of day, e.g. the onset of darkness. All these items must be considered, bearing in mind that the student may eventually go round several times, or be faced with having to orbit the field for a time if the runway or landing area became blocked by unserviceable aircraft.

It is good practice for instructors to get out of the aircraft at the holding point after the Pre-Take-off checks have been completed and ATC informed of the solo flight. They should also watch their student's first solo, as the information gained thereby can be useful in subsequent instruction.

CIRCUIT CONSOLIDATION

This should consist of two or three circuit periods dual/solo to consolidate and improve the student's performance of take-offs, circuits, approaches, landings and the handling of missed approach and mislanding situations. If not already coverered this will be the time to introduce and practise Crosswind, Glide and Flapless landings, and in the case of tailwheel aircraft, wheel landings.

If not already necessitated by the training environment, e.g. airfield surface and length the Short and Soft Field take-offs and landings may also be introduced at this stage provided the student's rate of progress is sufficient. The following additional emergencies should also be included during this consolidation period:

Altimeter Failure.
ASI Failure.
Suction System Failure.

AIRMANSHIP

The student's progress at implementing the various airmanship considerations and the development of his captaincy qualities will be a particular priority during this period of his training. Good habits developed whilst practising solo circuits at this stage will have considerable effect upon his ability to make sensible and safe decisions during his future solo flying.

LOCAL AREA CONSOLIDATION

Bearing in mind the student will have been confined to the circuit for some time since his earlier flights on basic exercises, it will be necessary to give a dual period to revise or introduce for the first time the following procedures and exercises:

Airfield Departure Procedure.

Map Reading and Identification of Local Landmarks, Danger Areas, Controlled Airspace etc.

Turning onto and Maintaining Headings by Reference to the Magnetic Compass (without the use of the Gyro Heading Indicator).

Obtaining and using QDM's.

Procedure for Rejoining the Circuit.

BEFORE THE EXERCISE

The student should be given a short briefing to review or introduce these exercises before commencing the flight.

DURING THE AIR DEMONSTRATIONS

The method of climbing out from the circuit and selecting an area suitable for the exercises authorised should be covered with emphasis on ATC procedures, wind strength and direction, vicinity of other airfields, airways or similar areas.

At an airfield where training circuits are being carried out, it is normally advisable (dependent upon ATC requirements) to climb out straight ahead and above circuit height before turning left or right. This prevents any confusion to pilots of following aircraft, and shows more clearly that a departure from the circuit is being made.

An important factor will be to provide the student with a sense of orientation, for which knowledge of use of the compass and of local landmarks will be needed.

MAP READING

This part of the exercise will continue at intervals throughout the flight and basically consists of ensuring that the student is capable of identifying towns, landmarks etc. in the local area to the extent that he will be able to recognise his position, and develop a sufficient sense of orientation and use of headings to return safely to the airfield during the solo flight which follows this dual period. It is important that he is capable of identifying any Danger, Restricted or Controlled Airspace which may be in the vicinity of the local flying area.

THE USE OF THE MAGNETIC COMPASS

The heading indicator should be caged or covered during the initial practice of compass turns and uncaged or visible to show acceleration/ deceleration errors. The correct method of re-setting the heading indicator with the magnetic compass must have been taught.

USE OF THE RADIO
Whenever facilities permit, the student should be shown how to obtain a QDM and also made to practise this from time to time in later flights. In order to instil confidence and understanding of this procedure, the QDM should be flown long enough to bring the aircraft in sight of the airfield. When possible at least one QDM should be obtained from an airfield other than base, but when this is not possible it should be accomplished during early navigation practice.

REJOINING THE CIRCUIT
In practice there are various methods used for joining the circuit pattern, and the use of any particular method will depend upon ATC requirements, weather in relation to visibility and cloudbase, or to demonstration and practice considerations. The method used at individual airfields will therefore vary, and all the variations of the rejoining procedure must have been demonstrated and practised before the student is authorised for his first solo navigation flight.

COMMON ERRORS
During compass turns a very common error is attempting to read the magnetic compass without allowing sufficient time for it to settle down following a turn. This can often be corrected by the instructor covering up the compass for some 20 to 30 seconds immediately following the completion of the turn, whilst the student maintains heading by reference to some outside feature.

Any errors in reading the altimeter or setting incorrect pressure settings must be watched for carefully. Although a student operating in VMC is unlikely to get dangerously near the ground without becoming aware of the situation, flying at inaccurate heights may lead to unauthorised penetration of controlled airspace and a hazardous operation when carrying out airfield arrival and circuit procedures.

Students often become so absorbed with their air exercise practice and maintenance of position that the periodic checks in the form of engine oil temperature and pressure, re-synchronisation of the heading indicator etc. are forgotten. The instructor, by meticulous prompting must ensure that these checks become an instinctive habit.

Many students have trouble when rejoining the circuit and commonly get mixed up between the downwind leg and 'dead side'. This can usually be overcome by relating the circuit pattern to its commencement and visualising the pattern from the take-off run onwards.

NOTE: The procedures for using ENTRY/EXIT lanes when the training airfield is within or below Controlled Airspace will be dependent upon individual ATCU requirments. The broader aspects of using these particular procedures are covered under 'Operation at Minimum Level'.

First Solo and Consolidation

Long Briefing

FIRST SOLO

OBJECTIVES
The aim of the 'First Solo' flight is fairly obvious, but it can be defined as the successful achievement of the first stage of flying training, and one which will prepare the student for the future flight exercises to be practised both dual and solo.

INTRODUCTION
The first solo flight is an important step in a pilot's training and one from which his confidence and ability to make decisions entirely on his own will emerge. It is from this stage on that the student will be able to develop his captaincy and also analyse his own errors and successes, as both of these qualities are necessary steps in his progress towards the required task of operating an aircraft with safety.

Following 'First Solo' a period of consolidation will take place, firstly during further dual and solo take-offs, circuits and landings and secondly during a revision of the procedures to adopt in the local flying area.

CONSOLIDATION

CIRCUIT CONSOLIDATION
This period will consist of two or three flights during which the student will have the opportunity to improve his ability to handle the aircraft and the various situations which occur during the take-off, circuit, approach and landing phases. It will also be used to introduce and review as necessary further types of take-off, approach and landing.

The period is a flexible one, as the particular contents of the flights will be determined by the instructor, but will include such additional items as crosswind, glide, and flapless approaches and landings. The student will also be introduced to the procedures for handling the following situations:

Failure of the:
   Altimeter.
   Airspeed Indicator.
   Suction System (where applicable).

CONSOLIDATION OF LOCAL AREA PROCEDURES
When the student has completed the circuit consolidation period to the satisfaction of his instructor, he will be given a dual flight designed to revise and, where necessary, to introduce the following:

Airfield Departure Procedure. The procedures used for entering Entry/Exit Lanes when the base airfield is within or below controlled airspace are covered later during 'Operation at Minimum Level'.

Map Reading and identification of landmarks within the Local Flying Area, including Danger/Restricted Areas and Controlled Airspace when applicable.

The use of the magnetic compass (without reference to the heading indicator).

The method used to obtain a Homing to the airfield when radio is fitted and the base airfield has a Radio Direction Facility.

The proecedures used for rejoining the circuit.

LEAVING THE CIRCUIT
The method used for the initial stage of airfield departure will depend upon the local regulations, and where applicable, the requirements of ATC. As a general practice, it is advisable to climb out straight ahead until clear of the circuit pattern. This prevents confusion in the minds of students who may be carrying out circuits and are not clear as to the intention of the aircraft which has just taken off.

Due regard must however be given to the standard rejoining procedure used at the airfield and where a downwind joining method is in current use, it will be more conducive to safety on departure to make a 45° change in heading away from the circuit direction once the aircraft is above 500 feet a.g.l.

Figure 14-1 shows the possible departure routes a student may be requested to follow or which he may determine to use according to the prevailing circumstances. The path indicated by 3 illustrates the straight ahead climb out procedure and 4 and 5 are alternative methods. When climbing out straight ahead, due consideration must be given to the obscured area ahead and below the aircraft nose, and in these circumstances slight changes of heading to the left or right will be advisable.

Fig. 14-1

The departure track shown at 4 could be used in circumstances where rejoining aircraft are arriving on the crosswind leg for circuit re-entry, and the path shown at 5 would be a good method to use where the rejoining procedure is for aircraft to arrive directly on the downwind leg.

All training airfields have a defined Local Area in which the student will carry out his solo practice. When leaving the circuit the student will need to plan the second stage of his departure procedure to arrive in this local area, and it is normal to set the Area QNH on the altimeter sub-scale at a suitable stage in the departure procedure.

MAP READING AND LOCAL AREA LANDMARKS

Throughout the period spent in the local area, the wind strength and direction must be kept in mind and headings should be chosen to ensure that the aircraft does not get drifted continuously downwind during the practice of authorised exercises.

The use of the map and identification of local towns and landmarks will be used as a basis for orientation in relation to the direction and position of the airfield and any Prohibited, Restricted or Controlled Airspace.

USE OF THE MAGNEIC COMPASS

Throughout the training previously carried out, the heading indicator will normally have been used for heading reference and this instrument will have to be checked and when necessary re-synchronised with the magnetic compass at approximately 15 minute intervals. However, should the heading indicator become unserviceable at any time during flight the pilot will have to rely solely on the magnetic compass for heading reference. The magnetic compass does not have the deadbeat accuracy of a gyro instrument and it also exhibits certain errors during use. To ensure an understanding of the two major transient errors the following demonstrations will be given.

Compass Errors During Turns

Turning error is the most pronounced of the in-flight errors to which the magnetic compass is prone. This occurs because when an aircraft is banked the compass heading ring and needle are also banked, and the angle of dip caused by the vertical component of the earth's magnetic field cause the end of the compass needle to dip to the low side of the turn giving an erroneous indication.

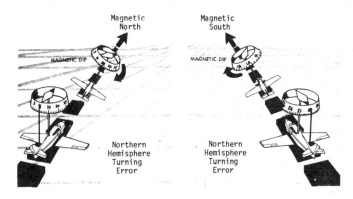

Fig. 14-2

When making a turn onto North the resultant indication is a lead into the direction of heading change and this will apply when turning through East or West onto a Northerly heading. The correction is applied by rolling out of the turn when the compass reading is still some 30° from North, when operating in latitudes covered by the United Kingdom. This correction is however based upon the aircraft making a rate 1 turn (bank angle approximately 15°).

When turning onto a Southerly heading the error is reversed in relation to the readings of the compass card and the correction will be to roll out some 30° after the compass has indicated a Southerly heading. Turning error is maximum when turning onto North or South and nil when using a rate 1 turn onto East or West. Therefore if the heading required is 045° or 315° the turn error correction will be approximately 15°.

Acceleration and Deceleration Error

This occurs on Easterly and Westerly headings, and when accelerating on East or West an apparent turn towards North will be indicated when the aircraft is actually maintaining a constant heading. When decelerating on Easterly or Westerly headings the apparent turn will be in the opposite direction, i.e. to the South.

Fig. 14-3

There is little point in memorizing the direction of the acceleration or deceleration errors as the pilot can do nothing to correct them, but knowledge of their existence is necessary so that the pilot understands these indications should be ignored. Therefore whenever a positive acceleration or deceleration occurs the aircraft should be kept on a constant heading by use of an outside visual reference.

Obtaining and using QDM's

Many ATC units are equiped with VHF direction finding equipment, which permit them to take bearings on radio transmissions emitted by aircraft in flight. Airfields equipped with this facility are notified in the COM section of the U.K. Air Pilot, and the designated call sign is the airfield name with the additional word 'Homer'. A call on the notified frequency will enable the pilot to receive either his true bearing from the station (QTE), or his magnetic heading to steer to reach the ground radio station (QDM). When a QDM is used to home to an airfield, the pilot will have to allow for any drift created by the prevailing wind at the aircraft's altitude.

One very important factor affecting the use of VHF radio facilities is the height of the aircraft in relation to its distance from the airfield. VHF radio signals follow a 'line of sight' and therefore it is important for any effective VHF transmission to be made when the aircraft is sufficiently high to permit an uninterrupted 'line of sight' to the airfield concerned. Figure 14-4 illustrates this effect and the aircraft at (b) is unlikely to be heard by the ground station because it is too low for good reception to take place. Although the strength of radio transmissions varies with atmospheric conditions and the vicinity of surface obstructions, a rule of thumb for good quality reception would be to ensure the aircraft is at an altitude of 1000 feet per 15 miles of distance to the station being called.

Fig. 14-4

Classification of Bearings

According to the known accuracy of the QDM or QTE the air traffic controller will classify the bearing as:

Class A – Accurate to within ± 2°
Class B – Accurate to within ± 5°
Class C – Accurate to within ± 10°
Class D – Accuracy less than Class C

Whenever a Class D is passed to the pilot he must treat it with considerable caution.

Some airfields have a 'Radar' facility (radio detection and ranging), and the method of using this service will be introduced to the student at an appropriate stage of his training. Radar equipment has the advantage of providing position information and aircraft surveillance, both of which will be valuable aids to the maintenance of flight safety. However, due to technical reasons which give variations in signal strength, radar cannot be relied upon implicity, and when surveillance is being given the student must still abide by the 'see and be seen' concept, and maintain a good lookout.

REJOINING THE CIRCUIT

Due to the different operational requirements which are involved at many airfields used by both small and large aircraft and mixed VFR and IFR procedures, there is no longer a standard method which can be used to join a circuit except at non ATC airfields or those airfields which do not utilise an RTF 'Advisory Service'. However it must be appreciated that the method of joining the circuit may vary at any airfield due to for example, glider winching operations and other similar activities.

When no regulations or instructions apply to the contrary, the normal method of joining the circuit at airfields which have no ATC or RTF Advisory Facility will be to fly overhead at least 2000 feet a.g.l. and examine the signals area, to determine the landing direction and whether a left or right circuit pattern is being used. Figure 14-5 shows a plan view of this procedure.

Having established the circuit and landing direction, the aircraft should be positioned to commence a continuous descending turn on the side opposite to the downwind leg, this area is more commonly known as the 'dead side'. The rate of descent and the flight path must be controlled to bring the aircraft close to the upwind end of the active runway or landing path at the published circuit height. By positioning the aircraft in this manner maximum separation is provided between rejoining aircraft and those taking off. This method can also be used at ATC controlled and other airfields, when confirmation of this pattern has been established by RTF prior to commencing the joining procedure.

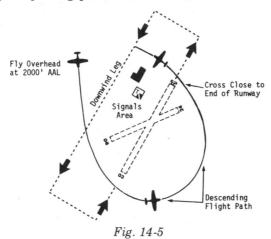

Fig. 14-5

Another method of joining which is becoming universally used at ATC controlled airfields, is to ascertain the airfield QFE, runway and circuit direction, some 5 miles from the destination airfield, and then position the aircraft for a descent well clear of the circuit area and in a position where a continuous straight and level flight path will bring the aircraft into the downwind leg.

Figure 14-6 illustrates this method which has the advantage of not requiring a descent from above those aircraft who may already be in the descent pattern or on the circuit. When using this method the descent must be completed bearing in mind that the run into the downwind leg will be made with a tailwind component, resulting in a high groundspeed. The rejoining aircraft must already be at circuit height before running into the downwind leg, or there will exist a danger of still being in the descent to circuit height during the initial stages of the downwind leg, and the consequent hazard of descending on top of aircraft already in the circuit. In addition to these two methods, at radio-equipped airfields the student must be prepared to receive joining instructions which direct him to join on a left or right base leg or even on long finals. Although at such airfields the ATC facility will clearly be of benefit in controlling the positions of the respective aircraft leaving, joining, or already in the circuit, it is in these last two situations that added vigilance will be necessary, both in relation to lookout and listening out to assess the position and height of other air traffic in the immediate vicinity. An important point to remember is that joining on long finals or base leg should never be attempted at non-radio airfields unless some particular circumstance necessitates this procedure.

Fig. 14-6

Regardless of the actual method used to enter the circuit pattern, there are some important checks to be carried out prior to commencing any joining procedure. These 'Airfield Approach' checks will vary slightly according to the type of aircraft and training environment, but the following items will always apply:

Fuel State and Tank Selection (Fuel Pumps ON when fitted).
Engine Oil Pressure and Temperatures Checked.

Suction and Ammeter Gauge Readings Noted.
Heading Indicator Re-Synchronised with the Magnetic Compass.
Harnesses Secure and Tight.

When applicable a radio call should be made on the correct frequency for joining instructions and the altimeter re-set to the airfield QFE. The exact order in which these checks are carried out will vary with the aircraft type and sequence laid down by the training organisation, but the fuel check should normally be made first. This is to ensure that if a change in tank selection is made, a short time will elapse to prove that fuel is flowing correctly from the selected tank, before the engine is throttled back for the descent.

AIRMANSHIP
A pilot must always keep in mind his responsibility for continuously maintaining a vigilant lookout, regardless of his position in relation to airfields, other air traffic or cloud. It must be remembered that most 'near miss' situations between aircraft have in the past occurred in conditions where the pilots could have seen the other aircraft.

A visual scan must take in all directions and should be made with the knowledge that the performance capabilities e.g. speed, rate of climb, etc., vary between aircraft, and that high closure rates are quite common. This limits the time available for detection, correct decisions and evading action.

At least 50% of near-miss incidents occur within or near the traffic pattern of airfields, and these particularly involve aircraft which are climbing during departure, or descending towards the airfield and joining the circuit. During descending turns, there will always exist blind areas below the aircraft and when descending into busy airfields hazardous situations can more easily occur.

PRE-FLIGHT BRIEFING
LOCAL AREA CONSOLIDATION

Aim

To prepare you for solo operation within the Local Flying Area.

What

This period consists of an introduction to, or revision of the procedues involved in leaving the circuit, map reading within the Local Flying Area, corrections to compass errors and obtaining and using QDM's for homing to the airfield. Upon returning to the airfield the rejoining procedure(s) will be demonstrated.

Airmanship

All normal airmanship considerations will apply, particularly in relation to the maintenance of a high standard of lookout, geographic orientation and remaining clear of any controlled or similar type of airspace.

How

Leaving the Circuit:

Detailed reference to the procedure(s) in current use at the base airfield.

Map Reading and Local Area Landmarks:

Folding the map to ensure a clear reference to the Local Flying Area. Orientation of the map during use. Convenient location for map stowage in the cockpit.

Compass Errors (Northern Hemisphere)

The aircraft will be set up on a Westerly or Easterly heading and the heading indicator caged or covered. Rate one turns will apply throughout.

Turn onto North and note 30° overshoot.

Corrrection will be to undershoot by 30°.

No turn error on East or West.

Obtaining and Using QDM's:

Fly at a suitable height compatible with the aircraft range from the D/F facility.

Use correct frequency and RTF procedures.

Note QDM (its class) and allow for the effect of drift during homing.

Revision of radio failure procedure.

The position of, and when applicable the lower and upper limits of Special Rules and Controlled Airspace, Danger Areas etc, in or adjacent to the Local Area.

Orientation in relation to wind direction and precautions to avoid being drifted too far downwind.

Implementation of en-route checks every 10 to 15 minutes.

Student Practice.

Turn onto South and note 30° undershoot.
Correction will be to overshoot by 30°.

When turning onto headings either side of North or South turn error is less, e.g. 045°, 315°, 135° and 225° turn error is 15° therefore correction is 15°.

Acceleration and deceleration errors are maximum on East and West. Whenever a positive change in airspeed occurs ignore the magnetic compass and use outside visual references to maintain heading.

Student Practice.

Rejoining the Circuit:
Detailed reference and application of the current procedure(s) in use at the base airfield.

Student Practice.

First Solo and Consolidation

Flight Demonstration

INTRODUCTION

At the appropriate stage of training the student will be sent on his 'First Solo' flight following a satisfactory dual period on the circuit procedures, take-offs and landings. This period will also include practice in the Engine Failure After Take-off procedure and will be immediately preceded by a short briefing in the cockpit from the instructor.

CIRCUIT CONSOLIDATION

Following the first solo flight at least two or three further dual and solo periods of take-offs, circuits and landings should be completed before the student proceeds with his next stage of training.

These dual circuit periods will be used to improve the student's basic ability at normal take-offs and powered approach landings plus an introduction to crosswind, glide and flapless approaches, or further practice of these approach and landings if they have already been introduced prior to the first solo flight. Further emergencies of different types will also be included for practice during this period.

The Short and Soft Take-off and Landing may, if convenient, be introduced during this stage or, if it is more practical, covered at a later stage before the solo navigation exercises.

LOCAL AREA CONSOLIDATION

This flight is designed to refresh the student on the methods of leaving the circuit, map reading, identification of local landmarks and the procedure to rejoin the circuit. It will where applicable also be used to introduce the student into the use of the magnetic compass without reference to the heading indicator and how to obtain and use QDM's.

DEMONSTRATION 1.   COMPASS ERRORS

Flight Lesson	Demonstration Sequence
The practical use of the magnetic compass Following the airfield departure procedure and review of local landmarks Turn Errors	The aircraft will be flown on a heading of West or East. The heading indicator will now be caged or masked. Carry out a rate one turn until the compass lubber line reads North. Roll level, ignore the compass and maintain heading by outside visual references. Note the error is an overshoot by approximately 30°. To correct for this it will be necessary to roll out some 30° early. Commence a rate one turn until the compass reads East. Roll level, maintain heading and note the compass reads East – no error incurred. Commence a rate one turn until South is indicated on the compass. Roll level, ignore the compass and maintain heading by outside visual references Note the error is an undershoot by approximately 30°. To correct for this it will be necessary to roll out some 30° after South is indicated. Commence a rate one turn until West is indicated by the compass. Roll level, maintain heading and note the compass continues to read West – no error. Summary: In the northern hemisphere when turning onto North undershoot the required compass heading by some 30°, and when turning onto South overshoot the required compass heading by some 30°. No turn errors are experienced when rolling out on West or East, but halfway between East or West and North or

	halfway between East or West and South the turn error is halved, therefore the correction applied must be halved.
Acceleration Error (Aircraft on West)	Uncage the heading indicator and re-synchronise it with the compass if necessary. Place the aircraft into a shallow dive. Simultaneously note the readings of the heading indicator and the magnetic compass. The magnetic compass shows a positive error. When the airspeed settles at the new higher speed the compass returns to an indication of West.
Deceleration Error (aircraft on West)	Place the aircraft into a climbing attitude and simultaneously note the readings of the heading indicator and the magnetic compass. The magnetic compass shows a positive error. When the airspeed settles at the new lower speed the compass returns to an indication of West.
	Summary: The magnetic compass must be ignored during changes of airspeed.

Student practice: The student should now be given practice at completing rate one turns onto various headings making allowance for the applicable degree of turn errors.

Use of radio to obtain QDM's	*Use of VHF D/F*

This consists of practical instruction and practice in the method used and applicable RTF phraseology to obtain QDM's followed by their application in flight. |

Student practice: The student should be given adequate practice in this procedure to ensure he is capable of implementing the correct procedure when solo.

Returning to the airfield and rejoining the circuit pattern	*Rejoining the circuit*

This consists of a review of the 'Airfield Aproach Checks' and instruction in the |

method(s) of rejoining the traffic pattern as applicable to the base airfield.

Note: When this does not include the procedure used from overhead the airfield the overhead method of letting down and joining the crosswind leg must be demonstrated and practised at a suitable stage prior to solo navigation.

Whichever method is not used at the base airfield, must be demonstrated and practised before the student commences solo navigation exercises.

Student practice: The student must demonstrate his competency at locating his position in the local flying area and estimating headings to reach the base airfield before he can be sent solo off the circuit.

NOTE: The use of Entry/Exit lanes relative to Controlled Airspace is covered under 'Operation at Minimum Level'.

Advanced Turning

Instructor's Guide

The initial objective is to teach the student advanced control co-ordination, not rapid entries, and this latter aspect should be left until the student has become competent at co-ordinating the control movements including the use of power and maintaining the airspeed and altitude.

Although instrument reference should be limited in the early stages, the significance of how to utilise the attitude indicator for pitch and bank reference, and the use of the vertical speed indicator as a trend instrument in relation to maintenance of altitude should eventually be covered.

AIRMANSHIP

The importance of lookout before and during the turn must be stressed, particularly as an added workload is involved in relation to aircraft handling, achieving a constant bank angle with the aircraft in balance and the airspeed and altitude constant.

It is not strictly correct to say that lookout is more important during this exercise, as lookout is important at all times, but it can be said that due to the higher rates of turn involved the lookout takes on a greater degree of urgency. As with the lookout for normal turns, the lookout which must precede each entry must include looking round and behind into the area away from the intended direction of turn, as well as into the direction of the intended turn.

Orientation can easily be lost during successive steep turns, and the student must be taught to re-assess his geographic location at short intervals, and keep in mind the direction of the prevailing wind.

Although the standard safety checks such as those used in Stalling and Spinning practice are not necessarily applicable unless stalling or spinning from the turn is intended, the student should be made aware of the dangers of loose articles, slack or insecure harnesses, and such items as orientation and lookout, and he must become meticulous at checking these items before practising steep turn manoeuvres.

BEFORE THE EXERCISE
The Long Briefing should cover the following:

Objectives
The Forces
Use of Power
Effect of Load Factor:
   Structural Considerations
   Increased Stalling Speed
Physiological Effects
Rate and Radius of Turn
Steep Level, Descending and Climbing Turns
Stalling in the Turn
Incipient Spin Entry/Recovery from the Turn
The Spiral Dive
Unusual Attitudes
Airmanship
Common Errors

The short Pre-Flight Briefing should be based upon the practical aspects of that part of the Long Briefing in relation to the Air Exercise to be covered.

DURING THE AIR DEMONSTRATION
Where possible the effect of altitude upon turning performance should be demonstrated. The excess horsepower over and above that required to maintain level flight at higher altitudes is fairly limited, and this has a significant effect upon turning performance when flying at altitudes above 5000 feet. For example, if the total horsepower developed at sea level drops by 25% at 5000 feet an aircraft equipped with a 100 HP engine and which has an excess thrust capability of 50 HP will have lost 50% of its ETHP and this will be reflected in its performance of Advanced Turns.

   The student must be proficient at early recognition of the stall and incipient spin and also the onset of a spiral dive during the practice of advanced turns. He must also be capable of recovering from any of these situations including the developed stall before he can be permitted to practise this exercise solo.

THE STEEP LEVEL TURN
It will save time to give the student an approximate idea of the power required to maintain the entry speed during turns of 45° and 60° of bank respectively. Insufficient power can lead to low airspeeds during the turn at a time when the stalling speed will have increased and too much power will produce a strong tendency for the aircraft to gain altitude.

Although the student will have difficulty in maintaining the exact speed at entry throughout the turn, any appreciable lowering of airspeed cannot be considered an acceptable performance standard.

THE STEEP DESCENDING TURN

Due to the lower nose attitude and the tendency for the airspeed to increase quite rapidly the student will have to increase the rate at which he scans the ASI. When an increase of speed occurs point out that reducing the bank slightly whilst increasing back pressure will have a significantly greater effect upon airspeed control than just increasing the back pressure.

During any steep descending turn, set a minimum height limitation for recovery. This is to avoid a student over concentrating on the exercise in hand, and allowing the aircraft to descend to an altitude not conducive to flight safety. This is particularly important during steep gliding turns, due to the high rates of descent which are involved.

THE STEEP CLIMBING TURN

Although these turns are not of any particular operational significance, they are valuable as advanced manoeuvres in co-ordination. It should be appreciated however that the angle of bank will have to be limited dependent upon the excess horsepower available from the particular type of training aircraft.

STALLING IN THE TURN

In order to achieve realism in this practice, the instructor should explore the easiest way for his particular training aircraft to enter a stall at steep angles of bank, taking into account the normal factors which may lead up to this situation. Many modern training aircraft are reluctant to stall in a steep turn without the use of excessive force on the control column. For this reason the flight demonstrations should be mainly confined to setting up lower speed situations from which the stall condition can more easily occur without such gross misuse of the controls.

SPINNING FROM THE TURN

The objective in this part of the exercise is to speed up the student's recovery actions at the incipient stage of a spin. The additional power used during advanced turning can cause a greater than normal degree of unbalance at the stall and many aircraft will exhibit a rapid wing dropping manoeuvre.

If the intention is to eventually proceed to the entry and recovery from a developed spin during a steep turn the instructor must check with the Flight/Owner's Manual/Pilot's Operating Handbook to see whether the aircraft is cleared for deliberate spin entries from steep turns with power applied.

THE SPIRAL DIVE

Care must be exercised to avoid excessive airspeeds and load factors during the practice of this manoeuvre, the engine RPM limitation must also be strictly complied with, and with regard to this latter item it will be advisable to have the RPM set to no more than a cruise figure for the entry.

During the development of a spiral dive there normally exists a condition of yaw away from the turn direction, or alternatively a slight sideslip into the direction of turn. Under these circumstances a strong back pressure applied to the control column can more easily raise the aircraft nose than when it is in a condition of balanced flight. As the object is to teach the correct recovery from a flight condition in which back pressure alone will worsen the situation, it will be necessary to ensure the aircraft is correctly balanced during that moment of the demonstration when the student is asked to apply back pressure and note its ineffectiveness in producing a recovery action.

MAXIMUM RATE AND MINIMUM RADIUS TURNS

The use of maximum rate and also those of absolute minimum radius are not really applicable to private pilot operations and any attempt to carry out such manoeuvres at low altitude by a pilot who may only fly some 5 hours a year would clearly be hazardous. It is for these reasons they are not included in the air exercise section of the Private Pilot Syllabus.

However the student must have an appreciation of the factors involved and in the case of minimum radius turns these would most probably be approached in a practical sense when flying in poor visibility and attempting to keep a small landing area or geographic feature in sight. Under these circumstances the use of a small amount of flap will be a safer proposition than adopting a very steep bank angle. This aspect should therefore be introduced at an appropriate stage of the student's training.

COMMON ERRORS

A tendency to rush the entry or recovery from the turn is quite common. Stress that the object is to achieve smooth co-ordination throughout the manoeuvre and speed of entry or recovery is not a requirement during the learning stage.

● A tendency to tense up once the turn is established often leads to the controls being held rigidly. It should be pointed out that throughout the whole of the entry, maintenance of the turn, and the recovery, the controls will need to be continuously and slightly on the move or large errors will occur.

● When quicker entries and recoveries are being practised the need to use more positive rudder application during the initial commencement of the rolling action is often forgotten. During this faster type of entry and recovery it will be necessary to stress the importance of using the rudder sufficiently to overcome the adverse yaw due to roll and so maintain a balanced flight condition.

● The student will usually need reminding of the necessity to maintain a very good lookout during steep turns. Deficiency of lookout will normally be due to a tendency to concentrate his vision directly upon that part of the natural horizon line ahead of the aircraft whilst attempting to maintain the correct pitch attitude.

● If the attitude indicator is introduced too early during the initial stage of practice, the student may attempt precision flight earlier than his capabilities will allow.

● Neglecting to check before entry that the aircraft is not grossly out of trim nose-up or nose down, often leads to a poorly performed steep turn.

● Late application of the extra power required, coupled with rapid application of bank, will usually result in loss of altitude followed by overcorrections.

● During practice of recoveries from the spiral dive be prepared for the student to use insufficient control pressure to level the wings prior to easing out of the dive.

Advanced Turning

Long Briefing

OBJECTIVES

Advanced turning is an exercise which is intended to improve the student's co-ordination and competency in handling an aircraft at steeper angles of bank. Additionally it will improve confidence and also be of benefit should the need to take sudden evasive action arise.

INTRODUCTION

Although advanced turning is primarily taught to further develop the pilot's ability at co-ordination and aircraft handling, it must also be appreciated that incorrect handling of the aircraft during this practice can lead to overstressing the aircraft and/or stalling at higher airspeeds.

However it is not difficult to avoid either of these situations if the pilot has a thorough understanding of how incorrect control techniques can lead to circumstances which may place the aircraft and occupants at risk. During this exercise it is not the intention to teach private pilots to operate an aircraft to its limits, and the steepness of the turns and the airspeeds at which they are conducted must be carefully controlled with this knowledge in mind.

THE FORCES

The disposition and variation of magnitude of the forces acting on the aircraft during turning flight have already been covered in the exercise on Medium Level Turns. The angles of bank which are commonly used during advanced turning concern those from 45° to 60° and fig. 15-1 reviews the position and strength of the forces at these two bank angles. The load factor is defined as the proportion between the lift being developed and the aircraft weight.

The turning capability of any aircraft will be limited by three basic factors:

The Maximum Lift Capability.
The Maximum Power Available.
The Airframe Load Factor Limitations.

Fig. 15-1

Maximum Lift Capability

For the case of the steady co-ordinated turn at a constant altitude the vertical component of lift must equal the weight. The additional total lift required when the aircraft is operating at large angles of bank is considerably greater than when carrying out medium banked turns, for example, at 60° of bank the total lift requirement to maintain the turn and remain at a constant altitude is twice that required for level flight, and at 75° of bank the lift requirement will be four times as great.

The pilot can obtain the additional lift by increasing the angle of attack through the application of back pressure on the control column during the turn. However, at the high angles of attack required to produce the large increases in total lift the induced drag is considerable, resulting in very positive reductions in airspeed which in turn leads to a reduction of the lift which could otherwise have been maintained. Typical values of increases in the induced drag during a level steep turn are as follows:

At 45° of bank the induced drag is increased by 100%.
At 60° of bank the induced drag is increased by 300%.

USE OF POWER

The only way to combat the increase of drag and remain at constant altitude is to increase the power as the bank is increased to the higher angles required for the performance of steep turns. However to avoid any initial fall off in speed the power needs to be increased, together with the increase in bank angle. If the application of power is made after a significant speed reduction it will take some time to accelerate the aircraft back to the original speed unless altitude is deliberately lost.

Maximum Power Available

If an airspeed reduction occurs at high bank angles in the region of 50° to 60° or above, the average small training aircraft will not have the power capability to produce an increase in speed if constant altitude is maintained. This is due to the high drag values being experienced and the limited excess thrust horsepower available. Therefore when carrying out advanced turns it will be necessary to maintain the airspeed by synchronising the throttle opening with the rate at which the aircraft is rolled into the turn.

Failure to carry out this action will lead to a drop in airspeed causing a reduction in lift and loss of altitude, any attempt to regain altitude by increasing the back pressure on the control column will only lead to a further reduction in airspeed causing further loss of altitude or eventually a stall.

The limiting condition for a sustained steep turn at constant altitude will be a combination of $C_{L_{max}}$, lowest wing loading (the ratio of all-up weight to wing area) drag equal to maximum thrust available, and the limiting load factor. Such a combination will produce the maximum possible rate of turn capability.

EFFECT OF LOAD FACTOR

All aircraft are constructed to withstand reasonable load factors which may be imposed upon them during flight, but the limiting load factor varies with different types of aircraft. The operation of any aircraft is subject to specific strength limitations and overstressing can reduce the aircraft life and when severe can lead to catastrophic failure in flight.

Aircraft which are designed to be operated in the Normal Category must meet minimum structural strength limits of +3.8g. However if certification is required in the Utility Category this limit must be a minimum of +4.4g. This latter limit is also accepted for the Semi Aerobatic Category in the U.K. but some countries, for example the U.S.A., require +6g. capability to obtain certification in the Aerobatic Category.

Structural Considerations

The differences between the structural strength limitations of different aircraft types has a significant bearing when carrying out advanced turning or similar manoeuvres which can impose high load factors on the airframe. The importance of understanding this can be seen by referring to fig. 15-2 which illustrates a basic V_n envelope i.e. airspeed versus load factor for a representative modern training aircraft which operates in the Utility Category.

The V_n (or V_g) diagram is used to illustrate the operating strength of the aircraft and is in a form where the horizontal scale represents

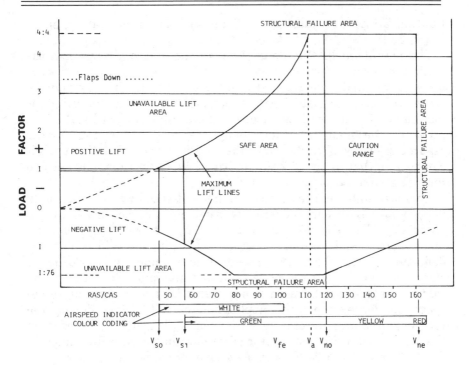

Fig. 15-2

airspeed (V) and the vertical scale represents the load factor (n). The presentation of the aircraft strength is based upon four factors being known:

1. The all-up weight of the aircraft.
2. The configuration i.e. flap, landing gear up or down.
3. The symmetry of loading e.g. if the aircraft is being rolled at the same time as 'g' is being applied the structural limits are reduced by one third.
4. The altitude, this latter however is of small consequence to light aircraft which operate below 10,000 feet, and will not be considered in this briefing.

Load factors are positive (+) when a positive 'g' is being pulled as for example in a steep turn or 'pull up' manoeuvre, and negative (−) in the case of pushing the control column forward. High negative loadings are rare due to pilot discomfort and the abnormal attitudes required to acheive them and because of this, aircraft need not be designed to withstand negative load factors as great as positive load factors.

The aircraft to which fig. 15-2 relates has a limiting positive load factor of 4.4g and a limiting negative load factor of 1.76g. The limiting airspeed is just over 160 kts and the basic stalling speed V_{S1} is 50 kts.

The maximum lift line (stall line) in the diagram represents the maximum load factor which can be produced at the various speeds between V_{S1} and V_a without stalling. For example, the maximum 'g' which can be pulled at 70 kts is just under 2 and at this point the maximum lift line will be exceeded i.e. the aircraft will stall. This prevents the pilot from increasing the load factor any further regardless of how abrupt or hard the pull force is applied. From this it can be seen that in fig. 15-2 the limiting load factor cannot be reached until the airspeed is just over 110 kts.

This last statement leads to an important speed which is normally defined for all modern general aviation aircraft, i.e. 'manoeuvring speed' (V_a). This speed is the maximum speed at which the pilot can make abrupt and extreme control movements involving their full deflection. Once above this speed it is possible to overload the structure, and for this reason, abrupt and maximum deflection of the controls should not be used when operating above the manoeuvre speed, as for example the application of full rudder during the recovery from an autorotative spiral. The V_a is generally based upon the $V_{S1} \times \sqrt{}$ limiting load factor. Therefore in the case illustrated in fig. 15-2 this would be $57 \times \sqrt{+4.4}$ or approximately 120 kts.

The colour coded dials of airspeed indicators are directly related to the V_g envelope for the particular type of aircraft. The bottom of the white band shows the stalling speed with flap down, no power and a load factor of 1. The bottom of the green band indicates the stalling speed under the same conditions but with the flap up.

The top of the white band indicates the limiting speed with flap lowered (V_{fe}) and it can be seen that this also coincides with the maximum 'g' which can be pulled without exceeding the maximum lift line or in other words the example shows that the maximum load factor permitted is 3.4g which in the illustration is directly in line with the flap limiting speed.

Once the speed exceeds the V_a the pilot will be able to pull 'g' forces in excess of the structural limitations and this has to be borne in mind, particularly if the nose is allowed to drop during turns at steep angles of bank, following which the pilot will have a natural tendency to apply greater load factors to the aircraft through any application of further back pressure in an attempt to raise the nose. This can, however, be avoided by reducing the bank before applying any further back pressure to the control column.

The top of the green band (V_{no}) relates to load factors produced by gusts during turbulent conditions. Gusts are associated with both vertical and horizontal velocity gradients in the atmosphere. The effect of vertical gusts is the important factor in relation to structural considerations in that they cause rapid changes to the angle of attack in the same way that a pilot does when suddenly applying a large back pressure to the control column.

When a sudden backward pressure is applied to the control column the aircraft will respond by a change in its attitude but inertia will prevent it from altering its flight path until a few moments have elapsed, during this time the angle of attack will have been increased and with it the load factor. Figure 15-3 shows the effect of a vertical gust in relation to its effect upon changing the relative angle of attack.

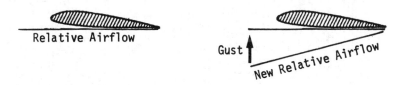

Relative Airflow

Gust

New Relative Airflow

Fig. 15-3

The higher the airspeed the greater will be the increase of load factor due to gusts. Small training aircraft are usually designed to safely encounter gust velocities of 30 feet per second (20 m.p.h.) which is greater than those likely to be experienced during normal flight operations. However airspeed will still be a decisive factor regardless of the gust intensity, and as such the V_{no} is laid down to ensure that pilots do not operate the aircraft at speeds during turbulent conditions which in the event of meeting a 30 f.p.s. gust will overstress the airframe.

Figure 15-4 shows the load factor related to bank angle for a constant height turn at any speed. It can be seen that the load factor increases very slowly in the moderate bank range and even at 45° of bank it has only increased to 1.4. However at 60° it has increased to 2 and thereafter rises extremely rapidly for only small increases of bank.

From this graph it can also be seen that a bank angle of 75.5° will produce a load factor which is the limiting load factor for an aircraft in the Utility Category. With this information a pilot will have some idea of the 'g' forces being applied even though a 'g' meter is not fitted. Note that between 70° and 75° the load factor increases by almost 1.5, therefore any aircraft stressed to +4.4g and flying at a 70° bank angle would only need to be subjected to a moderate gust factor and the structrual limitations could be exceeded.

INCREASED STALLING SPEED
During the turn at constant speed and altitude, the angle of attack

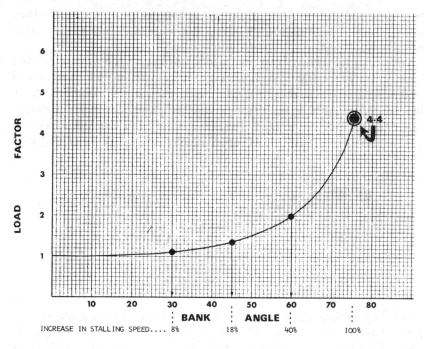

Fig. 15-4

will have to be increased to produce the extra lift required to support the aircraft. This causes an increase in the stalling speed which is directly related to the bank angle. Figure 15-4 illustrates the percentage variation of stall speed with angle of bank. Therefore as the bank angle is increased two factors of importance occur, both the stalling speed and the drag increase. The increase in drag will cause the airspeed to decrease unless sufficient power is available to combat the added drag and keep the airspeed constant. It can therefore be seen that if insufficient power is available to overcome the additional drag the flying speed will move toward the already increasing stalling speed as the angle of bank increases. A condition of stall will then occur at a substantially higher speed than that realised when the aircraft is flown in a condition where the load factor is 1.

PHYSIOLOGICAL EFFECTS

During normal steep turn manoeuvres the body will experience positive 'g' loadings which will not usually be in excess of 2. This means that if a person weighs 75 kilos he will experience a body weight of 150 kilos at 2g. This effect of added 'g' force can be quickly adjusted to and the effect will hardly be noticeable after several practice periods of Advanced Turning.

If the aircraft inadvertently gets into a low nose attitude during the turn and the pilot increases the load factor through the application of a large back pressure on the control column then a further effect of 'g' will become apparent. This is the effect of the blood draining down from the head towards the feet. At high accelerations, this draining of blood from the head can cause a 'greying out' and at higher accelerations a complete 'black out' of vision will eventually occur. The latter however, will normally be experienced only after the airframe of a Normal or Utility aircraft has passed its limiting load factor, though it will also depend upon the pilot's degree of physical fitness.

Notwithstanding the comments made in the previous paragraph it should nevertheless be appreciated that if a pilot causes a very sudden increase of 'g' to occur it will be possible to momentarily increase the 'g' loading to in excess of 8g before the effect of blood draining from the head and the consequent loss of oxygen to the brain causes a 'black out'. Due to this resilience of the human body any sudden application of high 'g' loadings must be avoided or over-stressing of the airframe will more easily be incurred.

During normal application of 'g' the pilot will begin to see spots before his eyes at about 3g as the greying out process begins and this is a signal that back pressure must be released and the aircraft rolled into a laterally level attitude where it can be returned to normal level flight without excess 'g' force being exerted. Due to the different values of 'g' at which different pilots grey out this last statement must not be used as a means of assessing the load factor being applied.

Negative 'g' is more uncomfortable than positive 'g' but normally large negative 'g' forces are much more difficult to achieve either deliberately or inadvertently, but if they do occur the blood in the body will be forced up into the head and a 'redding out' condition will occur.

RATE AND RADIUS OF TURN
The turning performance of an aircraft can be measured by the maximum rate of turn and the minimum radius of turn. The conditions under which each is obtained will however vary:

The rate of turn achieved at any given airspeed whilst maintaining a constant altitude will depend upon the amount of sideways force available to cause the turn. This force is the horizontal component of the total lift force produced by the wings. Initially the rate of turn will be increased by increasing the bank angle and so increasing the size of the horizontal component. There will, however, be a limiting angle of bank at which the power is no longer able to overcome the increase of drag and the airspeed will commence to decrease leading to a reduction in the total lift force unless altitude is lost to maintain the speed.

Airframe limitations must also be considered and in those cases where power is still available to maintain speed or when the aircraft commences to descend the limiting load factor will be the ultimate limitation in rate of turn.

Because airspeed is a factor in producing the total lift force it can also be appreciated that higher airspeeds will also permit higher bank angles leading to a greater rate of turn and a smaller radius of turn. Therefore the greater the speed at which the available power can balance the drag the greater will be the rate of turn and the smaller the radius of turn. Referring back to fig. 9-3 in the section on Medium Level Turns the various rates and radii of turn can be equated against different airspeeds and bank angles.

In considering minimum radius turns the ability to turn in a small radius will also be affected by the use of flap. Lowering flap gives additional lift for any given airspeed, but added drag will also be created. However, bearing in mind the operational use of minimum radius turns it will be quite likely that they will be performed during poor visibility when a pilot is attempting to keep a landing area in sight. In these circumstances he will probably be at a low altitude where an inadvertent stall could be disastrous.

Therefore from a practical viewpoint and one allied to the operation of the aircraft, the use of partial flap will lower the stalling speed and produce a safer situation which avoids the use of limiting bank angles. By limiting the bank angle and using a low safe speed the pilot will be able to divert reasonable attention to the location of ground features, whilst maintaining a reasonably small turning radius.

STEEP LEVEL, DESCENDING AND CLIMBING TURNS

Steep angles of bank can be achieved during level, descending or climbing flight, but an increased rate of turn will be possible in the descending turn, providing structural limitations permit. This is because the emphasised effect of gravity while descending makes available more power to maintain the aircraft in the turn. Conversely, because more power is required to climb the aircraft it can be appreciated that the maximum rate of turn attainable in a climb will be less than during level flight.

Although the operational requirements for steep turns do not come within the range of normal flight procedures, the practice of these manoeuvres will improve co-ordination and enhance the pilot's ability to handle his aircraft in unusual situations.

ENTRY AND MAINTAINING THE STEEP LEVEL TURN

Having first ascertained the aircraft position in relation to known landmarks, and ensured that the surrounding airspace is clear of other air traffic, note the airspeed and initiate the entry in exactly the same way as for a medium level turn. As the bank angle reaches 30° increase the power, and continue the roll to a 45° bank angle whilst increasing the back pressure on the control column.

The added power should be just enough to maintain the airspeed and the increased back pressure sufficient to maintain the altitude. Rudder should be used throughout to maintain the aircraft in a balanced condition. During the steep turn the controls are all used in the same way as for normal turns, i.e. ailerons are used to maintain the bank angle, elevators to control the attitude in pitch, and rudder to maintain balance.

Whilst one aim during the practice of steep turns will be to maintain altitude it is important not to achieve this at the expense of airspeed, and whilst small variations in speed are acceptable, it should be remembered that a significant lowering of airspeed can lead to a stall condition. Therefore if altitude is being lost whilst speed is being maintained, further power will be required as well as an adjustment to back pressure. Simply adjusting the nose to a higher pitch attitude will result in a decrease of airspeed, leading to a decrease in lift and after a short while the aircraft will start losing altitude again.

Whereas small changes in airspeed are controlled in the normal way by use of the elevators, if altitude is being lost and the airspeed is increasing significantly in relation to the entry airspeed then application of back pressure alone will also serve to tighten the turn due to the steepness of the bank attitude. This will lead to a tendency for the nose to drop still further and the airspeed to continue to increase. This is the beginning of a spiral dive during which structural limitations can easily be exceeded. The only correct method of recovery will be to decrease the bank at the same time as the added back pressure is applied and when the attitude in pitch has been re-adjusted any required increase in bank angle can be re-applied using the controls in the same way as the entry.

Recovery From the Steep Level Turn

This is effected by using the controls in the normal way, reducing the power at the same time and as this is an exercise in advanced co-ordination the power reduction should be timed so that the cruising RPM setting is achieved as the wings become level. Due to the added back pressure required during the turn care should be taken to release all of this back pressure progressively during the roll out or the aircraft will commence to climb as the bank is reduced.

The object throughout is to achieve a smooth manoeuvre, and hurried entries or recoveries should be avoided. Later, as a higher level of competence is achieved quicker entries and recoveries can be practised, but again it must be stressed that smooth and balanced flight will always be the requirement in practice situations.

The Steep Descending Turn
These turns wil be practised from powered descents or glides. The control functions are exactly the same as for steep level turns, but due to the lower nose attitude in relation to the horizon line (particularly in the gliding case) it will be a little more difficult to maintain a constant airspeed. With descending steep turns the entry airspeed should be higher than for a normal glide descent, and this speed increase should be in relation to the pre-selected bank angle, i.e. the higher the intended bank angle the higher the airspeed. This is to ensure an adequate margin above the increased stalling speed during the turn.

Referring to fig. 15-4 the increase of stall speed at 45° is 18% and at 60° is 40%. Ignoring power effects on the stalling speed and assuming a V_{S1} of 50 kts this will mean that at 45° of bank the stalling speed will have increased to 59 kts and at 60° of bank to 70 kts. Therefore a good principle would be to increase the normal descent or glide speed by 10 kts for a 45° banked turn and 20 kts for a 60° banked turn.

During steep descending turns the tendency for the nose to lower will be more marked and a quicker reaction to this must be made by bank reduction and increase in back pressure. A useful practice manoeuvre is the steep descending turn with flap lowered to stimulate a situation where the pilot is inadvertently operating at steep bank angles during the final stages of a spiral type descent whilst positioning for a final approach for an actual forced landing without power.

The procedure is exactly the same as for a gliding steep turn with flaps up, but the actual speed used will have to be compatible with the flap limiting speed, and wherever possible the speed chosen should be at least 10 kts lower than the maximum speed permitted with flap down. The main difference in handling will be in the steeper nose attitude necessary to maintain a safe speed, and the rapid lowering of the airspeed when the nose is raised even by quite small amounts.

The Steep Climbing Turn
The use of full power will be needed if not already being used during the climb. The amount by which the angle of bank used impairs the rate of climb will depend upon the excess horsepower available for the particular aircraft, but the object will be to practise this type of steep

turn up to bank angles of 40° to 45°.

Higher bank angles usually lead to a large reduction in climb rate and result in a situation where the aircraft is doing a steep turn with a higher than normal nose attitude and a very small rate of climb. The normal climbing speed will be appreciably lower than the entry speed for a level steep turn, so the considerations in relation to an increased stall speed will apply and care must be used to avoid a stall occurring.

STALLING IN THE TURN

As stated and demonstrated during the exercise of stalling, an aircraft can be stalled from a level, descending or climbing turn. Stalls which occur from incorrect handling during a turn, particularly at steeper bank angles, are often dynamic and associated with a positive wing drop action when the aircraft is flown with an aft c.g. As with the standard stall recovery the correct procedure to return the aircraft to a normal flight condition will be to move the control column forward and reduce the angle of attack.

Application of additional power will not have much effect if high power settings are already being used, as in the case of level and climbing steep turns. In the descending steep turn the nose will already be low and application of power will usually only serve to accelerate the aircraft along the downward flight path, leading to unnecessary altitude loss.

Rudder should be used in the normal sense to correct for further yaw which in most cases is present during dynamic entries to the stall. The stall characteristics will vary between aircraft and even aircraft of the same type, e.g. differences in location of the c.g., flaps up or down and the amount of power and bank angle used.

Either wing may drop regardless of the direction of turn, but generally a slight sideslip angle predominates just prior to the stall, causing yaw opposite to the direction of turn, and this leads to the higher wing stalling first. Other aspects such as asymmetry of wing or fuselage rigging can however alter this action and the bottom wing can sometimes be the first to stall.

If the predominant yaw is in the direction of the lower wing, e.g. too much bottom rudder being applied, then the inner wing will stall first. If the yaw is in the opposite direction then the outer wing will be the first to stall. In either case recovery is made by a positive forward movement of the control column by an amount which will only be learned by practice.

Clearly gross mishandling of the controls will be required to stall an aircraft when the speed is relatively high; this is because strong aerodynamic forces are involved and physical effort must be used to bring the aircraft through to the stall condition. However, it must also be clearly understood that when the speed is low and the aircraft is at a high angle of attack only a small movement of the control column is required, and due to the lower speed the controls are very light and can easily be moved. These facts suggest that the most probable reason for an inadvertent stall to occur during a turn is inadequate speed control rather than excessive bank angles.

Entering the Stall During a Steep Turn

Having completed the safety checks the aircraft should be placed in a steep turn and the increase of power delayed until the speed is below 1.5 the V_{S1}. At this stage the back pressure should be increased whilst maintaining the bank angle. The backward movement of the control column must continue without hesitation until the aircraft stalls.

At the stall some buffet may be felt and one wing will usually tend to drop, the rapidity of this wing-drop action will depend upon the type of aircraft, the position of the c.g., and the amount of bank at the time of the stall.

The Recovery

Recovery at the incipient stage is easily effected by relaxing the back pressure on the control column and either continuing with the turn or returning to the level attitude. Recovery from the developed stall follows the same lines, but a positive forward pressure on the control column will be required or the aircraft may be slow to recover, and during this period a wing-drop action can be very rapid and could lead to the aircraft becoming inverted.

Rudder is used to stop further yaw, and the power adjusted as applicable depending upon the nose attitude in pitch at the time of the recovery action.

SPINNING FROM THE TURN

The most probable reason for an inadvertent spin to occur during an advanced turn is lack of attention to airspeed, or gross over controlling of the aircraft. The former is the more likely event under normal conditions. To avoid large stresses being imposed on the aircraft structure by the pilot during practice it is advisable to reduce speed during the turn and make the entry to the incipient spin below 1.5 V_{S1}.

Once the safety checks have been completed and the steep turn initiated the entry may be set up by reducing the speed to below 1.5 V_{S1} and applying rudder into the intended spin direction whilst moving the control column back until the incipient spin occurs. Due to the added effectiveness of the controls with a relatively high power in use, they will require a smaller movement to produce an incipient spin entry. It will nevertheless be necessary to check with the Flight/ Owner's Manual or Pilot's Operating Handbook to ensure this type of spin entry is permissible.

A return to normal flight is effected by the use of the previously learned incipient spin recovery procedure, but due to the extra power being used the aircraft could quickly enter the developed stage of a spin. It will therefore be necessary to make a positive and rapid forward movement of the control column to ensure the aircraft recovers at the incipient stage.

Provided the aircraft is cleared for deliberate spin entries (refer to the aircraft manual) from advanced turns the instructor may decide to include entry to the developed spin and recovery. In which case the spin recovery method as shown in the aircraft manual should be implemented. However especial care must be used to ensure the throttle is closed immediately following entry to the spin.

THE SPIRAL DIVE

If the nose is allowed to lower significantly during the turn, this will be the result of not applying sufficient back pressure for the angle of bank being used, and the correction for this situation has already been covered during the procedure outlined under Steep Level, Desending and Climbing Turns. However if recovery action is delayed or further back pressure is applied without also reducing the bank angle, a condition can occur where the turn tightens up and the nose drops still further.

This condition is known as a 'Spiral Dive' and the use of back pressure alone will only serve to tighten and steepen the spiral as well as possibly overstressing the airframe. The correct recovery action is to close the throttle completely and positively roll the wings level, following this the aircraft can be eased out of the dive. When levelling the wings it must be appreciated that at the higher speeds associated with the spiral dive condition, the pilot will need to apply higher than normal control forces to the ailerons in order to roll the wings level.

UNUSUAL ATTITUDES

Basically there are two types of unusual attitude taught during training, one where the aircraft nose is high and one where it is low. As these attitudes are being considered under Advanced Turning it can be assumed for the purpose of the following recovery procedures that a steep bank angle is present in either case.

Recovery Procedures

If the nose is high and the bank is steep:

Roll the wings level, using ailerons and rudder. At the same time ease forward on the control column and increase power smoothly (if additional power is available).

Care must be used to handle all controls gently as the aircraft may be in the region of the stall.

If the nose is low and the bank is steep:

The recovery from this condition is similar to the recovery from a spiral dive.

Close the throttle.

Use aileron and rudder to roll the wings level and then recover from the dive in the normal way.

USE OF INSTRUMENTS TO ACHIEVE PRECISION FLIGHT

During advanced turns, the attitude in pitch can change rapidly, and this will be aggravated by any tendency to overbank once established in the turn. A further difficulty is imposed in that due to the urgency of maintaining a good lookout the scan of the flight instruments must of necessity be very rapid.

The bank angle established by visual refrence between the cockpit or cowling line and the natural horizon can be verified by a glance at the position of the bank angle pointer on the attitude indicator, and when radial lines are incorporated in this instrument, the attitude of the index aircraft wings relative to these lines can also be noted.

Once proficiency at steep turns is gained, a useful aid to accuracy in maintaining altitude during reasonably smooth weather conditions will be the trend indications of the VSI. This instrument reacts more quickly to altitude change than the altimeter, and frequent monitoring of the VSI needle alerts the pilot to any tendency to climb or descend.

AIRMANSHIP

It is the pilot's responsibility to ensure that the cockpit is free from loose articles, and that harnesses are tight and the surrounding airspace is clear of other air traffic before commencing practice steep turns. The height (a.g.l.) must be adequate to ensure sufficient time is available to put into effect any recovery action required from inadvertently entering an unusual attitude, stall or spin.

The location must be one which is clear from departure or arrival lanes near airfields and at a reasonable distance from any controlled airspace, aerodrome traffic zone, danger areas or similar airspace.

Orientation will remain an important aspect of airmanship

throughout the exercise and the student must monitor his geographic location between each manoeuvre to ensure that he is not drifted too far downwind, and does not depart too far from the area previously assessed as suitable for the practice. At appropriate times during the practice he should pause and re-set the heading indicator with the magnetic compass as well as carrying out the normal periodic cockpit checks. Particular care must be exercised to re-synchronise the heading indicator with the magnetic compass upon completion of the steep turn practice.

A point worth noting is that during advanced turns the aircraft is flown at relatively high angles of attack, and in this condition it will produce moderate wake turbulence. Thus if the aircraft loses some 20 to 40 feet of height during a 360° turn it will be flown through its own wake vortex, and this should be anticipated.

Supplement No. 3 pointed out that the strength of a vortex was related to the weight of the aircraft i.e. the greater the weight the greater the required angle of attack for any given airspeed. Once the effect of wake turbulence produced from a light aircraft has been experienced it will be easier to obtain a better physical appreciation of the considerably greater effect and added dangers of the wake turbulence produced by large General Aviation aircraft or airliners.

Flight/Owner's Manual and Pilot's Operating Handbooks clearly state the airframe limitations which apply to a particular aircraft and due caution must be exercised when practising advanced turning manoeuvres, to ensure these stress limitations are not exceeded. In the event that a pilot thinks that overstressing has occured at any time, his duty must be to report this to his instructor or to a ground engineer. Remember that in relation to overstressing an aircraft, a pilot not only has a responsibility for the safety of his aircraft and passengers, but also for those who may fly in the aircraft afterwards.

 Lookout Assumes a Greater Degree of Urgency During Advanced Turning.

PRE-FLIGHT BRIEFING

ADVANCED TURNING

Demonstration 1.   The Steep Level Turn

Aim   To teach you how to achieve a co-ordinated turn at steep angles of bank whilst maintaining a constant altitude and airspeed.

What   A turning manoeuvre at angles of bank in the region of 45° to 60°. Although not fundamentally an operational procedure, practice of steep turns will improve the pilot's co-ordination and competency.

Airmanship   All normal airmanship considerations will apply and in particular there will be a greater urgency for lookout. Ensure that no loose articles are present in the cockpit and that all harnesses and lap straps are secure and tight.

How   Initially an observation turn will be carried out for you to note the bank angle, pitch attitude, increased RPM and constant airspeed, altitude and balance.

The Turn Entry
Orientation established and lookout completed.

Normal turn entry.

Gradually increase power whilst increasing bank to 45° and increase back pressure on the control column to achieve pitch attitude for the maintenance of constant altitude. Rudder is used throughout the entry to maintain the aircraft in balance.

Maintaining the Turn
Maintain a careful lookout.

The angle of bank is still controlled by the use of the ailerons.
Pitch attitude is still controlled by the elevators.
Balance is still achieved by use of the rudder.

Airspeed is controlled by power and attitude in pitch.
Continuous small control pressures will be needed to maintain the aircraft in a correct steep turn.

Student Practice.

Recovery to Straight and Level Flight
Maintain a careful lookout.

Recover as from a normal turn whilst decreasing power in co-ordination with the rate of roll out.

Aim to reach the cruise power RPM at the same time as the wings become level.

Steep turns will be practised in both directions. Initially a slow rate of entry and recovery should be used.

PRE-FLIGHT BRIEFING

ADVANCED TURNING

Demonstration 2. Stalling in the Steep Turn and Recovery from a Spiral Dive

Aim

To teach you to recognise the symptoms of the stall during steeply banked turns, and the characteristics and correct recovery procedure from both incipient stage and developed stalls entered from this flight condition. Additionally to show you the most likely method of entering the spiral dive and teach you the correct recovery procedure.

What

The entry to and recovery from stalls and spiral dives incurred during steeply banked turns.

Airmanship

All normal considerations will apply, but in addition, emphasis must be given to the Safety Checks prior to stalling and the aircraft structural and engine limitations, as well as the altitude loss during the spiral dives.

How

Stall Entry and Recovery (Incipient Stage)

When the safety checks and lookout have been completed, enter a steep turn.

Delay power increase, raise the nose and when below 1.5 the V_{s1} increase the back pressure until the stall symptoms occur.

Note the higher speed at which these symptoms occur.

Recovery:

Release the back pressure and continue with the turn.

Stall Entry and Recovery (Developed Stage)

When the safety checks and lookout have been completed, enter a steep turn.

Delay power increase, raise the nose and when below 1.5 the V_{s1} increase back pressure until the developed stall occurs.

Recovery:

Positive forward movement of the control column.

Prevent further yaw with rudder.

Adjust power as required, i.e. if the nose is low reduce power, or if the nose is level or high increase the power (if available).

The higher stalling speed should be noted during a following demonstration.

Student Practice.

The Spiral Dive

Orientation established, check that a clear area and sufficient height a.g.l. is available.

Set cruise power (or less if required) to avoid exceeding the RPM limit or the V_{ne}.

Final lookout.

Enter a steep turn and allow the bank to steepen and the nose to drop.

Note:

Rapid increase of speed and loss of altitude.

Back pressure on the control column is ineffective at raising the nose when in a steeply banked attitude.

Recovery:

Close the throttle.

Roll the wings level (firm pressure).

Ease the aircraft gently out of the dive.

Note: Effective recovery.

Student Practice.

PRE-FLIGHT BRIEFING
ADVANCED TURNING
Demonstration 3.   Descending and Climbing Steep Turns

Aim   To teach you to turn the aircraft at steep angles of bank during descending and climbing flight.

What   A controlled and co-ordinated steep turn whilst the aircraft is in the descending and climbing phases of flight.

Airmanship   All normal airmanship considerations will apply and additionally the awareness of any tendency towards a lowering airspeed during the climbing phase and the need to monitor the altitude frequently during the descent.

How

The Descending Steep Turn
From the Descent Using Partial Power.

Orientation established, altitude sufficient and lookout completed.

Suitable airspeed selected.

Turn entry and maintenance as for a level steep turn, but without additional power.

Monitor airspeed and altitude.

Increasing airspeed controlled by a combination of bank angle reduction and increase in back pressure.

Student Practice

From the Glide Using Idle Power.

Repeat as above but note the higher rate of descent.

Student Practice.

Note: Stall entry and recovery at the incipient and developed stages will be practised. Entry and recovery will be the same as for a level steep turn.

Student Practice.

The Climbing Steep Turn
From the Climb.

Orientation established and lookout completed.

Turn entry and maintenance as for a level steep turn, maximum power applied (if not already used). Monitor and maintain the climbing speed and limit the bank angle to ensure a reasonable rate of climb is maintained.

The higher stalling speed will require a close monitoring of the airspeed.

Student Practice.

Note: Stall entry and recovery at the incipient and developed stages will be practised. Entry and recovery will be the same as for a level steep turn.

Student Practice.

PRE-FLIGHT BRIEFING

ADVANCED TURNING

Demonstration 4. Recoveries from Incipient Spins and Unusual Attitudes

Aim
To teach you to recognise and recover from the incipient spin entered during a steep turn. Additionally to teach you the correct procedures to recover from flight situations during which the aircraft assumes an unusual attitude.

What
The entry to and the recovery from incipient spins and unusual flight attitudes incurred during steeply banked turns.

Airmanship
All normal airmanship considerations will apply but in addition emphasis must be given to the Safety Checks prior to incipient spins, and the aircraft structural and engine limitations during the recoveries from unusual attitudes.

How

Incipient Spin – Entry & Recovery

When the safety checks are completed, lookout and enter a steep turn.

Delay the power increase when entering from level or climbing turns.

Raise the nose and reduce speed to below 1.5 the V_{S1}.

Final lookout and ensure a positive degree of unbalance is present (a small amount of rudder may be used to achieve this) whilst moving the control column back until the incipient spin occurs.

Recovery at the incipient stage is the same procedure as that used for the spin from the medium turn. There will however normally be some difference in the degree of movement of the controls.

* If the aircraft enters a developed spin the recovery procedure as shown in the aircraft manual should be used. If no specific recovery procedure is shown the standard spin recovery should be used.

Student Practice.

Recovery from Unusual Attitudes

Orientation established and lookout completed.

Adopt a steeply banked attitude with the nose high and a low airspeed.

Recovery:
Ease gently forward on the control column whilst levelling the wings and increasing power.

Return the aircraft to the normal level flight attitude.

Student Practice.

Adopt a steeply banked attitude with the nose low and airspeed increasing.

Recovery:
Close the throttle.
Level the wings.
Ease gently out of the dive.

Return the aircraft to the normal level flight attitude.

Student Practice.

* The Flight/Owner's Manual/Pilot's Operating Handbook must be checked to ensure whether spin entries with 'power on' are permitted and whether any differences from the Standard Spin Recovery apply.

Advanced Turning

Flight Demonstrations

INTRODUCTION

The contents of this exercise may be conveniently divided into the following specific demonstration groups:

1. The Level Steep Turn.
2. Stalling in the Turn.
   The Spiral Dive.
3. Descending and Climbing Steep Turns.
4. Incipient Spin Entry/Recovery from Advanced Turns.
   Recoveries from Unusual Attitudes.

Demonstration 1 will be mainly occupied with the initial demonstration and practice of Steep Turns at 45° bank angles. During this period the student will learn to appreciate and adjust to the physical 'g' forces which are experienced and the increasing weight on his body and limbs as the angle of bank is increased.

Demonstration 2 will be an extension of the stalls already practised during medium turns, and the introduction to the Spiral Dive and correct recovery procedure.

Demonstrations 3 and 4 will be introduced at convenient times during the general practice of this exercise.

Airmanship items will be an extension of those already covered during previous training plus an introduction to the considerations of safety in relation to keeping structural stresses within the limits permitted for the aircraft being used.

DEMONSTRATION 1.   THE STEEP LEVEL TURN

Flight Lesson	*Demonstration Sequence*
Turning flight at steep bank angles	
From straight and level flight.	The observation turn. Note the airspeed and altitude.

	Lookout and safety procedures completed. Once in the turn: Note the bank angle and pitch attitude, increased RPM, altitude and balance being maintained. Added power maintains the airspeed.
The turn entry from straight and level flight	Ensure that no loose articles are present in the cockpit, and all harnesses are secure and tight. Ensure the aircraft is in a suitable area and the surrounding airspace is clear of other air traffic. Complete a final lookout. Enter as for a normal medium turn. As the bank reaches 30°, increase the power (sufficiently to maintain airspeed) whilst increasing the bank to 45°, and increasing the back pressure on the control column. Rudder is used throughout in the correct sense to maintain balance.
During the turn	Maintain the lookout. Use the ailerons to adjust and maintain the bank angle, elevators to control the pitch attitude and rudder to maintain balance. Continual small pressures will be needed to maintain the bank, altitude and balance.
Returning to straight and level flight	Smoothly roll the wings level whilst at the same time decreasing the RPM and back pressure, and using rudder as required to maintain balance. The RPM should be smoothly adjusted to reach cruising power at the same time as the wings become level.

Student practice: The student will now be given the opportunity to practise steep turns. If the aircraft is equipped with side-by-side seating, the practice turns at this stage should be confined to the direction used during the demonstration.

When aircraft with side by side seating are used the turn should now be demonstrated in the opposite direction.	
From straight and level flight	Orientation established and lookout completed. Enter and maintain the turn in the same way as before.

Note the changed position of the nose in pitch as seen by the pilot, relative to the horizon.

Student practice: The student should now take over control and maintain this turn, with recovery to straight and level flight, followed by repetition as required. Following this, a demonstration of the added use of instruments to achieve precision flight should be given.

NOTE: The student will not be allowed to practise steep turns solo until he has had Stalling in Steep Turns and the Spiral Dive demonstrated, and become competent at the respective recoveries.

DEMONSTRATION 2. (A) STALLING IN THE STEEP TURN (B) THE SPIRAL DIVE

Flight Lesson	Demonstration Sequence
(A) Stalling and recovery from steeply banked turns	
From level flight	Complete the Safety Checks. Lookout followed by turn entry.
Stall entry and recovery at the incipient stage	Delay power increase during entry and raise nose slightly to reduce speed to below 1.5 the V_{S1}. Final Lookout. Continue to move the control column backwards in one continuous movement until the first symptoms of the stall occur, e.g. horn, light or buffet. Note the higher speed at which this stall warning occurs. Recover by releasing the back pressure. The aircraft can now be re-established in a correct steep turn or rolled back to straight and level flight.

Student practice: The student should now be given the opportunity to practise recoveries at the incipient stage.

Recovery from the developed stage of the stall	Complete the Safety Checks. Lookout followed by turn entry. Approach the stall as in the previous demonstration and continue to move the control column back in a firm manner until a positive stall occurs.

Recovery:
Move the control column positively forward.
Prevent further yaw with rudder.
Adjust power as required, e.g. if the nose is level or high, increase power, if the nose is low, reduce power.

Repeat the demonstration to show the higher stalling speed.

Student practice: The student should now practise stall entries and recoveries from the developed and incipient stages and from both left and right steep turns. Practice must continue until the student is proficient at the correct recovery procedures.

(B) The spiral dive entry and recovery	NOTE: Due to the increase of airspeed and RPM during these demonstrations it is advisable to practise them at a lesser RPM than normally used for steep turns.
From level flight	Orientation established and lookout (particularly below and to either side) completed. Enter a steep turn at reduced power. Allow the bank to steepen and the nose to drop well down below the horizon. Note: Rapid increase of airspeed, and altitude loss. Back pressure on the control column is ineffective in raising the nose and the bank steepens. Recovery: Close the throttle and roll the wings level. (Firm application of ailerons.) Ease gently out of the dive.

Student practice: The student should be given the opportunity to feel the control forces and aircraft reactions during the application of back pressure during the initial part of the demonstration. Practice must be continued until the student is competent at the correct recovery procedure.

DEMONSTRATION 3.   DESCENDING AND CLIMBING STEEP TURNS

Flight Lesson	Demonstration Sequence
Turning at steep angles during the descent and climb	
From the descent using partial power	Orientation established, altitude sufficient, and lookout completed. Select an airspeed compatible with the intended bank angle. Entry and maintenance of the turn is the same as for level steep turns, but without increasing the power. If the airspeed increases at bank angles above 45° the use of ailerons to reduce bank will be more effective in reducing the speed than the use of elevators alone. If the speed increases, use ailerons to reduce bank and elevators to reduce the pitch attitude. Note the high rate of descent. If the bank is not accurately controlled during steep descending turns the airspeed can increase rapidly, leading to a spiral dive situation.
From the glide descent	Demonstration and procedure as above but note the higher rate of descent.

Student practice: The student should be allowed to practise steep descending turns with partial power or no power at bank angles between 45° to 50°. Higher bank angles should only be used if the student's competence permits.

From the climb	Orientation established and lookout completed. Entry and maintenance of the turn is the same as for level steep turns. Maintain climbing speed. Note: Limiting angle of bank (appropriate to type) if a climb is to be maintained. Note: The stalling speed is higher during the turn and the need to maintain the correct climbing speed is vital.

Student practice: Steep climbing turns are not a recommended operational procedure but provided the bank angles are not made too steep they form a useful co-ordination exercise.

> Note: Where it is practical for the aircraft type the student will be taught the stall entry and recovery at the incipient and developed stage during steep descending and climbing turns.

DEMONSTRATION 4.   RECOVERY FROM INCIPIENT SPINS ENTERED DURING ADVANCED TURNS

Flight Lesson	*Demonstration Sequence*
Recovery at the incipient stage	Complete the Safety Checks. Lookout followed by turn entry. Where applicable, e.g. level and climbing turns, delay power increase during the entry and raise the nose slightly to reduce the speed to below 1.5 the V_{S1}. Final lookout. Ensure that a positive yaw is occurring (use rudder if necessary) and keep moving the control column back until the stall occurs with a positive wing drop. Recovery:
	The recovery at the incipient stage is the same procedure as that used during a medium turn. The basic difference will only occur in the degree of control movements. Note: The amount of rudder application required for entry will vary depending upon the aircraft type, c.g. position, the direction of turn relative to propeller rotation, and the amount of power being used.
Refer to the particular Aircraft Manual to ensure whether spin entries with power on are permitted, and whether	Note: If the aircraft enters a developed spin, use the spin recovery method as shown in the aircraft manual or if no specific method is shown the standard spin recovery should be implemented.

any differences from the
Standard Spin Recovery
apply.

Student practice: The student should now practise incipient
spins and recoveries from level, descending and climbing
steep turns.

	Recoveries from unusual attitudes
	Orientation established and lookout completed.
From level flight, descending and climbing attitudes	Adopt a steeply banked attitude with the nose high, at a low airspeed. Recovery:
	Ease forward on the control column whilst gently levelling the wings and increasing power.
	Return the aircraft to a normal level flight attitude. Adopt a steeply banked attitude with the nose low and airspeed increasing. Recovery:
	Close the throttle. Level the wings. East gently out of the dive.
	Return the aircraft to a normal level flight attitude.

Student practice: The student should now be given the opportunity to
practise returning the aircraft to normal level flight from unusual
attitudes developed from level descending and climbing flight.

Operation at Minimum Level

Instructor's Guide

During the formative stages of a student pilot's flying, the ability to appreciate the dangers of deteriorating weather and the experience to recognise the onset of such conditions will be such that even after careful briefing he could lack the sense of awareness which comes only with experience.

This fact must be accepted, and to prepare him for possible situations which may develop when flying solo in the Local Flying Area and in the circuit, he will need formal training to develop the ability to handle the aircraft safely and apply sensible procedures when forced to fly at lower levels to avoid cloud.

The training objectives of this exercise must therefore be based upon the situation brought about by an unplanned descent to low altitudes due to weather deterioration. The student's state of mind in these circumstances must be taken into consideration and the training must be planned to ensure he is able to handle this situation with complete safety.

Additionally there will often be occasions when a pilot may have to operate between 800 to 1500 feet to comply with ATC requirements when using Entry/Exit Lanes or Special Local Rules which may apply at certain airfields within controlled airspace.

It is for these reasons that this exercise has been introduced into the Private Pilot Syllabus. However the wider considerations of having to adopt unplanned low-level operation due to the onset of bad weather during cross-country flight is covered later during the Long Briefing of Pilot Navigation under the sub heading of 'Navigation at Minimum Level'.

Although the number of weather-induced accidents do not form a substantial part of the total accident figures such accidents do form a significant part of the total fatal accidents. Therefore it is fundamental to the instructor's role to ensure that this exercise is covered adequately and as soon as possible after the student has completed his initial solo consolidation period.

AIRMANSHIP

In a sense the whole of the procedural part of this exercise can be considered as airmanship. It will encompass such items as a sense of weather awareness, knowledge of geographic position, the direction and strength of the wind, the approximate height of the underlying terrain, the need for a good lookout, self discipline, the capability to make firm 'Go No-Go' decisions and recognition of the best course of action are just some of the many airmanship facets which apply to this exercise.

BEFORE THE EXERCISE

The Long Briefing should cover the following:

Objectives.
General Considerations.
  Planning Requirements Prior to Flight in Entry/Exit Lanes.
  ATC Rules, Pilot Qualifications and Aircraft Equipment.

Low Level Familiarisation:
  Entry/Exit Lanes and Areas where Specific Local Rules Apply.
  Actions Prior to Descending.
  Visual Impressions and Height Keeping at Low Altitude.
  Effects of Speed and Inertia During Turns.
  Effects of Wind and Turbulence.

Low Level Operation:
  Weather Considerations.
    Low Cloud and Good Visibility.
    Low Cloud and Poor Visibility.
    Avoidance of Moderate to Heavy Rain Showers.
  Effects of Precipitation.
  Joining a Circuit.
  Bad Weather Circuit, Approach and Landing.

Airmanship.
Common Errors.

The short Pre-Flight Briefing should be based upon the practical aspects of that part of the Long Briefing in relation to the Air Exercise to be covered, e.g. regulations pertaining to specific Entry/Exit Lanes, operation at low level or bad weather circuits.

DURING THE AIR DEMONSTRATION

Introduce the exercise by allowing the student to become familiar with the changed aspect of the ground when flying at the lower levels.

Following this he should be taught to identify features on the ground and relate these to his map. Avoid over-concentrating on the map and point out that terrain 'high spots' (when available) often stand out clearly and can be valuable aids in pin-pointing the aircraft position.

Once the student has been acquainted with the added workload involved whilst operating at lower levels it will give him a better appreciation when making decisions, such as to continue or divert when weather deterioration occurs.

It will be essential to have conditions of reasonable wind strength i.e. 15-20 kts when demonstrating the effect of wind closer to the ground, or the full value of this part of the demonstration may be lost, and could lead to a failure to appreciate the effect of wind during turning manoeuvres when an actual operation at minimum level occurs.

LOW LEVEL OPERATION

From the commencement of this stage clearly define the weather condition to be assumed for this purpose, so that the student appreciates what action he must take if such conditions are met in reality.

Be particularly careful not to allow the aircraft to get too low at any time. Personal self discipline coupled with a sense of the need to avoid annoying persons on the ground and frightening livestock will be essential. One purpose of this exercise is to establish the minimum height that a student will permit himself to be forced down to. It could be said for example, if the cloud is such that a pilot is forced to fly below safety altitude then he has illustrated a lack of weather awareness coupled with an inability to make a more correct decision, i.e. to proceed to an alternative airfield at an earlier stage.

Insist upon the student meticulously checking his fuel state and performing the other en-route checks at appropriate times, and physically demonstrate the procedures to be followed when carrying out diversion action.

If a suitable airfield exists within or in close proximity to the Local Flying Area it will be invaluable experience for the student to actually land there, but if this is not practical the aircraft should at least be established en-route to such a diversion airfield for a period of time.

The opportunity to demonstrate bad weather circuit joining, including approaches and landings during actual bad weather conditions will usually occur at some stage during his course, and demonstration and practice in these actual conditions will be of greater benefit than feigning bad weather. However, if such an opportunity does not occur the practice of this part of the exercise must not be omitted, and an assumed weather situation can be adopted for this purpose.

COMMON ERRORS

Most errors in handling the aircraft and making decisions will stem from a lack of anticipation and awareness.

Operation at Minimum Level

Long Briefing

OBJECTIVES

The purpose of this exercise is to teach you how to operate the aircraft in safety when circumstances dictate the need for the aircraft to be flown at significantly lower heights than those normally used during the en-route stage of a flight. Such a height can be considered as being from 1500 feet to below 1000 feet a.g.l.

INTRODUCTION

There are two basic circumstances when flight in these conditions will be necessary:

1. The unplanned operation of an aircraft at lower than normal altitudes due to deterioration of weather, either in the circuit, in the Local Flying Area, or during navigation flights.
2. The planned entry into the VFR Entry/Exit Lanes associated with certain Controlled and Special Rules Airspace. The regulations governing the use of such lanes often require that VFR movements be flown at lower altitudes to provide a safe vertical clearance from IFR traffic.

Without doubt one of the greatest problems the pilot has to face is the weather and its attendant hazards during flight. The ability to recognise the warning symptoms of weather deterioration and the knowledge needed to carry out the necessary procedures if caught out in these circumstances is a vital necessity to the achievement of flight safety.

GENERAL CONSIDERATIONS

Although there are several considerations applicable to operating an aircraft at lower levels, only two are specified in this Long Briefing. These are:

1. The pre-planning required to ensure observance of any special rules applicable to the use of Entry/Exit Lanes in controlled airspace through which a pilot may have to operate in order to depart from and return to his base airfield.

2. The specific flight training required to operate an aircraft safely
   when flying at lower than normal altitudes in the Local Flying
   Area and the circuit.

The broader considerations of low-level operation due to deteriorating
weather during cross-country flying are covered in the Long Briefing
on Pilot Navigation under 'Navigation at Minimum Level'.

**Planning Requirements Prior to Flight through Entry/Exit
Lanes**
It is a legal requirement for all pilots to carry out careful pre-flight
planning.

The particular planning requirements for VFR transit between
those airfields situated within or below controlled airspace will need
to be carried out with reference to the longitudinal, lateral, and
vertical limits of such lanes. When such information is not
overprinted on navigation charts the pilot should mark these on his
chart before departure. Further to this it will be necessary to know
the RTF frequencies to use and the procedures to be followed. The
exact procedure and height band to use will vary between specific
Entry/Exit Lanes and can only be determined from local ATC
regulations or from the U.K. Air Pilot.

The U.K. is divided into controlled and uncontrolled airspace. The
former consists of Airways, Control Zones, Terminal Areas and
Special Rules Airspace, and as changes are made from time to time to
the regulations governing flight in such areas, it is not possible in
this manual to cover more than the broad principles involved.

A clearance must be obtained from the applicable ATC facility
which controls the particular airspace and this is done by filing a
flight plan by telephone or in writing (completing a written flight
plan) prior to flight, and receiving a clearance for the flight to be
made. When a change of plan en-route dictates a requirement for
VFR traffic to obtain such a clearance the request can be made to the
relevant ATC authority by RTF during flight, and in either case the
pilot will have to conform to the established entry or departure
procedures. It must be borne in mind that a pre-requisite for flight in
these areas is that pilots must ensure they remain clear of cloud and
in sight of the surface.

ATC Rules, Pilot Qualifications and Aircraft Equipment
Conforming with Entry and Departure procedures may sometimes
require the pilot to fly lower than the legal minimum height for flight
over towns or built up areas. Although on such occasions the pilot
will be absolved from observing this minimum height rule, it is still
the pilot's responsibility to ensure that he operates his aircraft at

such a height that he can alight clear of towns or built-up areas in the event of an engine failure. He is also bound by the 'low flying rule' which makes it illegal to fly closer than 500 feet to any person, vehicle, vessel or structure except when carrying out a normal take-off or approach to land.

A pilot's licence and associated ratings gives the holder certain privileges. The actual exercise of these privileges will nevertheless be constrained by certain weather limitations, e.g. cloud base and visibility, and it is the pilot's responsibility to ensure he has the necessary privileges, and that the forecast weather is such that he can reasonably expect to remain within his limitations during any planned flight. The pilot must also ensure that his aircraft is suitably equipped and that the required equipment is functioning correctly prior to such a flight.

At certain airfields, normally in the vicinity of Control Zones or under TMA's special local rules apply to VFR flights. These are evolved to improve co-ordination of air traffic movements when mixed VFR and IFR flights occur in fairly close proximity. The U.K. Air Pilot gives details of these airfields and the local rules which apply.

This information contains such items as:

Maximum altitudes to fly, these may vary dependent upon the runway in use at the nearby major airfield(s) upon which the controlled airspace is centred.
The geographic limits within which these altitude restrictions apply.
The minimum flight visibility in which VFR flights may take place.
Any other pertinent information.

An example of these local rules and Entry/Exit procedures is shown pictorially in fig. 16-1. Normally when transit takes place below TMA's and Special Rules Areas the airfield QNH should be used to determine altitude.

LOW LEVEL FAMILIARISATION
During the operation of an aircraft at minimum level the pilot will need to understand certain environmental factors which he will not normally meet during flight at higher altitudes, for example the requirement to map read, interpret ground features and identify his position will become more difficult at lower levels. Further, due to the associated reasons necessitating operation at minimum level such as low cloud often in combination with poor visibility the exercise requires a higher standard of flying ability, self discipline and decision-making qualities, all of which must be displayed during conditions which are more difficult than when flying normally at safer altitudes.

Fig. 16-1

PRELIMINARY ACTIONS PRIOR TO DESCENDING

Immediately before descending to the lower levels associated with this exercise it is necessary to complete the following checks:

FUEL

Mixture selected to 'Rich'.

Fuel contents noted and fullest tank selected, when tank selection is changed at this stage it should be performed several minutes prior to the descent to ensure that fuel is being drawn from the newly selected tank, and before the aircraft is taken to the lower level where height may be insufficient to rectify a fuel starvation situation. When fitted, the electric fuel pump should be switched 'ON'.

RADIO

This should be selected to the required frequency, and the Squelch and Volume controls suitably adjusted. Remember that at the lower levels below 1500 feet the range of radio transmissions and reception is markedly reduced. This reduction in range will also apply to any Radio Navigation equipment being used.

ENGINE   Pressure and temperatures should be carefully
                  checked to ensure that the engine is performing
                  correctly.
                  The use of Carburettor Heat should be con-
                  sidered, also the advisability of a powered descent
                  rather than a glide.

SYSTEMS   The Ammeter and Suction Gauge readings
                  should be noted to establish the serviceability of
                  their respective systems.
                  The Heading Indicator should be re-checked with
                  the Magnetic Compass and carefully synchron-
                  ised. Once in the lower levels this action will
                  usually become more difficult due to the possibil-
                  ity of added turbulence and the greater need to
                  maintain a vigilant lookout.

ALTIMETER   Ensure that the altimeter is set to the appro-
                  priate datum, and when applicable the next
                  required altimeter setting noted, e.g. that for the
                  destination airfield QNH, or QFE as required for
                  ATC procedures.

HARNESS   The pilot and passenger seat belts/harnesses re-
                  checked as secure and tight.

POSITION   Check the position of the aircraft immediately
                  prior to the descent, and include a review of high
                  ground, obstructions, danger and similar areas
                  within or adjacent to the local flying area. The
                  changed wind velocity at the lower levels will
                  also need to be anticipated.

The descent should be planned in relation to both time and position to
ensure that it can be safely made without entering or becoming very
close to cloud. The inadvertent entry to cloud in this type of operation
would be particularly hazardous to a VFR pilot and if descending
through gaps or broken layers of cloud, the pilot can easily experience
spatial disorientation which would again lead to a hazardous
situation.

Selection of Airspeed and Configuration
In small training aircraft the normal cruising speed will usually give
an adequate margin for avoiding action in relation to high ground,
obstructions or other aircraft. In the event that the flight is taking
place in conditions of very poor visibility it would be advisable to
operate at a low safe cruising speed, but as this normally produces a

higher nose attitude in level flight it would be beneficial to use some 10° of flap which will permit flight to be made at the same speed with the nose lower.

Although range or endurance are not significantly affected at lower levels in small training aircraft, an appreciation of the fuel remaining and that needed to return to the airfield must be conducted at short intervals. This will become of increasing importance if the pilot has to circumnavigate the weather.

Visual Impressions and Height Keeping at a Low Altitude

Once the aircraft has been levelled off at the selected height the student will be able to more clearly appreciate the changed perspective of ground features and the difficulties experienced in maintaining the selected height by reference to the ground. Although one aim in this exercise is to develop the student's ability to judge his height over the surface by visual reference, the altimeter should not be ignored as it will be of value as a secondary reference.

The lower the aircraft is flown the more oblique will be the view of the ground features which will lead to map reading becoming more difficult. One object of this exercise therefore will be to give the student an opportunity to study this changed perspective, so that with practice he will be able to relate this changed impression of the ground features to his interpretation of the information shown on the map.

If snow has fallen the effect will be to mask certain ground features blending them with one another, affording greater difficulty in establishing the aircraft position.

In order to develop the student's ability to map read when flying at lower levels the aircraft will be flown at heights between 1000 feet and 600 feet during which the student will get a first-hand impression of landmarks viewed from an oblique angle. It will be important to keep in mind that symbols are not shown on air navigation charts for obstructions less than 300 feet above local ground level, and unmarked obstructions of all kinds may be present up to a height of 299 feet above ground level.

In view of this, pilots must make due allowance for unmarked obstructions up to this height in addition to the required terrain clearance, when determining minimum safe height, and although it is unlikely that there will be any need to fly at such very low heights, it must nevertheless be considered as a possibility when flying in areas where the ground has sharp vertical irregularities and the visibility is poor.

In relation to the weather conditions prevailing, it should be appreciated that poor visibility alone is no reason for flying at heights below 1500 feet. In these cricumstances map reading can become very difficult and the pilot will be much safer staying at a reasonable altitude. This will give him more time to concentrate on map reading and determining his position. Although at higher altitudes the slant visibility factor will reduce the pilot's visual range this effect is minimal at heights of 1500 to 2000 feet as shown in fig. 16-2.

Fig. 16-2

Effects of Speed and Inertia During Turns

Whenever an aircraft turns, a degree of inertia will be present; this is highest at increased speed and less at reduced speeds. Whereas at altitude the effect of inertia is not particularly important it does become significant when operating near the surface. Whilst at low level the student will be shown the visual effect during turns and made to appreciate the need for early decisions whenever obstacle clearance requires a change of direction.

Effects of Wind – Misleading Visual Impressions

During flight at lower altitude certain misleading visual impressions can occur, for example when flying across the prevailing wind direction the amount of drift experienced can be clearly seen as shown in fig. 16-3. However when turning the aircraft to a downwind heading a distinct visual impression of 'slipping in' during the turn will occur, fig. 16-4.

When turning upwind the opposite will be the case and the pilot will obtain the visual impression that the aircraft is in unbalanced flight and skidding towards the outside of the turn (fig. 16-5). It is during these moments that a pilot must rely upon his balance indicator to assist him in maintaining a balanced flight condition. Due to the tailwind component when flying downwind the impression of speed is greater and the pilot must guard against any instinctive tendency to reduce power in order to reduce what is only an apparent increase of airspeed.

These effects will be demonstrated by the instructor flying the aircraft across the wind to enable the student to experience the visual effect of drift at low height. The aircraft will then be flown into wind and a medium turn downwind will be carried out and during this the

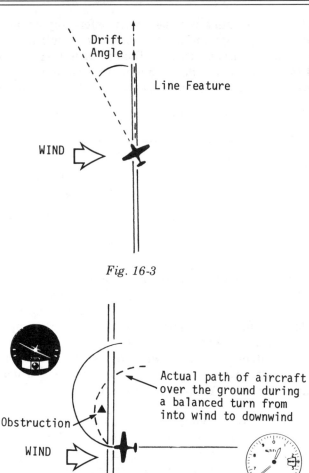

Fig. 16-3

Fig. 16-4

impression of 'slipping in' will be clearly seen. Finally the aircraft will be turned into wind so that the apparent effect of 'skidding out' can be appreciated.

Effect of Turbulence
When flying at relatively low altitudes over general terrain which is less flat and with more surface obstructions than an airfield, mechanical turbulence and wind shear effects are more marked, particularly in moderate to strong winds.

Turbulence and eddies will always exist in the vicinity of, and especially downwind of woods, forests, or hilly and undulating

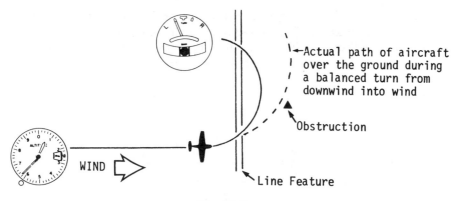

Fig. 16-5

ground. Such turbulence can become a very real hazard to an aircraft in flight and the use of added power to avoid sudden height loss must be anticipated.

Wind shear effects will also assume greater importance. The effect of vertical gusts upon the aircraft flight path has already been covered in Advanced Turns but the vertical variation of wind strength due to sharp velocity gradients can be seen more clearly by reference to fig. 16-6.

Fig. 16-6

The action of horizontal shear will cause sudden changes in the wind component and its effects upon the aircraft flight path, leading to sharp variations of airspeed. For example, when flying in a wind of 35 kts on a heading which gives a 30 kt headwind component the occurrence of wind shear as shown in fig. 16-7 will produce a drop in airspeed of 20 kts, and a consequent sudden decrease of lift and loss of height will occur, the pilot must therefore be ready to counteract such effects when flying at the lower levels.

Horizontal Wind Shear

Fig. 16-7

LOW LEVEL OPERATION

Operations in Entry/Exist Lanes between 800 to 1500 feet a.g.l. during good weather will not normally be difficult, provided the ability to map read and navigate at these levels has been practised. However when low-level operation is forced upon the pilot due to worsening weather conditions, the situation will change and the ability to map read, navigate and maintain an optimum level of safety will incur a degree of practical urgency.

Self discipline, methodical cockpit procedures and the development of an awareness of the problems will be essential for such a flight operation to be safely conducted.

When a low cloud-base occurs with good visibility underneath ground features can be seen well ahead and to either side of the aircraft flight path. However an awareness of the position of the aircraft in relation to high ground and obstructions will be necessary, and the importance of knowing the exact position prior to descending deserves special emphasis.

When conditions of both low cloud and poor visibility are experienced considerable care must be used to maintain a close check on the aircraft position, and an accurate appreciation of ground speed and intelligent use of the clock will be essential. It is just this type of weather condition which may call for a change in plan and an estimated heading and time required to an alternative airfield. During local area operations it is good airmanship to have accessible the basic details and radio frequencies of airfields adjacent to the local flying area in order that a diversion airfield can be quickly selected.

Whenever a situation necessitating low level operation or diversion procedure occurs (and radio is available) the pilot should inform his base or destination airfield of his flight situation and whether he will be attempting to continue to the airfield or divert to an alternative one.

Some of the factors to be considered when arriving at a decision to continue or divert are listed below:

Returning to Base Airfield:
The anticipated minimum base of the cloud in relation to the terrain to be overflown.
The likelihood of the weather deteriorating still further.
The visibility range to be expected when operating below the cloud, including the effect of precipitation.
The degree of difficulty likely to be experienced in map reading and maintaining a reasonably accurate track in the existing weather conditions.

Diverting to an Alternate Airfield:
The fuel state and daylight remaining in relation to the distance to the nearest suitable airfield.
The weather conditions anticipated along the diversion route.
The type of terrain to be overflown.

If moderate to heavy showers occur during flight in the Local Area the base of the associated clouds can often be very low and visibility in the precipitation can be markedly reduced. In these circumstances the correct action will be to remain at a normal altitude and in a clear area until the shower has passed and the route to the airfield (including the airfield itself) is clear. ATC should be informed of the situation and care must be taken not to 'hold off' downwind of the shower activity. A marked ground feature should normally be chosen to assist in the continued maintenance of orientation relative to the base airfield.

Effects of Precipitation

Light rain does not normally produce a visibility problem of any great extent but heavy rain, sleet or snow can seriously reduce forward visibility. Sleet or snow will often reduce forward visibility to nil and, must therefore be avoided even though it may mean diverting to another airfield.

Care should be exercised during flight at low level whenever rain in the form of large drops is present. Raindrops on the windscreen cause distortion to forward visibility due to refraction and diffusion of light waves, and this effect can mislead pilots into thinking they are higher than they really are. Figure 16-8 shows this effect during flight for both the en-route and landing case.

Fig. 16-8

Whenever precipitation is encountered the windscreen demister (if fitted) should be selected and added alertness to the possibility of carburettor icing will be necessary. When the aircraft is equipped with a pitot heater this too should be switched on preferably before precipitation is encountered. Whereas an unserviceable ASI can cause minor difficulties at higher levels, the loss of airspeed indications when operating at minimum level can become a hazard and create additional problems at a time when the workload may already be high.

Joining an Airfield Circuit

During operation at minimum levels it will clearly be hazardous to rejoin overhead the airfield as the height being flown to avoid cloud could be close to or below the usual circuit height.

When radio is available the joining procedure will be as directed by ATC or as advised by the Advisory Facility. Other aircraft already in the vicinity of the airfield or in the circuit will be advised as necessary of any rejoining traffic and at times as this the use of radio is an invaluable aid to flight safety.

A decision made to proceed to an alternate airfield at the right time would increase the possibility of the pilot being able to join the circuit in the normal manner, making low-level operation unnecessary.

When the weather conditions necessitate operating below circuit height it will be advisable to establish the Visual Manoeuvring Height for the airfield concerned. This height is published in the U.K. Air Pilot, or obtained from ATC. In the U.K. the visual manoeuvring height is based upon a 300 feet clearance of any obstructions within a 4 n.m. radius of the airfield and to fly below this height during the rejoining procedure would be very hazardous particularly during conditions of poor visibility.

The maintenance of lookout for other aircraft will be absolutely vital during this period. Attention can easily be diverted completely due to the associated problems of orientation, and aircraft positioning in relation to the active runway, and during this period the pilot may find himself in conflict with the tracks of aircraft climbing away after take-off, following the circuit pattern, or approaching to land.

Bad Weather Circuit, Approach and Landing
Once the aircraft is established in the pattern particular alertness is necessary so as not to lose sight of the airfield, and to keep a mental check on the position of other aircraft which have announced their position through normal RTF procedures. It must also be appreciated that at those airfields where instrument approaches are being carried out, some aircraft may not be on the same frequency as the circuit traffic and additional alertness will be required during the base leg and final approach.

Accurate headings must be flown and the clock used to time each leg of the circuit. This will be invaluable if the visibility is such that difficulty is experienced with keeping the airfield in view or if the pilot is forced to widen or lengthen his circuit to avoid getting too close to other air traffic.

The pilot must not hesitate to inform ATC if he becomes uncertain of his position during the circuit, and any ATC instructions must be carefully obeyed. Air Traffic Controllers are competent persons whose duty it is to render every assistance to aircraft in flight and they must be relied upon in such circumstances.

When poor visibility exists without low cloud being present many of the foregoing considerations will apply, but it may be advisable when safe to do so, to establish a positive position from overhead the airfield well above circuit height, then continue on a fairly tight overhead let down followed by a slightly closer than normal circuit pattern. Be careful however to be at circuit height before crossing the take-off path at the upwind end of the airfield.

Fig. 16-9

AIRMANSHIP

From the foregoing it can be seen that a continued state of awareness is essential for weather deterioration to be dealt with in a safe and sensible fashion. A lack of awareness coupled with unpreparedness can lead to hazardous circumstances in which a pilot who lacks decision making capability can be forced into a situation where he is unsure of his position or completely lost and flying into worsening weather, getting nearer the ground and becoming a potential hazard to himself and persons on the ground.

Whenever operating at low levels the visibility range will be reduced regardless of the weather conditions. Therefore extra care must be taken to maintain an accurate position check in order to remain clear of Controlled Airspace, Special Rules Zones and Areas, and Military Air Traffic Zones unless permission to fly in such airspace has been obtained.

Lookout in relation to other aircraft is just as important at the lower levels as it is during operations at normal altitudes. It is sensible to assume that if a pilot is forced to fly low because of bad weather then other pilots may also be in the same situation.

Engine handling will assume an even greater degree of importance during low level operation. Mistakes or carelessness in items such as fuel management, involving for example the incorrect selection of fuel tanks, can create engine failure when insufficient height or time is available for the mistake to be rectified. The mixture control should be set at full Rich (this may not always apply over high mountainous areas) and a close watch kept for any symptoms of carburettor icing. This latter can be aggravated in conditions of high humidity associated with low cloud and rain. Instruments must be checked regularly so that the pilot is alerted to any symptoms of engine or systems malfunction.

In poor visibility conditions and regardless of the height being flown, the pilot should not hesitate to use the aircraft external lighting, and such aids as rotating beacons, navigation lights and (when fitted) strobe lights should be switched on. However in certain conditions, notably in poor light, rotating beacons and particularly strobe lights may cause reflections from water droplets or particles in the atmosphere. Caution must therefore be exercise and when such conditions occur these lights should be switched off. This is because such reflections can often become distracting to the pilot and lead to the onset of vertigo or spatial disorientation.

Near the Ground Hazards Abound

Be Alert for
Airspace
Restrictions

PRE-FLIGHT BRIEFING
OPERATION AT MINIMUM LEVEL

Aim

To teach you the correct procedures when using Entry/Exit Lanes or Special Local Rules and how to map read and handle the aircraft at low altitudes.

What

A flight conducted at low level due to specific ATC regulations or deterioration of weather conditions during flight.

Airmanship

The extreme importance of abiding by ATC instructions and a vigilant lookout for other aircraft, obstructions, villages, towns and controlled or restricted airspace. Correct handling of the aircraft systems is a requirement.

How

Demonstration 1.

The Use of Entry/Exit Lanes

Pre-Flight Preparation:

The need for checking ATC information.
Making of the map.
Obtaining a clearance for flight within Entry/Exit Lanes or Areas which are governed by special local rules.

During Flight:

Flight operation in accordance with ATC procedures.
The importance of maintaining a strict lookout.
Careful adherence to entry/exit routes and height limitations.
Correct use of RTF procedures.

Student Practice.

Demonstration 2.

Low Level Familiarisation

Actions Prior to Descending:

To include checks on fuel state, engine systems, correct altimeter setting, security of harnesses and knowledge of position.

At Low Level:

The changed aspect of ground features will be seen and the difficulties of map reading appreciated. Villages and towns must be avoided, together with controlled and restricted airspace. A careful lookout must be maintained for other aircraft and obstructions.
The effect of speed and inertia during turns will be shown. Crosswind flight along a line feature will show drift angle. Turning downwind will give an impression of 'slipping in' towards the turn.
Turning into wind will give the impression of 'Skidding outwards' during the turn.

Note the importance of resisting false impressions and maintaining airspeed and balance.

Note the increased effects of turbulence when near the ground due to surface irregularities, wind shear, gusts etc.

Student Practice.

PRE-FLIGHT BRIEFING
OPERATION AT MINIMUM LEVEL

Aim To teach you how to conduct a flight during conditions of marked weather deterioration in the Local Area or circuit.

What The procedure to adopt if weather deterioration, with low cloud base or poor visibility occur during flight.

Airmanship Awareness of the weather state, and the considerations applicable when forced to fly at low level.

How

Demonstration 3   Low Level Operation
When weather deterioration occurs a decision must be made to return to the base airfield or divert.

Returning to the Base Airfield
Complete checks, establish position positively, review the type of terrain and obstructions along the route back to the airfield.
Descent to a suitable height (200 feet below cloud base).
Anticipate use of power to clear rising ground or varying the aircraft height to remain clear of cloud. Importance of frequent positon and en-route checks. If cloud ahead continues to lower, a decision to turn back and re-plan may be required.

Diversion Procedure
Assess weather expected en-route to diversion airfield.
Check fuel state, daylight remaining, distance from the alternative airfield and type of terrain to be flown over.
Plan best route, assess heading and time to alternate airfield. Note time when setting heading and inform ATC of intentions. Reselect radio frequency as required.

When low cloud and poor visibility exist, an increased urgency of lookout and a preparedness to turn back and make alternative plans will be necessary.

Student Practice.

Demonstration 4.   The Bad Weather Circuit
Circuit Joining
Whilst still well clear of the airfield, obtain ATC clearance, circuit direction and runway in use.
Check the minimum 'Visual Manoeuvring Height'.
Establish position and orientation in relation to the circuit pattern and runway in use.
Decide on joining route or act on ATC instructions.
Monitor all RTF calls to establish the approximate position of other aircraft.
Avoid crossing the take-off or landing paths when close to the airfield except when instructed by ATC.

The Bad Weather Circuit, Approach and Landing
Establish position on the downwind leg, allow for drift and maintain heading. Monitor the time on this leg. RTF call 'Downwind'. Maintain a vigilant lookout and complete the pre-landing checks.

Turn onto base leg and maintain a searching lookout for other aircraft and the 'lead in' lights.
RTF call 'Base Leg' (if applicable).
Maintain a time check on base leg, and if runway sighting is not achieved, turn to finals on the basis of time.

Throughout the final approach maintain a wide visual search either side of the aircraft nose to obtain a sighting of the runway.

Student Practice.

Operation at Minimum Level

Flight Demonstrations

INTRODUCTION

The contents of this exercise can be conveniently divided into the following specific demonstration groups:

1. The use of Entry/Exit procedures and application of Special Local Rules for VFR flights when departing or arriving at airfields within or below Controlled Airspace.
2. Low Level Familiarisation.
3. Low Level Operation.
4. Joining a Circuit at Low Level.
   Bad weather circuit, Approach and Landing.

Demonstration 1 may have already been covered earlier in the course when training is being conducted from airfields at which such Special Rules apply.

Demonstration 2 is essentially a practical exercise to get the student acquainted with and permit practice of handling the aircraft below 1000 feet a.g.l.

The contents of demonstration 3 would be best presented during weather conditions which require this type of flight operation. However when this is not practical the instructor will describe the conditions which will be assumed for the demonstration, e.g. the imaginary cloud base and visibility.

Demonstration 4 will be given at the end of demonstration 2 or 3 or at any other time to fit in with existing weather conditions or the course programme.

Airmanship items related to this exercise will be introduced and developed at the appropriate time during each demonstration.

DEMONSTRATION 1.   USE OF ENTRY/EXIT PROCEDURES AND APPLICATION OF SPECIAL LOCAL RULES

Flight Lesson	Demonstration Sequence
Pre-flight planning and application of procedures	The correct procedures must be clearly noted. The map should be clearly marked. ATC clearance must be obtained. Flight operation according to local procedures. RTF as necessary. Student Practice.

DEMONSTRATION 2.   LOW LEVEL FAMILIARISATION

Flight Lesson	Demonstration Sequence
Operation of the aircraft at lower than normal altitudes	Use of Entry/Exit Lanes (as applicable).
Actions prior to descending	Fuel, Radio, Engine, Systems, Altimeter, Harness and Position Checks.
From level flight over a suitable area descent to approximately 600 to 800 feet a.g.l.	Importance of lookout. Establish level flight at cruise power. Trim. The oblique view gives a marked change in the aspect of ground features, and an impression of increasing airspeed. The altimeter datum (area QNH) is related to sea level, a visual assessment of height will be necessary. Note the possibility of added turbulence due to surface temperature, proximity to uneven ground, obstructions or wooded areas. Maintain a safe speed and be ready to use power as necessary to maintain height above irregular surface contours. En-route checks. Check geographic position at frequent intervals. Avoid villages and towns, and

	observe the 500 feet rule in relation to buildings, persons and livestock.
	Be alert to obstructions such as power cables on rising ground.
	Student practice.
Effect of speed and inertia during turns.	Lookout and carry out medium turns in either direction.
	Note turn radius becomes more obvious at lower levels.
	Student practice.
Effects of wind: Crosswind effect.	A straight line feature at 90° to the wind will be selected.
	Position the aircraft to track along the selected ground feature.
	Note that the drift angle is more clearly seen at lower levels.
Turning downwind.	The aircraft will be headed directly into wind.
	Lookout and commence a medium turn through 180°.
	Note the effect of wind on the aircraft track relative to the ground.
	Close visual contact with the surface gives an impression of 'slipping in'. .
	Note: Do not attempt to correct for non-existent 'slip'.
	The aircraft will be flown directly downwind. Note the increased ground-speed for a constant airspeed.
	Caution: Do not reduce power.
	Lookout and commence a medium turn through 180°.
	Note the effect of wind on the aircraft track relative to the ground gives an apparent impression of 'skidding out'.
	Note: Do not attempt to correct for non-existent 'skid'.
	NOTE: It will be necessary to take the effect of drift into account when turning to avoid obstacles.
	Student practice.
Effect of turbulence.	Note this is most marked over uneven ground and downwind from large woods etc.
	Use the map to determine position and return to a normal altitude.

Student practice: The student will fly the aircraft at 600 to 800 feet a.g.l. to practise turns and map reading whilst adjusting himself to the changed visual impressions of ground features and when applicable the increased turbulence.

DEMONSTRATION 3. LOW LEVEL OPERATION

Flight Lesson	Demonstration Sequence
An assumed weather situation will be described and a demonstration of the correct procedure given	
Assumed weather:	
Conditions of moderate to heavy shower activity	Actions: Decide to return to base or hold off in the clear. Note the dangers of a low cloud base with reduced visibility in precipitation. Inform ATC of intentions. Proceed to, or remain in a clear area and avoid positioning the aircraft downwind of shower clouds. Maintain a safe height and position relative to clearly defined ground features. Monitor fuel state and aircraft endurance When the route to the airfield is clear return to base and rejoin in the normal manner.
Assumed weather:	
Conditions of low cloud with good visibility below	Actions: Remain clear of cloud and decide whether to return to base airfield or divert. Check fuel state, daylight remaining and distance to the nearest suitable airfield. Inform ATC of the situation and intentions. Returning to base airfield: Complete the Checks prior to descending. Check position and type of terrain and obstructions to be anticipated en-route. Review the route back to the airfield.

16

When the checks and route preparation are completed descend to a suitable height to remain at least 200 feet clear below cloud. Adopt cruising speed and re-trim.

Importance of lookout.

Be prepared to vary the height to remain clear of cloud and anticipate the need for added power when over irregular surface contours.

Maintain a close check on geographic position, e.g. map reading, accurate headings and time checks.

Take early action to avoid villages, etc. Be particularly alert to obstructions on rising ground.

Complete en-route checks at regular intervals.

NOTE: If cloud ahead is dropping below acceptable limits in relation to en-route terrain . . . TURN BACK.

If the original decision is to divert:

Inform ATC of decision and the chosen alternate airfield.

Plan route in relation to:

Fuel state, anticipated weather en-route and daylight remaining.

Note the assessed new heading, distance to go, groundspeed anticipated and time to alternate airfield.

Reselect radio frequency as required.

Student practice.

Assumed weather:
Conditions of low cloud and bad visibility

Actions:

Remain clear of cloud and decide whether to return to base airfield or divert.

Check fuel state, daylight remaining and distance to nearest suitable airfield.

Inform ATC of the situation and intentions.

Returning to base airfield:

The considerations and actions will be basically the same as for the previous demonstration but due to the reduced visibility there will be an increased urgency of lookout.

	Map reading will be more difficult and an increased alertness to the possibility of worsening weather conditions will be necessary. Be prepared to make an early decision to . . . TURN BACK and re-plan when in a clear area.
	If the original decision is to divert:
	The considerations and actions are as for the previous diversion demonstration.
	Student practice.

DEMONSTRATION 4.   JOINING THE CIRCUIT, BAD WEATHER CIRCUIT APPROACH AND LANDING

Flight Lesson	*Demonstration Sequence*
Entering and completing a circuit when operating at minimum level	
Joining a circuit	Obtain ATC information, e.g. runway in use and circuit direction before getting close to the airfield. Bear in mind the 'minimum visual manoeuvring height' for the particular airfield. Establish position and orientation in relation to the circuit pattern. Monitor all RTF transmissions to mentally establish the position of other aircraft. Maintain a vigilant lookout and remember that non-radio aircraft may be in the vicinity. Avoid crossing the take-off or approach paths when close to the airfield unless otherwise directed by ATC.
The bad weather circuit, approach and landing	Establish position on the downwind leg not less than the visual manoeuvring height. R/T call 'Downwind'. Maintain heading, allow for drift and monitor the time. Carry out normal pre-landing checks. Turn onto base leg and carry out a powered approach. Maintain a searching lookout for any aircraft on final approach.

Look for the runway 'lead in' lights and be prepared to alert other aircraft by making an additional RTF call 'Base Leg'.

When runway visual contact is uncertain estimate a time to turn onto the final approach.

Bear in mind the effect of a tail/headwind component in relation to the estimated time on this leg.

Final Approach:

In poor visibility conditions maintain a wide search either side of the nose to obtain a visual sighting of the runway.

Student practice: The student should practise bad weather circuits under actual or simulated conditions with an emphasis on lookout, accurate headings and timing of the circuit legs.

Forced Landings

Instructor's Guide

It can be said that during the early days of flight, every time an aircraft took to the air a state of emergency existed. Today, due to the high reliability of the modern aircraft, emergencies caused by engine or airframe malfunction are very rare. However it can also be said that any aircraft is safe until the pilot steps on board after which many things can go wrong. For example, statistics reveal that some 20% of the total aircraft accidents occur because of engine failure due to the pilot mismanaging one of the associated engine systems and in particular the fuel supply.

Therefore although this exercise is primarily concerned with what a pilot should do after an engine failure, it is vital not to lose sight of the importance of preventing an engine from failing, and this will only be brought about by the pilot having a thorough understanding of the engine systems, fuel consumption figures and the need to plan correctly prior to every flight. It is the instructor's responsibility to ensure that the seeds of good aviation practices are not only sown during training, but are also developed properly throughout the student pilot's course.

Adherence to correct planning and drills and the development of a sense of awareness as to how systems can be mismanaged is just as essential during training as the teaching of take-offs and landings, and the instructor must make every effort to see that his student is fully trained to think and act correctly before emergencies occur as well as afterwards.

Forced landing practice must never be allowed to become an academic exercise which is done just to satisfy a syllabus. It must be treated as an exercise in survival in which positive and clear thinking backed up by good judgement, confidence and competence must be exercised if it is to be of real value to a pilot.

FORCED LANDING WITHOUT POWER

When the exercise is first demonstrated good instruction principles will demand that it should be presented along the lines of an ideal forced landing situation, i.e. the throttle will be closed when the aircraft is within easy reach of a suitable field and with plenty of height available. This will give the instructor sufficient time to teach, and the student time to comprehend, the various aspects of the descent plan which are being unfolded. Once the student has practised and grasped the principles and procedures involved, then alternative situations more natural and more difficult can be created.

Simulated forced landings should be introduced as early as possible after first solo and only consistent practice will produce the required skill to handle them correctly. Therefore regular practice must be phased in throughout the whole of the training period, because occasional practice will have little real value. Whilst appreciating the relatively short time available during this section of a Private Pilot Course, the utilisation of short periods on a consistent basis should not markedly interfere with the practice of other exercises.

AIRMANSHIP
Provided good airmanship in respect of correct drills, procedures and systems management is implemented the possibility of this emergency occurring will be rare.

In the event that engine failure does occur, a sound knowledge of the factors involved in selecting a landing area and initiating a descent plan will further a state of confidence, and materially assist the successful outcome of the forced landing procedure.

During practice periods the instructor must stress the importance of correct engine handling, control of airspeed, and the need to avoid giving annoyance to persons or livestock. The student should be shown by the instructor's example that there is no need to descend too low in order to assess the outcome of the forced landing practice. In this respect the dangers of coming too low when turbulence exists must be clearly pointed out, and it should be noted that downdraughts from turbulence and wind shear at low levels in the open countryside can present severe hazards, regardless of which type of forced landing is being practised.

BEFORE THE EXERCISE
The Long Briefing should cover the following:

Objectives.
Forced Landing Procedures.
Choice of Landing Area.
  Provision for Change of Plan.
Gliding Distance Considerations.
The Descent Plan.
  Key Positions.
  Engine Failure Checks.

Use of Radio.
The Base Leg.
The Final Approach.
The Landing.
Actions After Landing.
Aircraft Security.
Airmanship.
Common Errors.

The short Pre-Flight Briefing should be based upon the practical aspects of that part of the Long Briefing in relation to the Air Exercise to be covered.

In order to strike a balance between efficient utilisation of airborne time and the need for realism in searching for and selecting a suitable landing area, it will be advisable for the instructor to have one or two suitable areas already located for use during the introduction of the flight exercise. Later, when the student has practised and grasped the principles involved, practice can be carried out over other areas.

When giving the short briefing prior to the practice of the exercise the instructor should describe the layout of the field to be used and any significant ground features which may be available to assist recognition from the air.

DURING THE AIR DEMONSTRATION

Ensure that the field selected for the introduction of forced landings without power is clearly identified and pointed out to the student prior to commencing the exercise. This will avoid the frustration of having to break off in the middle of explaining the procedure during the descent phase to re-identify the field, or finding out in the final stages that the student had misunderstood which field was originally chosen.

During the first demonstration avoid too much emphasis on the failure checks, as the first priority is for the student to concentrate on how the planned descent is progressing. He will need to follow the methods used to position the aircraft throughout the descent in relation to the aircraft height and its distance from the selected touchdown point. In this respect special emphasis should be given to orientation in relation to the prevailing wind, and how it affects the aircraft during the implementation of the descent plan.

A good principle is to initially plan the 'aiming point' to be in the centre of the chosen field, as this will reduce the risk of under-shooting. During the final stages of the base leg and/or during the final approach flaps can be used in conjunction with aircraft positioning to bring the 'aiming point' back to a quarter or one third of the way into the field.

Although the use of a 1000 feet key area at the end of the downwind leg will be an important guide for positioning it will also be valuable to select further key areas for the commencement of the crosswind and downwind legs. This will facilitate judgement in that the student will soon learn to appreciate that if he is to arrive at the end of the downwind leg at approximately 1000 feet a.g.l. he will need to pass through a key area at the commencement of the downwind leg with at least 1500 feet a.g.l. remaining, or adopt an alternative route closer in or further out from the field. It can also be said that the aircraft will need to be at about 2000 feet a.g.l. at the start of the crosswind leg, and if significantly lower at this point he must immediately set up an alternative route to bring the aircraft inside the path originally planned in order to achieve 1500 feet at the beginning of the downwind leg.

It will be important to ensure the student does not lose sight of the chosen field, and that he can anticipate the effect of wind upon the aircraft track throughout each leg of the descent route.

Make good use of the time in transit to and from the local flying area to develop the student's reactions in quickly selecting the best field within range. This can best be done by initially pointing out various suitable landing areas, and later by temporarily closing the throttle without warning and asking him to choose a field and plan a descent.

After the student has grasped the principles involved it will be of value to occasionally practise a forced landing without power from overhead the airfield. This will then permit the final outcome of the practice to be accurately assessed. Added care however must be used to avoid hazardous 'near miss' situations developing when other aircraft are in the circuit.

COMMON ERRORS

A lack of accurate trimming for the correct gliding attitude will lead to a greater necessity to concentrate on flying the aircraft. This will adversely affect the time available for planning and could lead to errors in judgement.

• It is not uncommon to find that the student has mistakenly planned to land downwind, leading to an extremely dangerous situation. Ensure that the student locates an approximate landing run into wind first, and then plans his descent procedure based on this datum.
• When height is plentiful the initial stage of the plan (to the first high key position) is not a vital one necessarily affecting the remainder of the descent pattern, however it can be crucial at lower heights. Therefore special emphasis must be placed upon getting the priorities right between commencing a descent plan and carrying out cockpit procedures. Failure checks and an RTF call must be done in

the correct order, and fulfilling the required descent plan must have the first priority.

• Students are particularly prone to ignoring any headwind/tailwind component on the base leg when a crosswind approach has to be made. This omission is particularly hazardous if there is a headwind component during base leg, as it could lead to the development of an undershoot situation.

• During practice of the failure checks ensure that the student carries out drills by statement of intent, or by 'touch drills' only, and at no time during practice should he re-select fuel tanks after or immediately before the engine is throttled back.

• The natural concentration on the planning and execution of the descent will commonly lead to a failure to clear the engine at regular intervals, thereby allowing the possibility of a real engine failure to develop.

• An actual case of engine failure could lead to an unnecessary state of anxiety to hasten the aircraft's arrival onto the ground, and this action must be guarded against. To a certain extent this can be covered during simulated engine failure practice at the airfield, but the environment used in this case will not be conducive to the realism experienced when using an ordinary field the length of which will invariably be substantially shorter than a normal airfield. Ensure this aspect is covered adequately during the ground briefing.

FORCED LANDING WITH POWER

This exercise must be covered before the student commences the solo navigation stage. It is an important part of the flight training syllabus and should be related to the various circumstances which may demand its implementation. Such factors as deteriorating weather, low fuel state, and failing daylight will be the main contributing causes.

AIRMANSHIP

The application of good airmanship together with correct decisions taken early will normally preclude the necessity for this type of forced landing to develop, and emphasis must be given to this point. During practice there will be a particular need to select an area where annoyance to persons and livestock will be avoided.

BEFORE THE EXERCISE

The Long Briefing should cover the following:

Objectives.
Occasions necessitating
  In Flight Conditions.

Field Selection.
Landing at a Normal Airfield.
Landing at a Disused Airfield.
Landing on an Ordinary Field.
Circuit and Approach.
Actions After Landing.
Aircraft Security.
Airmanship.
Common Errors.

The short pre-Flight Briefing should be based upon the practical aspects of that part of the Long Briefing in relation to the Air Exercise to be covered. Many of the instructional points made in the forced landing without power are common to this exercise and should be introduced when applicable.

DURING THE EXERCISE
Paint a clear word picture to the student to illustrate the weather conditions being simulated during practice, and ensure that he is competent at assessing the suitability of a selected field before he is sent on solo navigation flights.

COMMON ERRORS
When this procedure is used in actual circumstances, the student will usually be in a state of anxiety. It is most important therefore that he demonstrates his ability to make positive and correct decisions sufficiently early to permit as many of the alternative plans to be possible, e.g. landing at an active airfield, disused airfield or an ordinary field.

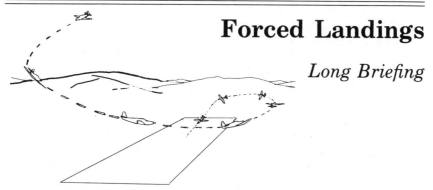

Forced Landings

Long Briefing

FORCED LANDINGS WITHOUT POWER

OBJECTIVES

The purpose of this exercise is to teach you the procedure to adopt in the event of an engine failure occurring during flight at medium to high altitudes. The practising of this emergency procedure must be aimed at developing the required level of competence to handle this type of situation.

INTRODUCTION

Development of competence will only come from frequent practice during training and additional practice at intervals thereafter. When learning the procedures involved following an engine failure, it must be appreciated that in training to handle any emergency situation there are two fundamental aspects:

1. The prevention of an emergency situation.
2. The action to be taken should an emergency situation occur.

Whereas this exercise is primarily concerned with the second of these aspects, you should appreciate that most engine failures occur because of the mismanagement of the aircraft systems by the pilot, e.g. fuel tank mis-selection, mixture control, carburettor heat etc. Mechanical failure is extremely rare.

Accident analysis reveals that some 20% of all engine failure occurrences are caused by fuel starvation, the definition of which is:

● The interruption, reduction or complete termination of fuel supply to the engine, although ample fuel is aboard the aircraft for normal flight operations.

Bearing this fact in mind it can be seen that if consistent care is taken to employ good operating practices, the forced landing without power situation will rarely occur.

For instructional purposes the complete procedure is divided so as to introduce the many items involved in a clear sequential manner. It must therefore be understood that in the introductory stages of this exercise a certain amount of academic principle will be involved, i.e. the aircraft will be placed in the best position and at an ideal height in relation to a pre-chosen landing area. However this is only to simplify the initial task of demonstration and practice.

Later more realistic situations will be created, and many variations of the initial procedure will be practised in order to cover the numerous possibilities following an actual engine failure.

To sum up therefore, the exercise will initially commence following selection and identification of the landing area. During this a review of the aircraft's intended route and the procedure to be followed will be outlined, and only then will the throttle be closed to simulate the emergency situation.

Towards the latter stages of training the throttle will be closed at varying heights and in different flight situations, leaving the student to assess the immediate best course of action in relation to the wind direction, aircraft height, selection of landing area and the most suitable procedure to adopt.

FORCED LANDING PROCEDURES

The following procedures are mainly concerned with the execution of the forced landing without power, but there may be circumstances when partial power is available, and the decision to carry out a forced landing will then depend upon:

The amount of power remaining and whether or not there are indications that a total power loss will follow.
The distance to the nearest airfield.
The type of terrain below the aircraft at the time and the nature of the surface en-route to the nearest airfield.
Whether other factors, e.g. engine fire, are involved.

In such situations the pilot will have to weigh up all the factors before continuing to the nearest airfield using partial power, or

closing the throttle and initiating a forced landing without power, or
carrying out a forced landing using partial power.

Such a decision can only be made at the time, but a cautionary note can be covered here, and that is if partial power is used to assist in the forced landing, the basic procedure once over the selected landing area should follow that used when no power is available.

This is to guard against the possibility of the engine stopping completely at some stage during the descent around the selected landing area. In other words if some power is available, use it when needed, but never rely upon it during the planning of the final descent route.

For training purposes the exercise is divided into two basic types of situation:

1. Engine failure at 2000 feet a.g.l. or above.
2. Engine failure at lower heights.

Introductory practice will commence with an assumed engine failure between 2500 to 3000 feet above ground level and in a position which is within easy reach of the pre-selected landing area. The exact height chosen will depend upon such factors as cloud base or other restrictions which may apply in the particular area e.g. the base of a Special Rules Area, etc.

During the desent phase the route will be one that takes the aircraft towards and around the landing area. This will be achieved by establishing a descending circuit pattern during which a cross-wind, downwind, base leg and final approach will be carried out. The distance out from the landing area will vary with the aircraft height at the time and its position in relation to the touch down area. Two possible variations of this circuit pattern are shown in fig. 17-1.

The dotted lines show alternative routes which can be used if at any stage the aircraft is estimated to be too low in relation to its position in the pattern.

To what extent either path is followed will depend mainly upon the position and height of the aircraft relative to the chosen landing area at the time of the engine failure. Further to this, the strength and direction of the wind may require frequent amendment to the planned descent route.

In the case of engine failure occurring well below 2000 feet a.g.l. the prior practice of forced landings from higher altitudes will stand the student in good stead, as he will be able to appreciate where the aircraft should fit into this previously practised pattern compatible with the aircraft position and the height available.

The student will have had frequent practice at flying rectangular patterns about an airfield, incorporating downwind and base legs, and the use of a similar pattern during a forced landing would be familiar to him. However being able to achieve this type of descent pattern will depend upon the aircraft position relative to the selected landing area, together with the wind velocity and height available at the time of the engine failure.

Initial practice will commence from a position equivalent to the 'dead side' of a left hand circuit. This will give the student a reasonably uninterrupted view of the landing area throughout the procedure, and make it easier to anticipate the effects of the wind in relation to the aircraft headings and the touch-down area.

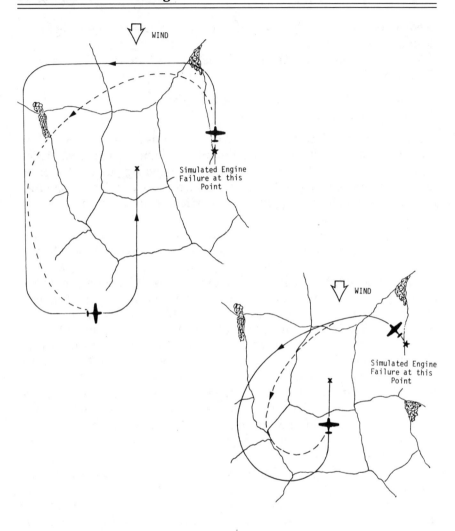

Fig. 17-1

CHOICE OF LANDING AREA

The selection of a landing area must be made as early as possible following the engine failure. This enables a wider choice to be made, compatible with the greater height which will be available. Nevertheless, when choosing a landing area from heights of 2500 to 3000 feet a possibility will always exist that the initial choice will be unsuitable, due to the inability to discern from height such hazards as power cables suspended from small wooden poles, or ditches and stagnant streams with a greenish surface, any of which would cause considerable damage during the landing run (fig. 17-2).

Fig. 17-2

Provision for Change of Plan

Therefore when initially selecting an area to land it is advisable when possible to select a group of fields, choosing one of them which conforms to the requirements and is centrally situated. Having done this, a misjudgement or the discovery that the original choice is unsuitable, will enable a change of plan to be made in reasonable time. Figure 17-3 shows how an alternative choice of landing area can be implemented. The broken lines in the diagram show the alternative routes which can be followed.

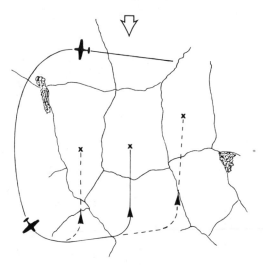

Fig. 17-3

For the student to get the best value from this practice, any re-selection of a landing area should be completed at the latest during the base leg, or the incentive to develop and improve gliding judgement will be reduced.

The Landing Surface
The surface of the landing area should preferably be grass or firm stubble. The presence of young crops indicates the surface will have been recently ploughed, and ripening crops will be long, leading in either case to a 'nose over' situation. The same will apply if the surface is particularly green, as this would indicate swampy ground with a very soft surface. Identification of suitable surface areas will only come from practice and recognition, and this will normally be carried out during earlier flights.

A marked ground slope will pose hazards and difficulties which increase with the degree at which the ground slopes up or down. Down slopes should in particular be avoided as these will normally lead to a greatly increased landing run.

Field size and shape must be considered, and obviously if all other factors are equal the greater the size the better will be chances of success, but shape will also be important, because a squarish field will offer alternative landing paths in the event that the aircraft is too low or too high at the end of the downwind or during the base leg. Figure 17-4 shows the benefits available from a square field and the restrictions of a long narrow field.

The overshoot, and particularly the undershoot area, must be free of obstructions as far as possible. Isolated trees can be negotiated if

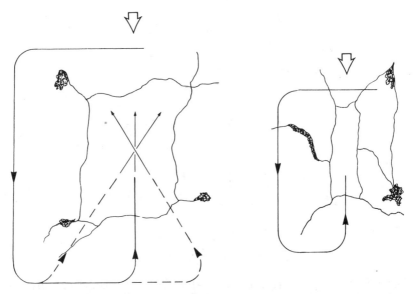

Fig. 17-4

the aircraft is on the low side during the final stage of the approach, but copses or woods can form a hazard which cannot easily be dealt with when little manoeuvring height remains.

GLIDING DISTANCE – CONSIDERATIONS

The choice of landing area must be made so that the aircraft can reach its vicinity at a height which enables the pilot to plan a descent pattern. A minimum of an angled base leg will be required to allow the pilot to re-adjust heading as necessary compatible with his height and the wind velocity, in order to reach the touch-down area.

A base leg permits adjustment for height and position

Fig. 17-5   Fig. 17-6

Gliding distance is a direct function of the aircraft lift/drag ratio. A L/D ratio of 10:1 simply means that the aircraft will travel 10 feet forward for every one foot down (in conditions of zero wind). Zero wind is rare, therefore a further complication will be introduced in that the aircraft may have to travel into wind or downwind to get to the required position.

In the limited time available during this type of emergency, mathematical calculations and judgement of distances are not easily made. However when estimating the distance an aircraft can glide (assuming zero wind) one factor which remains constant is the descent angle. Therefore a radius about the aircraft will be the easiest method to use when judging gliding distance.

Fig. 17-7

THE DESCENT PLAN

If a partial or complete engine failure occurs the actual descent plan will have to be based upon the circumstances prevailing at the time. However, during the introduction of this exercise a simple descent plan will be used commencing from a high key position. When the student is competent at this procedure, variations of aircraft height and position relative to a suitable landing area will be introduced so that the student obtains practice in handling more difficult situations.

The procedure to adopt in general follow the principal steps outlined below:

● Adopt the glide, re-trim and search all around the aircraft for a suitable area within gliding distance. Turn towards this area and estimate the wind direction and strength.

● Select the best field within the chosen area bearing in mind the size, shape, surface, slope and surrounds.

● Choose the key position for the entry point of the descent pattern compatible with the height available. Assess the height of the ground in the immediate area and bear in mind that the altimeter will only give an approximate indication of height above ground regardless of what datum is being used. Choose a key area 1000 feet above the ground which is coincident with the end of the proposed downwind leg. Review any intermediate key areas at 500 feet intervals to aid judgement in arriving at the 1000 feet area.

● Complete the specified checks (for the particular aircraft type) in an attempt to rectify the engine failure. Detailed considerations relating to causes of engine failure are covered later in this briefing.

● When carrying out checks and drills ensure that adequate surveillance of the selected landing area is maintained, together with the aircraft's progress towards the chosen key areas. Maintain or modify the descent route relative to the landing area as required, and if no rectification of the fault which caused the engine failure can be made, transmit a 'Distress Call' using the appropriate RTF frequency.

● Use of Radio. During an actual emergency situation care must be taken not to get involved in a lengthy interchange of information as this will increase the pilot's workload and divert attention from the primary aim of getting the aircraft safely on the ground. Normally when operating at en-route heights of 2500 to 3000 feet there will be little time available to pass more than the aircraft

ADOPT GLIDE – TRIM –
SEARCH – W/V – PLAN DESCENT

FAILURE
CHECKS

CRASH
DRILL

SHORT
MAYDAY
CALL

PRE-LANDING
CHECKS

Fig. 17-8

callsign, position, height and intentions and unless the aircraft is in the immediate vicinity of the airfield at which the ATC facility is based, the air traffic controller will only be able to alert the emergency services nearest to the aircraft position.

When the aircraft is at substantially higher altitudes there may, dependent upon the aircraft's distance from the ATC facility (if based on the airfield) be the opportunity for ATC to assist in 'Homing' the aircraft to the overhead position or into the circuit pattern of the airfield concerned, and by so doing play a signficant role in getting the aircraft down safely.

● The Downwind Leg. During that portion of the descent pattern which most closely approximates the downwind leg the normal pre-landing checks should be carried out. However during a real forced landing procedure these checks should be replaced by the 'Security Drills' which consist of turning OFF the fuel and ignition, and ensuring the harnesses are very tight. During practice these latter drills should not be physically carried out but just said aloud. Where electrically operated flaps are fitted, the master switch must be left ON until the final flap selection has been made. If a combustion heater is being used for cabin heating or windscreen de-misting or de-frosting it is important that this is turned OFF during these drills.

The end of the downwind leg terminates at the key area of 1000 feet a.g.l. This area can be considered as a cube of airspace at which both the estimated height over the ground and the aircraft's position relative to the touch-down point will need to be assessed, together with the wind strength and direction, when considering the exact point to turn onto the base leg.

● The Base Leg. The main value of the base leg lies in the fact that during this part of the descent the pilot can manoeuvre the aircraft into a position for the final approach, and at this stage the aiming point should be halfway into the field. Flap should be used as required during this leg, but it is not recommended to use more than about half. This will then leave some flap available for use to adjust the descent rate during the final approach. Airspeed should be monitored closely during turns, and when lowering flap. The aircraft position can be varied in relation to the selected touch-down point by diverging from the field if the aircraft is too high or converging if the aircraft appears to be too low. Alternatively if the aircraft is significantly low or high at this stage the landing line can be changed and the aircraft turned onto final approach earlier or later than originally planned. If a narrow field has had to be selected and an excess of height occurs on the base leg, then the aircraft's heading can be altered to diverge away from the field until the final turn. If this action is insufficient the aircraft can be flown past the approach centreline followed by a shallow S turn to bring the aircraft back onto the approach path.

In the event that engine failure occurs low down the procedure will have to be modified compatible with the actual height above the ground, and the aircraft position relative to a suitable landing area. Some examples of alternative routes are shown in fig. 17-9.

Fig. 17-9

● The Final Approach. Up to this stage the aim should be to make the touch-down point approximately half way into the selected field. When it becomes obvious that this point could be reached, then maximum flap should be selected to steepen the approach path and bring the touch-down point back to approximately one third to one quarter the distance into the field. If due to misjudgement excess height still remains, then the airspeed may be increased to dive off the surplus height.

When large flap selections are made, the float period resulting from the extra speed is rapidly lost on rounding out.

The use of a sideslip is normally confined to aircraft without flap as sideslipping an aircraft with full flap lowered could in certain circumstances lead to a situation where the rate of descent becomes dangerously high.

It must be appreciated that with large angles of flap selected the downwash effect over the tailplane is such that the effectiveness of both the rudder and elevators could be impaired. This can apply to either high or low wing aircraft to an amount dependent upon the flap design and position relative to the tailplane. This loss of effectiveness is normally insufficient to cause problems in a clean glide, but it can be seen that when a sideslip is used in conjunction with flaps, then the rate of descent can be considerable.

From this it is obvious that when recovering from a sideslip when flaps are lowered an appreciable anticipation must be used and failure to take recovery action early enough would have disastrous results.

● Going Round Again. As soon as the outcome of the practice forced landing can be clearly seen, the aircraft should be climbed away. It is however important not to leave this until the aircraft is very low, and the minimum height to which the aircraft should be allowed to descend is approximately 250 feet a.g.l. Normally it will not be necessary to descend to this height and in any event the 500 feet rule must be adhered to. This states that no aircraft must be flown within 500 feet of any persons, vehicles, livestock or structures. Caution must be used when raising the flaps and this should be carried out compatible with achieving a safe airspeed.

● The Landing. During an actual forced landing consideration must be given to the method of landing on an unprepared surface. Ideally the final approach will have been started so that full flap selection will need to be made at the point where the pilot is sure of landing approximately one third of the distance into the field. This will then ensure that that the minimum stalling speed without power can be achieved at touchdown, thereby reducing the stresses and shocks imposed on the aircraft and occupants if the landing surface is rough.

Due to the short length of landing run which is usually associated with landings made in ordinary fields, there will be a strong tendency for the pilot to place the aircraft onto the ground before the correct touchdown speed is reached. This may be a necessary action when available ground distance is becoming obviously short, but the pilot must resist giving away to unwarranted anxiety in this respect, or the aircraft and occupants may be exposed to the hazard of nosing over. Bearing this point in mind it will nevertheless be advisable to place the aircraft firmly on the ground if an obvious overshoot is imminent, as this action will utilise the deceleration effects of surface friction, leading to a reduced landing run.

The brakes can also be employed earlier, but care should be used to apply them intermittently, increasing the pressure as the aircraft slows down, particularly if landing on a wet surface. In the event that the aircraft will clearly not stop before reaching the far hedge or an obstruction, a controlled ground loop should be initiated. This will obviate the sudden deceleration which occurs on collision with obstacles. This ground looping action will also hold good when the aircraft is running towards a ditch or similar ground feature at a moderately low speed.

If the aircraft is equipped with a retractable landing gear, it will normally be advisable to have it down for landing. This is because in the event of a landing occurring on rough ground, the landing gear will absorb a large amount of the impact forces and reduce the risk to the aircraft occupants. However, if the only available landing area is extremely short it will usually be preferable to leave the landing gear retracted, as a gear up landing will always produce a substantially shorter landing run.

● Actions After Landing.   Immediately the aircraft comes to rest, safety harnesses should be released and the aircraft evacuated. When passengers are on board the pilot in command must give clear orders to this effect, and ensure that safety straps or harnesses are not unfastened until the aircraft has come to a complete stop.

When clear of the aircraft the pilot can take stock of the situation, returning to the aircraft to ensure that everything is switched off correctly, and such items as control locks and the pitot cover are placed in position and any personal effects removed.

The pilot's next concern will be to protect the aircraft as far as possible, and in this connection it should be borne in mind that cattle are very inquisitive by nature and can easily damage an aircraft. Once the aircraft has been secured and the doors locked, the student should find the nearest telephone and inform his CFI of the situation, including details of any damage or personal injury incurred.

NOTE: Even if a student finds out the reason for the engine failure and can correct it he must on no account attempt to take-off again.

CAUSES OF ENGINE FAILURE

Typical items which could be mismanaged by the pilot and therefore rectified during the 'Engine Failure Checks' are:

Fuel, Mixture Control, Carburettor Icing and the Ignition System.

During these checks the throttle should be set to approximately one third open, this will avoid stress being placed on the engine as it suddenly goes from nil to high power if the fault is rectified, or alternatively if the engine failed during the glide the throttle being open during the failure checks will reveal whether the cause of failure has been discovered.

Fuel. When two or more tanks are fitted that can be selected independently, it may only be a matter of selecting another fuel tank to rectify the failure. The correct procedure for changing fuel tanks should be followed, and when an electric pump is fitted, the tank and pump selection should be made in the correct order as recommended in the Flight/Owner's Manual/Pilot's Operating Handbook for the aircraft type.

Regardless of whether the fuel gauge shows fuel available in the original tank, a re-selection should be made, because the fault may be due to a blockage at the tank filter or a damaged fuel line, or water contamination.

In low wing aircraft the mechanical fuel pump is supplemented when required by an electric fuel pump, and if the mechanical pump fails it will only be necessary to switch on the electric pump to rectify a fuel starvation situation.

Finally it should be appreciated that in the event of a fuel supply problem due to a partially disconnected fuel line, or semi blocked filter etc., a reduced power setting can often keep the engine running. Most light aircraft will maintain height at low speed down to approximately 40% power, and in this case the aircraft can be kept safely airborne until an active airfield is reached. Caution must nevertheless be exercised in this type of situation as it is not always possible to determine whether the cause of the problem will worsen. In such a case, this could lead to a complete engine failure when the aircraft is no longer over suitable terrain.

NOTE: In relation to the failure checks, re-selection of fuel tanks should not be done physically during practice situations. This is because the fuel flow from the newly selected tank cannot be checked whilst the aircraft is gliding, and if fuel is not flowing correctly this fact will only be discovered during the climb away, when the aircraft will be too low for failure checks to be instigated and rectification action taken.

Mixture.   If mixture is being used when the engine fails, it should be returned to the Full Rich position. However if the aircraft is at higher altitudes it may simply be that the mixture needs further adjustment to a more Lean position (due to over-richness). In any case either action may be tried if necessary to see whether the cause of failure can be found.

When a manual carburettor priming system is installed, it is possible for incorrect mixture to occur if the priming pump is open when the engine is operating in a particular RPM range; therefore check to ensure the priming pump is secured in the locked position.

Carburettor Icing.   Normally when the engine is under power, early symptoms of carburettor icing will show in the form of power reduction, followed by the engine running roughly. These indications will usually occur well ahead of any situation in which a large build-up of ice creates engine failure. However, if the icing has occurred and the engine actually failed during a glide, or operation at very low power, it can remain unnoticed until the throttle is opened during for example, the transition from the descent to level flight, or for engine clearing purposes.

The source of carburettor heat is the engine, therefore if carburettor heat is selected after engine failure, there may not be sufficient heat available to melt the ice inside the induction system. It is in fact for this very reason that selection of carburettor heat prior to reduced power operation is normally a recommended procedure.

Despite the foregoing comments, carburettor heat should when applicable be selected as a means of rectifying ice in the carburettor, as sufficient heat may still be available. In any event this action will provide an alternative air source if the fault lies with a blocked intake which has been incurred due to airframe icing or other reason.

NOTE: In certain environmental circumstances carburettor icing can occur with extreme rapidity.

Ignition system.   Aircraft are equipped with a dual ignition system so that the engine will continue to run if one part of the system fails. It is nevertheless possible for the pilot to place the ignition key inadvertently to a single magneto position. When tumbler switches are fitted it is possible for one to be moved inadvertently to the 'OFF' position, for example, an ignition switch can be mistakenly turned off instead of an electric fuel pump.

If a situation exists where only one magneto has been selected and it fails, the engine will stop. However, selecting the other magneto or placing both switches in the 'ON' position will immediately rectify the situation and the engine will function again. It is therefore essential to check and ensure that both switches are 'ON' during the search for the cause of an engine failure.

In the event that rough running has been the problem and no cure has been found, the magnetos should be individually selected in turn and if the engine runs smoothly again the flight should be continued on the one serviceable magneto.

Finally at some stage the oil temperature and pressure gauges should be checked to establish whether a mechanical failure has occurred. In the event of loss of oil pressure or lack of oil, the oil temperature will rise rapidly to the red line on the temperature gauge.

AIRMANSHIP

It will be important during the glide descent to open up to the half throttle position at intervals to ensure the engine is continuing to run correctly, to keep the plugs clear of excess carbon deposits, and to maintain a reasonably warm engine. The throttle should be left in the half open position for two or three seconds to be of value, and sudden and full power applications avoided as this will interfere with the smooth maintenance of the descent plan. In order to avoid upsets of judgement during the final stages of the approach the last opening of the throttle should be done at approximately 1000 feet a.g.l. or at the latest during the base leg.

In relation to lookout it must be appreciated that other aircraft may also be involved in forced landing practice within the Local Flying Area, therefore the need to stay constantly aware of the position of other air traffic must be emphasised. This is necessary because of the danger of becoming over-absorbed in the procedure to be followed, and the need to spend frequent intervals looking at the chosen landing area, and assessing the aircraft height and position and whether modifications are necessary to the originally planned route.

This aspect of lookout is particularly important when specified fields are used for forced landing practice, especially in light winds when decisions as to the best final approach direction may vary between different pilots using the same forced landing area.

The minimum height down to which this exercise is practised will depend upon the rules of the training organisation and the local environment. In any event the 500 feet rule must be observed, and it is very important that nuisance is not created to persons or livestock during the latter stages of the exercise.

During practice the selection of a suitable landing area must include an appraisal of the 'climb away' area. If this is covered with woods, buildings etc., then a totally unnecessary hazard will exist in the event of an actual engine failure occurring during the climb away phase. Therefore always ensure the climb out path is over relatively flat open countryside.

FORCED LANDING WITH POWER

OBJECTIVES

The purpose of this exercise is to teach you the procedures to be followed should conditions occur which force you to land at a disused airfield or on an unprepared landing surface (an ordinary field) or an unknown airstrip.

INTRODUCTION

A forced landing when power is available can be considered as any unplanned landing which is forced upon the pilot due to circumstances encountered during flight. These circumstances normally relate to:

- Deteriorating Weather.
- Becoming Lost.
- A Low Fuel State.
- The Impending Onset of Night.

In view of these factors it can be seen that the major airmanship consideration in relation to this exercise is that through the use of good airmanship and sound captaincy the pilot would normally have landed safely at an active airfield before circumstances reached the stage where he is forced to carry out an 'Off Airfield' landing.

When practising this exercise, the basic procedure used will apply to most landings made away from an active airfield, however variations will be dictated by the specific weather conditions at the time, e.g. cloud base, visibility, wind strength, and the type of terrain. One point to note is that the method of performing an approach and landing into a small field will also be applicable to the method used for landing at small airstrips. Therefore this part of the exercise will serve two purposes.

OCCASIONS NECESSITATING

The circumstances leading to a forced landing with power can be many and varied, but they usually arise from becoming lost, weather deterioration, running short of fuel or daylight. The difficulties encountered are normally of a compound nature, e.g. if the weather deteriorates, the likelihood of becoming lost is increased, and when navigation difficulties occur they can often result in unplanned additional airborne time leading to a shortage of fuel or the onset of darkness.

The important message emerging from these factors concerns the need to develop a state of awareness and the ability to take positive decisions before the situation changes from one of 'Urgency' to one of 'Emergency'. In this respect and when radio is available, contact should normally have been established with an ATC facility and assistance obtained at an early stage. The procedure for this will be covered during the Long Briefing on Pilot Navigation. In view of the foregoing it can be seen that when bad weather has led to the situation where a forced landing with power is necessary, many of the considerations are complementary to the lesson learned during Operation at Minimum Level.

In Flight Conditions.

The type of weather existing at the time will play a large part in deciding the exact procedure to use, for example if the cloud base is relatively high, but visibility is poor, the need to fly a low circuit will not exist, but if the cloud base is low a lower than normal circuit will probably have to be used. If visibility is very poor it will be advisable to select some identification checkpoints at the time the inspection runs are being made to check the surface suitability and the approach and overshoot areas. This action will then assist the pilot to orientate himself on any subsequent circuits which are necessary.

Field Selection.

Ideally the first choice of a landing area would be an active airfield, or when circumstances preclude this, a disused airfield may offer a suitable alternative. Failing the availability of an airfield or airstrip, a landing will have to be made on an ordinary field.

LANDING AT A NORMAL AIRFIELD

Fly at a safe height overhead the airfield and if it is identified and the RTF frequency is known, landing instructions can be obtained in the normal way. When an active airfield is found which cannot be identified, such RTF information will be lacking. Extreme caution must therefore be exercised, and the landing direction or runway in use must be determined visually either by inspection of the signals

area, or by movements of other aircraft using the airfield.
If it is a large airfield with long runways, it
could be a military airfield or a civil airport,
and in either case additional care must be
used, as movements may be in the form of
large and fast jet aircraft. In these circumstances, and depending upon the degree of
urgency e.g. fuel state, rate of weather deterioration or daylight time left, it may be more
advisable to fly away from the area as quickly
as possible, rather than attempt a landing
unannounced in an air traffic environment of
large passenger carrying or military jet
aircraft.

Whether the decision is to fly clear of the area or to land it will be
advisable to switch 'ON' all the aircraft external lighting such as
navigation, strobe and landing lights in order that the aircraft can be
more easily seen by other air traffic.

In the event that the fuel state, remaining daylight or weather
conditions preclude any other action but to land, the pilot should
signify his intention to do so by flying parallel to the active runway in
the correct landing direction at approximately 500 feet above airfield
elevation. Whilst doing this the navigation lights should be switched
'ON' and 'OFF' at short irregular intervals. The ATC facility will
normally flash standard light signals, and these should be obeyed as
far as possible compatible with the state of emergency.

LANDING AT A DISUSED AIRFIELD
At many geographic locations disused airfields are plentiful, but
these can present many unsuspected hazards. For example, at height
the surface of the runways may appear to be serviceable and in good
condition, whereas in actual fact large cracks and surface debris may
abound. Wire fences are also commonly found across and along the
runways of disused airfields and these are often difficult to detect
until a fly-past inspection has been made.

Provided fuel and weather conditions permit, at least one inspection run and preferably more should be made from a relatively low
height. The actual procedure used for this purpose is covered under
the next heading.

LANDING ON AN ORDINARY FIELD
When the previous alternatives are not available a suitable field
must be selected, and in assessing its suitability several factors must
be taken into account. However, the time available, e.g. fuel state,
onset of darkness, and weather conditions will determine the scope of

the search, and the choice may be restricted due to lack of time. The factors to bear in mind during the field selection are:

1. The length of the landing run available in relation to the wind direction and strength.
2. The nature of the ground surface and whether a pronounced slope is present.
3. The presence of obstructions in the vicinity of the undershoot and overshoot areas, keeping in mind that it may be necessary to go round again should the first approach to land be unsuccessful.

Having established that these criteria are satisfactory, standard 'airfield joining checks' should be carried out, with the altimeter set to the last known QNH. During these checks the aircraft should be manoeuvred to a position which is into wind and slightly to one side of the selected landing path. The first inspection run should be done at 5/600 feet a.g.l. and a low safe cruising speed maintained. The height will have to be assessed visually for this purpose.

CIRCUIT AND APPROACH PROCEDURE

During the first inspection run the magnetic heading of the selected landing path should be noted together with any drift and a reciprocal heading worked out for use on the downwind leg. The approach path must be assessed for suitability, and the position of any obstructions in relation to the descent path noted.

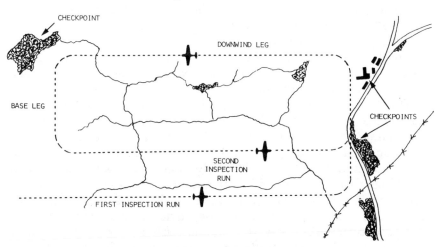

Fig. 17-10

By flying along one side of the intended landing path the surface will be more easily inspected for hidden ditches, light wire fences, rocks and other surface irregularities. The general appearance should be assessed in relation to whether it is relatively flat or sloping. If the inspection so far indicates the field is suitable the overshoot area should be checked for any obstructions, e.g. trees, power cables etc., which may be a hazard should the first approach have to be converted into a 'go round again' situation.

Once the pilot is satisfied so far with his selection, the aircraft can be put into a circuit around the field and the normal considerations of a bad weather circuit will usually apply. However small fields are easily lost to view, and therefore careful attention should be given to the headings and time on each leg. When the visibility is poor, it will be of assistance to note the most easily identifiable ground features at or in the vicinity of the selected turning points around the circuit. The pre-landing checks should be completed as a matter of course for each circuit which is made around the field.

Provided conditions permit, a second inspection run should be made, but this time an approach down to approximately 100 feet a.g.l. should be flown, to coincide with the centre line of the selected landing path. It is advisable not to use more than half flap for this approach, which will permit a better rate of climb and improved obstacle clearance during the climb back up to the required height for the final circuit.

The second inspection run will give the pilot a final opportunity to re-assess all the points he was looking for during the first inspection and a more accurate assessment of the landing surface can be made. Provided the results of this run establish the field to be satisfactory, the final circuit and approach can be commenced.

The previous inspection runs will enable the pilot to judge his approach line and rate of descent more easily, so as to bring the aircraft to a point where it touches down about one quarter to one third of the way into the field.

Whilst assessing the airspeed and amount of flap to use for the final stages of this approach it should be borne in mind that the length of the landing run is affected by threshold speed and the strength and direction of the wind. In general terms this means that when the wind is light and the field is relatively small a low speed and full flap should be used during the final stages of the approach. If the wind is strong a higher airspeed will be required for better control and the use of full flap may not always be advisable due to the risk of increased turbulence near the ground with possible sudden down draughts. Strong winds will however mean lower ground speeds, and consequently the length of the landing run will be shortened accordingly.

The final stages of the approach and landing procedure should be the same as for the Short or Soft Field Landing, depending upon the nature of the ground surface.

ACTIONS AFTER LANDING

Wait until the aircraft has come to rest before releasing the seat harness. After this the normal shutting down and after flight checks should be carried out and the aircraft inspected for damage. Due to the possible hazards which may exist or be partially hidden by long grass, e.g. identations, drainage strips etc., it is not advisable to taxy the aircraft after the landing is completed. In the event that the aircraft has to be moved to a safer position, e.g. shelter from the wind etc., a thorough inspection of the ground surface should be made on foot, and only after ensuring that the ground is suitable for taxying should the aircraft be restarted and moved to the required position.

Once the aircraft is secured and protected as far as possible from damage by persons or animals, a message must be sent to the training organisation to inform them of the situation. Finally under no circumstances should a student attempt to take-off again, even though the aircraft may be undamaged and the weather conditions improved.

AIRMANSHIP

As in the case of Operation At Minimum Level the initial emphasis in relation to airmanship is the development of a sufficient sense of awareness to weather conditions, fuel state etc. so that the situation of a forced landing with power would never become more than a landing at an alternative airfield. This will only be achieved by correct decisions made early, rather than delaying the issue until the situation occurs where the aircraft has to be landed in whatever suitable field can be found.

During practice the emphasis on airmanship will lie in the need to choose a suitable field which not only meets the requirements of the exercise, but also one which will permit the practice to take place without infringing the 500 feet rule or causing annoyance to persons or livestock.

Due regard must be given to the maintenance of safety throughout the procedure, and adequate speed for the inspection runs and approaches must be maintained. This is particularly important when moderate or strong winds, gustiness and downdraughts are present.

During an actual situation:

Provided fuel state and weather conditions permit it will be essential to 'go round again' from the final approach to landing if the aircraft is not in the right position at the correct height and airspeed after the boundary of the field has been crossed.

If the opportunity permits, remember to turn 'OFF' the master switch before landing. This will reduce the possibility of a fire hazard should the aircraft be damaged during landing.

PRE-FLIGHT BRIEFING
THE FORCED LANDING WITHOUT POWER

Aim To teach you how to carry out a safe descent, approach and landing in the event of the engine failing during flight.

What The procedures and methods used to bring the aircraft and occupants safely down on the ground when an emergency involving power loss occurs.

Airmanship All normal airmanship considerations will apply but in addition, extra emphasis must be placed upon safe operating procedures and the need to avoid annoyance to persons and livestock during the practice of this exercise.

How *Preparation.*
From approximately 2500 feet a.g.l. select a suitable landing area and specify a particular field. Determine the best descent route and ensure it will remain clear of other aircraft.

Use carburettor heat as applicable and close the throttle to simulate the engine failure.

Descent Plan to the 1000 feet Area.

Adopt the glide, trim and proceed to the 'High Key' area.

Adjust the route according to the aircraft height and position relative to the selected touch-down area.

Anticipate the wind effect in relation to the selected route.

Open the throttle to the halfway position for a few seconds.

Complete the 'Engine Failure Checks', Mayday call as applicable and the Pre-Landing Checks/Security Drills. Re-select the landing area if necessary and maintain a lookout for other aircraft.

Base Leg.
When in the vicinity of the 1000 feet area commence the base leg. Vary the approach route as necessary.

Select initial flap if height and position permit. Final use of throttle to clear the engine.

Final Approach
Maintain a safe airspeed and avoid steep turns.

When sure of getting well into the field, use additional flap as required. MAINTAIN A SAFE AIRSPEED.

During an actual forced landing turn the master switch 'OFF'.

Climb away at a safe height and avoid infringing the 500 feet rule.

Obtain a safe airspeed before raising the flaps.

Student Practice.

From Lower Altitudes.
Establish a suitable landing area and ensure the surrounding airspace is free from other air traffic. Simulate engine failure and complete the immediate actions.

Monitor the height and position from the selected touch-down area.

Anticipate the wind effect on the descent route.

Use the throttle to clear the engine and complete the Pre-Landing Checks/Security Drills.

Adjust the base leg as required and adopt a curving path if necessary onto the final approach.

Select the initial and final flap settings at the appropriate times.

Climb away at a safe height and obtain a safe airspeed before raising the flaps.

Student Practice.

PRE-FLIGHT BRIEFING

THE FORCED LANDING WITH POWER

Aim
To teach you how to carry out an unplanned landing away from an active airfield.

What
The procedure used to land the aircraft when away from an airfield should an emergency occur involving severe weather deterioration, becoming lost, or running short of fuel or daylight.

Airmanship
All normal airmanship considerations will apply, but in addition emphasis must be placed upon safe operating procedures and the need to avoid annoyance to persons and livestock during the practice of this exercise.

How

In Flight Conditions.
Assess the time available:

Note fuel state, hours of daylight and rate of weather deterioration.

Note the wind direction and search for a suitable landing area.

Selection Factors:

Field length, surface condition, surface gradient and obstructions on the approach and overshoot areas.

Note the magnetic heading of the most suitable landing run.

During practice ensure no persons or livestock are in the immediate vicinity.

Student Practice.

Inspection Procedure.
First Inspection Run:

Position the aircraft to the right and parallel with the landing path at 500 feet a.g.l. Maintain a low safe cruising speed and check:

The approach path for obstructions.
The surface for suitability.
The approach/overshoot areas for obstructions and noting any drift.

If satisfactory, commence a circuit noting any clearly identifiable ground features, and complete the Pre-Landing Checks.

Subsequent Inspection Run:
Set up a simulated approach down to 100 feet a.g.l. using no more than half flap and maintaining a safe airspeed.

Re-assess the approach path, landing surface and overshoot areas. If satisfactory complete a further circuit.

Student Practice.

Approach and Landing.
Maintain a safe speed and if conditions permit lower full flap.

Aim to touch down one quarter to one third of the distance into the field.

During practice initiate the 'Go Round Again' procedure at a safe height.

Remember the 500 feet rule and the need to avoid annoyance to persons and livestock during practice.

When the practice is carried out at the airfield a Short or Soft Field landing should be made to conclude the exercise, according to the simulated conditions.

Student Practice.

Forced Landings

Flight Demonstrations

INTRODUCTION

The contents of this exercise can be conveniently divided into the following specific demonstration groups:

1. The Forced Landing Without Power from altitudes in excess of 2000 feet a.g.l. with the descent procedure being commenced in close proximity to the selected landing area.
2. The Forced Landing Without Power commenced below 2000 feet a.g.l. in the vicinity of the selected landing area.
3. The Forced Landing With Power conducted at a disused airfield or ordinary field.

The suitability of landing areas should preferably have been covered on previous flights.

Demonstration 1 is essentially an introductory exercise requiring practice at intervals until you are competent enough to be introduced to demonstration 2. During the early stages of practice, the checks and drills may be performend by your instructor.

The contents of demonstration 3 should be preceded by the instructor specifying the simulated weather conditions and type of situation which will prevail during the practice.

Airmanship items which are specifically related to this exercise will be introduced and developed at the appropriate time during each demonstration.

DEMONSTRATION 1.   THE FORCED LANDING WITHOUT POWER FROM ALTITUDES ABOVE 2000 FEET A.G.L.

Flight Lesson	*Demonstration Sequence*
The planning and implementation of an emergency procedure after engine failure	
From approximately 2500 feet a.g.l.	Select a suitable landing area and outline the Descent Plan to be used. Lookout for other air traffic (particularly below). Position the aircraft in the vicinity of the 'High Key' position (use carburettor heat as applicable) and close the throttle to simulate engine failure.
	Immediate Actions: Adopt the gliding attitude, trim, head for the high key position and initiate the descent plan.
	Subsequent Actions:
	Assess the approximate height above ground and select a specific field (if not previously chosen). From the high key position onwards, continually review the aircraft height and position relative to the selected touch-down area. Commence the 'Engine Failure Checks' whilst monitoring the aircraft height and position relative to the field. At intervals open the throttle to the halfway position for a few seconds to keep the engine warm and prevent the plugs from fouling. Anticipate the effect of wind on the aircraft flight path and revise the descent route as necessary. Maintain a good lookout for other aircraft. In the event of an actual engine failure which has not been rectified at this stage, transmit a 'Mayday' call on the frequency in use. Continue towards the 1000 feet key area and during practice situations complete the pre-landing checks.

Following this the 'Security Checks' should be initiated but confined to 'Touch Drills' during practice.

The base leg

The base leg should be commenced in the 1000 feet area. If the assessed height a.g.l. indicates the aircraft to be low at this stage, consider using a re-aligned approach path to shorten the length of the base leg, and thereby bring the aircraft into the 500 feet key position as the final turn is commenced.

If the assessed height a.g.l. indicates the aircraft to be high at this stage, consider slightly delaying the turn onto the base leg. If significantly high at this stage consider using a re-aligned approach path to increase the length of the base leg, and thereby bringing the aircraft into the 500 feet key position as the final turn is commenced.

When possible the first stage of flap selection should be made on the base leg and the aircraft re-trimmed.

NOTE. If at this stage or earlier during the descent it becomes clear that the choice of field is obviously unsuitable or serious misjudgement in positioning the aircraft has occurred, it may be a wiser course to select an alternative field.

Maintain a continuous review of the aircraft height and position relative to the selected touch-down area, which should up to this stage be one third to halfway into the field.

From this stage onwards the judgement of height and position relative to reaching the touch-down area successfully will become progressively easier.

If at this point it is felt that the aircraft is too high, a slight divergence of heading away from the field should be made, and if too low a change of heading should be made to converge towards the field.

To avoid any upset in judgement and unnecessary interference with attitude and speed control, the final use of throttle to warm the engine should be made before the end of the base leg. The aircraft should be in a position to turn onto the final approach at 5/600 feet a.g.l.

The Final Approach

Once it is judged that the aircraft will definitely reach the selected touch-down area, full flap can be selected to increase the descent rate and bring the actual touch down area within one quarter to one third of the distance into the field. If any possibility of an undershoot situation exists, further flap should not be used.

Note: During the turn onto final approach, and while lowering flap extreme care must be exercised to maintain a safe airspeed.

Aircraft with Electrically Operated Flaps:

When the final flap selection is completed the Master Switch should be turned to the 'OFF' position.

Note: During the practice of this exercise a climb away must be initiated at a safe height compatible with surface obstructions in line with the climb-out path and the degree of turbulence being experienced. This height must not conflict with the 500 feet rule, e.g. an aircraft must not fly closer than 500 feet to any person, vehicle, structure or livestock.

Student practice: The student should now practise this procedure from a suitable 'high key' position until he is competent at quickly forming a descent plan, carrying out all the procedures, including checks and drills, and adjusting the aircraft flight path to demonstrate his ability to arrive safely in the vicinity of the touch-down area. During this practice it will often be convenient to climb up to the 1000 feet key area and just practise the base leg and final approach section. This will permit more intensive practice of the important final stages.

DEMONSTRATION 2.   THE FORCED LANDING WITHOUT POWER FROM ALTITUDES BELOW 2000 FEET A.G.L.

Flight Lesson	*Demonstration Sequence*
The implementation of an emergency descent plan following engine failure	
From varying altitudes below 2000 feet a.g.l.	Establish a suitable landing area and review possible routes which could be used. Position the aircraft as required rela-

tive to a selected landing area, (use carburettor heat as applicable) and close the throttle.

Immediate Actions:

Adopt the gliding attitude, trim and head for the 1000 feet key area.

Subsequent Actions:

Commence the descent plan, adjusting the route as necessary compatible with:

The aircraft position relative to the selected touch-down area.
The height available.
The wind velocity.

Complete as many Failure Checks and Security Drills as possible before reaching the 'Break-Off Height'.

Note: Due to the reduced time available when simulated engine failure is practised from lower heights, it will be necessary to pay particular attention to the suitability of the 'climb away' area following the practice. Any obstructions in this area must be noted early as they will often affect the height at which the descent must be terminated.

Student practice: Initially the student should establish a suitable landing area and together with the instructor review the possible descent routes before the throttle is closed. Towards the end of this practice a more realistic situation must be introduced, in which the throttle is closed without warning and from which the results of the foregoing practice can be assessed.

DEMONSTRATION 3.   THE FORCED LANDING WITH POWER

Flight Lesson	Demonstration Sequence
The procedures involved during an unplanned landing away from an active airfield	
From level flight at a height dictated by the circumstances.	The simulated conditions leading to this operation will be described by the instructor.

Assuming an active airfield is not available for reasons of being lost in conditions of deteriorating weather or running short of fuel or daylight.
The decision is made to land in the first suitable area.
The procedure will be the same whether a disused airfield or an ordinary field is chosen.
If applicable, take up a suitable heading to remain clear of:

> Deteriorating weather,
> Controlled airspace,
> Mountainous areas, and obstructions.

A downwind heading will permit more ground to be covered while searching for a suitable landing area.

Note: In poor visibility it is sometimes advisable to lower a small amount of flap to improve forward view and facilitate ground scan.

If fuel state is low or poor visibility exists use a low cruise power setting.
Note time available, e.g. weather conditions, fuel state, hours of daylight remaining.
Search for a suitable landing area.
Factors which determine the suitability of a landing area are:

> Length of landing run available in relation to wind velocity.
> Nature of the ground surface including gradient.
> The presence of obstructions on the undershoot and overshoot areas.

When an initial selection has been made, note the magnetic heading of the most suitable landing path and set up the required inspection procedure.
First Inspection Run:

> Position the aircraft to the right of and parallel with the intended approach path. Descend (as required) to approximately 500 feet a.g.l. This height will have to be assessed visually.

Note:
> Obstructions in the approach area.
> Condition of landing surface and whether surface obstructions exist e.g. fences, ditches etc.
> Obstructions or rising ground in the overshoot area.
> The degree of drift being experienced.

Initiate a climb to the intended circuit height or remain at 500 feet if cloud conditions dictate. Commence a circuit of the landing area, paying particular attention to the headings flown and noting any clearly identifiable ground features.

Perform pre-landing checks during this stage. If fuel state and weather conditions permit commence a further inspection run.

Second Inspection Run:

Carry out a simulated approach to 100 feet a.g.l. using no more than half flap, and maintaining a low safe cruising speed. Inspection items will include all those applicable during the first inspection run.

If satisfied with the suitability of the field, climb back to the required circuit height and commence a second circuit. Complete the pre-landing checks and set up an approach for landing. If conditions permit use full flap during the approach and aim to touch-down one quarter to one third of the way into the field.

When practice is conducted away from an active airfield initiate the 'Go Round Again' procedure at a safe height.

Note:

The type of landing e.g. Soft Field, Short Field or Normal will depend on the available landing distance and nature of the ground surface. The practice of this final stage of the procedure will be conducted at the base airfield.

Student practice: The student should now complete at least one full practice using the field selected for the initial demonstration, following which the situation can be re-set in a different location. During this further practice the student will have to select his own landing area and complete the full procedure to 'Break-Off' height. This exercise must be practised until the student has reached the necessary level of competence to safely implement the procedure should its use become an operational necessity.

Pilot Navigation

Instructor's Guide

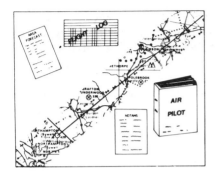

The operation of an aircraft in accordance with the privileges given to the holder of a Private Pilot Licence will require the ability to navigate the aircraft safely and remain aware of the problems associated with the division of the airspace system. The special rules which apply to controlled airspace, and the general Air Traffic Rules which apply at all times, will have to be observed during flight and must be included in the considerations of pre-flight planning.

Navigation is a cockpit activity demanding extra mental and physical work from the pilot in addition to all the other normal functions to be fulfilled during flight. With this in mind, the methods used to achieve pilot navigation must be capable of being carried out by the student without prejudice to his normal operation of the aircraft.

Any method of pilot navigation, as distinct from map reading, will inevitably involve calculations, but if the instructor is to be successful and teach the student to navigate rather than 'track crawl' the methods used and the calculations involved will need to be sufficiently simple for the student to be able to use them successfully during flight, thereby developing trust and confidence in his own ability.

An essential requirement to a successful navigation flight will be thorough pre-flight planning, achieved in such a way that the pilot's workload during flight can be organised in a methodical manner. In this way the flight can be conducted more efficiently in relation to handling the aircraft and maintaining an adequate lookout.

AIRMANSHIP
Although the term 'Airmanship Begins on the Ground' is applicable to any flight, it has a particular emphasis in relation to navigation flights. When a trip is well planned with due consideration to the aspects of weather information, care in calculations and the observance of good operating practices, its outcome will normally be successful. However inattention to standard planning procedures increases the workload in flight and commonly leads to situations where the pilot becomes lost.

Cockpit activity which is methodical and pre-planned will permit the pilot to maintain an adequate lookout for other air traffic as well as identify check-points and make brief essential log entries.

BEFORE THE EXERCISE
The student must have demonstrated his competence in relation to the following items before he is authorised to conduct solo navigation flights:

Flight Planning
Objectives.
Weather Forecast and Actual(s).
Map Selection and Preparation.
Choice of Route:
Controlled Airspace.
Danger, Prohibited and Restricted Areas.
Safety Altitude.

Calculations:
Magnetic Heading(s) and Time(s) En-Route.
Fuel Consumption.
Weight and Balance.
Weight and Performance.

Flight Information:
Notams etc.
Noting of Required Radio Frequencies.
Selection of Alternate Airfields.
RTF PAN Procedure.

Aircraft Documentation.
Notification of the Flight.
Booking-Out Procedure.
Flight Plans – Form CA 48.

Airfield Departure
Organisation of Cockpit Workload.
Departure Procedures:
Altimeter Settings.
Setting Heading Procedures.
Noting of ETA(s).

En-Route
Maintenance of Altitudes and Headings.
Revisions to ETA and Heading.
Log Keeping.

Use of Radio (including VDF if applicable).
Minimum Weather Conditions for Continuance of Flight.
'In Flight' Decisions.
Procedures for Flight within Regulated Airspace.
Navigation at Minimum Level.
Uncertainty of Position Procedure.
Lost Procedure.

Arrival Procedures
Airfield Joining Procedures.
  Altimeter Setting, ATC Liaison etc.
  Entering the Traffic Pattern.
  Circuit Procedures.
Parking Procedures.
Security of Aircraft.
Refuelling.
Booking In.

The pre-flight planning and associated briefing should cover those items of the Long Briefing which are applicable to the stage of navigation training and the particular route to be followed.

The AOPA Private Pilot Syllabus recommends the following order of dual navigation training flights:

No. 1 Dual Map Reading Triangular Cross Country (to include flight planning, departure, en-route and arrival procedures).

No. 2 Dual Pilot Navigation (to include procedure for penetration of regulated airspace, uncertainty of position procedure, an unscheduled diversion and away landing.

No. 3 Dual Pilot Navigation (to include Operation at Minimum Level and implementation of 'Lost Procedure').

This sequence permits a good introduction to be made, coupled with sufficient time and opportunity to develop the necessary experience for the student to carry out a diversion and land at an away airfield should the need arise during his initial solo cross country.

The sequence actually used by the particular training organisation may, of necessity, vary from this ideal due to local constraints or operating practices. Nevertheless, the pre-flight planning and associated briefing should cover those essential items of the Long Briefing which are applicable to the particular cross country to be flown. It will also be sensible training practice to ensure whenever possible that the student is given an adequate dual period of map reading outside the Local Flying Area before commencing a planned navigation flight.

In relation to pre-flight planning, the instructor must ensure that the student understands how to apply his knowledge of the technical subjects in a practical manner. He must also establish that the student is capable of obtaining the relevant information, completing the flight log, and making correct decisions on whether or not it is safe to undertake the flight.

Checkpoints selected for use en-route must be as distinctive and unique as possible, bearing in mind the terrain to be overflown. The number of checkpoints to be used should be limited, otherwise the trip could easily turn into a map reading exercise, instead of one designed to develop navigation ability.

Impress upon the student the importance of relating time to the distance flown, as many students become confused and search for checkpoints which could not possibly have been reached in the elapsed time. Furthermore the maintenance of heights and headings will become progressively more inaccurate if time is spent checking a large number of ground features.

A systematic approach to carrying out en-route position and time checks, is to associate time with quarter, half or three quarter distance points. This enables the pilot to more easily ensure that he is not only at the right place at the right time, but also that he is maintaining the correct heading in relation to the use of the heading indicator and the magnetic compass.

DEPARTURE PROCEDURE
Due to the constraints of controlled airspace at some training airfields it may not be possible to introduce setting heading overhead the airfield. If this is the case, and bearing in mind that the overhead procedure is rarely used after the training stage, little benefit will be obtained by introducing it later.

LOG KEEPING
One easy way to become lost is to attempt pilot navigation with a badly written or illegible flight log. Although neat entries are often difficult to make in flight without diverting significant time from accurate flying or lookout, all entries must be clearly readable as they will often form the basis of rectifying an 'uncertainty of position' or 'lost situation'.

DIVERSION PROCEDURE
This is an important part of a student's training and it must be practised during flight. Merely covering the procedure by ground briefing is inadequate. Remember there is no substitute for the practical application of the lessons learned on the ground.

NAVIGATION AT MINIMUM LEVEL

Whenever possible a short length of one dual cross-country flight should be used to consolidate the procedures and knowledge gained during Operation at Minimum Level. Care must be used to avoid implanting in the student's mind that flying below the selected safety altitude is automatically an acceptable procedure if the weather deteriorates and the cloud base lowers.

UNCERTAINTY OF POSITION AND LOST PROCEDURE

In addition to practising diversion procedure, it is the responsibility of an instructor to simulate situations of being uncertain of position and of being lost, before the student is sent on solo navigation flights. The benefits gained by the small expenditure of flight time in practising these procedures in flight will be more valuable than several hours of talking about them on the ground.

ARRIVAL PROCEDURES

Stress the importance of an RTF call to the destination airfield made early enough to enable the student to visualise and orientate himself correctly, prior to arriving in the circuit area. Ensure that the airfield approach checks are methodically carried out, and that the student prepares himself and the aircraft for the particular circuit joining procedure to be used.

COMMON ERRORS

Anxiety will quickly set in if the student is unable to pinpoint himself at any stage en-route. Stress the importance of time checks and point out that it is quite common during pilot navigation to be temporarily unable to fix the aircraft's exact position over the ground.

• When the situation of being uncertain of position looks as though the lost procedure should be implemented and there is the possibility of the aircraft getting close to controlled airspace, the student must not hesitate to obtain early radio assistance when this aid is available. One of the most common errors in this situation is to delay asking for assistance until a perfectly safe situation has developed into one which is rapidly becoming hazardous, e.g. inadvertent penetration of controlled airspace, running short of fuel or daylight or flying into worsening weather conditions. It is in just these circumstances that the full benefits of the Air Traffic Services can be achieved, but ATC cannot do their job unless the pilot does his. The axiom 'Communicate, Confess and Comply' is one which demonstrates good airmanship and not shame.

• When arriving at a strange airfield many students have initial difficulty in orientating themselves. Ensure students give themselves sufficient time to assess the runway and landing direction visually prior to entering the traffic pattern, and point out that it may sometimes be advisable to orbit clear of the airfield or overhead at a safe height until they are quite sure of carrying out the circuit entry correctly.

• Failure to re-set the altimeter to airfield QFE is also a common error, and this could lead to a substantially incorrect circuit height at an unfamiliar airfield, particularly one which is well above mean sea level.

Pilot Navigation

Long Briefing

OBJECTIVES

The purpose of this exercise is to teach the student to navigate the aircraft safely under Visual Meteorological Conditions without infringing the rules governing Controlled Airspace. This will involve adding further knowledge and skills to those already acquired.

INTRODUCTION

Prior to any flight the pilot will be required to undertake certain pre-flight actions. When a navigation flight is planned, the depth and amount of these actions will be increased, all of which must be carried out in a detailed and meticulous fashion if the pilot is to fulfil his responsibilities and prepare himself adequately for all normal and abnormal situations which may be encountered en-route.

During the preparation for any cross-country flight the pilot will need to satisfy himself that:

1. The flight can safely be made taking into account the latest information available as to the route(s) to be flown, the airfields to be used and the weather conditions likely to be met during flight.

   He must also prepare for alternative courses of action should the aircraft become unserviceable, or the weather deteriorate during flight or whilst on the ground at an away airfield, and also for any unplanned landings which aircraft unserviceability or worsening weather dictate. The selection of one or more alternate airfields will therefore be necessary during the pre-flight preparation.

2. The equipment required either by regulation or the dictates of common sense and good operating practice is carried and is fit for use during the flight.

3. The aircraft is in every way fit for the intended flight, and the Certificate of Airworthiness, Maintenance Certificate etc., are in force at the time.

4. The aircraft is being operated within the maximum all-up weight permitted and the c.g. is within the required range.

5. Sufficient fuel and oil is carried for the flight, with a safe margin allowed for contingencies, e.g. diversions, becoming lost etc.
6. The departure, destination and selected alternate airfields are suitable and of such size that a take-off and landing can safely be made.

With these facts established a suitable check list of pre-flight actions can be evolved, and each is discussed in this Long Briefing.

The working plan for any pilot navigation flight will be the 'Flight Log Sheet' and this should contain all the essential information which will be needed en-route. It must include details of the route(s), compass headings, altitudes (including safety altitudes), and air-speeds to be flown, times en-route, ETA's, fuel calculations, required radio frequencies, airfield information, pressure settings etc. A typical Flight Log Sheet is shown at fig. 18-1.

Fig. 18-1

In order that navigation can be accomplished by a pilot flying solo, who already has many other tasks to perform while handling the aircraft and exercising airmanship, the procedure must be reduced to a simple and completely workable one, excluding the need for intricate calculations. A private pilot will be required to navigate his aircraft with only limited aids, yet it must be possible for him to conduct his pilot navigation safely. Therefore the most important aspects will lie in his preparation before flight, an understanding of the basic principles involved, the ability to map read and apply simple 'dead reckoning' techniques.

Those items which concern pilot navigation are covered thoroughly in the Technical Subjects Section of the Ground Training Syllabus, it is therefore only intended to review the practical aspects of this knowledge in the following paragraphs.

FLIGHT PLANNING

THE WEATHER FORECAST AND ACTUAL WEATHER REPORTS

The pilot must obtain current weather information which covers the

---

METEOROLOGICAL OFFICE - AREA FORECAST

date 3rd August 1984

Area forecast for 30NM Radius of Luton Airport

METFORM 2324A
(Revised 3/79)
(All heights in feet above MSL)

Period (date/times) 3 Aug 1984   Valid 0600 to 1200   Time standard GMT

Special features of the meteorological situation

A SLOW MOVING DEPRESSION OVER SOUTHERN IRELAND CONTINUES TO
MAINTAIN AN UNSTABLE SOUTHWEST AIRSTREAM OVER THE AREA.

Winds (degrees true and knots)   Temperatures (C)
Surface   210 to bec 15

10,000Ft.   230 25 Zero

5,000Ft   230 20 PS 08

2,000Ft   220 25 PS 12

Cloud CLOUD BKN STSC BASE 800 FT LYRD TO 8000 FT (HIGH GROUND COVERED) LIFTING &
       BREAKING TO SCT CU BASE 2500 FT TOP 8000 FT LATER LOC ISOL CU CB BASE 1500 FT
       TO 24000 FT IN SHOWERS. SCT OCNL BKN AC LYR BASE 10000 FT TOP 14000 FT.

Surface visibility
       ABOVE 15 KM BEC 8KM IN SHR WITH PROB OF 4000M IN HVY SHWR LATER LOC
       BELOW 300M IN HILL FOG.

Weather SCT LIGHT SHWR PERHAPS LATER BEC MOD OR HVY. LOCAL HILL FOG PATCHES
        UNTIL 0800Z.

Height of OC isotherm 10000 FT.

Airframe icing
        MOD BUT LOC SEV IN CB

Barometric changes SMALL

Remarks Warnings Turbulence

        LOC SEV TURB VICINITY OF CU CB

Further outlook to

        UNTIL 031800Z SIMILAR WITH PROB OF ISOL THUNDERSTORMS

FOR FORECASTER ....

Fig. 18-2

period of the flight. In the U.K. he has several methods of obtaining this information, as follows:

1. Studying the current 'Area Forecast' issued by the appropriate meteorological unit. This forecast is available at airfields served by ATC units. It is normally issued every 6 hours commencing from 0001 hours. Figure 18-2 shows an Area Forecast which covers a radius of 60 n.m. from a stated datum, in this case the airfield of LUTON.

2. Another method of obtaining an Area Forecast is to telephone the 'General Aviation Visual Flight Weather Service'. This service is operated specifically for the private pilot flying under VFR. Areas of the U.K. are numbered (see fig. 18-3) and the pilot selects the area(s) through which his intended route passes, obtaining from the published telephone number a pre-recorded forecast for the area(s) concerned. The phone number together with a printed pro forma for entering the weather details (see fig. 18-4) are on the reverse side of the numbered area map and issue through the Aircraft Owners and Pilots Association of the U.K. Forecasts are updated every 3 hours and each forecast is valid for 6 hours.

Fig. 18-3

Fig. 18-4

3. When long routes are planned a Route Forecast should be obtained from the appropriate meteorological unit, and this is normally issued in the form of a Significant Weather Chart covering the

whole of the route length. At least 2 hours' notice will be required by the meteorological unit prior to the issue of a route forecast and when the route length is over 500 miles 4 hours' notice will be required. Figure 18-5 shows a significant weather chart and fig. 18-6 illustrates the associated method of displaying wind information.

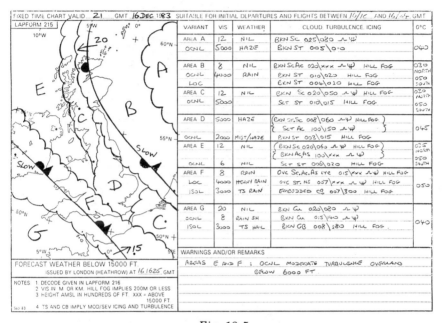

Fig. 18-5

4. An 'Actual Weather Report' for the destination airfield can only be obtained by contacting the airfield concerned. It will also often be possible to obtain the weather trend expected for a short period ahead.

When it has been established that the weather is forecast to remain suitable for the flight to be conducted, the next stage of the flight planning can begin.

MAP SELECTION AND PREPARATION
The two most commonly used aeronautical maps are the ICAO Aeronautical Chart (scale 1:500,000), and the Topographical Air Chart (scale 1:250,000). The former chart is the most useful as it shows all controlled airspace, whereas the latter only shows the lower limits of controlled airspace with bases below 3000 feet a.m.s.l. In addition the 1:500,000 chart covers the U.K. with three separate charts whereas some 18 1:250,000 charts are required to cover the same area.

Fig. 18-6

Whichever chart is used, care must be taken to see that the overprinted information concerning controlled airspace is current, as periodic changes occur. The chart legend will show the date up to which this information is correct and after this date the pilot will need to refer to AIPs and Notams.

Whenever the intended route is close to the edge of the chart, the overlapping chart should be studied during flight planning and also carried during the flight. Otherwise in the event of an unplanned route change due to bad weather or other circumstance, the pilot may find himself over terrain which is not covered by the chart carried.

Methods of map preparation will vary between pilots, with the use of time scales, proportional division of track lines, standard distance marks, or 5° and 10° drift lines being used to aid calculation of wind effect and drift while airborne. Regardless of the methods used, the map must be folded correctly to display the area at least 25 miles either side of the intended track and all marks and lines must be drawn in clearly. Suitable checkpoints should be noted along and in the vicinity of the track lines. These checkpoints should be sufficiently prominent to make their identification as easy as possible.

It has already been stated that pilot navigation must be simple and practical, but it must also be reasonably accurate, and one method of assessing and correcting track errors and revising estimated arrival times is known as the '1 in 60 rule'. The basis of this method is the fact that one nautical mile subtends an angle of one degree at a distance of approximately sixty miles.

Whereas calculations can be carried out in relative ease whilst on the ground when distractions or limitations on time available do not interfere, their use during flight must clearly be simplified. An example of this simplification is to state the 1 in 60 rule as follows:

A heading error of 1° will result in the aircraft being 1 n.m. 'Off Track' after flying 60 n.m., e.g. 6° equals a track error of 6 n.m. in 60 n.m. (fig. 18-7).

Fig. 18-7

Therefore, given the distance off track and the distance flown, the track error can be calculated by using the following simple formula:

$$\frac{60}{\text{Distance Flown}} \times \text{Distance Off Track} = \text{Track Error in Degrees}$$

Doubling this error and applying it to the heading towards the required track will result in the aircraft regaining the originally planned track at a point approximately double the distance already travelled. Figure 18-8 illustrates this correction. After flying for 20 n.m. the pilot fixes his position 2 miles to the left of track. This reveals a track error of 2 miles in 20 which would equal 6 miles in 60 or 6°. Therefore the heading alteration required is 12° to the right until track is regained. At this stage the aircraft heading should be altered 6° to the left to maintain the original track, (fig. 18-8).

The application of this procedure will be satisfactory as long as the alteration to heading is carried out at or before the half way position

Fig. 18-8

of the leg, after this it may result in the aircraft arriving back on a line which is an extension of the required track beyond the actual destination. Therefore when insufficient distance remains for the aircraft to return to the required track using this procedure another method will be needed as follows:

Original Track Error (established by the previous method) plus

$$\frac{60}{\text{Distance To Go}} \times \text{Distance Off Track} = \text{Heading Alteration in Degrees. (Closing Angle).}$$

This method is not absolutely accurate but is eminently suited to pilot navigation, and an example is shown at fig. 18-9. In this case the aircraft has drifted 4 n.m. off track, and the distance to reach destination is some 20 n.m. Therefore application of the 1 in 60 rule would be as follows:

$$\text{Original Track Error} = \frac{60 \times \text{Distance Off Track}}{\text{Distance Gone}}$$

$$= \frac{60 \times 4}{40} = 6°$$

$$+ \frac{60 \times \text{Distance Off Track}}{\text{Distance To Go}}$$

$$\text{Closing Angle} = \frac{60 \times 4}{20} = 12°.$$

Correction to reach destination = 6° + 12° = 18° to the right.

Another method of assessing track error and making the necessary corrections is through the use of 5° or 10° bearing (or drift) lines. By drawing in lines either side of the track the pilot can estimate the track error in degrees at a glance and calculate a new heading to arrive back on track.

Fig. 18-9

For example, fig. 18-10 shows bearing lines drawn 5° either side of track. If after flying for 10 minutes the aircraft position is identified at (c) it will have been following a line 5° to the left of the intended track. A heading change of 10° to the right will return the aircraft to track in the same time it took to reach (c). Once back on track the heading should be altered 5° to the left in order to remain on track.

Fig. 18-10

Although the use of the 1 in 60 rule will give the required heading to regain track or to reach destination it cannot always be used to revise ETAs for checkpoints en-route or destination. One simple way to obtain this information would be to divide the track line into quarters (or halves) and re-calculate ETAs at these quarter or halfway points. Figure 18-11 illustrates this procedure.

Fig. 18-11

After flying for 15 minutes the aircraft is abeam the halfway point and therefore the time taken to reach destination will also be 15 minutes. This same calculation for revising ETA will be equally applicable if the aircraft is on track at the halfway position.

CHOICE OF ROUTE
During the pre-flight planning stage the intended route should be studied for its proximity to Controlled Airspace, Danger and

Prohibited Areas etc., and when applicable the track must be offset to avoid such areas. Also when drawing in the track any need to use Special Entry/Exit lanes in relation to Controlled Airspace must be considered.

Information regarding Prohibited and Restricted Areas is clearly shown on the Aeronautical Charts, however although Danger Areas are shown with their code numbers and the altitude(s) to which they extend above mean sea level the times during which they are active are not displayed on the Aeronautical Charts used for pilot navigation. It will therefore be necessary to refer to the Chart of Airspace Restrictions and Danger Areas, see fig. 18-12. This chart will show in its legend the code number of the Danger Area and whether it is active during laid-down specific periods, or is Notified. The term Notified means that it is active at irregular intervals and for varying periods, these intervals and periods are published in Notams.

Full details of all Danger and Prohibited Areas in the U.K. can also be found in the Air Pilot (RAC section). Other information on the Chart of Airspace Restrictions and Danger Areas concern those areas where High Intensity Radio Transmissions take place, and advice regarding the avoidance of such areas and/or the minimum height which should be used when flying in their locality. Bird sanctuaries are also shown, together with the heights and any date restrictions. Areas of intense military aircraft activity are also listed. Figure 18-12 illustrates a sample legend of an Airspace Restriction and Danger Area Chart.

Following a study of this information the pilot will be able to decide on whether a direct route to destination is possible, or whether additional tracks will need to be drawn.

Once the track line(s) have been laid out on the aeronautical chart, the route, including a safe distance either side (at least 5 to 10 n.m. depending upon the length of the leg) should be checked for surface obstructions, including high ground. This information will be required in arriving at a decision as to what minimum altitude can safely be used during the flight should the weather deteriorate. There are several methods used for determining a safety altitude en-route but a fairly simply guide would be to ensure at least 1000 feet vertical clearance over any obstructions or high ground, within 5 or 10 n.m. either side of track.

USE OF A SAFETY ALTITUDE

The purpose of determining safety altitude(s) during the preparation stage is to be able to assess the minimum safe altitude if a decision to descend is required in the event of a lowering cloud base. Such

LEGEND

The upper limit of an area is shown as altitude in thousands of feet following the
identification number or name of the area.
Where the base of an area is not at ground or sea level this is also shown as
altitude in thousands of feet followed by the upper limit. e.g. 15-55

DANGER AREAS

National Prefix EG

† D001	H24 }	ST MAWGAN 126·5
† D001A	H24	
§ D002	H24 M·F	ST MAWGAN 126·5
† D005	Day M·F & Notified }	
† D006	H24	CULDROSE 134·05
§ D007	H24 }	
§ D007A	Notified	ST MAWGAN 126·5
D008	Notified	
D009	H24	
D009A	H24	
D009B	H24	
D010	Notified	
* D011	H24	
* D011A	Notified Day	

Scheduled Danger Areas are shown by solid outline. ───────
Notified Danger Areas are shown by pecked outline. ----------------
† Crossing Service available from identified unit.
§ Activity Information Service available from identified unit.
⁞ The upper limit is occasionally raised by Class 1 Notam.
* Contain Airspace to which Byelaws apply which prohibit entry during the
  Period of Danger Area Activity. See UK AIP RAC 5·1·1.
₪ For those Scheduled Danger Areas whose upper limit change at specified times
  during its Period of Activity, only the higher of the Upper Limits is shown on the chart.
Day.....0800-1800L Winter, 0700-1700L Summer.
M·F....Monday to Friday inclusive
L........Local
Ⓔ........See UK AIP AGA 3·3·2 for details of Entry/Exit lane for Dornoch AD.

PROHIBITED AREAS

National prefix EG

P047	Winfrith	¶P424	Armagh
P311	Capenhurst	¶P425	Ballykinler
P413	Calder/Winscale	¶P426	Bessbrook
¶P414	Lisburn	¶P429	Crosmaglen
¶P415	Lurgan	¶P430	Forkill

RESTRICTED AREAS

National prefix EG

R101 Aldermaston Flight permitted for the purpose of landing at or taking-off
                   from the helicopter landing area at Aldermaston. PPR.

R102 Harwell Flight permitted within 2NM of Harwell at not less than
               ALT1268ft for the purpose of making an instrument approach
               to land on R/W 36 at RAF Abingdon

¶R421 Belfast Except for take-off and landing at Belfast Harbour under ATC

¶R428 Enniskillen Except for take-off and landing at St Angelo, subject to prior
                    notification by A/C Commander to FIS St Angelo.(0365 22771)

¶ INADVERTANT ENTRY. Pilots are urgently warned against inadvertant entry into
Prohibited or Restricted Areas in Northern Ireland. Such entry could entail a danger
that the flight might be judged to have hostile or criminal intent and the aircraft
could be liable to counter-measures.

Fig. 18-12

information will be necessary in order to determine whether it is safe
to continue the flight.

The pilot must avoid any tendency to fly below the pre-determined
safety altitude in the hope that the cloud base will become higher
further along the route. It would always be more prudent to assume

that lowering cloud base en-route is indicating a continuing trend, one which is more commonplace.

Finally, remember that the aircraft will have to be flown 1000 feet vertically clear of cloud in order to maintain VMC above 3000 feet a.m.s.l., and when below this height there will still be a need to remain well clear of cloud to achieve a safe distance and time interval from any aircraft which may be descending or in transit through cloud along the route.

CALCULATIONS

Magnetic Headings and Times En-Route
The weather information which has been obtained will include the wind velocities and temperatures for selected heights a.m.s.l., and once the tracks are drawn and the altitude to fly decided, the magnetic headings and ground speeds can be calculated. These should be entered in the flight log together with the time(s) en-route which can also now be estimated.

Determination of the 'Compass Heading' can only be made and entered in the flight log when the compass correction card in the aircraft has been studied. Similarly, the ETA for destination or the first turning point cannot be entered in the log until the aircraft has been established on the appropriate heading, and the actual commencement time for the leg noted.

Fuel Consumption
Although the navigation flights which are carried out during a private pilot course are of relatively short duration, the importance of fuel calculations cannot be neglected. Once the habit has been established during training the pilot will be equipped to apply such fuel calculations on the longer flights which are often carried out after obtaining a private pilot licence.

Fuel consumption tables or graphs are normally shown in the

PILOT	
FUEL COMPUTATIONS	
G.P.H	
Route Time	
Total Carried	
Total for Route	
Reserve	
Total Required	
Fuel Remaining	

Fig. 18-13

aircraft operation section of the Flight/Owner's Manual or Pilot's Operating Handbook. Reference to this information will provide the pilot with the fuel consumption rate at particular power settings and altitudes. Range and endurance figures can also be read off directly or calculated from the published information.

Within the training environment it is common practice for fuel tanks to be filled prior to solo cross-country flights, but this does not absolve the student from making the required calculations to ascertain how much fuel will be used during the flight including the start-up, taxying period, climb to altitude, and the let down, circuit, and approach at destination.

When calculating flight times it is good aviation practice to include at least 45 minutes to 1 hour of additional flight time to allow for such contingencies as diversions around possible bad weather, proceeding to an alternate airfield or becoming lost.

A final note in respect of fuel consumption is that normally the published consumption rates, and the range and endurance figures are based upon the use of mixture control. If the mixture is left in the Rich position throughout the cross-country or a substantial part thereof, it will be necessary to increase the consumption rates by approximately 15% and to decrease the range and endurance figures by about the same amount.

Weight and Balance
Prior to taking off on a cross-country flight the pilot must ensure the aircraft is loaded so that it is within the permitted all-up weight and c.g. limits. Overloading an aircraft will result in a positive reduction in its climb performance, and increase overall fuel consumption. The stalling speed will also be significantly increased and the aircraft structure can more easily be overstressed if turbulence is encountered.

Supplement No. 2 to Straight and Level Flight explains in detail the method used for weight and balance calculations, and although there will be many occasions when the pilot will know that the aircraft is within the limits, there will also be occasions when doubt will exist, e.g. when passengers and baggage are carried. Under these circumstances a prudent and sensible pilot will carry out all the required calculations to ensure that he complies with his accepted responsibilities.

Weight and Performance
The available take-off and landing lengths at the destination airfield(s) should be obtained from the AGA section of the Air Pilot, and cross reference made between these figures and the take-off and landing distance and run required figures shown in the Flight/

Owner's Manual or Pilot's Operating Handbook. The latter will have to be interpreted in relation to the wind velocity, air temperature, aircraft weight, ground surface and airfield elevation.

A mental note should also be made in relation to the maximum crosswind component which can be expected during take-off and landing at the destination airfield(s). This figure must be one which is within the crosswind limitations of the particular aircraft.

FLIGHT INFORMATION

The Air Traffic Services have a responsibility to provide information for the use of pilots using the Airspace System. This information is made available by the publishing of relevant details in the Air Pilot, Notams, Information Circulars etc., and through radio communication established at ATC units.

The latest information published and relevant to the intended route should be reviewed by the pilot during the flight planning stage, together with the Altimeter Setting Regions through which his route passes.

During flight the pilot can communicate by RTF with the appropriate Flight Information Region which is marked on the aeronautical chart. The frequency to use will be found on the chart, and it can be confirmed by reference to the COM section of the Air Pilot. In addition this section of the Air Pilot can be used to determine the appropriate frequency for the VOLMET weather broadcast. VOLMET is a continuous tape recorded broadcast which gives actual weather reports from specific airfields, and the information is transmitted with a time prefix for each airfield to show when the weather observations were made.

Noting of Required Radio Frequencies

Information on the radio frequencies available for both the en-route section of the flight and those relative to the destination airfields can be obtained from the COM section of the Air Pilot. Although certain frequencies, e.g. Flight Information Centres, MATZ and Special Rules Zones are displayed on the Aeronautical Charts they should be verified with the Air Pilot and Notams in case of any recent changes. Frequencies of those airfields which are close to the intended track will be useful and should be noted in the flight log.

Selection of Alternate Airfields

Even though care has been used to obtain an adequate forecast, and one which indicates that VMC will prevail during the period of the flight, it must be appreciated that weather conditions can occasionally change in an unpredicted fashion. On such occasions deteriorating weather conditions can present problems to the pilot, with a need to make positive decisions as to whether to turn back or divert to an alternate airfield.

Clearly it will be of considerable help in making such decisions to have essential details of suitable alternate airfields entered in the flight log. Such details should include radio frequencies, airfield aids, and whether an ATC unit and grass or runways are available.

A review of the track(s) which have been planned will reveal the relative positions of suitable alternate airfields, and information relating to their facilities, e.g. radio frequency, landing distances available etc. can be obtained from the Air Pilot. This information should be entered in the flight log.

AIRCRAFT DOCUMENTATION

The final part of the preparation stage should be to review the documents of the particular aircraft to ensure that the Certificate of Airworthiness is in force, and the Maintenance Release or equivalent document is current. The aircraft Weight and Centre of Gravity Schedule will normally have already been referred to if any doubt existed as to whether the aircraft load is such that it may be outside the permitted limits.

NOTIFICATION OF THE FLIGHT

A pilot intending to make a flight shall inform ATC at the airfield of departure, and this procedure is known as 'Booking Out'. Another procedure which involves the completion of a special form (CA Form 48) is known as 'Filing a Flight Plan'.

A private pilot may if he wishes, file a flight plan for any flight he undertakes. Normally flight plans are filed for IFR flights, or those VFR flights during which the route is partly or wholly over sparsely populated or mountainous areas, or during overwater flights if the route takes the aircraft more than 10 n.m. from the coast.

The basic purpose of filing a flight plan during VFR flights is to ensure that prompt search and rescue action can be taken if a forced landing or ditching occurs. If a flight plan is to be filed it should be received by the appropriate ATC unit at least 30 minutes prior to the aircraft departure time.

Normally most training flights will occur in circumstances which do not necessitate the filing of a flight plan, but Booking Out is a mandatory requirement and can be achieved either by RTF, or when no radio is fitted, by telephone to the appropriate airfield authority. Minimum details should include the:

● Aircraft registration letters.
● Endurance and expected flight time en-route.
● Destination.
● Number of persons on board.

AIRFIELD DEPARTURE

ORGANISATION OF COCKPIT WORKLOAD
In order to reduce the cockpit workload involved in flying and navigating the aircraft at the same time, it is important to institute a methodical procedure whereby the Flight Log and the required maps are easily accessible and immediately available for reference throughout the flight.

The map should be folded in a sensible manner and one which allows the ground detail to be clearly read for at least 20 n.m. either side of the intended track. A pen or pencil must be available for the pilot to make entries in the Flight Log or to make marks on the map during the en-route phase and it will be advisable to have at least one spare should the original get broken or mislaid.

The format of the Flight Log should be clear and easily read, this will also apply to any of the information written on it during the planning stage. Many pilots have become lost quite unnecessarily due to misreading badly written figures in relation to headings and times.

DEPARTURE PROCEDURES
During initial training in navigation it will be preferable to set heading from overhead the departure airfield at the en-route altitude and airspeed, which will facilitate accuracy and reduce workload. However this procedure will be impractical when departing from larger airfields handling IFR traffic, therefore later practice must involve climbing en-route following take-off. In the case of a small number of training airfields this second type of departure procedure may be necessary from the commencement of navigation due to the presence of Special Entry/Exit Lanes.

The altimeter setting to use on the en-route section of the flight will normally be the Area QNH for VFR cross country flights, largely due to the fact that most training cross countries for the private pilot licence will be conducted at or below 3000 feet a.m.s.l. Even when operating at or above 3000 feet there will often be difficulties in selecting an appropriate 'flight level' in accordance with the quadrantal rule, and one which will at the same time ensure the maintenance of VMC, e.g. the aircraft remaining clear of cloud by at least 1 n.m. horizontally and 1000 feet vertically.

Once established on the required heading, the time must be noted and entered in the Flight Log, following which the ETA can be calculated and inserted in the appropriate column.

EN-ROUTE

MAINTENANCE OF HEIGHTS AND HEADINGS
During the en-route stage it is important to avoid becoming absorbed in map reading to the detriment of flying accuracy. The object of cross-country training is to develop the ability to navigate, map reading being only one of the factors involved. Navigation requires the ability to use a map to fix the aircraft position and also deduce where the aircraft will be at a pre-determined time ahead. This achievement will be prejudiced by over-concentration on consulting the map, as this could cause inaccuracies in heading maintenance, altitude keeping and airspeed.

Checkpoints should be selected during the pre-flight planning stage which are easily recognised from the air. These checkpoints need not coincide exactly with any distance or track division line but should be in locations where simple assessments of the aircraft position relative to such lines can be made.

The map should be orientated so that the track line being followed points in the same direction as the way the aircraft is going, thus facilitating recognition of ground features and estimates of distance.

The first checkpoint should be chosen so that it falls between 5 to 15 miles along the track from the point of commencement. This will be an invaluable early check on whether the heading calculations were performed correctly, and will establish whether the wind velocity used is the actual one being experienced. If the aircraft remains on track to the first checkpoint on each leg then this will be a good indication that the navigation which follows will be reasonably accurate, provided the pilot continues to fly the aircraft accurately.

REVISIONS TO ETA AND HEADING
If the aircraft is maintaining its correct track then the only revision which may be necessary will be to the ETA, and this can easily be calculated according to the method used in marking the track line, e.g. distance or time marks.

When the aircraft has drifted off the track line, it will be necessary to estimate the distance 'off track' for the distance flown and apply the 1 in 60 rule to calculate the track error, then take up a new heading to regain track or destination. An entry should be made in the Flight Log whenever a new heading has to be calculated or an ETA revised.

LOG KEEPING
The primary purpose of maintaining an airborne log is to provide the pilot with sufficient information to plan ahead (D.R.) and also to re-fix his position at any time. It is of particular value should any

uncertainty of position occur, or in the event of becoming lost. Therefore even when the flight is progressing exactly as planned it is still a good practice to maintain position and time entries. Entries must however be made legibly, and the most important items to record are:

- Departure time.
- ETAs and revised ETAs.
- Time relative to checkpoints or distance marks.
- Fixes.
- Changes of heading, altitude or airspeed, together with the time.

Groundspeed is important for ETA revision, and can be calculated easily on a distance/time basis. That is, if a distance of 10 n.m. has been travelled in 6 minutes, it would normally take a further 6 minutes to travel another 10 n.m., and a groundspeed of 100 kts is being experienced. Reasonable approximations are acceptable if they simplify the procedure used, for example, the previous calculation would represent about one and a half n.m. per minute. Such approximations will often be less likely to produce errors than trying to work out an exact groundspeed.

USE OF RADIO INCLUDING VDF

When radio is fitted it will be a valuable safety aid, and is there to be used when needed. Consequently the pilot should listen out on a frequency appropriate to the stage of the flight. During the en-route section, the FIR frequency should be selected so that if assistance is required the ATC services can be quickly alerted. Similarly, when passing close to active airfields whilst en-route, the frequency of the relevant airfield should be selected and either a call made to inform the ATC unit of the aircraft position and pilot's intentions or merely to listen out for information concerning the activities of other aircraft in the vicinity.

When contacting an airfield en-route, ensure that the content of the message is planned before transmitting. The ATC unit will appreciate the following information:

- Aircraft Call Sign.
- Altitude.
- Heading and Approximate Position.
- In-Flight Conditions, i.e. VMC.
- Intentions.

NB. Always make a call notifying the intention to leave one frequency for another.

Although the primary purpose in basic PPL navigation is to be able to develop the ability to navigate the aircraft safely by reference to aeronautical charts and the ground, the pilot should not hesitate to make use of VDF facilities (when available) for navigational purposes should assistance be needed to re-establish the aircraft position, or for Homing purposes.

This method of assistance is often neglected until the pilot has become completely lost. There is nothing derogatory in using such an aid to navigation should the need arise and the service is available.

MINIMUM WEATHER CONDITIONS FOR CONTINUANCE OF THE FLIGHT
The term 'Weather' to any pilot basically revolves around the following:

● Visibility.
● Wind Velocity.
● Precipitation.
● Cloud Base.

It will be primarily due to changes in these factors that such 'In Flight Decisions' as to continue, turn back, or proceed to an alternate airfield will be based.

Visibility

VFR navigation demands an environment in which the pilot can see a resonable distance, and during training any reduction of visibility below 5 km. will seriously affect the pilot's ability to navigate successfully.

Reduced visibility during navigation flights is usually caused by haze, produced from smoke and similar particles in the atmosphere, or precipitation. Fog and mist are normally associated with lowering air temperature and/or an association with precipitation or near precipitation conditions.

Haze can cause a considerable reduction to the 'In Flight' visibility, particularly if heading into sun. Sometimes it can be avoided by increasing the aircraft altitude, but if this action is taken it must be borne in mind that a different wind velocity to that used during the calculations of heading and groundspeed may exist, and the pilot must be alert for this change.

The occurrence of fog or mist can be forecast with reasonable accuracy, but the pilot will have to maintain a weather eye for their development, particularly if frontal conditions exist, or whenever the temperature is nearing the dewpoint and a light wind prevails, or shortly after sunrise if the cross country is commenced early in the day. A light wind or heating from the sun's rays striking the ground will often produce the necessary mixing action for fog to occur if other conditions are favourable to its formation. Flying during the early morning or evening will therefore require an added awareness for the possibility of fog formation, and should this likelihood exist, an early decision to land at the nearest suitable airfield should be considered rather than a continuance and discovery too late that the ground can no longer be seen.

Wind Velocity

Strong winds and light aircraft combine to produce a hazardous situation during take-off and landing. Most small training aircraft should not be operated in wind strengths above 35 kts. The area forecast will normally reveal any anticipated high winds, but sometimes these occur without warning, confronting the pilot with a difficult landing situation at his destination.

In these circumstances a pilot must be aware of the effect of a changed wind strength upon his original heading and groundspeed calculations and ETAs. He must also be alert to the crosswind limitations applicable to the particular aircraft type when landing, and be prepared to go round again if necessary.

Precipitation

The effect of rain and snow upon 'In Flight' visibility has already been covered during 'Operation at Minimum Level', but students are reminded of the dangerous effects of flying into falling snow during which the visibility can be reduced to a few metres. Heavy rain showers or thunderstorm activity en-route will automatically require a diversion from track to be made in order to circumnavigate such conditions. Good log keeping will be required during this procedure as the possibility of becoming lost will be increased.

Light rain falling from high cloud may occasionally occur, but this alone will not normally be a reason to turn back or divert to an alternate airfield. A close monitoring of the weather situation will nevertheless be necessary in case the cloud base lowers to an unacceptable level for the safe continuance of the flight.

Cloud Base

By the time navigation is introduced into a student pilot's training programme he should have developed a sufficient sense of safety awareness to appreciate the reduction in flight safety whenever an aircraft is operated at lower than normal heights, particularly if this is necessitated by bad weather.

It is for this reason that a 'Safety Altitude' is estimated for particular tracks, and to deliberately ignore this limitation when adopting any available alternative action, would be foolhardy.

'IN-FLIGHT' DECISIONS

The weather will often be a changeable factor during any flight regardless of forecast conditions, and as a result a pilot will most likely be faced at some time during his flying with a situation where the weather deteriorates, necessitating a change from his original plan.

However, a safe and sensible pilot will develop the ability to make sound decisions sufficiently early so as to avoid hazardous situations from occurring. In relation to weather changes this decision will involve one of three actions:

- To continue to destination.
- To turn back.
- To proceed to an alternate airfield.

Due to the variation of circumstances which can occur during any flight, it is extremely difficult to lay down hard and fast rules for the making of 'In-Flight Decisions', however a few simple and valuable rules are outlined as follows:

Continuing to Destination

This should only be attempted if the cloud base is such that the aircraft can be flown clear of cloud at or above the selected safety altitude. If these conditions are being met only marginally, the pilot during the continuance .of the flight should have his next alternative decision already planned, i.e. turn back, or proceed to an alternate airfield if the cloud base lowers further. However, should the pilot have the destination airfield in sight when the cloud base forces him to fly lower than his safety altitude it will often be sensible to continue to destination, but he will need to be constantly aware of any obstructions in the vicinity of the destination airfield.

Turning Back

The pilot in command has sole responsibility for the safety of the aircraft and its occupants. If a pilot decides to turn back in the face of what appears to be deteriorating weather ahead, whilst the weather behind remains good, he has made the right decision, and one that cannot be criticised. The pilot who aborts a flight for this reason and returns to his departure airfield in clear weather conditions has not only made the right decision, but he has made it at the right time.

A pilot who in similar circumstances eventually aborts the flight and returns to the departure airfield in marginal weather conditions, has also made the right decision but not at the most opportune time.

Proceeding to an Alternate Airfield

The purpose of planning for alternate airfield(s) en-route is to counter the case of aircraft malfunction, or that of running into unexpected weather conditions in circumstances when to turn back is not a practical proposition. With this fact in mind the pilot must not hesitate to put a pre-planned procedure into effect. This will reduce the possibility of becoming lost as a result of continued flight into adverse weather conditions.

Additional care must however be used to double check the 'in-flight' calculations used to estimate the heading and ETA for the alternate airfield.

Procedures for Flight within Regulated Airspace

In addition to the general aerodrome air traffic rules, special rules are prescribed in the Rules of the Air and Air Traffic Control Regulations for certain aerodromes. These additional rules are made to provide a further safeguard to aircraft using, or flying in the vicinity of these aerodromes.

Details of these Special Rules Zones and/or Areas are obtained from the UK AIP (Air Pilot) RAC section and it is the pilot's responsibility to ensure that he complies with these rules.

NAVIGATION AT MINIMUM LEVEL

All the considerations involved during the practice of 'Operation at Minimum Level' will apply to a cross-country flight, but as the pilot will often be a relatively long distance from the base airfield, and the terrain being overflown will usually be unfamiliar, a state of anxiety can more easily lead to the pilot becoming lost.

Therefore, whenever forced to fly low during a cross-country flight due to weather deterioration there will be a special need for correct preparation prior to descending. The decision to continue under these conditions will normally be made because the weather generally has worsened, preventing the pilot from changing his plan and heading for an alternate airfield or adopting a heading to return to the departure airfield.

Before descending to avoid cloud, determine whether it is possible to alter heading and circumnavigate the area where the cloud base is low, or whether proceeding to an alternate airfield would obviate the necessity to operate at low level.

If the decision is to continue, a check should be made of the safety altitude assessed for this portion of the flight, and a review conducted to establish the height of ground or obstructions, and whether any towns or airfields lie on or close to the track line.

Having decided that there is no alternative but to continue the flight at low level, the cockpit checks learned during Operation at Minimum

Level should be carried out, the geographic position noted, and the time of the descent entered in the flight log. If facilities are available it may be advisable to obtain a QTE or QDM if the aircraft position is not accurately known prior to descent. Remember that the range of VHF decreases rapidly below 2000 feet.

Once established at the lower altitude the need to fly accurately will be increased, because the difficulty of map reading at low levels leads to a greater dependence upon D.R. navigation techniques.

Generally the wind velocity will be different from that used in the flight planning or previously corrected for during the en-route phase, and this will affect both the groundspeed and required heading. If a revised time check (groundspeed) can be established between the first two checkpoints during the low level phase it will be of significant help in maintaining a D.R. position for the rest of the leg.

Any attempt to map read and identify ground features in a completely continuous fashion will rarely be successful, and it will be more sensible to look for the most easily identifiable ground features. This method will permit more time to be spent in flying the aircraft accurately, and it will also be less likely to lead to confusion and worry.

During flight at low levels there is an inevitable tendency to concentrate vision fairly close to the aircraft, which can lead to a lack of awareness of obstructions, high ground, or cloud lowering still further ahead. Therefore be very careful to avoid looking at the ground close to the aircraft for any longer than is necessary.

The lower the aircraft is being flown the more difficult it will become to make entries in the flight log, but times over checkpoints should, where possible, be entered. If a checkpoint does not appear at the appointed D.R. time, do not worry unduly over this, as at low level even minor distractions can lead to it being missed. Therefore assume it has already been passed and prepare to identify the next checkpoint.

There may be occasions when a clearly identified line feature such as a coastline, major river, railway line or motorway will be available, and if this terminates in the vicinity of destination it may be wiser to proceed to such a feature and follow it. In this event more time will be available for keeping a lookout in relation to obstructions etc. However, when following any line feature the aircraft should be positioned along its right side.

Uncertainty of Position Procedure

During any form of navigation (as distinct from map reading) there will be times when a pilot will not be able to fix his exact position by reference to his map and the ground features being overflown. This is a perfectly normal situation and one which must not give cause for undue alarm.

Navigation calls for the maintenance of accurate headings and identification of ground features, i.e. checkpoints at pre-determined intervals, and if a particular checkpoint is not identified on time it may be due to a number of reasons. In this situation the pilot should initially assume that the checkpoint has been overflown, and continue to maintain his heading until the next checkpoint is identified. In the event that a second checkpoint does not appear at the appointed time it can be assumed that a situation is developing which may call for the implementation of 'Lost Procedure'.

LOST PROCEDURE

Within the U.K. it can normally be said that when a pilot has not been able to establish his position for some 20 to 30 minutes it can be assumed that the situation has changed from being uncertain of position to becoming lost. This will call for an assessment of the current situation, which will include ascertaining the fuel state, daylight remaining, and a re-appraisal of previous calculations and headings flown.

Although it is not possible to detail the order of checks and procedures to be carried out in all circumstances, the following list of actions represent a general guide to be followed in the event of becoming lost.

Check to ensure that the Safety Altitude for the route sector is being maintained and note the fuel state and airborne time remaining:

- Ensure that the gyro heading indicator is correctly synchronised with the compass.
- Re-check the flight log to ascertain that the correct heading is being flown.
- Re-assess the ETA for the last checkpoint which has been missed.
- Estimate the present D.R. position and mark on the map a circle of uncertainty, radius 10% of the distance flown since the last reliable checkpoint.
- Assuming visual contact with the ground, search for an identifiable feature within the circle of uncertainty, reading from the ground to the map.

The causes of becoming lost can generally be listed as follows:

- A marked change in wind velocity.
- An incorrectly synchronised or faulty gyro heading indicator.
- Mis-reading the heading or time calculations in the flight log.
- Incorrect identification of a previous checkpoint.
- Weather deterioration involving reduced visibility and/or increased cockpit workload.

● Unscheduled diversions from the original track.

Taking these factors into account, a systematic check should be made to establish which of the above items was the reason for becoming lost. If the cause was due to setting the heading indicator incorrectly prior to a change in heading over a turning point, the heading indicator should be correctly synchronised with the magnetic compass, and an estimate then made of the track which has actually been followed. The radius of the circle of uncertainty should then be based upon 10% of the estimated track distance covered since setting heading over the last turning point. If the aircraft position is positively re-established, it would be advisable to return to the turning point and then start afresh. Figure 18-14 illustrates this type of situation.

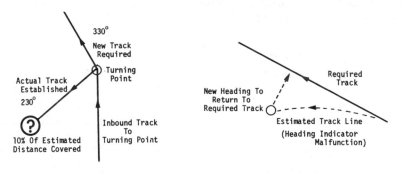

Fig. 18-14   Fig. 18-15

In the event that the gyro heading indicator has precessed significantly, then provided en-route checks are being methodically carried out at 10 to 15 minute intervals, the aircraft will have only been flying on erroneous headings for this period. In this case a rough assessment of position can be made, and a new heading selected in order to return towards the originally planned track. Figure 18-15 illustrates this procedure. If the search for a fix becomes protracted or fruitless, the pilot should declare the situation through an RTF PAN call on the frequency being used, and comply with any instructions received. If no two-way communication is established on this frequency the pilot should transmit a PAN call on 121.5 MHz.

If assistance is not available or radio is not fitted, the best course of action will be to maintain a steady heading and continue to search for ground identification features or an active airfield. Then a safe landing may be made before a reduced fuel state dictates the carrying out of a forced landing with power away from an airfield.

ARRIVAL PROCEDURES

During the early days of aviation, the absence of radio facilities and the relatively small difference between the approach speeds of small training and large passenger-carrying aircraft allowed practical simplification and standardisation of arrival procedures. Today, small slow aircraft often share the same airspace as large military and passenger jetliners, and whereas it is still possible to keep them apart en-route, they will of necessity be operating closer together when arriving at many of the medium-sized and larger airfields.

Therefore as a result of the large changes which have occurred to aircraft size and speed, and the development of procedural let-downs and landing systems, it is no longer possible to have a standard airfield joining procedure which will apply to all airfields and aircraft. The methods of joining the circuit and approaching to land will consequently vary according to the circumstances.

AIRFIELD JOINING PROCEDURE

When the destination airfield is small and radio facilities do not exist, the standard method of joining the circuit will (unless instructions to the contrary have been received prior to take-off) be to fly at a safe height overhead the destination airfield. Initially this height should be at least 2000 feet a.g.l. to remain clear of the aerodrome traffic zone. Whilst carrying out this procedure a very good lookout must be maintained, and an inspection of the airfield signals area can be made to determine the circuit and landing direction.

The aircraft should then be positioned on the side opposite to the downwind leg and on a heading co-incident with the take-off and landing direction. This type of arrival procedure has already been shown during the Local Area and Consolidation exercise and is illustrated in fig. 14-5. Unless instructions have been received to the contrary this method of circuit joining should be followed at all non-radio airfields, unless prevented by difficult weather conditions or proximity to controlled airspace. It is significant to note that accident statistics clearly reveal that most 'near miss' situations and airborne collisions occur at non-radio airfields, due to arriving pilots joining the circuit on base leg or final approach.

Altimeter Setting and ATC Liaison

When RTF is available arrival and landing may be under the direction of an Air Traffic Controller, or alternatively only Advisory Information may be relayed. When radio is used the pilot should contact the facility before arriving in the immediate vicinity of the airfield (normally 5 to 10 miles away) and obtain ATC instructions or Advisory Information.

The QFE should be set prior to flying overhead the airfield, or if the overhead procedure is not being used, it should be set prior to commencing the final descent phase to circuit height. Once radio contact has been established, a continuous listening watch must be maintained until the aircraft has reached the parking area.

Entering the Traffic Pattern

Once in the vicinity of the airfield a search should be maintained for other air traffic movements so that the entry into the traffic pattern can be phased safely between other aircraft.

Whether or not radio is available it is of paramount importance that a continuous and vigilant lookout is maintained throughout the arrival, during the circuit, and in the approach and landing and taxying-in phase.

The 'Airfield Approach Checks' should be completed prior to arrival in the airfield vicinity so as not to detract from lookout within the congested area around the airfield.

Circuit Procedures

When applicable, RTF calls should be made at appropriate positions during the circuit, which will normally be carried out at 800 or 1000 feet a.g.l. It is usually advisable to set up a powered approach when landing at a strange airfield, to ensure greater accuracy in controlling the approach path and position of touch-down.

When arriving at an unfamiliar airfield, the student will tend to be more prone to errors in judgement due to the strangeness of his surrounds, therefore he must be particularly alert and prepared to go round again if the situation demands.

PARKING PROCEDURES

After landing caution must be exercised, and on grass landing areas the safest procedure is to bring the aircraft to a stop, look around both sides and behind before turning left through 90°. In a high-wing aircraft, flaps should be raised to improve lookout before this initial turn.

When at 90° to the landing direction, another good lookout should be made into the approach and landing path area to ensure that it is still safe to taxy clear of the manoeuvring area. When taxying on strange airfields be particularly alert for bad ground which can often be hidden by long grass, and maintain a watch for 'boundary markers' or other ground signals which indicate areas unfit for taxying aircraft.

Once the parking area has been reached ensure the aircraft is parked in a position which does not restrict the movement of other aircraft.

SECURITY OF THE AIRCRAFT

Upon arrival in the parking area, carefully note the fuel state and complete the running down and switching-off procedure. Place the control locks and pitot cover in position and when a handbrake is not fitted the aircraft should be securely chocked. The final entries in the flight log can now be completed and an 'after flight' inspection of the aircraft carried out.

REFUELLING

It will be the responsibility of the pilot to determine whether re-fuelling is required prior to further flight, and he must also ensure that the correct grade of fuel is used. To aid the decision on whether uplift of fuel is necessary, a check should be made of the time estimated for the flight and compared with the actual time taken.

Sometimes the wind may have been stronger than forecast, and if a headwind has been experienced this could lead to a significant increase in the fuel used. If a diversion or a state of being lost has been incurred these also could have significantly increased the fuel consumed.

BOOKING IN

This procedure should be carried out at the end of each flight and normally consists of paying the appropriate landing fee and supplying a representative of the airfield management with the following information:

Aircraft Registration.
Pilot's Name.
Airfield of Departure.
Next Point of Intended Landing (if appropriate).

PRE-FLIGHT BRIEFING
PILOT NAVIGATION

The pre-flight briefings given for each cross country will be appropriate to the routes which are used at a particular training organisation.

The introduction of such items as diversion procedures, landing away and lost procedure will depend upon the specific routes flown and the training programme used. For this reason no attempt is made to itemise pre-flight briefings or navigation techniques.

However, a format considered to be acceptable for the introduction and practice of this exercise is given in the Flight Demonstration section. Alternatively, the instructor will be able to select and utilise the items shown in the sequence he requires.

Pilot Navigation

Flight Demonstrations

INTRODUCTION

The total coverage of this exercise will involve the student with many new items to be learned and although these items will initially be covered during your ground training it will take several hours of practical pilot navigation in the air before competence in this exercise can be achieved.

The following sequence of flight training represents one convenient method of ensuring demonstration and practice of the essential items in a logical manner:

No. 1. Dual Map Reading Triangular Cross Country (to include flight planning, departure, en-route and arrival procedures).

No. 2. Dual Pilot Navigation (to include procedure for penetration of regulated airspace, uncertainty of position procedure, an unscheduled diversion and away landing.

No. 3. Dual Pilot Navigation (to include Operation at Minimum Level and implementation of 'Lost Procedure').

NAVIGATION FLIGHT TEST

Your instructor may vary the content and sequence of these flights depending upon local circumstances and the procedures used at the particular Flying Training Organisation. However, the contents of the dual navigation flights as outlined on the following pages will normally have been introduced and practised prior to your first solo navigation flight.

Specific airmanship items which are related to cross-country flying will be introduced and developed at the appropriate time during each navigation flight.

DEMONSTRATION 1.   PILOT NAVIGATION NO. 1. DUAL MAP READING CROSS COUNTRY

Flight Lesson	*Demonstration Sequence*
Map reading Map reading will already have been introduced and practised during previous exercises but normally the first demonstration of your pilot navigation training will consist of a flight specifically undertaken to enable you to practise map reading whilst maintaining accurate altitudes and headings.	

DEMONSTRATION 2.   PILOT NAVIGATION NO. 2. DUAL CROSS COUNTRY

Flight Lesson	*Demonstration Sequence*
Pilot navigation procedures	
Complete the Pre-Flight preparation in the aircraft.	Calculate compass headings and enter in the flight log. Ensure the necessary navigation equipment e.g. map(s) flight log, pencils etc. are available and stowed in an easily accessible location.
After take-off	The setting heading procedure will be conducted from overhead the airfield or during the climb after take-off. Set the appropriate ASR QNH. Note the time on commencement of the first heading and enter this in the flight log, together with the ETA for destination. Maintain accurate heading, altitude and planned airspeed. Ensure the map is orientated in the direction of the track. Confirm correct heading and approximate maintenance of track by the use of local ground features within a few minutes of setting heading.
En-route	Observe a good standard of lookout and prepare to identify the first checkpoint. Use distant ground features ahead and to either side to obtain a rough guide of the track being made good. Avoid random alterations of heading

and wait to obtain a positive fix relative to the first checkpoint.

Radio: Remain on airfield approach frequency or select FIR frequency as required.

Read from the map to the ground and establish a fix relative to the first checkpoint. Assess position in relation to the track required.

If the aircraft is 'Off Track' calculate a heading correction and adopt the new heading. Note time and the ETA to regain track. Log entry as required.

Upon regaining track, adopt new heading to maintain track.

Maintain accurate headings between checkpoints and rely on D.R. navigation over featureless areas.

En-route checks: Gyro heading indicator re-synchronised.
Fuel state.
Engine oil pressure and temperatures.
Vacuum and alternator check.
Altimeter setting change when crossing into new ASR.

Maintain a state of awareness in relation to the weather and carburettor icing during the progress of the flight.

Note ETA of first turning point, and set new heading from overhead.

Carry out en-route checks.

Initial confirmation of correct heading by reference to ground features in the vicinity of the turning point.

Note ETA of next checkpoint.

Establish fixes relative to checkpoints and calculate new headings if necessary and revise ETAs as required. Log entries.

At a suitable stage assume the weather ahead is deteriorating markedly, and adopt diversion procedure

Estimate heading and distance for alternate airfield and assess safety altitude for the route.

Note time of setting new heading and calculate ETA. Enter position, heading, distance to run and ETA in flight log.

Review facilities and radio frequencies at the alternate airfield from the information given in the flight log.

Re-check heading and ETA calculations for the alternate airfield.

Carry out en-route checks.

If the intention is to land at the alternate airfield	Contact ATC when 5 to 10 miles away from the airfield. Note joining instructions, adjust altimeter pressure setting, and copy runway and circuit information. Join the circuit according to ATC instructions or Advisory Information. After landing complete the flight log, 'book in' and inform base airfield of your situation.
If for training purposes the intention is to proceed towards the alternate airfield and then alter heading for the original destination or base airfield	At the required position calculate a new heading and ETA for the original destination, base airfield or to regain original track. Assess safety altitude for the route. Set heading as required and enter heading, distance to run and ETA in the flight log. When established along the new track re-check heading and ETA calculations. Carry out en-route checks.
Arrival procedure	Contact ATC when 5 to 10 miles away from the airfield. Airfield approach checks. Comply with joining instructions, adjust altimeter pressure setting and note runway circuit information. After landing complete the flight log and 'book-in'.

Student practice: During the flight both the instructor and student will participate in flying the aircraft and carrying out the navigation procedure. Towards the end of the flight the student should be completing the total task by himself.

DEMONSTRATION 3.   PILOT NAVIGATION NO. 3. DUAL CROSS COUNTRY

Flight Lesson	Demonstration Sequence
Pilot navigation procedures	
Complete the Pre-Flight preparation in the aircraft	Calculate compass headings and enter in the flight log. Ensure the necessary navigation equipment e.g. map(s), flight log, pencils etc. are available and stowed in an easily accessible location.
After take-off	The setting heading procedure will be conducted from overhead the airfield or

	during the climb after take-off. Set the appropriate ASR QNH. Note the time on commencement of the first heading and enter this in the flight log, together with the ETA for destination.
En-route	Maintain accurate heading, altitude and planned airspeed. Ensure the map is orientated in the direction of the track. Observe a good standard of lookout and carry out normal navigation procedures for fixing position, estimating track errors and calculating new headings and ETAs as applicable.
Assume weather deterioration with a lowering cloud base	For training purposes the decision will be to continue at a lower level, but not below the planned safety altitude. Carry out the normal checks before Operation at Minimum Level and descend from a known position. Enter the time in the flight log prior to the descent. Navigation at lower levels will require greater reliance upon D.R. navigation and the noting of times at checkpoints. A vigilant lookout will need to be maintained. Reduce the number of log entries if the workload becomes too high.
Return to the originally planned altitude, and at a convenient stage the Uncertainty of Position procedure will be introduced	Re-check the time over the last identi-fied checkpoint. Note present time and estimate the D.R. position of the aircraft. Read from ground to map and if two further consecutive checkpoints are not identified carry out the Lost Procedure.
Lost Procedure	Ensure the safety altitude is being observed. Note the fuel state and deter-mine airborne time remaining and hours of daylight left. Ensure the heading indicator is synchronised with the magnetic compass. Re-check with the flight log to ensure the correct heading has been flown and that the correct ETA at checkpoints is being used. Re-assess the ETA for the last checkpoint which has been missed.

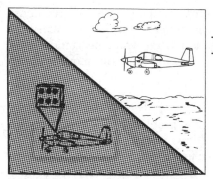

Introduction to Instrument Flying

Instructor's Guide

This exercise is a requirement for the PPL course and is allotted 4 hours in the air. It is essentially an introduction to the problems of 'instrument flying' and should include demonstrations in the clear and under-simulated instrument conditions. The purpose of the exercise is to ensure the student can measure his limitations, and enable him to appreciate that flying an aircraft by sole reference to the instruments is not a task which can be safely achieved without undertaking a recognised course of instrument training.

During his course so far the student has been taught to adjust and maintain the aircraft attitude and performance by visual reference using external cues, complementing this by using the instrument indications to achieve more precise flight. However this practice of 'precision flight' does not equip a pilot to maintain control of the aircraft if outside visual reference is lost.

Although an instructor should normally encourage positive motiv-ation during learning, i.e. all practice should be towards the development or achievement of a particular accomplishment, this exercise is one which puts emphasis on negative motivation in that it places stress on what not to attempt rather than what to achieve. In essence it must carry a firm warning against any deliberate decision to fly solely by the use of instruments without first completing a formal course of training in instrument flying.

Nevertheless sound teaching principles can still be observed, in that the student whilst being taught his limitations can also gain the foundation of an insurance policy to get him out of trouble should he inadvertently find himself in cloud or weather conditions where outside references are such that instrument flight becomes necessary.

For this reason the instructor should ensure that upon completion of this exercise his student will at least have the ability to maintain control of the aircraft, and turn back out of adverse weather should such a situation arise.

AIRMANSHIP
The lesson of airmanship in this exercise is for the student not to get

himself into a situation where flight completely by instruments becomes necessary. For the instructor, airmanship lies in a constant awareness of the need for lookout at a time when he could easily become absorbed by the instrument readings and the monitoring of the student's instrument practice.

OBJECTIVES
1. To acquaint the student with the problems of controlling an aircraft by sole reference to the flight instruments.
2. To give the student sufficient instrument flight training to ensure that he is capable of controlling the aircraft and safely returning to visual flight conditions in the event of inadvertent entry into instrument weather conditions.
3. To ensure that the student will appreciate the need for him to undertake further instrument flying training before deliberately planning to fly or navigate in instrument weather conditions.

During the four hours of instrument flying training the instructor should plan his flight demonstrations and student practice periods to ensure the student has obtained approximately two hours and thirty minutes of practice in simulated instrument flying or a combination of simulated and actual instrument flying.

Upon completion of the exercise the following should have been covered:

The Flight Instruments:
   Pressure Instruments.
      Air Speed Indicator.
      Altimeter.
      Vertical Speed Indicator.
   Gyroscopic Instruments.
      Attitude Indicator.
      Heading Indicator.
      Turn and Balance Indicator/Turn Co-ordinator.

Physiological Considerations:
   The Three Primary Senses.
   Spatial Disorientation.
   Sensory Illusions.

Instrument Appreciation:
   Attitude Instrument Flight.
      Instrument Indications.
         Pitch Attitude.
         Bank Attitude.
         Heading and Balance.
      Attitude, Power and Performance.

Attitude Instrument Flying.
  Control Instruments.
  Performance Instruments.
  Effect of Changing Power.
  Cross Checking the Instruments.
    Instrument Interpretation.
  Selective Radial Scan.

Instrument Limitations (Including System Failures).
Airmanship.

Instrument Flight – The Basic Manoeuvres.
  Straight and Level Flight.
    At Various Airspeeds and Aircraft Configurations.
Climbing and Descending.
Standard Rate Turns.
  Level Turns   ⎫
  Climbing Turns   ⎬ Including Turns Onto
  Descending Turns   ⎭ Pre-selected Headings.

Recoveries to Straight and Level Flight from:
  Climbing and Descending Turns.
  Spiral Dives.

The short Pre-Flight Briefing should be based upon the practical aspects of that part of the Long Briefing in relation to the Air Exercise to be covered.

DURING THE AIR DEMONSTRATION
This period should start with a demonstration of the physiological problems associated with the loss of outside visual cues. Following this the student should be convinced of the need to rely upon his instrument references rather than the use of his physical sensations in order to determine the aircraft attitude.

There are many demonstrations or combination of demonstrations which can be used to show the susceptibility of the human senses to disorientation, but it should only be necessary to show a few of them. Two examples are as follows:

The False Sensation of Turning
Whilst in straight and level flight ask the student to close his eyes and lower his head, pointing out that he should resist any temptation to look out, otherwise he will miss the sensations normally received during instrument flight.
Lower the right wing very gently and then positively roll the wings level whilst raising the nose attitude without changing power. At this stage ask the student what attitude the aircraft is in. His

balance and postural sensations will normally lead him to conclude that the aircraft has entered a turn to the left.

The False Sensation of Climbing

Whilst in straight and level flight ask the student to close his eyes and lower his head. Enter a medium turn to the left using a positive entry, then very gently change to a turn to the right whilst applying consistent back pressure to the control column. At this stage ask the student to tell you what attitude he thinks the aircraft has assumed. The physical sensation he has received will be that the aircraft is in a climbing left turn.

Once the student has seen that the physical sensation received from the senses of balance and posture can be misleading, he will have a better appreciation of the need to be able to fly by instrument reference before attempting to enter cloud or any other condition where outside visual references are minimal or completely absent.

NOTE:

It is not necessary to handle the aircraft violently or adopt extremes of attitude to achieve the effects of disorientation.

INSTRUMENT APPRECIATION

This term is used to describe the initial period of the flight exercise known as 'Introduction to Instrument Flying', during which the student is taught how to interpret the various flight instruments in relation to instrument flying and the basic elements of scanning technique.

The student should regard the exercise as a natural extension of his task in learning to become a competent pilot. The student will already have been taught the elements of 'precision flight' in relation to visual manoeuvres and therefore he will have a grasp of the instrument indications and a general understanding of how they show specific aspects of aircraft performance.

A student's rate of progress will be significantly improved if at an early stage of his instrument flight training plenty of emphasis is placed on the need to quickly interpret and react to the instrument indications. It will also be important for him to be introduced to the use of the various instruments in a progressive fashion, so as to gradually increase his workload until at the end of the total instrument flying exercise he has become competent to fly the aircraft safely whilst carrying out the basic manoeuvres without the use of outside visual references.

The use of the instrument visor (hood) or other means of restricting the student's vision to outside references should not be introduced until he is able to interpret the aircraft's attitude and performance and react correctly to achieve the desired results by reference to the instruments alone without the visor being lowered. This procedure will apply to each of the basic manoeuvres. Restricting his vision at an earlier stage will normally have a strong claustrophobic effect and delay his progress.

COMMON ERRORS

Normally the two most common errors will be in appreciating the small pitch adjustments required to the index aircraft of the attitude indicator and the ability to set up a reasonably continuous scan rate without gazing at any one instrument.

Other errors which can occur will be the trusting of physical sensations rather than instrument readings, and also tensing up on the controls. Either of these will be difficult to detect and the instructor must be sympathetic and re-assuring throughout the exercise in order to create an atmosphere in which the student can relax.

Introduction to Instrument Flying

Long Briefing

OBJECTIVES

This section is incorporated into the PPL syllabus so that the student will learn to appreciate the problems of Instrument Flying whilst at the same time giving him sufficient flight training to enable him to maintain control of the aircraft whilst returning to a *Visual Flight* situation in the event of inadvertent penetration into instrument weather conditions.

INTRODUCTION

In the past a number of fatal aviation accidents have been incurred wholly or partly by bad weather. Few of these accidents were due to a total disregard of the weather at the time of take-off but rather to pressures during flight which led to a situation in which the pilot displayed an inability to make a correct decision, and either turn back, or divert to an alternative airfield when faced with conditions of deteriorating weather.

Analysis of the causes of weather induced accidents reveal that in most cases the pilot 'pressed on' and attempted to fly in partial instrument flight conditions which often developed into full instrument conditions.

The basic Private Pilot Course does not equip a pilot to conduct or continue a flight in either of these circumstances, therefore any attempt to operate the aircraft under these conditions cannot possibly provide an adequate level of safety. These remarks are also applicable to pilots who have obtained a little instrument flying training or those who are not in current instrument flying practice.

The sole person responsible for the safety of the aircraft and its occupants once in flight is the pilot. He has the primary responsibility to seek and obtain up to date weather information, and ensure within the constraints often associated with this information (weather forecasts can often go awry) that the weather conditions are suitable for the successful completion of the planned flight.

Commenting upon air safety during the early days of flight the aviation pioneer, Wilbur Wright warned against 'carelessness and overconfidence' on the part of some pilots, such as lack of adequate pre-flight planning, risky weather decisions and lack of visual alertness for other aircraft. His warning still stands and in view of the increase in air traffic movements and the pressures of the modern world is probably ten times more applicable today. However what is also true is the fact that the pilot's weather safety 'check list' is a simple one and can be summed as follows:

1. Adequate Pre-Flight Planning, including the latest weather information, is essential for every flight.
2. The use of 'Go, No-Go' decisions are part of a pilot's responsibilities and when decisions to continue, turn back or divert to another airfield are required during flight they must be recognised early and made at the **right time**.

THE INSTRUMENT PANEL
The following paragraphs contain a brief summary of the flight instruments. A fuller explanation of all these instruments including the magnetic compass is given in Technical Manual No. 3 of the Ground Training Series.

The layout of the instrument panel will vary between aircraft of different makes and sometimes between different types of the same make. The student will have by now become accustomed to the composition and layout of the instruments fitted to the type on which he is training. However he must appreciate that when flying an aircraft which has a different instrument layout his initial ability to scan and read these instruments will be reduced.

The normal 'Full Panel' consists of three pressure instruments, the ASI, VSI, and Altimeter, and three gyro instruments comprising the Attitude, Heading and Turn Indicators, the latter also being fitted with a facility to show any condition of unbalance. Other instruments will also be required for instrument flying, amongst which are the Magnetic Compass and Tachometer. The two last mentioned will require less frequent reference than those previously mentioned.

The Air Speed Indicator

This instrument may be marked in knots or miles per hour or in many cases in both calibrations on the same instrument. During flight, whenever an attitude change occurs it will take several seconds before the ASI will accurately indicate the airspeed compatible with the new attitude. This fact will have already been learned by the student during his use of the instruments in relation to Visual Attitude Flight. However when flying solely by the use of instruments this lag between attitude selection and the inertia of the aircraft in arriving at the new airspeed will pose some difficulty to the pilot, and he must adopt a firm resistance against any tendency to 'chase the airspeed'.

The Altimeter
Many variations exist between altimeters in the presentation of altitude information. The most common display is the three-needle type which indicates 10,000's 1000's and 100's of feet. The subdivisions in the 100-ft band are normally in 20 foot or 50 foot increments. Within the United Kingdom millibars* are used as the units of pressure, but occasionally the pressure datum of an altimeter may be calibrated in inches of mercury. In such a case, when receiving QFE or QNH in millibars a conversion into inches will have to be made before the altimeter can be re-set. The standard datum of 1013.2 mb equals 29.92 inches and therefore when operating at a flight level with an altimeter calibrated in inches the figure of 29.92 inches should be set.

New altimeter presentations now gradually being introduced into General Aviation aircraft have a window through which a digital display gives a read out of height in thousands of feet, whilst a single pointer gives height in hundreds of feet. There are other combinations of digital display but they all have at least one pointer measuring hundreds of feet, in order to give the pilot a quick reference to any tendency of the aircraft to change its height.

The Vertical Speed Indicator

Apart from its use as a rate of descent or climb instrument, it is also a trend instrument, one which can be used to determine any consistent tendency for height variation to occur. This latter function is quite useful as it indicates a rate of height change a little more quickly than the average altimeter, and can therefore be invaluable for precision flight. However, one disadvantage is its tendency to 'hunt' during turbulent conditions and

---

* ICAO has now introduced the SI unit hectopascal as the standard unit for measuring atmospheric pressure. Values of hectopascals and millibars are equal (i.e. 1013 mb = 1013 hPa). The use of hectopascals in the U.K. has not, at present, been agreed by the CAA but could be adopted in the future.

in such circumstances its value is reduced, so that primary reference should be restricted to the altimeter.

Another aspect worthy of note is that if sudden movements of the elevators are made the instrument will temporarily indicate a reversed trend, i.e. a sudden backward movement of the control column will cause the VSI pointer to indicate a small rate of descent for a few moments before it gives the correct reading, in this case a rate of climb.

The Attitude Indicator

This is commonly referred to as the 'Master Instrument' because its pictorial presentation of aircraft attitude in pitch and bank requires a minimum of interpretation effort. It must however be fully appreciated that the indications obtained from this instrument relate only to the aircraft attitude, they do not reveal aircraft performance e.g. constant height, climbing or descending.

(a)   . (b)   (c)

Fig. 19-1

There are several types of attitude indicator in current use and fig. 19-1 (a) shows a modern-day presentation. At (b) the aircraft is being banked to the right at an angle of 15 degrees. Earlier versions as shown at (c) have a bank index pointer which moves to the left when a right bank is occurring. The pilot must therefore exercise extreme care to establish which of these presentations he is using.

The Heading Indicator

Bascially there are two presentations of heading indicator in current use and these are illustrated in fig. 19-2.

(a)   (b)

Fig. 19-2

The presentation at (a) is easier to use in that a complete visual indication of the various points of the compass together with the heading of the aircraft are present in the one picture.

The principle utilised in the function of the attitude indicator and heading indicator is that of 'gyroscopic rigidity' and the gyro is driven by an air source or electricity. The most common source in use for small aircraft is air, and a diagram of a typical system is shown in fig. 19-3.

Fig.19-3

The Turn Indicator and Turn Co-ordinator

Several types of presentation are currently in use and these are shown in the following fig. 19-4.

(a)   (b)   (c)

Fig. 19-4

All these instruments incorporate a balance indicator, either in the form of a pointer as shown at (a) or a ball or disc presentation as shown at (b) and (c). The turn indicator shown at (b) and the turn co-ordinator shown at (c) may be calibrated to show either a two-minute or four-minute turn through 360 degrees, and due to the different presentations of the turn index marks it will usually be advisable to check the position of the turn needle or index aircraft relative to the turn markers during flight to establish the correct indication of a rate one turn. In most modern aircraft these instruments are operated by electricity.

PHYSIOLOGICAL CONSIDERATIONS
The three primary senses used to establish physical orientation are those of sight, motion and posture. During flight the sense of sight permits direct reference to the natural horizon and also the position and aspect of the ground. These visual cues are used by the pilot to determine his position in space, i.e. whether level, banking or climbing, etc. During Instrument Flight all references to the natural horizon or ground are lost, and interpretation of the aircraft attitude and performance will have to be perceived through the indications given by the flight instruments.

Whilst on the ground any one of these senses will normally determine which way the human body is orientated, i.e. standing up, lying down, leaning to one side etc. However, during flight the only reliable sense which can be used on its own to determine the aircraft attitude is that of sight.

During flight the three basic senses will be perceiving messages and transmitting them to the brain, when all of these sense are passing the same information, the brain can interpret the messages clearly but if conflicting information is passed, the brain is unable to respond correctly and confusion will exist, which could lead to incorrect control actions being taken.

IF MESSAGES CONFLICT
CONFUSION WILL EXIST
AND LEAD TO –
DISORIENTATION

During instrument flight the sense of sight may sometimes disagree with the information being perceived by one or both of the supporting senses, e.g. motion and posture. When this happens a condition called spatial disorientation will occur, the severity of which will depend upon the individual, his proficiency and the acuteness of the situation which caused the misleading information in the first place.

Whereas the sense of sight is not easily misled the senses of motion and posture can be confused fairly easily during flight. The sense of motion originates within the balance mechanism (vestibular organ) of the inner ear, which has the faculty to register linear and rotational acceleration and deceleration. However this balance mechanism can misinterpret attitude changes in flight because it is not capable of distinguishing between centrifugal force and gravity or detecting between constant airspeed and small changes in airspeed.

The effects of gravity and centrifugal forces are closely related during flight manoeuvres and the resultant of these forces can only be interpreted by the sense of vision. Because of this the sense of motion will often become unreliable and must be disregarded. The sense of posture obtains its perceptions through the variation of pressure on the body muscles and tendons. With the eyes closed, it is still possible to detect whether one is standing up, lying down or sitting down because of the information transmitted to the brain from the muscles. However, as with the sense of motion, the postural sense will not be capable of differentiating for example between an aircraft attitude change involving entry to a climb or entry to a turn.

To sum up, false sensations or sensory illusions may occur at any time during flight and are far from uncommon. These illusions are most likely to occur when attempting to fly visually without adequate external cues, or during any period when sole reference to the aircraft instruments is required. Therefore in order to operate an aircraft safely during instrument flight a pilot must train himself to ignore false sensations and rely on his correct visual interpretation of the instruments.

INSTRUMENT LIMITATIONS
The respective operating limitations, errors and serviceability checks are covered in Technical Manual No. 3 Aircraft Instruments. However it will be of benefit to review the operating limits of the gyro instruments at this stage.

Attitude Indicator
There are several types of attitude indicator which may be fitted into small aircraft, and they are usually operated from a vacuum system. Earlier types of attitude indicator have defined limitations in relation to pitch and roll due to the geometrical arrangement of the gimbals and their freedom of movement in relation to the construction of the fixed and moving parts of the instrument. This effectively limits their freedom to approximately 110° in roll either side and about 60° in pitch up or pitch down. When these limits are exceeded the instrument will topple and take about 10 minutes to re-erect and become reliable again.

Later models of vacuum operated attitude indicators have been designed in such a way that complete freedom in roll is achieved and if the instrument is brought to the vertical attitude in pitch (up or down) the properties of precession are so harnessed to permit the gyro assembly to roll through 180° as the vertical attitude is reached, thereby indicating an inverted attitude as the aircraft movement is continued through a looping manoeuvre. The net effect is to present an instrument which is normally topple free. However if the aircraft is rolled when in a near vertical attitude the instrument will topple and take several minutes to re-erect and become of use again.

Heading Indicator
As with the attitude indicator the toppling limits of this instrument will vary dependent upon its make and type. The older directional gyro indicator as illustrated in fig. 19-2 (b) has toppling limits of 55 degrees in both pitch and roll. However it will have complete freedom in pitch or roll if the heading of the aircraft coincides with the axis of rotation at the time of the pitching or rolling movement. Later versions of heading indicators may be of the type which is limited in pitch and roll whilst others may have topple free characteristics.

Due to the effects of bearing friction and the normal drift of the gimbal system about its vertical axis due to the earth's rotation it will be necessary to re-set the heading indicator with the magnetic compass approximately every 10 to 15 minutes.

Turn Indicator or Turn Co-ordinator
Although this instrument uses a rate gyro system it only has one gimbal ring and will not topple, it does in one sense have a limitation in that it will be limited to the maximum rate of turn it can indicate. Some types are limited to show just over a rate 1 turn and others can show up to a rate 4. In the case of those instruments which are limited to show no more than a rate 2 turn, the pilot will have no reliable indication of greater rates of turn. This could present a problem in the case of a spiral dive whilst flying on instruments.

INSTRUMENT SYSTEM FAILURES
There are basically three types of systems involved in the operation of the flight instruments, these are:

1. The Pitot/Static System
    The pitot system conveys ram air pressure to the air speed indicator via an externally mounted pressure head, whilst the static system is incorporated together with the pitot tube or as a separate flush fitting to the fuselage. The static system is used to vent the altimeter, vertical speed indicator and air speed indicator to the surrounding atmosphere.

2. The Vacuum System
    This provides a suction source to drive the mechanism of the gyro instruments. The most common method in use consists of an

engine driven suction pump, but a small number of aircraft, usually of older manufacture, utilise the principle of an externally mounted venturi assembly. The disadvantage of this latter method lies in the fact that its operational efficiency is impaired at low airspeeds, and is also prone to icing.

3.   The Electrical System
     Electricity is often used to drive one or more of the gyro instruments and for fail/safe purposes a common arrangement is that where a vacuum system is used to operate the attitude and heading indicators, an electrical system is utilised to operate the turn indicator or turn co-ordinator.

     Electricity is also employed to supply a heating element in the air speed indicator to prevent malfunction of this component during heavy rain or icing conditions. Some engine and other instruments, e.g. fuel, temperature and flap gauges are also frequently operated by an electric current.

Due to the importance of having correctly functioning instruments during instrument flight, it is vital that the pilot knows the source from which each instrument is operated, and any remedial measures he could employ during flight should any system malfunction.

Although the power instruments, i.e. manifold pressure gauge and/or tachometer, are considered as part of the flight instruments for the practical purpose of instrument flying, the failure of these instruments is not considered under this heading.

The Pitot/Static System

Damage to or blockage of either the pitot tube (or when fitted the static vent) will produce erroneous or even zero readings to the instruments operated by the system.

If a blockage occurs in the static system during flight and the aircraft is maintaining altitude at the time, there will be no reaction from the altimeter or vertical speed indicator, both will continue to give a steady reading, unfortunately these readings will also remain constant should the aircraft climb or descend. However the air speed indicator used in conjunction with the attitude indicator will normally give an indication that the static source is not functioning correctly.

For example, referring to the basic principle of operation of the air speed indicator, it will be remembered that the value of the indicated airspeed is a measure of the dynamic pressure in the pitot tube after the static pressure either side of the capsule has been cancelled out.

If the static pressure line becomes constricted or blocked, the static pressure within the system will remain relatively unchanged during a descent, but the value of the static pressure in the pitot line will increase as the altitude decreases. This will result in an increase in the instrument reading even though the actual airspeed remains unchanged.

This increase is quite marked and depending (to a certain extent) upon the actual construction of a particular pitot/static system and the altitude band through which the aircraft descends, the indicated airspeed could double during a descent through 1000 feet.

Therefore an aircraft with a red line speed (V_{ne}) of 160 knots which is slowly desending from 3000 to 2000 feet at an actual airspeed of 80 knots could have an indicated airspeed of 160 knots upon reaching 2000 feet. If this situation occurred during flight in cloud the psychological effect on the pilot could lead to a circumstance whereby reference to the air speed indicator on its own might cause the pilot to continuously raise the aircraft's nose and so create a stall condition. On the other hand, the proper reference and interpretation of the control instruments, i.e. the attitude indicator and power gauges would enable a pilot to recognise this situation and permit him to handle the aircraft safely.

The reverse of this condition will occur if the aircraft ascends, when the indicated airspeed would gradually decrease. Again, proper reference to and interpretation of the attitude indicator and power instrument readings will enable the pilot to assess the true state of affairs.

If the pitot tube becomes restricted or blocked during flight the opposite effect will result, in that, as the aircraft descends the air speed indicator will show a decreasing airspeed, or if the aircraft ascends an increasing airspeed will be indicated.

In either situation reference to the attitude indicator and power instruments will enable a pilot to identify the true situation and so avoid a hazardous flight condition.

Icing is a common cause of blockage to the pitot/static system and because of this it is vitally important that flight in instrument weather conditions should never be planned without a pitot heater being available and switched on prior to cloud penetration or when flying in heavy rain or in snow. It must be appreciated that heavy rain and even light snow can reduce outside vision to almost nil, thus making instrument flight essential.

The Vacuum System
Failure or malfunction of the vacuum system, either through clogged filters or malfunction of the suction pump can produce marked

erroneous indications from the gyro instruments. The pilot must therefore be alert to any significant changes to the reading of the suction gauge and/or conflict between the readings of the gyro and pitot/static instruments.

Items such as worn gimbal bearings and dirty filters usually give an early warning to the pilot through the sluggish erection or excessive vibration of the gyro instruments during the pre-flight phase. An alert pilot will take note of these warnings by placing the aircraft unserviceable before an in-flight failure occurs.

Where an externally mounted venturi is used to drive the gyro instruments, correct functioning will depend upon the speed of the airflow passing through them. The integrity of this system can only be checked once the aircraft is airborne and a reasonable speed has been attained. It will therefore be very important to monitor the readings of the gyro instruments in the very early stages of a flight, i.e. during the initial climb after take-off to identify any malfunction.

The Electrical System

Most flight instruments driven by electricity incorporate a warning flag to show the pilot when the electricity supply to the particular instrument is fluctuating or has been cut off. When scanning such instruments prior to or during flight any visible signs of this flag will be an indication that the system is suspect and that the instrument cannot be relied upon.

In these circumstances the appropriate fuse or circuit breaker should be checked and replaced or re-set in an attempt to rectify the situation.

Important Note:

All instrument indications should be checked as far as is possible prior to flight and during the take-off and initial climb out. This may ensure an early warning of any impending instrument problems during a flight.

Normally, if any instrument is giving indications of an erroneous reading or is sluggish in response whilst the aircraft is on the ground the flight should be cancelled. If similar indications are noted during flight the flight should be terminated as soon as it is safely possible.

If any ambiguous instrument indications are observed during flight, the aircraft should be held in or returned to the straight and level attitude and the cause investigated.

If it is considered that the attitude indicator is giving reliable readings then it should remain the master instrument. If the attitude indicator is considered unreliable then utilise the indirect information from two or more of the other performance instruments to establish the aircraft attitude.

In the case of a suspect or known malfunction of the gyro instruments, check that the suction or electrical supply is available, and bear in mind that in the case of externally mounted venturi systems a minimum airspeed will be needed to allow the gyro instruments to give reliable indications.

If insufficient suction is the cause and an alternate source is available, e.g. on multi-engine aircraft a selection to the alternate source should be made. If a failure in the electrical supply occurs, the appropriate fuse or circuit breaker should be changed or re-set and it might be necessary to consider reducing the load on the electrical system.

In the case of a suspect or known malfunction of the pitot/static instruments when an alternate static system is fitted it should be selected immediately. If an alternate source is not available and it is essential to obtain accurate altitude information for the descent, e.g. the cloud base is not high enough to permit a descent to VMC below without altitude information the glass of the vertical speed indicator can be broken thus permitting cockpit static air to enter the system.

This source of static air will normally be at a slightly lower pressure than the air surrounding the aircraft and therefore the pressure activated instruments will give slightly inaccurate readings. Any errors will normally be small, e.g. approximately 50 feet in altitude and 5 knots in airspeed.

Providing the pilot has been trained in instrument flying by reference to a limited number of instruments, he will usually be able to control the aircraft using the appropriate standard power settings and initiate a safe descent through cloud. However when cloud bases are below the relevant safety altitude a functioning altimeter may become a necessity if the descent is to be conducted safely.

AIRMANSHIP

Apart from the hazards which are always present when a pilot operates in flight conditions beyond his capabilities, the situation of flight in very poor visibility requires increased skills in the use of instruments, and brings added dangers in the form of airborne collision risk. The following illustration shows the time taken at different distances for two aircraft to come together at a closing speed of 360 m.p.h.

The columns on the right indicate the distance and time available to manoeuvre the aircraft into an avoiding turn and the column on the left shows the average time needed to commence the turn from the first moment a sighting is made.

The aircraft used in the illustration has a wing span of 32 feet and to obtain the correct impression of size for the respective distances shown, the reader should stand back about 9 feet from the picture.

Seconds

	Miles	Seconds
	10	100
	6	60
	5	50
	4	40
	3	30
	2	20
	1	10
	$\frac{1}{2}$	5

	Seconds
See Object	0.1
Recognise Aircraft	1.0
Become Aware of Collision Course	5.0
Decision to Turn Left or Right	4.0
Muscular Reaction	0.4
Aircraft Lag Time	2.0
Total Time	12.5

In using these figures an allowance will have to be made for the fact that it would be rare for a pilot to spot an approaching aircraft the moment it came within visual sighting range, because in poor visibility conditions the increase in cockpit workload will be high, e.g. the greater use of flight instruments, and the frequent use of map and ground scanning to identify the aircraft position.

INSTRUMENT APPRECIATION

ATTITUDE INSTRUMENT FLIGHT

During initial training a pilot is taught attitude flight through the use of visual cues obtained from outside references, e.g. the natural horizon and the aspect of the ground relative to the aircraft.

Following this, precision flight is introduced and achieved by co-relating outside visual references with fairly frequent scanning of the aircraft flight instruments, and in this way any small deviations from altitude, heading or airspeed, are more quickly perceived and corrected.

When flying by sole reference to the instruments however, attitude flight is still achieved but now the visual cues are obtained through scanning the instruments alone and interpreting the aircraft attitude and performance from their readings. The attitude indicator can be considered as the *Master Instrument* for this purpose, for though it does not give performance indications, e.g. speed, rate of climb, etc. it does give the pilot a direct picture of the aircraft attitude, e.g. wings level or banked, nose high or low.

Pitch Indications
Direct information regarding the aircraft's attitude in pitch is obtained from the attitude indicator by noting the position of the miniature aircraft (index aircaft) in relation to the artificial horizon line. Alternatively or in addition to the information given by the attitude indicator, indirect pitch information can be obtained from the air speed indicator, altimeter and vertical speed indicator.

With regard to the use of the attitude indicator some instruments display pitch information in degrees, above and below a zero (neutral) position, the increments of degrees so displayed, vary between instruments and the actual angle is not always denoted against the pitch lines which are shown on the instrument face.

Apart from the information obtained by the use of pitch lines another term known as *Bar Width* is currently used in order to describe the actual amount of movement of the index aircraft in the pitching plane. Due to the differences in instrument presentation the index aircraft wings are sometimes thicker than the artificial horizon line and sometimes the artificial horizon line is thicker than the wings of the index aircraft. Therefore to aid the pilot in the measurement of index aircraft movement the term bar width should be applied to either the index aircraft wings or artificial horizon line whichever of the two is the thickest.

Many attitude indicators used in light aircraft are equipped with an index aircraft symbol in which the basic relationship of the index aircraft symbol to the artificial horizon line is adjustable by the pilot, and it is essential that pilots of aeroplanes fitted with this facility should be aware of the dangers of misuse of the adjusting facility in flight.

If the position of the aircraft symbol is altered while flying on instruments the pilot's reference for corrective action is no longer valid and the chances of a prompt recovery or in extreme cases a successful recovery, to normal flight may be jeopardised.

The occasions when a pilot may be tempted to adjust his horizon datum in flight will usually occur during prolonged turns, climbs and descents, when there may be a gap between the horizon line and the index aircraft. It is not considered that such adjustments are either necessary or advantageous for successful instrument flying. In fact, it is a necessary adjunct to good instrument flying that a pilot becomes familiar with the appropriate pitch attitude of the index aircraft symbol in relation to the artificial horizon in various phases of flight. Any variation of this basic reference feature will interfere with the acquisition of such knowledge.

It is therefore recommended that, in fixed wing aircraft fitted with attitude indicators which have a pitch datum adjusting facility, the reference aircraft symbol should be aligned correctly before flight, and that no further adjustment should be made during flight.

Bank Indications
Figure 19-5 (b) shows the picture given by the attitude indicator when the aircraft is banking to the left in level flight. The number of degrees of bank is shown by the position of the pointer at the top of the instrument face. Behind this pointer the periphery of the instrument is marked out with 10 degree lines up to 30°, thereafter lines are marked out at 60° and 90°.

(a)   (b)

Fig. 19-5

The instrument shown in fig. 19-6 indicates the aircraft is in a low nose attitude and banking to the right. It must be clearly understood that the attitude indicator shows a direct picture of the aircraft's attitude and not of its performance, e.g. climbing, descending or turning. Information relative to aircraft performance has to be obtained from the other flight instruments.

Different Dial Presentations
The information given by the instrument does to a certain extent

Fig. 19-6

depend upon the specific make of instrument and time of manufacture, in that some earlier models have a bank pointer at the bottom of the instrument face and some have bank pointers which indicate degrees of bank in the opposite sense to the actual direction of bank and this can be confusing (fig. 19-7).

Fig. 19-7

In more recent models this bank pointer is synchronised with the direction of turn, i.e. when the aircraft is banking to the right the bank pointer indicates to the right (fig. 19-8).

Fig. 19-8

Introduction to the Use of the Attitude Indicator
During the flight demonstration the aircraft will be placed in level flight and trimmed, following which, the position of the index aircraft in relation to the artificial horizon line must be noted.

Pitch Attitude
The aircraft will then be placed in a high-nose attitude and cross reference made to the position of the aircraft's nose to the natural horizon and the index aircraft's position relative to the artificial horizon.

After this the index aircraft will be returned to the level attitude in relation to the artificial horizon and this attitude confirmed by outside visual reference. The demonstration will be repeated for a low-nose attitude.

Bar Widths

The effect of displacing the index aircraft by one bar's width in pitch will be shown, to establish the marked effect on aircraft attitude when a change of one bar width is made. The effect of such a pitch change should be noted by holding the new attitude for approximately one minute to see its effect upon the performance instruments, i.e. in this case the ASI, altimeter and VSI.

It will be seen that this relatively small movement of the index aircraft can cause very significant changes in airspeed and initial rates of ascent and descent, thus highlighting the need for very small movements of the controls when re-adjusting the position of the index aircraft to a constant attitude in pitch.

Bank Attitude

After an appreciation of control in pitch through the use of the attitude indicator, the indications of bank can be ascertained. The aircraft will be placed in banked attitudes of 10°, 15°, and 20° and the position of the index aircraft together with the bank pointer readings should be noted.

In the case of those attitude indicators which have radial lines on the lower half of the instrument face, the angle of bank which results when the index aircraft's wings are aligned with the first radial line can also be ascertained by reference to the bank angle pointer.

Having established the bank indications by reference to the index aircraft and bank scale, the aircraft should be rolled level by reference to the index aircraft and artificial horizon, this attitude can then be confirmed by reference to the natural horizon.

In the initial stage of the introduction to attitude instrument flying the student will be given practice in maintaining the aircraft in the laterally level and constant pitch attitude, by reference to the attitude indicator alone. During this period a student should be developing the physical skills necessary to interpret and apply the correct control pressures to maintain the index aircraft in the correct position relative to the artificial horizon line.

Heading and Balance

The maintenance or change of an aircraft's heading is an aspect of its performance and is established by reference to the heading indicator and/or the magnetic compass. Although under normal flight circumstances an indication of bank on the attitude indicator usually implies the aircraft is turning it must nevertheless be appreciated that the presence of a small degree of bank can quite easily be inadvertently counteracted by a small amount of opposite rudder. Although this will prevent the aircraft from turning it will be out of balance. Alternatively, the index aircraft may show the aircraft wings are laterally level but if the aircraft is not in balanced flight it could be slowly changing its heading.

In addition to the foregoing points it is sometimes possible for a bank error to be present in the attitude indicator. This error is most commonly caused by the turning or acceleration errors which are normally inherent in the instrument. As a result of these errors the artificial horizon line may take a short while to settle down and give an accurate reading following a turn or sudden acceleration.

In these circumstances, although the index aircraft has been correctly aligned with the artificial horizon the aircraft will still be slightly banked. In such a situation the aircraft will be turning slowly and any attempt to use rudder to hold a constant heading will result in the aircraft being out of balance. Providing the pilot is aware of these errors in the attitude indicator and the reasons why they occur, the problem will not be a significant one.

For the purpose of accurate instrument flight it will be necessary for a pilot when straightening the aircraft from a turn, to cross check with the heading and balance indicators. For these reasons the heading indicator is the primary instrument for control of heading, but it should be used in conjunction with the balance indicator to confirm that the aircraft is in balance during straight or turning flight.

Attitude, Power and Performance
Whether the aircraft is being flown using outside visual references or instrument references the concept of attitude flight remains the same, i.e.

Power + Attitude = Performance
where: *Power* is related to the thrust delivered by the engine and,
Attitude relates to the aircraft attitude in pitch, lateral level or bank, and direction and balance.
Performance is the airspeed and direction of the aircraft's flight path, e.g. flying level, climbing, descending (including rate of climb or descent) during straight or turning flight.

Attitude Instrument Flying
Attitude instrument flight entails controlling an aircraft's attitude and performance through the instrument indications when the

natural horizon cannot be seen. The pilot interprets the attitude of the aircraft through the readings of the instruments available to him, and then, as in visual flight, changes the attitude and power until the desired performance is achieved.

Aircraft performance essentially depends upon how the pilot arranges the attitude of the aircraft in relation to the thrust being used. Therefore when a full instrument panel is being used, the power instruments (tachometer and/or manifold pressure gauges) and the attitude indicator are termed the *Control Instruments*.

The instruments which give performance information, i.e. the air speed indicator, altimeter, vertical speed indicator, heading indicator and turn and balance indicator (or turn co-ordinator) are termed the *Performance Instruments*.

When a full instrument panel is being used the idea of referring to instruments by two groups in the above manner is consistent with the development of current day instrument flying techniques, however should a full set of instruments not be available, e.g. due to the lack of, or the unserviceability of the attitude indicator the group termed *Performance Instruments* will have to be used to provide both performance and attitude information.

There are five steps employed in Attitude Instrument Flight to achieve a given performance; these are:

1. Adjust power and attitude with reference to the power instruments and attitude indicator. Referrring to the balance indicator to confirm that the correct balance is being maintained and then adjust the trimming control(s).
2. Allow time for the aircraft to become stabilised at a constant airspeed, pitch and lateral attitude, altitude or rate of ascent or descent.
3. Use the performance instruments to assess the accuracy of the performance achieved.
4. Adjust attitude and/or power as necessary to obtain the desired performance.
5. When the desired performance is achieved, a final adjustment to the trimming control(s) will be needed.

It will be remembered that when changing an aircraft's attitude to a new position, e.g. raising the nose, a small reversed pressure on the control column will be required immediately following completion of the initial movement. This is necessary to prevent the nose continuing to rise beyond the point selected.

Apart from this action, it must also be appreciated that during flight by the combined use of outside references and instruments, the pilot will subconsciously be making use of his peripheral vision. However during flight by the sole use of instruments a pilot's visual reference area will become appreciably narrower, because at any one moment he will tend to look directly at a particular instrument. Added to this it must also be appreciated that small movements of the index aircraft on the attitude indicator are not always easy to detect. Therefore positive emphasis must be given during deliberate attitude changes to the sequence of, Change – Check – Hold – Adjust – Trim as depicted below.

Effect of Changing Power
During normal flight, attitude and/or power changes are made to establish or change the aircraft's performance in relation to altitude, airspeed or rate of climb or descent.

Once the required performance is decided upon the pilot must make the necessary change to the attitude and power. Although the attitude indicator meets the requirements of accurately indicating changing attitude it will not show how much change will be required, and this information must be obtained from the performance instruments.

If for example the desired airspeed is not being achieved for a constant altitude a change to the attitude and power will be needed. A pilot will learn from experience the approximate combination of attitude and power to be used for a particular flight condition and once these have been set and the aircraft established on a given flight path, only small changes in attitude and/or power should be required.

To sum up therefore, any change in performance will require a change in attitude or power. If any alteration is made to the power setting it will affect the pitch trim of the aircraft, and in addition there will be the less marked but still significant effect of slipstream and torque.

Therefore the control pressures which are necessary during this transition period must be anticipated, and during instrument flight it will also assist if the rate at which the throttle and/or propeller pitch control movements are reduced. This will allow the pilot to achieve smoother control over the aircraft when he is flying with limited reference features, i.e. by the flight instruments alone.

The flight demonstration for this exercise will consist of establishing an attitude and power setting and then changing the power and attitude to achieve significantly different airspeeds while maintaining a constant altitude.

Cross Checking the Instruments

The basis of all instrument flying is the correct division of attention to and interpretation of the flight instruments. A continuous process of cross reference must be devised between the *Control* and *Performance* instruments in a fashion which is both comprehensive and efficient.

Fig. 19-9

However looking at the appropriate instrument at the right time can only produce the desired results provided the pilot is able to understand and evaluate what he sees. Therefore, a proper division of attention and *Interpretation* are the two essential elements of any cross-check technique.

Instrument Interpretation

The student will already be aware of the direct indications of the various instruments which comprise the instrument flight panel, and it will be appreciated that the *Control Instruments*, i.e. the attitude indicator and the power instruments, give immediate and direct information in response to control changes.

The performance instruments will give both direct and indirect indications but they are also subject to lag. For example the altimeter gives a direct indication of altitude (subject to a small lag) and an indirect indication of pitch, i.e. if the altitude changes for a constant power setting the pitch attitude of the aircraft will have changed.

In the case of the air speed indicator, this will give a direct indication of airspeed which if constant also means that for a given power setting the pitch attitude is remaining unchanged. The air speed indicator therefore also gives an indirect indication of pitch.

The following table lists the direct and indirect indications given by the performance instruments:

INSTRUMENT	INDICATION	
	DIRECT	INDIRECT
AIR SPEED INDICATOR	AIRSPEED	PITCH
ALTIMETER	ALTITUDE	PITCH
VERTICAL SPEED INDICATOR	RATE OF CLIMB OR DESCENT	PITCH
HEADING INDICATOR	HEADING	BANK
TURN INDICATOR	RATE OF TURN	BANK
BALANCE INDICATOR	BALANCE	YAW/BANK

The instrument cross-check technique or sequence will vary with different phases of flight, however pilots must become familiar with the various factors to be considered when dividing their attention between instruments. They must also know how to interpret the symptoms which enable them to assess whether their cross-check techniques are correct for any particular flight manoeuvre.

The ability of the instruments to give direct and indirect indications has already been mentioned, so has the effect of lag, which often occurs in the performance instruments and which is aggravated when rapid control movements are made.

Instrument lag is due to the inertia of an aircraft and the operating mechanism of the instruments. Therefore inevitably some degree of instrument lag must be accepted as an inherent factor.

When the attitude and power are properly controlled, the lag in the performance instruments should not appreciably affect the tolerance within which the pilot controls the aircraft, nor should it interfere with the maintenance of, or the changing of, either attitude or power indications.

With this in mind the pilot must appreciate that the performance instruments will take a little time (a very little time if small control movements are made) to stabilise, and this must be allowed for, otherwise a situation develops where the pilot makes direct control movements in response to the lag factor which in turn leads to erratic control movements, and additional changes to the instrument indications, with consequently yet more instrument lag effects.

A further point to note under this heading is that the use of the instruments alone causes a greater workload on the pilot. This, together with the fact that a change in aircraft attitude is often more quickly discernible through the performance instruments, than would be the case when using the natural horizon will lead to a tendency for the pilot to over react to any change in the instrument readings.

The most effective way of combating such a situation is to give adequate attention to the *Control Instruments* and move the controls slowly when making attitude or power changes, this will reduce any tendency to 'chase' the performance instruments, minimise the possible errors, and lead to the development of a smoother instrument flying technique.

Selective Radial Scan

When instrument flying techniques were first being developed there were few instruments available for use as control and performance indicators, but today the number of flight instruments including those used for radio navigation may be ten or more.

Due to the smaller number of instruments the older methods of scanning were largely centred on a technique in which the pilot scanned each instrument in turn, directing his gaze in a clockwise or anti clockwise fashion around the instrument panel. Many experienced instrument pilots still use this system, but pay more attention to those instruments which have more importance to the particular stage of the manoeuvre.

Today, the instrument training technique which is most favoured is called *Selective Radial Scan*. This is a technique where, when a full panel is used, the attitude indicator is established as the *Master Instrument* and the particular performance instruments needed for any stage of a manoeuvre are termed the *Supporting Instruments*. Supporting instruments can be divided into *Primary* or *Secondary* depending upon their importance at different stages of a manoeuvre.

In this technique a selective process is used so that each instrument is interrogated according to its degree of importance at any given moment. Additionally the frequency of interrogation of a particular instrument can be varied to suit any stage of a manoeuvre.

To give a practical example of this, first consider the relative importance of the various instruments during straight and level flight. Once this flight condition has been established at a given altitude and airspeed with the aircraft correctly trimmed, the air speed indicator, vertical speed indicator, altimeter, heading indicator and balance indicator will be the performance instruments for the monitoring of constant airspeed, altitude, heading and balance. If the power and altitude remain constant, the airspeed should not change, and providing the aircraft wings are level and the heading is constant the aircraft should be in balance. From this it can be seen that in maintaining straight and level flight the air speed indicator and balance indicator will require less monitoring than the other instruments. The primary supporting instruments will therefore be the vertical speed indicator/altimeter and the heading indicator, whilst the attitude indicator will remain the *Master Instrument* at all times for the reasons given in the following paragraphs.

The word 'radial' inserted into the term *Selective Radial Scan* applies to the technique of using the attitude indicator as a *Control* or *Master Instrument* in that all attitude changes are made by reference to this instrument, from which the pilot also radiates his interrogation scan of the other instruments, as shown in fig. 9-10. Note the scan moves radially outward from the attitude indicator to the particular performance instrument and then directly back again.

Fig. 19-10

In this method the scan always returns to the attitude indicator before radiating out to another performance instrument and therefore two performance instruments are never scanned in succession. This procedure permits the most frequent attitude check compatible with establishing the aircraft's required performance.

Fig. 19-11

The greater the frequency with which the instruments can be scanned the less time there will be for significant deviations to occur, and the smoother the instrument flying will become. The frequency or number of times the instruments can be scanned in any given period will clearly be greater if the pilot can reduce the number of instruments to check during his scan cycle.

This will also permit a more efficient utilisation of the pilot's scan technique in that he will be able to devote more scan time to an instrument which is more subject to deviation than the others.

For example, once an aircraft has been stabilised and trimmed in the straight and level attitude the altitude will be less likely to change than the heading. Therefore when using the selective technique it will be advisable to scan more often between the attitude indicator and the heading indicator than the attitude indicator and the altimeter, this principle will increase the rate of scan where it is most needed and as a result reduce the number and size of heading deviations.

To summarise, the technique of *Selective Radial Scan* is simply a method whereby the pilot radiates his scan out and back from the attitude indicator to the chosen performance instrument. This action is repeated for each performance instrument selected as being important to the particular part of a manoeuvre or to the continued maintenance of a flight condition.

The development of the selective radial scan can only come through practice and in this respect the student should be introduced gradually to the technique during flight.

Note: In the illustration below and those shown on the following pages, the thickness of the arrows indicate the relative frequency in which the instruments are scanned.

In the early stages the aircraft will

be established in level flight and only the attitude indicator and one of the performance instruments will be scanned, e.g. the attitude indicator and the altimeter.

Fig. 19-12

Fig. 19-13

Once the student has developed sufficient proficiency at maintaining the wings level at a constant altitude under instrument conditions the scope of the scan should be increased to include the heading indicator.

After which the selective process should be continued so that the secondary supporting instruments are gradually brought into the scan sequence at the appropriate intervals, see figs 19-14 and 19-15.

Fig. 19-14

Fig. 19-15

One very common problem during the development of scan technique is *Fixation*, this is the tendency to stare at a particular instrument. This often occurs when the pilot finds it difficult to hold a steady indication on a particular instrument or when a large deviation from a required indication takes place. Any form of fixation will inevitably lead to a worsening of the pilot's accuracy, because whilst he is staring at one instrument probably with increasing tension, another instrument changes its reading unnoticed and accumulated errors will follow.

The quicker a pilot can develop a continuous scan without stopping to stare at any one instrument, the easier and quicker the situation can be interpreted, and correct control responses effected.

A further point regarding selective radial scan techniques is that it is not necessary for a pilot to commit to memory the scan patterns for the various manoeuvres, because as long as the principle is understood he will in general instinctively be able to assess which instruments must be monitored and scanned more frequently.

THE BASIC MANOEUVRES

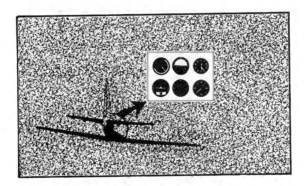

The sequence used when referring to the flight instruments to obtain and maintain any desired flight attitude and performance condition is best discussed under three headings, these are:

Achieving, Maintaining and Correcting.

Note: Although straight and level flight should be covered in its entirety before proceeding with the other basic manoeuvres, the exact sequence in which the various parts of Climbing, Desending and Turning are introduced will depend upon the particular instructor's technique which must take into account the prevailing circumstances, e.g. weather considerations, student's progress, etc.

Straight and Level Flight
At the commencement of the air exercise the aircraft will initially be placed in a condition other than straight and level flight.

Achieving:

The aircraft will be placed in the approximate straight and level attitude by reference to the attitude indicator and with cruise power set. (Control Instruments.)

Monitor the attitude indicator, heading indicator and altimeter (Primary Supporting Instruments) whilst the aircraft is being trimmed. If the attitude in pitch is correct for the power being used the altimeter reading will remain constant.

If an altitude change is being indicated by the altimeter the index aircraft should be lowered or raised as appropriate. A half bar width or less should normally be sufficient. At this stage a fine trim adjustment should be made.

If the aircraft wings are level and the heading indicator is showing a constant heading, the aircraft will be maintaining straight flight in a balanced condition.

If the heading indication is changing, first ensure that the index aircraft wings are level and then check the balance indicator (secondary supporting instrument). If the latter is indicating an out of balance condition keep the wings level and apply rudder as necessary.

If the index aircraft wings are level and the balance indicator shows that balanced flight is being achieved, but the heading indication is changing, it will be indicative of an artificial horizon error. In this case apply a slight bank as appropriate to the index aircraft and re-adjust rudder pressure as required to maintain a balanced condition.

Maintaining Pitch:

Once straight and level flight is achieved and a proper scan rate is used, the primary supporting instruments will be the heading indicator and the vertical speed indicator. The altimeter and air speed indicator become secondary supporting instruments and should be included in the scan as required.

The emphasis on the use of the vertical speed indicator lies in the fact that it is a more useful *trend* instrument in that it usually responds to altitude changes a little more quickly than the altimeter, and it will also give an indication of the magnitude of the pitch error.

When reacting to indications from the vertical speed indicator, the index aircraft should only be moved a maximum of a ½ bar width at a time as the instrument is very sensitive to altitude variation.

Note: When turbulent weather conditions (even light turbulence) are being experienced in a light aircraft the needle of the vertical speed indicator will tend to fluctuate and it will become difficult to interpret it accurately. Therefore when turbulence is present the pilot should in the main reduce his scan to the attitude indicator and altimeter to maintain altitude.

Maintaining Heading & Balance:

In relation to the maintenance of a constant heading with the aircraft in balance, this can normally be achieved by the use of the attitude indicator and the heading indicator. However the balance indicator should occasionally be brought into the pilot's scan as a secondary supporting instrument.

Correcting:

Attitude in Pitch

If the aircraft is allowed to descend below or climb above the required altitude a correction to the pitch attitude will have to be applied and the aircraft returned to the desired altitude.

Small errors in altitude will only require small changes to the position of the index aircraft and normally not more than one bar's width should initially be used.

If the error is in excess of approximately 100 feet a small power alteration may be required to assist in returning the aircraft to the original altitude, particularly if an altitude loss has occurred.

CORRECTING

Once a correction is started the altimeter will become the primary performance instrument instead of the vertical speed indicator. Remember that the rate of closure to the desired altitude will depend upon the *amount* by which the index aircraft has been altered in conjunction with any change in power. Just before the correct altitude is reached commence to apply control pressure to re-adjust the position of the index aircraft and the power setting (if applicable)·. Reintroduce the vertical speed indicator into the scan as the altitude and airspeed stabilise.

Heading and Balance
When small directional changes are required to regain a heading, apply bank equal to one half the number of degrees to be turned, i.e. when the error is 20° the correcting bank angle should not exceed 10°.

If the aircraft is correctly trimmed only a nominal back pressure on the control column will be required to maintain altitude during the change. During the period of heading correction maintain the scan through the attitude indicator to the vertical speed indicator or altimeter and take care to avoid any fixation on the heading indicator.

Just before the correct heading is regained commence to level the wings of the index aircraft and maintain the normal scan but initially include a cross reference to the balance indicator.

Note: A fairly common fault is to attempt to regain the reference altitude or heading with too much haste. This usually results in over corrections and fixation on one instrument which then tends to cause unnecessary deviations in both pitch and lateral level. The emphasis on all corrections should be smoothness in aircraft control and small attitude changes. At this stage of a student's instrument flying practice the time taken to return to a specific reference altitude or heading is of less importance than the ability to interpret the correction required and put it into effect.

Straight and Level Flight at Various Airspeeds and Configurations

The aircraft will be flown in level flight at a specific altitude and correctly trimmed. After the airspeed has stabilised the pilot will then have to assess the amount of power alteration needed to achieve the nominated airspeed. Once experience is gained at flying in a specific aircraft at different airspeeds the pilot will know the approximate power settings required for the airspeeds most commonly used. Therefore after the initial 'achieving' phase of level flight at a particular airspeed has been carried out, the subsequent power adjustment (if any) will be fairly small.

Changing Airspeed

Having assessed the power change necessary to achieve the desired airspeed, smoothly adjust the power setting to that required and maintain the attitude of the index aircraft until the needle of the vertical speed indicator starts to move from the zero position. Therefore apart from a glance at the power instruments no change of scan is initially required.

As the needle of the vertical speed indicator moves, an appropriate pressure will be required on the control column to slightly raise or lower the index aircraft and return the needle to zero.

The direction of movement of the needle and the required counter movement of the index aircraft will depend upon whether the power and airspeed change is an increase or decrease.

After a short while the air speed indicator should be included in the scan. During the change in power, care must be used not to allow fixation on any one instrument to occur.

Once the new airspeed is stabilised the balance indicator should be momentarily included in the scan to check that the correct balance is being achieved. Then the aircraft should be finally trimmed and a reversion to the normal scan can be made.

Changes in Aircraft Configuration

This part of the air exercise is not necessarily related to any specific flight procedure, but forms a useful adjunct to the previous practice of maintaining straight and level flight under changing conditions. It should essentially consist of two typical situations as follows:

1. In level flight below Vfe a nominal amount of flap will be lowered and eventually raised whilst maintaining altitude throughout.

2. In level flight below Vfe a nominal amount of flap will be lowered and the airspeed reduced to a pre-determined figure. This is then followed by returning to the clean configuration and original airspeed. A constant altitude should be maintained throughout.

Climbing

The air exercise will commence from a condition of straight and level flight.

Achieving:

Apply climbing power and whilst maintaining lateral level and a constant heading change the aircraft's attitude in pitch placing the index aircraft in the approximate climbing attitude relative to the artificial horizon.

During this phase the scan should be concentrated upon the attitude indicator and the heading indicator with just a quick glance at the power instruments to confirm that climbing power is being achieved.

A coarse trim can then be made and at the same time the air speed indicator should be included into the scan sequence as a primary supporting instrument.

Maintain the attitude of the index aircraft and when the airspeed has stabilised make pitch adjustments as necessary until the correct climbing speed has been obtained. Normally these adjustments in pitch should not exceed $\frac{1}{4}$ to $\frac{1}{2}$ bar widths.

Confirm that balance is being achieved and make fine trim adjustments as necessary.

Maintaining:

Maintain the position of the index aircraft and scan the heading indicator and the air speed indicator via the attitude indicator.

The altimeter should be brought into the scan pattern at intervals and when close to the desired altitude the scan should be changed to bring in the altimeter instead of the air speed indicator.

Levelling Off:
Anticipate the 'level off' altitude by approximately 10% of the rate of climb, e.g. if the climb rate is 700 f.p.m. then commence to slowly lower the index aircraft to the level flight position 70 feet before the desired altitude is reached.

Note: The rate at which the index aircraft is lowered should be such that it reaches the level flight attitude coincident with the aircraft's arrival at the desired altitude.

Throttle back the power to that required for straight and level cruising flight.

At this stage the maintaining scan for straight and level flight is employed, but initially the airspeed indicator should be a primary supporting instrument until the correct airspeed has been achieved.

Note: As the airspeed increases to that required for level flight, there may be a tendency for the aircraft to climb. Maintaining the normal scan between the attitude indicator and the vertical speed indicator will alert the pilot to any pitch change required to the index aircraft's position. Once the aircraft has been stablised at the correct attitude and airspeed make fine trim adjustments as necessary.

Correcting:

The basic corrections during climbing concern the airspeed, heading and balance. Any pitch correction needed should be limited to $\frac{1}{4}$ or $\frac{1}{2}$ bar widths, allowing the airspeed to stabilise before continuing with a further correction. All control movements, whether they relate to airspeed, heading or balance should be slow and smooth and care must be taken to avoid a fixation on any one instrument.

Descending

The air exercise will commence from straight and level flight. Descents during flight in instrument weather conditions are normally confined to those using a reduced power setting rather than a glide. The descent rate normally used during training and most commonly afterwards is 500 f.p.m.

Achieving:

Check that the desired altimeter setting has been selected. After the descending airspeed and rate of descent is decided, and whilst maintaining the pitch attitude of the index aircraft, the power should be slowly reduced to the assessed setting required.

Note: This procedure is used when the selected descent airspeed is less than the level flight airspeed being flown.

Normally the descent speed will be less than the cruising airspeed in use. Therefore, initially continue to maintain the attitude of the index aircraft whilst maintaining a scan between the attitude indicator and the heading indicator.

Within a few seconds bring the air speed indicator into the scan and as the airspeed nears the chosen value lower the position of the index aircraft to commence the descent phase. After the airspeed has stabilised, balance can be confirmed and coarse trim action can be taken.

The vertical speed indicator is then included into the scan sequence. Note the rate of descent and make power and pitch adjustments as necessary to maintain the correct speed and achieve the desired rate of descent.

Confirm the aircraft is in balance and make fine trim adjustments as necessary.

Maintaining:

When the desired rate of descent is being acheived, maintain the position of the index aircraft and scan the heading indicator and air speed indicator via the attitude indicator.

At this stage the vertical speed indicator becomes a secondary supporting instrument and should be included in the scan less frequently.

The altimeter also should be brought into the scan pattern at fairly frequent intervals because of the dangers of descending below the assigned altitude. Initially it will be a secondary supporting instrument but when close to the required altitude the scan must be changed to bring it in as a primary supporting instrument.

Levelling Off:

Anticipate the 'level off' altitude by approximately 10% of the rate of descent and smoothly increase the power to that required for cruising flight.

Note: The rate at which the index aircraft is raised should be such that it reaches the level flight position coincident with the aircraft's arrival at the desired altitude.

At this stage the straight and level flight maintaining scan is used but initially the air speed indicator should be included as a primary supporting instrument until the required airspeed is established.

Confirm the aircraft is in balance and make power, attitude and fine trim adjustments as necessary.

Correcting:

The basic corrections during a descent concern the airspeed, rate of descent, heading and balance. Any attitude or power corrections which are needed should be confined to small changes. All control movements should be slow and smooth, with care being taken to avoid a fixation on any one instrument.

Standard Rate Turns

During instrument flight it is normal to limit a turn to the 'Standard Rate' (rate 1), i.e. 3° per second. In order to evaluate the bank angle required to carry out a rate 1 turn at a given airspeed, the following simple method may be employed:

Divide the airspeed (knots) by 10 and add 5,

$$\text{i.e. required bank angle (degrees)} = \frac{\text{Airspeed (knots)}}{10} + 5$$

e.g. for an airspeed of 90 knots the bank angle = 9 + 5

= 14° of bank for a rate 1 turn

This rule of thumb is fairly accurate up to airspeeds of 100 knots. Most light aircraft used in training normally have cruising speeds at or about the 100 knots figure, so a convenient bank angle of approximately 15° will normally suffice. When flying at speeds much above 100 knots the figure of 7 should be used instead of 5.

Both the turn entry and recovery will affect the pitch control of the aircraft, therefore as an aid to smooth precise flying it is important to apply or remove the angle of bank slowly, so that the pilot can more easily keep up with the changes of instrument indications and effect the correct control responses at the appropriate time. A simple rule will be to enter and recover from a turn on instruments at not more than half the rate applicable when flying using normal outside visual references.

The Level Rate One Turn

Achieving:

Referring to the index aircraft, apply the appropriate angle of bank and co-ordinate with rudder. As the correct angle is reached apply sufficient back pressure to raise the index aircraft slightly and cross refer to the vertical speed indicator to ensure the pitch attitude is correct for a level turn.

Except when turning through a small number of degrees the heading indicator can be left out of the scan until the turn is well established.

Maintaining:

The attitude indicator is used to maintain pitch and bank attitude. The turn and balance indicator is the primary supporting instrument in relation to the rate of turn and the aircraft balance.

The vertical speed indicator/altimeter must be retained in the scan as primary supporting instruments for altitude information. As the turn proceeds, progressively introduce the heading indicator into the scan so that the aircraft can be rolled out onto the correct heading.

Returning to Straight Flight
When rolling out onto a specific heading, anticipate recovery to straight flight by a number of degrees. A useful rule is to anticipate by half the number of degrees of the bank being used.

Adjust the rate of roll out, so that the wings level attitude coincides with the desired heading. During the roll-out release the slight back pressure held to maintain altitude and when the wings are level and the heading is constant momentarily include the balance indicator into the scan.

Revert to the normal scan for the maintenance of level flight.

Correcting:

The small reduction of airspeed resulting from a rate one turn can normally be ignored and the power setting may remain unchanged, but it must be borne in mind that any change of bank angle will also affect the aircraft's pitch attitude and balance.

If altitude is lost during the turn, the subsequent pitch alteration to the index aircraft should be kept small and a gradual return to the original altitude made, as any marked change in pitch will significantly affect the airspeed and lift, and as a result a further change in control pressure will be required.

Climbing Turns

The introduction to this exercise will normally be taught from climbing flight.

Achieving:

Using the index aircraft apply the appropriate angle of bank for a rate one turn. Maintain a scan between the attitude indicator, air speed indicator and turn and balance indicator.

Maintaining:

During the maintenance of the turn the scan will chiefly involve the attitude indicator and the air speed indicator. As the required heading is neared the heading indicator must be progressively introduced into the scan.

Returning to the Straight Climb

The recovery to a straight climb involves continuing the maintaining scan, except that the balance indicator will initially remain in the scan and the heading indicator must be incorporated more frequently into the scan as the required heading is neared.

Correcting:

The comments made when discussing the bank angle, pitch and balance during the level turn still apply, but additionally it must be appreciated that a slight back pressure will still be needed throughout the maintenance of a turn during a climb. This is because when an aircraft is banked there will be a tendency for the aircraft nose to drop to a lower pitch attitude.

It must also be remembered that at climbing power and airspeed the effect of slipstream, yaw and torque produced by the propeller will be quite marked. This will result in a tendency to overbank or underbank dependent upon the direction of propeller rotation in relation to the direction of turn.

Descending Turns

The introduction to this exercise will normally be taught from descending flight.

Achieving:

Using the index aircraft apply the appropriate angle of bank for a rate one turn. Maintain a scan between the attitude indicator, air speed indicator and turn and balance indicator.

Maintaining:

During the maintenance of the turn the scan will chiefly involve the use of the attitude indicator and the air speed indicator.

If the rate of descent has to be maintained and not allowed to increase, then additional power may be required and the vertical speed indicator must be introduced into the scan.

As the required heading is neared, the heading indicator must be progressively introduced into the scan.

Returning to the Straight Descent

The recovery to a straight descent involves continuing the maintaining scan, except that the balance indicator will initially remain in the scan and the heading indicator must be incorporated more frequently as the required heading is approached.

If the power has been altered during the turn it will need readjusting to maintain the correct rate of descent.

Correcting:

The comments made in relation to corrections during the climbing turn also apply to the descending turn, with the exception of the effects produced by the use of climbing power.

Recovery from the Spiral Dive

If the bank is allowed to become too steep and the nose of the aircraft assumes a low attitude in pitch, a spiral dive situation will occur. Pilots must therefore be capable of recognising this condition and returning the aircraft to normal flight through the use of the instruments. Practice for this situation will consist of the instructor adopting a spiral dive condition and demonstrating how this can be recognised from the flight instrument indications.

The recovery action can be considered in three stages and the first two shown below can be carried out simultaneously:

   1.   Level the wings.
   2.   Reduce the power.
   3.   Ease firmly back on the control column and place the index aircraft in the level attitude relative to the artificial horizon line.

Once back in the level attitude the power should be returned to the cruise setting and a normal scan of the instruments continued, noting in particular any spurious readings between the individual instruments in an effort to ascertain the cause of the unusual attitude and in order to prevent its recurrence.

PRE-FLIGHT BRIEFING
INSTRUMENT APPRECIATION

Aim
First to demonstrate to you that the aircraft cannot be controlled in safety without reference to the flight instruments when the outside visual references are lost. Secondly to ensure you fully appreciate that sustained instrument flight cannot be safely undertaken without a proper course of instrument flying training.

What
A demonstration to show that the physiological senses can be confused. Followed by an introduction to Instrument Attitude Flight including the effects of changing power and the development of 'Selective Radial Scan'.

Airmanship
All normal airmanship considerations will apply and additionally emphasis will be made on the need to avoid situations where instrument flight is necessary.

How
Physiological Effects: Initially you will be asked to close your eyes and attempt to determine the aircraft attitudes and movements. This demonstration will reveal how the senses of motion and posture can become confused.

Instrument Indications

Attitude in Pitch	Attitude Indicator Altimeter/VSI Air Speed Indicator

The movement of the index aircraft by one bar width and its effect upon the airspeed/rate of descent/ascent.

Attitude in Bank	Attitude Indicator Altimeter

The movement of the index aircraft with bank and the measurement of bank angle.

Heading and Balance	Attitude Indicator Heading Indicator Balance Indicator

Determination of lateral level, heading and balance.

Student Practice with Visor: Maintaining the aircraft attitude by reference to the attitude indicator alone.

Attitude Instrument Flight

Effects of Changing Power	Attitude Indicator, Power Instruments, Altimeter, Air Speed, Heading and Vertical Speed Indicators.

Student Practice: Maintaining a constant altitude and heading during change of airspeed.

Selective Radial Scan	Attitude Indicator Altimeter

Student Practice with Visor: Maintaining the aircraft attitude and altitude.

Selective Radial Scan	Attitude Indicator Heading Indicator

Student Practice with Visor: Maintaining the aircraft attitude and heading.

Selective Radial Scan	Attitude Indicator Heading Indicator Altimeter

Student Practice with Visor: Maintaining heading and altitude.

PRE-FLIGHT BRIEFING

INSTRUCTION TO INSTRUMENT FLYING
The Basic Manoeuvres

Aim The purpose of Demonstrations 2 & 3 are to teach you how to control the aircraft in Straight and Level, Climbing and Descending Flight by sole reference to the instruments.

What These exercises are concerned with the development of your instrument flying ability to ensure that you can maintain control of the aircraft should an inadvertent penetration into instrument weather conditions occur.

Airmanship All normal airmanship considerations will apply but particular care must be taken with reference to the aircraft's position in relation to Controlled and similar airspace. Additionally, weather considerations such as airframe icing, inadvertent flight into cumulo nimbus cloud, etc. must be borne in mind.

How *Demonstration No. 2*

Straight and Level Flight
Achieving: Use of the aircraft controls in relation to the attitude indicator and power instruments. Attitude and power in relation to the performance instruments.

Maintaining: The use of the correct scan technique between the 'control', 'primary' and 'secondary' supporting instruments.

Correcting:

Errors in Altitude – The importance of small movements of the index aircraft and the correct use of power.
Errors in Heading – The importance of using small angles of bank to return to a selected heading.

Student Practice with Visor.

Demonstration No. 3

Climbing
Achieving and Maintaining: Use of the aircraft controls and power in relation to the control and performance instruments.

The importance of the correct scan technique between the 'control', 'primary' and 'secondary' supporting instruments.

Levelling Off: The correct anticipation of the required altitude and the change in instrument scan sequence.

Student Practice with Visor.

Descending
Achieving and Maintaining: Use of the aircraft controls and power in relation to the control and performance instruments.

The importance of the correct scan technique between the 'control', 'primary' and 'secondary' supporting instruments.

Levelling Off: The correct anticipation of the required altitude/height and the change in instrument scan sequence.

Student Practice with Visor.

PRE-FLIGHT BRIEFING

INTRODUCTION TO INSTRUMENT FLYING
The Basic Manoeuvres — Turning Flight

Aim   To teach you how to enter, maintain and recover from level, climbing and descending turns, and spiral dives by sole reference to the instruments.

What   This exercise is an extension of your instrument flying technique.

Airmanship   All normal airmanship considerations will apply and particular care should be taken over orientation in relation to the aircraft's position over the ground.

Demonstration No. 4.

How

Rate One Turns – Level
Commencing from straight and level flight the student will receive a demonstration of entering, maintaining and recovering from a rate 1 turn onto a pre-selected heading.

Correct use of controls and instrument cross reference using the proper scan technique.

Achieving and Maintaining:
Use of the attitude and turn and balance indicators. Interpretation of the correct bank angle and use of the primary and secondary supporting instruments.

Recovery to Straight Flight:
Anticipation of the pre-selected heading. Smooth control movements and change of the instrument scan.

Student Practice with Visor.

Rate One Climbing Turns
Achieving and Maintaining:
Use of attitude and turn and balance indicators. Correct scanning of the primary and secondary supporting instruments.

Recovery to Straight Flight:
Anticipation of pre-selected heading.

Smooth control movements and change of the instrument scan.

Student practice with Visor.

Rate One Descending Turns
Achieving and Maintaining:
Use of attitude and turn and balance indicators. Correct scanning of the primary and secondary supporting instruments.

Recovery to Straight Flight:
Anticipation of pre-selected heading. Smooth control movements and change of the instrument scan.

Student Practice with Visor.

Recovery from a Spiral Dive
Recognition: Attitude Indicator – steep bank and low nose attitude.
   Airspeed Indicator – increased speed.
   Turn Indicator – increased turn rate.

Recovery: Throttle closed – wings levelled.
   Raise aircraft nose to level attitude and return to cruising power.

Student Practice with Visor.

Introduction to Instrument Flying

Flight Demonstrations

INTRODUCTION

The content of this air exercise is designed to give you the ability to maintain control of the aircraft for a limited period during flight by sole reference to the instruments. The training will be carried out initially using external and instrument references and then using the flight instruments alone.

The exercises will be limited to the following demonstrations:

1. Physiological Sensations.
   Instrument Appreciation.
      Attitude Instrument Flight.
         Instrument Indications.
            Pitch Attitude.
            Bank Attitude.
            Heading and Balance.
         Attitude Instrument Flying.
            Control Instruments and } Effect of Changing
            Performance Instruments } Power.
            Cross-Checking the Instruments.
            Selective Radial Scan.

2. Instrument Flight – The Basic Manoeuvres.
   Straight and Level Flight.
      At Various Airspeeds and Aircraft Configurations.

3. Climbing and Descending.

4. Standard Rate Turns.
      Level Turns   }
      Climbing Turns } Including Turns onto
      Descending Turns } Pre-selected Headings.

5. Recoveries to Straight and Level Flight from:
   Climbing and descending turns and,
   Spiral dives.

Airmanship items will be introduced at appropriate moments during the flight demonstrations.

The accomplishment of the air exercises covered in the demonstrations 2, 3, and 4, is intended only to develop the ability to maintain control of the aircraft for a short period of time during inadvertent flight into instrument weather conditions.

DEMONSTRATION 1.   INSTRUMENT APPRECIATION

Flight Lesson	Demonstration Sequence
Physiological sensations From straight and level flight.	The student will be asked to close his eyes and interpret the aircraft attitude through his physical sensations. Note: Physical sensations derived from motion and posture can become confused during flight.

Instrument indications –
Pitch
 	
From straight and level flight using both external and instrument references.
 	
Reference Instruments:
    Attitude Indicator.
    Altimeter.
    Air Speed Indicator.
    Vertical Speed
    Indicator.
	Note the airspeed and position of the index aircraft in pitch, relative to the artificial horizon line.
	Raise the index aircraft by one bar width.
	Note the rate of altitude increase and after a short while check the new airspeed reading.
	Return the index aircraft to the original position in pitch.
	Lower the index aircraft below the artificial horizon by one bar width.
	Note the rate of altitude loss and after a short while check the new airspeed reading.
	Return the index aircraft to the original position in pitch.
	
	Note: It can be seen from this simple demonstration that extremely small movements of the index aircraft in pitch will produce significant changes of altitude and airspeed.
	Therefore when flying on instruments very light control pressures will be

required to correct pitch deviations
and maintain a constant attitude.

Instrument indications –
Bank

From straight and level
flight using both external
and instrument
references.

Reference Instruments:
  Attitude Indicator.
  Altimeter.

Note the wings of the index aircraft are
level and the altitude and heading are
constant.
Bank the index aircraft until a 10°
angle is reached.
Maintain the bank angle and adjust the
pitch attitude of the index aircraft as
necessary to maintain a constant
altitude.
The exact angle of bank can be
measured from the index marks on the
attitude indicator.

Note: Bank angles of 15°, and 20° will
  also be shown.
Return the index aircraft to the laterally level position and re-adjust its pitch
attitude as required to maintain a
constant altitude.

Note: An immediate and accurate
  indication of bank angle or lateral
  level is displayed by the attitude
  indicator.
This demonstration will be shown in
banked attitudes to the left and to the
right.

Instrument indications –
Heading & Balance

From straight and level
flight using both external
and instrument
references.

Reference Instruments:
  Attitude Indicator.
  Heading Indicator.
  Balance Indicator.

Note the wings of the index aircraft are
level and the heading is constant with
the aircraft in balance.
Bank the index aircraft slightly and
apply sufficient opposite rudder to
maintain the aircraft's heading.

Note: Although the heading is constant the aircraft is out of balance.
Recover to normal straight and level
flight.
Maintain the wings of the index aircraft
in the laterally level position and use
rudder (as necessary) to create slight
unbalance.

Note: Although the aircraft's wings
  are laterally level the aircraft is not

	in balanced flight and the heading indicator will show that a change in heading is occurring. Recover to normal straight and level flight.
Attitude instrument flight From straight and level flight. Adjust visor and refer to the instruments.	Student Practice: Maintaining a laterally level and constant pitch attitude, by reference to the attitude indicator alone.

Attitude instrument flying
 	
Effects of changing power during straight and level flight. Use of both external and instrument references.
 	
Reference Instruments:
  Attitude Indicator.
  Power Instruments.
  Heading Indicator.
  Airspeed Indicator.
  Vertical Speed
  Indicator.
  Altimeter.
	Whilst maintaining a constant attitude make a significant but gradual increase to the power being used.
	Note that during smooth air conditions the vertical speed indicator will give a trend indication within a few seconds of the additional power being applied.
	The altitude and airspeed will also gradually increase.
	Apply the necessary control pressure to adjust the position of the index aircraft and maintain a constant altitude.
	As the airspeed continues to increase a further adjustment of the pitch attitude will be required.
	Note any heading change and 'out of balance' effects. Maintain the wings level and adjust rudder pressure as required.
	When the airspeed stabilises the aircraft can be re-trimmed.
	Student Practice:

Using external and instrument references.	The student should now practice maintaining altitude, heading and balance whilst changing the power and airspeed.

Attitude instrument flight
 	
'Selective Radial Scan'
 	
Maintaining altitude in straight and level flight – using visor.
 	
Reference Instruments:
  Attitude Indicator.
  Altimeter.
	Student Practice:
	
	With the aircraft correctly trimmed in straight and level flight use the attitude indicator and altimeter to maintain a constant altitude.
	Scan from the attitude indicator to the altimeter and back to the attitude indicator.

Use the appropriate control pressures to re-adjust the pitch attitude of the index aircraft if altitude deviation occurs.

Maintaining heading – using visor.

Reference Instruments:
Attitude Indicator.
Heading Indicator.

Student Practice:
With the aircraft correctly trimmed in straight and level flight use the attitude indicator and heading indicator to maintain lateral level and heading.
Scan from the attitude indicator to the heading indicator and back to the attitude indicator.
Use of the appropriate control pressures to maintain the wings level and the heading constant.

When the student is proficient at performing these two selective scan exercises the combined used of the attitude indicator, altimeter and heading indicator should be practised as follows:

Maintaining altitude and heading – using visor.

Reference Instruments:
Attitude Indicator.
Heading Indicator.
Altimeter.

Student Practice:
With the aircraft in straight and level flight, develop the scan technique radiating out from the attitude indicator to the heading indicator and back, then from the attitude indicator to the altimeter and back.
The frequency of the scan between the attitude indicator and the heading indicator should be greater than that used between the attitude indicator and the altimeter.

When the student is proficient at this task, the selective radial scan technique can be developed to bring in the secondary supporting instruments as discussed under the heading of Selective Radial Scan in the Long Briefing section.

DEMONSTRATION 2.   ACHIEVING AND MAINTAINING STRAIGHT AND LEVEL FLIGHT

Flight Lesson	Demonstration Sequence
The exercise will commence with the aircraft in a condition other than straight and level. The initial practice should be carried out using external and instrument references, following this the	*Achieving:* Apply control pressures as required to position the index aircraft in the level attitude whilst adjusting the power for cruising flight. Monitor the attitude indicator, altimeter and heading indicator, re-adjusting the aircraft attitude as necessary, by use of the elevators and ailerons.

exercise should be continued with the student's visor lowered.

All control adjustments should be smooth and gradual.
Re-trim.
Increase the scan to include the balance indicator and air speed indicator as secondary supporting instruments.
Complete final trim adjustments.

Maintaining:
The primary supporting instruments will be the heading indicator and (in smooth flying conditions) the vertical speed indicator.
The altimeter, air speed indicator and balance indicator are secondary supporting instruments.

Note: In turbulent weather conditions use the altimeter as the primary supporting instrument in pitch.

Correcting:
Errors in altitude
Small errors in altitude will only require small changes to the position of the index aircraft.
If altitude errors of more than 100 feet occur, use small power adjustments.

Errors in heading
When small heading corrections are required used a maximum bank angle equal to half the number of degrees in error.

When the student is proficient at achieving and maintaining straight and level flight at a pre-determined power setting he should be given practice at flying in straight and level flight at different airspeeds, followed by maintaining altitude during the selection of small flap settings.

DEMONSTRATION 3.   ACHIEVING AND MAINTAINING CLIMBS AND DESCENTS

Flight Lesson	*Demonstration Sequence*
	Climbing
The exercise will commence from a condition of straight and level flight. The initial practice	*Achieving:* Smoothly and gradually select climbing power and apply the necesary control pressures to place the index aircraft in the approximate climbing attitude

should be carried out using external and instrument references, following this the exercise should be continued with the student's visor lowered.

whilst maintaining a constant heading and balance.
Confirm the correct climbing power has been set and monitor the attitude indicator and heading indicator.
Complete an initial trim adjustment and increase the scan to bring in the air speed indicator as a primary supporting instrument.
When the airspeed has stabilised make small pitch adjustments as necessary to achieve the correct climbing speed.
Increase the scan to bring in the balance and vertical speed indicators as secondary supporting instruments. Note that a positive rate of climb has been established and re-trim.

Maintaining:
The primary supporting instruments will be the heading indicator and the air speed indicator.
The altimeter will initially be a secondary supporting instrument until the aircraft approaches the desired altitude. At this stage the altimeter will become a primary supporting instrument and the air speed indicator will become secondary.

Levelling Off:
Anticipate the required 'level off' altitude by 10% of the rate of climb.
Slowly return the pitch attitude to the level flight position and reduce power to that required for cruising flight.
The primary supporting instruments at this stage will be the heading indicator and altimeter.
Complete an initial trim adjustment and as the airspeed increases include the vertical speed indicator in the scan to check for any tendency to deviate from a constant altitude.
Confirm the correct airspeed is being achieved and make final balance and trim adjustments.

The exercise will commence from a condition of straight and level flight.

Descending

Achieving:
Re-set the altimeter datum as necessary and determine the required airspeed and rate of descent.

The initial practice should be carried out using external and instrument references, following this the exercise should be continued with the student's visor lowered.

Whilst maintaining a constant altitude gradually reduce power to the estimated setting.

Monitor the attitude indicator, heading indicator and airspeed indicator. When nearing the required descent airspeed apply the necessary control pressures to lower the index aircraft to the approximate descent attitude.

The primary supporting instruments at this stage will be the heading indicator, air speed indicator and vertical speed indicator.

Complete an initial trimming adjustment.

Make power and attitude adjustments as necessary to achieve the correct airspeed and rate of descent.

The secondary supporting instrument will be the balance indicator, confirm correct balance and complete final trimming adjustments.

Maintaining:
Once established at the required rate of descent and airspeed the primary supporting instruments will be the heading indicator and the air speed indicator.

The vertical speed indicator and altimeter become secondary supporting instruments.

As the desired altitude is approached the altimeter will become a primary supporting instrument and the air speed indicator becomes secondary.

Note: Because of the hazards of descending below the nominated altitude the transfer of the altimeter from a secondary to a primary supporting instrument must be made well before the nominated altitude is reached.

Levelling Off:
Anticipate the required 'level-off' altitude/height by approximately 10% of the rate of descent.

Smoothly increase the power to that required for cruising flight at a selected airspeed, and re-adjust the pitch attitude for level flight.

The primary supporting instruments at this stage will be the heading indicator

	and altimeter. Complete an initial trimming adjustment. At this stage the air speed indicator becomes a primary instrument until the correct airspeed is established. As the airspeed increases include the vertical speed indicator into the scan and check for any tendency to deviate from a constant altitude. Confirm the correct airspeed is being achieved and make final balance and trim adjustments.

DEMONSTRATION 4.   STANDARD RATE TURNS

Flight Lesson	*Demonstration Sequence*
The exercise will commence from a condition of straight and level flight. The initial practice should be carried out using external and instrument references, following this the exercise should be continued with the student's visor lowered.	*Level Turns – Rate One* *Achieving:* Gradually bank the aircraft until the bank pointer of the aircraft indicator reaches 15°. Maintain balance with rudder and as the correct bank angle is reached the index aircraft will have to be raised slightly to prevent a gradual loss of altitude. The primary supporting instruments during the turn entry will be the vertical speed indicator and the turn and balance indicator. Note: In turbulent weather conditions the altimeter should be used as a primary supporting instrument instead of the vertical speed indicator. *Maintaining:* The primary supporting instruments during the maintenance of the turn will be the vertical speed indicator and the turn and balance indicator. The turn pointer of this latter instrument will indicate the actual rate of the turn. The heading indicator will be a second-ary supporting instrument until nearing the required heading. Returning to Straight Flight: When a specific heading is required anticipate the recovery to straight flight

by half the number of degrees of the bank angle used.
Adjust the rate of roll-out so that the wings-level attitude coincides with arrival at the required heading.
During the return to straight flight the primary supporting instruments will be the heading indicator, the vertical speed indicator and the balance indicator.

The turn will be commenced from a straight climb.

Climbing Turns
Achieving:
The sequence of control movements will be the same as for the entry to a level turn.
During the entry the primary supporting instruments will be the air speed indicator and the turn and balance indicator.

Maintaining:
The primary supporting instruments will be the air speed indicator and the turn and balance indicator. The heading indicator will be a secondary supporting instrument until nearing the required heading.

Returning to the Straight Climb:
The sequence of control movements will be the same as the recovery from a level turn.
The primary supporting instruments will be the heading indicator, air speed indicator and the balance indicator.

The turn will be commenced from a straight descent.

Descending Turns

Achieving:
The sequence of control movements will be the same as for the entry to a level turn.
During the entry the primary supporting instruments will be the air speed indicator and the turn and balance indicator.
If the descent rate is to be maintained additional power may be necessary and the vertical speed indicator will have to be brought into the scan.

Maintaining:
The primary supporting instruments will be the air speed indicator and the turn and balance indicator. The heading indicator will be a secondary supporting

	instrument until nearing the required heading.
	Returning to the Straight Descent: The sequence of control movements will be the same as the recovery from a level turn. The primary supporting instruments will be the heading indicator, air speed indicator and the balance indicator.

DEMONSTRATION 5.   RECOVERY FROM A SPIRAL DIVE

Flight Lesson	Demonstration Sequence
From turning attitudes the aircraft will be allowed to enter a spiral dive condition	*Entering:* The bank will be allowed to steepen and the aircraft nose to drop. A steep bank and low nose attitude will be indicated by the attitude indicator. The turn indicator will show a rapid rate of turn and the Air speed indicator will show an increasing airspeed. *Recovery:* Close the throttle. Level the wings by reference to the attitude indicator. Raise the aircraft nose to a level attitude in pitch and return to cruise power.

Night Flying

Instructor's Guide

THE NIGHT RATING

A pilot who has received training in night flying will undoubtedly have additional competence which will stand him and his passengers in good stead whether it be in the flexibility of his flight operations or in the event of his being unintentionally airborne after nightfall.

All instructors should therefore encourage pilots who have no night flying experience to undergo training to qualify them for a night rating or to obtain at least sufficient dual experience at night, to ensure that they appreciate the dangers of being caught out, due perhaps to poor pre-flight planning, or psychological pressures which lead to taking chances in order to get home from an away airfield.

To operate an aircraft safely at night, the pilot will require a reasonable competence in 'instrument flying'. This is due to the fact that whilst by day a pilot controls his aircraft mostly by reference to ground features and the visual horizon, at night, reference to ground features including the natural horizon is limited or completely lacking, and the use of the flight instruments may be the only method of determining the attitude of the aircraft.

Normally the flight conditions at night enable the aircraft attitude to be interpreted by the perspective of and the pattern of ground lights and occasionally a dimly defined natural horizon. In these circumstances control of the aircraft will be achieved by a combination of visual and instrument references.

AIRMANSHIP

On clear nights the red/green navigation lights of other aircraft are relatively easy to pick out when operating at medium to high altitudes, however in the lower levels e.g. when the aircraft is in the circuit, aircraft navigation lights can easily merge into the light patterns of local towns and added vigilance will be necessary.

A particularly difficult aspect is the recognition of aircraft white tail lights and although such lights will only be seen when astern of aircraft on similar headings, a safe situation can easily change into a hazardous one if the preceding aircraft suddenly changes heading substantially.

The advent of tall television masts situated on high ground has also led to a particular need to recognise obstruction lights at an early stage, and emphasises the need for self discipline in maintaining planned minimum safety altitudes.

The natural hazard of weather deterioration will become more acute at night due to the difficulties experienced in recognising the development of a lowering cloud base or precipitation. It is essential that this aspect of airmanship in relation to weather is covered thoroughly during ground briefings and in-flight procedures.

Emergencies which are minor by day can be hazardous when operating at night and the student must be given ample practice in the appropriate emergency procedures during flight training as well as learning them on the ground.

A final point relating to both airmanship and organisation of duty periods is, that due to the financial constraints and difficulties involved in adequately scheduling small staffs to obtain suitable rest periods, an instructor may find himself in a situation where he is scheduled to give night instruction at the end of a long working day. In these circumstances and bearing in mind that fatigue can be the precursor of accidents he must ensure that he has a suitable rest period prior to giving night instruction.

BEFORE THE EXERCISE
The student must have obtained knowledge of and demonstrated competence in the following items before being issued with a night rating:

● **LEGISLATION REQUIREMENTS FOR NIGHT OPERATIONS**
Aircraft Equipment.
Aircraft Lights.
Flight Crew Licences/Ratings.
Aerodrome Licensing.

● **NIGHT OPERATIONS**
Preparation for Flight.
Taxying.
Take-off Procedures.
Airfield Departure and Arrival Procedures.
Approach and Landing Procedures.
Going Round Again.

● **NIGHT NAVIGATION**
Flight Planning.

In-Flight Procedures (including Lost Procedure).
Safety Altitude Considerations.
Weather Awareness.

NIGHT EMERGENCIES

PREPARATION BEFORE FLIGHT
Prior to the student's initial flight point out that night flying is a combination of visual and instrument flight and that the amount of visual reference will depend upon the clarity of the natural horizon and the availability of ground lights.

Ensure the student fully appreciates that a pilot flying at night will need to possess a greater alertness towards his own limitations and there will be a requirement to observe more caution than during day operations.

Brief the student so that he is thoroughly aware of the lighting systems in use at the training airfield and the various light signals to be expected from ATC in the event of radio failure.

Due to the limited visibility inside the cockpit the student must be given time to identify all the switches and controls required to operate the aircraft systems under conditions of limited cockpit illumination.

DURING THE FLIGHT DEMONSTRATIONS
Do not allow the restrictions in relation to cockpit lighting to adversely affect the quality of the student's drills and checks. Errors resulting in failure of the engine or aircraft systems will create greater hazards at night than by day and therefore cockpit drills will need to be more meticulous.

Do not lose any opportunity to demonstrate the need for a particularly careful lookout all around the aircraft prior to and after starting the engine.

Taxying at night often brings with it additional difficulties, but excess taxying speed, perhaps arising from reduced distance perception, is probably the one which will cause most difficulty.

Ensure the student is aware of the need for added vigilance in the region of the 'holding point', and that he appreciates how easily a single tail light from an aircraft ahead can easily be lost in the variety of lights which are used on and around airfields.

The Take-off
Stress the importance of looking well ahead down the lines of runway lights and ensure he consciously avoids the temptation to look at the lights in the immediate vicinity of the aircraft.

Once airborne the runway lighting will quickly disappear behind the aircraft leaving an apparent dark void ahead and along the aircraft track. It is for just this reason that transference to instrument flight is so necessary for the initial stages of the climb out.

Night Orientation

Give the student reasonable time to adjust to the changed visual cues experienced and get him to identify both ground lighting and aircraft navigation lights. When attempting to assess the approximate headings of other aircraft a student may often suffer a delay in remembering to which wing the red or green navigation light is fitted. This delay can be avoided by the use of the simple term 'red not right'.

The use of the 'Off Centre' technique when attempting to identify lights is an important feature of night vision so too is the integration of short pauses in eye motion during scanning techniques.

The student must be made aware of the difference in flying conditions and visibility on very dark nights with overcast skies, and those nights when starlight or moonlight is available. The illumination under these three conditions is very different, and in the first case it would be very easy to inadvertently fly into cloud.

When introducing the student to the airfield lighting system as seen from the air, point out the effects of uni-directional runway lighting if used. This will ensure that he does not become disconcerted or disorientated when looking for them from an upwind position.

Circuits and approaches are often more easily and accurately accomplished during calm nights with good visibility because of the better definition obtained by the use of airfield lighting systems and approach slope indicators. However the landing phase (when aircraft landing lights are not being used) will usually give some problems to start with, and the instructor must ensure that the student uses the impressions gained from the runway lights to assess his height above the runway during the flare and up to the point of touch-down.

Emergency procedures must be covered in a practical fashion and in order that the student is able to judge his approach path accurately in circumstances when VASIS or Angle of Approach Indicators are not available, he must be given practice at landing approaches with the approach slope lighting system switched off.

COMMON ERRORS

Most students will experience difficulty in estimating the distance of known lights and underestimation is the most common fault. Only experience, and guidance from an instructor will overcome this difficulty.

• An optical illusion which can mislead on a dark night is to confuse the stars with lights on the ground. This may produce vertigo if reference to the instruments is not carried out frequently.

• During ground handling, where the student is unsure of his correct taxy path he will often be reluctant to slow down or stop. On these occasions the instructor must not hesitate to point out that this is a case of the aircraft being in charge of the situation, and not the pilot.

• If the student fails to maintain an accurate heading after take-off it is often because he has transferred to the instruments too late or is too tense in his application of instrument flying, leading to an incorrect instrument scan.

• Students will often make unnecessarily wide circuits and long downwind legs, particularly if other aircraft are ahead. Point out the correct spacing required from the runway, and that the need to extend downwind will normally only arise when the aircraft ahead is carrying out a full stop landing.

• If the student persistently arrives at the final approach turn too low or too high it is usually because he is concentrating too much attention to the runway lights, and failing to monitor the altimeter with sufficient frequency.

• A fairly common fault during the landing phase is to look for the ground instead of assessing the aircraft height from the perspective of the runway lights. This will best be cured by reminders from the instructor during the hold-off period.

Night Flying

Long Briefing

OBJECTIVES

The purpose of night flying training is to enable a pilot to safely operate an aircraft at night and exercise the privileges of a night rating.

In relation to the U.K. Rules of the Air and Air Traffic Control Regulations the definition of 'night' is as follows:

'Night' means the time between half an hour after sunset and half an hour before sunrise, sunset and sunrise being determined at surface level.

INTRODUCTION

Although a mandatory amount of flying experience and training is a requirement to obtain a night rating on a pilot's licence, a lesser amount of night flying will still be of benefit to a pilot and provide for his greater safety.

Hazardous situations have occurred in the past in which pilots without night flying experience have found themselves unintentionally airborne after nightfall. Such situations have been brought about through inadequate pre-flight planning, or pressures relating to a desire to get back home, or other circumstances outside the control of the pilot.

Therefore the ability to operate an aircraft at night is a useful extension of a pilot's competence, and one which:

(a) Permits him greater flexibility in planning his flight operations.

(b) Provides for added safety should he inadvertently find himself airborne after nightfall.

In order to obtain this additional competence, proper training must be undertaken which will need to include a reasonable amount of instrument flying because of the changed visibility and conditions during the hours of darkness.

LEGISLATION REQUIREMENTS

Night operations by aircraft registered in the U.K. will have to comply with the requirements of the Air Navigation Order and The Air Traffic Rules and Regulations. The areas of compliance can be divided into:

Aircraft Equipment
Aircraft Lights
Flight Crew Licences
Aerodrome Licensing

AIRCRAFT EQUIPMENT

The details of equipment to be carried at night are covered in the ANO Schedule 5 and vary with the authorised all-up weight of the aircraft and whether or not it is flying for the purposes of Public Transport and whether it is flying outside or inside Controlled Airspace. A review of the table relating to 'Aircraft and Circumstance of Flight' in Schedule 5 will reveal that the minimum equipment to be carried for flight at night consists of Scales A, C and D.

Scale A

(i)   *Spare fuses for all electrical circuits the fuses of which can be replaced in flight, consisting of ten per cent of the number of each rating or three of each rating whichever is the greater;*

(ii)   *Maps, charts, codes and other documents and navigational equipment necessary, in addition to any other equipment required under this Order, for the intended flight of the aircraft, including any diversion which may reasonably be expected;*

*(iii)   *A safety belt or safety harness for every seat in use.*

Scale C

(i)   *Equipment for displaying the lights required by the Rules of the Air and Air Trafic Control;*

(ii)   *Electrical equipment, supplied from the main source of supply in the aircraft, to provide sufficient illumination to enable the flight crew properly to carry out their duties during flight;*

(iii)   *Unless the aircraft is equipped with radio, devices for making the visual signal specified in the Rules of the Air and Air Traffic Control as indicating a request for permission to land.*

Scale D

(i)   *Either*   *(a)*   *a turn indicator and a slip indicator; or*

   (b)   *a gyroscopic bank and pitch indicator and a gyroscopic direction indicator;*

(ii)   A sensitive pressure altimeter adjustable for changes in barometric pressure.

However when flying within controlled airspace, scale E will be required in place of D and additionally scale F will be needed. These scales are as follows:

Scale E
(i)   A turn indicator and a slip indicator;
(ii)   A gyroscopic bank and pitch indicator;
(iii)   A gyroscopic direction indicator;
(iv)   A sensitive pressure altimeter adjustable for changes in barometric pressure;
           Provided that any aircraft may, at the option of the operator, be equipped with an additional gyroscopic bank and pitch indicator in lieu of the turn indicator referred to in (i) of this scale.

Scale F
(i)   A timepiece with a sweep second hand;
(ii)   A means of indicating whether the power supply to the gyroscopic instruments is adequate;
(iii)   A rate of climb and descent indicator.

* Note: With effect from January 1978 every pilot's seat and any seat situated alongside a pilot's seat, must be equipped with a safety belt with one diagonal shoulder strap or a safety harness.

AIRCRAFT LIGHTS
All aircraft must display a minimum system of external lights when taxying or flying at night. These lights together with the appropriate colours are clearly laid down in Rule 9 of the Rules of the Air and Air Traffic Control Regulations.

In the interests of flight safety during night operations pilots must be able to distinguish between powered aircraft, gliders and balloons and for this reason, there are differences in the lighting systems of the varying classes of aircraft. These differences are shown in fig. 20-1 below.

Although anti-collision or strobe lights are not a requirement for small aircraft the use of such additional lighting systems will enhance safety. Their use however can lead to distraction or even spatial disorientation when flying in or close to cloud and in these weather conditions it will usually be advisable to switch them off.

In the event that part or all of the mandatory system of lights should fail during flight the pilot should land when in his opinion it is

Fig. 20-1

safe to do so, but in any event he must inform the appropriate air traffic control unit of the situation.

FLIGHT CREW LICENCES
The experience requirements and training syllabus for the Private Pilot's Licence does not include night flying training, and therefore the privileges of the licence are

United Kingdom Civil Aviation Authority

NIGHT RATING-AEROPLANES

Licence No.........

....the holder of
this Licence, is entitled to act as pilot in command of an aeroplane carrying passengers by night.

Signature of   Date and
Issuing Officer.........................   Stamp.........................

FCL1/4 310376

limited in relation to the carriage of passengers at night. The present regulations therefore require that a pilot carrying passengers at night must hold a night rating.

The night rating is a qualification which a private pilot may obtain to supplement the privileges of his basic licence, however the holder of a U.K. night rating must have within the previous six months carried out as pilot in command at least 5 take-offs and landings at night before he can exercise the privileges of his night rating. Although 'touch and go' landings may be accepted for this purpose, the solo landings required for the initial training for a night rating must be to a full stop.

An applicant for a U.K. night rating must have completed a total of 50 hours as pilot of aeroplanes to include:

25 hours as pilot in command.

5 hours instruction in instrument flying of which 2½ hours may be tuition in instrument flying in an approved simulated flight trainer.

The flying section of the U.K. night rating course consists of 5 hours of flight by night comprising:

A minimum of 3 hours of dual instruction including at least one hour of night navigation. The remaining hours may be solo during which at least one airfield departure and return, and 5 solo take-offs and landings shall be completed.

AERODROME LICENSING

The Air Navigation Order requires that an aerodrome must be licensed for night flying when the aircraft which are taking off or landing are engaged in flights for the purpose of public transport or flying instruction.

Aerodromes which are licensed for day operations including the giving of flying instruction may not necessarily be licensed for night flying unless certain conditions are met in relation to the suitability of lighting equipment.

Before an aerodrome may be licensed for use at night, lighting facilities must be provided in accordance with certain scales as laid down by the Civil Aviation Authority. These scales vary according to the type of night operation being performed e.g., public transport of passengers, flying training etc., and relate to runway, taxyway, approach and obstruction lighting. Additionally at those aerodromes where aircraft home by visual means or where night flying training is carried out, an aerodrome Light Beacon will also have to be provided.

NIGHT FAMILIARISATION

A familiarisation period will be necessary to introduce the pilot to the differences between day and night flying. This period will be so arranged as to cover the changed operational aspects which occur during flight preparation, taxiing, take-offs, in-flight procedures, circuits, approaches and landings.

PREPARATION FOR FLIGHT

Essentially this will follow the normal routine preparations which are used prior to day flying, but the following additional aspects will be necessary:

Equipment Required for Flight at Night.
Night Vision Accommodation.
Personal Safety Precautions in the Parking Area.
External/Internal Checks – Night Considerations.
Aeroplane Lights – Operation.
Start-Up Procedure – Night Considerations.

EQUIPMENT REQUIRED FOR FLIGHT

In addition to the normal equipment carried during flights in daylight hours, e.g. maps etc., and those items required by schedule 5 of the ANO relating to flights by night, it will be necessary to have a hand torch in order to complete a satisfactory external check of the aircraft condition and to illuminate those areas in the cockpit which may not be adequately covered by the internal lighting system. It will also be invaluable should the normal cockpit lighting fail, either partially or totally during flight.

NIGHT VISION ACCOMMODATION

In the past aircraft often operated at night from inadequately lighted airfields and night navigation was mainly carried out by the use of a map and ground reference features. There was therefore a need for a pilot to avoid bright lighting for some 30 minutes prior to flying and to use red lighting in the cockpit in order to retain his night vision accommodation.

Today, regulations require adequate minimum standards of airfield illumination, such that on take-off the act of just looking along the runway lights would greatly reduce the quality of night vision developed before take-off. Further to this the development of better cockpit lighting systems has brought with it the wider use of white lighting instead of red because of the changed philosophy in relation to such problems as the incorrect selection of fuel and other systems due to inadequate cockpit lighting. Items of this nature have now become more significant to safe flight than the ability to maintain maximum efficiency with regard to night vision.

Additionally, current navigation methods are greatly improved and radio navigation has in many instances replaced the older methods of determining position solely by the use of ground identification features and a map. Nevertheless all pilots should have an understanding of the facts concerning night vision adaptation so that they can obtain the most from their vision during night flying.

To start with it should be appreciated how the construction of the human eye enables it to pick up light wave impulses through the sensory endings of the retina. These impulses are then interpreted and transmitted to the brain via the optic nerve.

The retina is a screen upon which light rays are projected. It is composed of millions of tightly packed light sensitive receptors covering the transparent innermost layer of the eyeball. These sensors are made up of two types of receptors, rods and cones. There are two types because the eye has to accommodate for two widely differing periods, day and night.

Fig. 20-2

The clarity of an image depends upon light intensity and the angle at which it is perceived. The cones are used during conditions of bright light and the rods are used for seeing in dim light. The cones are concentrated where the point of focus normally occurs, and they distinguish colour and distant objects. The rods are concentrically distributed around the cones and detect objects only in shades of grey.

During the day the rods are used in peripheral vision but because they can operate in light which is only 1/5000th part of the intensity of that which the cones cease to function they play their most important part in night vision. They do however need more time to adapt to darkness than the cones need to adjust to bright sunlight, and whereas the cones can adjust to sunlight in a few seconds the rods require some 30 minutes to fully adjust to darkness.

Because the distribution of the rods around the cones results in their not being directly behind the pupil of the eye, at night it will be important to use an 'off-centre' technique, that is, looking a few degrees to one side of the object of interest. Another point is that the rods will not perceive an object whilst the eyes are in motion, it will therefore be important to integrate short pauses in eye movement when using scanning techniques.

Rods will lose their sensitivity after exposure to a light source but provided one guards against bright lights they will regain their

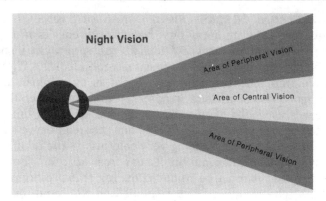

Fig. 20-3

sensitivity fairly quickly. Therefore pilots should keep cockpit lighting to a minimum intensity compatible with their needs, and when a hand torch is used it should be suitably masked to reduce its brilliance.

A further point relating to night vision is the phenomenon of 'Auto-Kinesis'. This can occur when looking at a fixed light source against a dark sky. After a while the light may appear to oscillate or be in motion and to prevent this illusion it will be necessary to avoid focussing on the light for too long a period.

Finally, good night vision will depend upon a pilot's physical condition. Factors such as the consumption of alcohol, smoking, fatigue, colds or medication can seriously impair the development and maintenance of good vision during the hours of darkness.

PERSONAL SAFETY PRECAUTIONS ON THE PARKING AREA

At night the normal safety precautions to be taken when moving around parked aircraft are particularly important. Ideally parking areas should be illuminated, but physical and financial constraints often prohibit this, so pilots should ensure they have a torch handy whenever they are in the vicinity of parked aircraft.

During engine starting operations pilots should arrange to keep cockpit illumination to a minimum compatible with operational necessity so that they can more clearly see persons outside in the close vicinity of their aircraft. Although good operating practice dictates that navigation lights and when available anti-collison lights are switched on prior to start up, persons on the parking area must not rely 100% on this being the case and should remain well clear of propellers at all times.

A particular hazard at night occurs when one or more aircraft are stationary or manoeuvring in the vicinity of the parking area; the engine noise they create will tend to drown out engine noise from other and closer aircraft on the move.

EXTERNAL/INTERNAL CHECKS – NIGHT CONSIDERATIONS

A torch will be needed to carry out the external checks in a proper manner. Any attempt to carry out an external pre-flight inspection with insufficient lighting could have catastrophic results if just one unserviceable item necessary for safe flight is overlooked. Bear in mind the importance of a clean windscreen and remember that dew can form readily on the windscreen and side windows during the cooling which occurs after sunset. If this has occured ensure that it is removed with a clean cloth. During very cold nights the pilot must be particularly alert for the formation of hoar frost or ice on the aircraft and if this is found it must be removed during this pre-flight phase.

The internal checks must be meticulous and the hand torch must be used to cover those areas which the normal cockpit lighting may not illuminate. A sound knowledge of the location and position of all switches, controls and levers will be a great asset to any pilot operating at night. Cockpit lighting should be adjusted to ensure that all instruments are visible, but maximum lighting intensity should be avoided whenever possible.

When 'warning lights' are fitted in the cockpit, their brilliance is normally arranged so that they are clearly visible during daylight. At night this brilliance will be distracting to the pilot and some method is normally incorporated to lower light intensity for night operations. On some aircraft they may automatically be dimmed whenever the navigation lights are switched on, alternatively they may be fitted with an adjustable iris which will have to be manually operated or set by the pilot.

A careful check should be made to ensure that the required number of spare fuses are available for the lighting circuits and other systems, with the exception of those protected by manual or automatic re-set circuit breakers.

AEROPLANE LIGHTS – OPERATION

The pre-flight inspection should include a careful check on the operation of navigation, taxy and landing lights. When fitted, the anti-collision light should be included in this inspection.

When red internal lighting systems are used the pilot should review any effect that red lighting has in reducing the clarity of the colour codes used on cockpit instruments, and fuel selector markings etc.

Note: Not all night flights start off in the dark and therefore whenever it is suspected that the intended flight might run into the hours of darkness the navigation lighting, taxy and landing lamps and cockpit lighting systems should be checked for serviceability as part of the pre-flight drills.

START-UP PROCEDURES

During the normal pre-starting checks ensure that the navigation lights and if fitted the anti-collision lights are switched 'ON'.

Adjust the cockpit lighting to a minimum acceptable level and complete a very careful lookout for any person outside and in close vicinity to the aircraft. Make sure one window is open and give a 'clear starting' call prior to engaging the engine starter.

When a ground marshaller is available during the start-up phase remember it is still the pilot's responsibility to ensure that it is all clear around the aircraft prior to starting up or commencing to taxy.

Once the engine is running it will be particularly important to ensure that the alternator/generator is functioning correctly and giving an adequate charge rate.

LOCAL PROCEDURES – INCLUDING ATC LIAISON

Prior to instruction in night flying a pilot should receive a general briefing on specific local procedures which are additional to, or changed from, those used during daylight operations. Such procedures will vary dependent upon the type(s) of airfield lighting equipment, air traffic activity and the airfield position relative to controlled airspace, restricted areas, large towns etc.

One of the pre-requisites of good airmanship is 'anticipation' and this can more easily be achieved when the pilot has a thorough knowledge of the procedures which he may be called upon to carry out.

Nowadays night flying training is seldom done without some form of Air Traffic Control or RTF Advisory Service being available, and a thorough knowledge of any additional or changed RTF procedures will be required if the pilot is to operate his aircraft in a competent and safe manner.

On those occasions where the ATC/RTF facility becomes unserviceable, or at airfields where no RTF is provided, the pilot will be controlled by lamp signals and therefore the table of visual light signals on page 20-16 should be reviewed.

TAXYING

Marshalling Signals

When marshallers are available for the guidance of aircraft manoeuvring on the ground, they will normally be equiipped with torches or illuminated wands.

The standard set of signals which they will use are clearly defined in the Rules of the Air and Air Traffic Control Regulations and the U.K. Air Pilot. These signals have identical meanings by day or by night and it would be useful to review them prior to operating at night. It would also be advisable to review the standard light signals shown below.

SIGNAL	MEANING TO AIRCRAFT ON THE GROUND	MEANING TO AIRCRAFT IN THE AIR
Intermittent Green Luminous Beam	Authorises: Movement on the Manoeuvring Area and Apron.	Aircraft is to: Return to the circuit, or remain in the circuit, at normal circuit height and to await signal for permission to land.
Continuous Green Luminous Beam	Authorises: Take-off.	Authorises: Landing.
Intermittent Red Luminous Beam	Aircraft is to: Move clear of the Landing Strip immediately.	Requires that: Owing to the aerodrome being unfit or for any other reason, a landing should be made elsewhere.
Continuous Red Luminous Beam	Movement on the Movement area is prohibited.	Requires that: The aircraft is to give way to other aircraft and continue circling.
Intermittent White Luminous Beam	Requires that: The aircraft return from the Movement Area to the Starting Place.	Requires that: The aircraft is to land at the aerodrome and proceed to the apron.
Red Pyrotechnic Light or Red Flare (not directed at the aircraft)		Prohibits aircraft from landing for the time being. Cancels any previous permission to land.

By day or by night, a series of projectiles discharged from the ground at intervals of 10 seconds, each showing, on bursting, red and green lights or stars		Shall indicate to an aircraft that it is flying in or about to enter a danger or similar area and is required to take such action as may be necessary to leave the area or change course to avoid the area

Parking Area and Taxyway Lighting

When taxying out from a lighted parking area the first major transition will occur on leaving the illuminated area and becoming orientated in relation to the position of the taxyway lights.

Depending upon the scale of lighting equipment used at the airfield the taxyway may be marked by blue lights positioned in line with the taxyway edges at intervals of 30 to 60 metres. Additionally green centre line lights may be fitted and positioned between 15 and 30 metres apart. The latter is a useful supplementary lighting system as it enables a pilot to more easily maintain a central position along the taxyway, thereby keeping the wing tips further away from any low obstructions which may be adjacent to the sides of the taxyway.

Judgement of Speed and Distance

Taxying at night will call for extra care and it will be important to reduce cockpit lighting to a minimum level.

The basic difference between taxying by day and by night relates to the changed vision characteristics. At night judgement in relation to distance and speed is deceptive and vision is more limited.

The collective effect of these factors can deceive the pilot and stationary lights will appear to be further away than they actually are. This leads to a tendency to taxy faster at a time when reduced visual perceptions require taxying speeds to be reduced. Therefore a pilot must make a positive effort to maintain a slow taxying speed, and relate his judgement of speed to those lights which are closest to the aircraft.

During prolonged taxying the alternator/generator charge rate should be monitored to ensure an adequate charge is being maintained and it may sometimes be necessary to taxy intermittently against the brakes to avoid the battery discharging.

Use of Aircraft Taxy Lights

A slow taxying speed will lead to shorter stopping distances in the event of a pilot becoming confused in relation to his taxying route, or if obstructions are encountered without previous warning.

When taxy/landing lamps are available the pilot should be fully aware of the exact location of the switches and know the correct switch movement. Practice at reaching out and switching on either of these lights should be included during the training period.

During taxying a situation can occur where the aircraft is pointing into the direction of the landing approach path and on these occasions care must be exercised to avoid dazzle to landing aircraft through indiscriminate use of taxy or landing lights. A similar situation obtains when the taxy track parallels a main road, and in such a circumstance care must also be used to avoid dazzling oncoming road traffic.

Avoidance of Hazards – Obstruction Lighting

A pilot taxying at night will often be faced by a variety of lighting and from a distance it is often difficult to detect the difference between red lights indicating hazards to aircraft in flight e.g. those fitted to tall obstructions such as masts, hangars etc., and those which are set much lower and warn the pilot of hazards during ground manoeuvring.

Obstructions which infringe runway or taxyway clearance limits will be lighted by one or more steady red lights. The light(s) will normally be fixed at the top of the obstruction and considerable care should be taken when manoeuvring in their vicinity. Red obstruction lights are also used by night at ground level to delineate areas which are unsafe for taxying, or to close off unserviceable parts of runways or taxyways. These steady red lights are normally positioned between 3 and 7·5 metres apart.

Any vehicle which is cleared for use on the surface of an aerodrome at night must be fitted with an obstruction light. This usually consists of a flashing yellow or blue light fitted to the highest point on the vehicle.

Instrument Checks

The importance of carrying out a flight instrument check whilst taxying at night lies in the fact that during night flying the pilot will need to rely upon them more frequently, for example, cloud is often more difficult to detect at night and even when it is not present the instruments will still need to be used and monitored closely during normal flight operations and particularly throughout the initial stages of the climb after take-off.

Bear in mind however that during these checks the cockpit illumination will probably need to be increased, and due to the added restriction to vision during taxying it will be advisable to reduce the number of instruments being checked during any one turn.

Holding Point – Lighting and Procedures

The 'holding position' at night is normally the same as by day, but as there is no laid-down lighting method to identify this area, it will be subject to the procedures used at the particular airfield. Sometimes reflective markers or several closely spaced taxyway lights are used. In any event the position of the runway lighting will be a useful guide in this connection, runway thresholds are marked at night by green lights. The latter, however, are not always readily visible from the postion of the holding point and care must be used to stop early in order that the pre-take-off actions can be completed whilst holding well clear from the active runway.

A cautionary point to bear in mind is that other aircraft may already be parked at the holding point and when they are not equipped with anti-collision lights they may only be recognised by a white tail light, which can easily be missed among the number of other lights in the vicinity of the runway.

Following completion of the power checks and pre take-off drills the pilot should re-adjust the cockpit lighting and be particularly careful to stow his hand torch in a secure but convenient position where it can be easily reached should the cockpit lighting fail at any stage during flight.

INITIAL FAMILIARISATION FLIGHT

Departure Procedure

Following take-off, the airfield departure procedure will normally be the same as that used by day, or as directed by ATC.

The airfield departure stage of the flight is a period when a pilot is still adjusting himself both mentally and physically to the requirements of night operation, and this period is also coincident with the need for added vigilance during flight in the vicinity of an airfield, including the mental adjustment required to determine the flight path of other aircraft from the colours presented by their navigation lights.

During the introductory stages of night flying the instructor will be giving directions to the pilot under training, in order to position the aircraft at a height and location from which the Local Area Night Orientation part of the flight can begin.

LOCAL AREA NIGHT ORIENTATION

The object of this first flight by night is to give the 'pilot under instruction' the opportunity to accustom himself to the many changed aspects of flight operations at night.

Apart from the identifications of towns from the area covered by lights and being able to recognise them by their respective positions in relation to one another, a pilot must be able to distinguish between distant moving lights from vehicles on the ground, and those of aircraft in flight.

The lack of a natural horizon and the need to back up visual flying techniques by reference to the flight instruments will be another item in this familiarisation exercise.

Prior to descending into the circuit, a short time should be spent studying the airfield recognition characteristics and the layout of its lighting system, including the identification beacon, approach and runway lighting, and the positioning and identification of the various obstruction lights.

SIGNIFICANCE OF LIGHTS ON OTHER AIRCRAFT

The ability to recognise navigation lights of aircraft in the air and to determine their approximate direction of flight has already been mentioned. Aircraft tail lights are normally the most difficult to distinguish, but when they are seen there is usually more time to assess whether a closing situation exists.

Anti-collision and particularly strobe lights stand out fairly clearly, the former because of their flashing characteristics which readily attract the human eye and the latter because of their flashing characteristics and brilliance.

A method used on some larger aircraft is an additional external lighting system (Tel-Tail Recognition Lights), whereby the whole tail section of the aircraft is illuminated during flight, thus giving more positive recognition.

GROUND OBSTRUCTION LIGHTS

 All man-made obstructions which extend 500 feet above the surface are lighted with one or more red lights during the hours of darkness. Sometimes obstructions which extend upwards between 300 feet and 500 feet are also lighted.

In the vicinity of airfields any obstructions (regardless of height) which are considered to be a hazard to aircraft in flight will show at least one red obstruction light. In the event that an obstruction above 500 feet is situated close to an airfield it will usually be marked by a flashing red light known as a hazard light.

Certain conspicuous mountains and hills in the United Kingdom are considered to be especially hazardous to aviation operations and these are also marked by red obstruction lights, details of which are shown in the U.K. Air Pilot.

DIVISION OF PILOTING EFFORT – EXTERNAL/INSTRUMENT REFERENCE

As with day flying the pilot will be faced with various weather conditions, but even on cloudless nights the use of the flight instruments will play a greater part in flying the aircraft.

During the hours of darkness there will seldom be a clearly defined natural horizon and visual flight will be achieved by the visual cues obtained from the varied pattern of lights on the ground. Disorientation during and after turning may occur, and the pilot will need to make frequent reference to the attitude indicator in order to confirm the attitude of the aircraft.

A process of adjustment to night conditions will occur during every flight and apart from IMC penetration, the greatest need to rely upon instrument reference will occur during the period immediately after take-off.

Once the aircraft has reached a height where the pilot is able to clearly assess the aircraft attitude by reference to the cues afforded by ground lighting, a division of effort will normally be necessary and the pilot will need to adapt his reference to include both external visual cues and the flight instrument indications.

The degree of effort between external visual and instrument reference will vary, and will be primarily dictated by the phase of flight, the visibility, and the amount of ground lighting within visual range. For example, over barren countryside or large areas of water, instrument flying will be more or less continuous, but over populated areas which normally afford plenty of external visual cues in the form of ground lights, instrument reference will normally tend to be reduced, and a greater vigilance in relation to normal lookout and visual navigation techniques can be employed.

REJOINING PROCEDURE
At night there are no fundamental differences in the methods used to join the traffic pattern. The local procedures should wherever possible be complied with in a meticulous fashion in order that an orderly and safe flow of air traffic movement is achieved.

It is important to bear in mind however that the aircraft will be entering an area where traffic intensity is often high and the ability to recognise other aircraft by their navigation lights and other forms of illumination, together with the prompt determining of their approximate headings will be vital.

AIRFIELD LIGHTING – APPROACH AND RUNWAY LIGHTING (INCLUDING VASIS)
Various types of approach and runway lighting are in current use, and the complexity, geometric arrangements, and numbers of lights involved, vary according to the operations being conducted and the lighting system being used at the aerodrome concerned.

Detailed information in relation to these various scales of lighting is outside the scope of this manual, and what follows can only be a general outline of the various component parts of a typical approach and runway lighting system.

The colour of and intensity of these lights will normally be of a steady or fixed character. When high intensity permanent electric lights are used, they normally show in the approach direction only but their intensity can usually be controlled to suit the prevailing conditions. A pilot finding the lights too dazzling can request ATC to adjust them.

Information on the specific lighting arrangements used at individual aerodromes is given in the U.K. Air Pilot, AGA 2 (Aerodromes for use by International Air Transport) see fig. 20-5, and AGA 3 (Aerodrome Directory) see fig. 20-6. Information on lighting arrangements at specific airfields is also given on Landing and Approach Charts, see figs 20-7, 20-8 and 20-9. These last three figures show the method of presenting lighting information on Aerad Charts produced by International Aeradio Ltd. Acknowledgements are made to the U.K. National Air Traffic Services Aeronautical Information Service for the reproductions from the Air Pilot, and to International Aeradio

Fig. 20-4

Ltd, Aerad Division for figs 20-7, 20-8 and 20-9.

A licensed aerodrome which does not have the full lighting facilities required by the CAA will be annotated in column 24 of AGA 3 as 'Not Licensed for Night Use', an example of this is shown in fig. 20-10. Further to this, when an unlicensed aerodrome is shown in AGA 3 with lighting facilities it does not necessarily imply that the lighting requirements for licensed aerodromes have been met, see fig. 20-11.

The Reference Information on pages 20-24, 20-25, 20-26 and 20-28 is to be used for Ground Training purposes ONLY.

If the runway lights are not of the flush type but are mounted above the surface this will be indicated by the abbreviation 'elev'. At certain airfields paraffin flares only are available, and this will be indicated in the Air Pilot by the word 'Goosenecks'. On certain

VISUAL GROUND AIDS

32   Taxying guidance system: Centre-line green lights on taxiways ABC and D. Elsewhere blue edge lights. Taxiway B also has blue edge lights. Taxiway stop bar and lead on lights from A to 26 threshold, from B to Runway 26 and from D to 06 threshold.

33   Visual aids to location: Aerodrome beacon alternating white/green

34   Indicators and ground signalling devices:

35   LIGHTING AIDS

Runway/ Run	Lead-in/Approach lights	Threshold lights	Runway lights	Angle of App. lights
a	b	c	d	e
08	439 m H.I. centre-line with 1 cross bar	H.I. Green with H.I.	H.I. elev bi-directional with omni-directional component. H.I. colour coded centre-line. Runway end lights red.	VASIS (3°) 131 m and 320 m.
26	882 m H.I. coded centre-line with 5 crossbars. Supplementary lighting, inner 288 m.	Green w. bars	H.I. elev bi-directional with omni-directional component. H.I. colour coded centre-line TDZ 900 m. Runway end lights red.	VASIS (3°) 150 m and 360 m.
17	910 m H.I. centre-line with 5 crossbars	H.I. Green	H.I. elev bi-directional with L.I. omni-directional component. Runway end lights red.	VASIS (3°) 152 m and 345 m.
35	522 m H.I. centre-line with 1 crossbar	L.I. Green	H.I. elev bi-directional with L.I. omni-directional component. Runway end lights red.	VASIS (3°) 143 m and 366 m.

36   Emergency lighting and secondary power supply: Yes   **37**   Obstruction marking and lighting: Yes

38   MARKING AIDS: Runway designation, threshold, centre-line, touchdown zone and fixed distance markings available on Runways 08/26 and 17, Runway designation and permanent displaced threshold markings available on Runway 35. Taxi-holding position markings.

39   Safety altitude (within 25 nm): 3,300 ft   (L) Obstruction lighted ....* and flashing   Aerodrome obstructions:

	Approach Areas					Sectors between Approach Areas								
Rwy	Object	Height (feet) aal	amsl	nm from Thr	Sector °T from ARP	Highest Object: Object	(feet) aal	amsl	Exceeding 150 feet aal within 2½ nm Bearing °T	Distance (nm)	Exceeding 250 feet aal 2½ nm—4 nm Bearing °T	Distance (nm)	Exceeding 500 feet aal beyond 4 nm Bearing °T	Distance (nm)
08	—				066/162	Trees	183	450	099	1·8				
26	Electricity poles on high ground	146	413	1·72		TV Mast(L)	1,432	1,699					112	8·1
						TV Mast(L)	1,461	1,728					119	8·1
17	—				162/246	—								
	—				246/342	—								
35	Electricity poles	56	323	0·71	342/066									
		47	314	0·82										
		48	315	0·98										

14 Nov 75   Civil Aviation Authority

Fig. 20-5

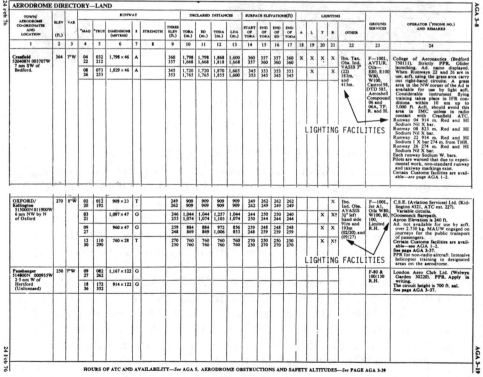

AERODROME DIRECTORY—LAND

TOWN/ AERODROME CO-ORDINATES AND LOCATION	ELEV (ft.)	VAR	RUNWAY °MAG	°TRUE	DIMENSIONS (METRES)	S	STRENGTH	THRES ELEV (ft.)	TORA (m.)	ED (m.)	TODA (m.)	LDA (m.)	START OF TORA	END OF TORA	END OF ED	END OF TODA	A	L	T	R	OTHER	GROUND SERVICES	OPERATOR (PHONE NO.) AND REMARKS
1	2	3	4	5	6	7	8	9	10	11	12	13	14	15	16	17	18	19	20	21	22	23	24
Cranfield 520408N 003707W 7 nm SW of Bedford.	364	7°W	04 22	032 212	1,798 × 46	A		360 357	1,798 1,668	1,798 1,668	1,868 1,818	1,600 1,668	360 357	357 360	357 360	360 360	X	X	X	X	Ibn. Tax. AVTUR. Oils— E80, E100 W80, Castrol 99, Aeroshell Compound 06 and 06A, TF, R. and H.	F—100L, Jet A1,	College of Aeronautics (Bedford 750111). Strictly PPR. Glider launching. Ad. name displayed. When Runways 22 and 26 are in use, acft. using the grass area carry out right-hand circuits. A grass area in the NW corner of the Ad is available for use by light acft. Considerable instrument flying training takes place in IFR conditions within 10 nm up to 3,000 ft. Acft. should avoid this area in IMC unless in radio contact with Cranfield ATC. Runway 04 914 m. Red and HI Sodium Nil X bar. Runway 08 823 m. Red and HI Sodium Nil X bar. Runway 22 914 m. Red and HI Sodium 1 X bar 274 m. from THR. Runway 26 274 m. Red and HI Sodium Nil X bar. Each runway Sodium W. bars. Pilots are warned that due to experimental work, non-standard runway and taxiway markings exist. Certain Customs facilities are available—see page AGA 1–2.
			08 26	073 253	1,829 × 46	A		345 353	1,720 1,765	1,720 1,765	1,870 1,855	1,665 1,600	345 353	353 345	353 345	353 345			X	X	VASIS 3° (22) 183m. and 413m.		
OXFORD/ Kidlington 515000N 011900W 6 nm NW by N of Oxford	270	8°W	02 20	012 192	909 × 23	T		249 262	909 909	909 909	909 909	909 909	249 262	262 249	262 249	262 249				X	Ibn. Ind. Obs. AVASIS 3½° left hand side 91m and 193m (02/27) and (09/27).	F—100L, Jet A1, Oils W80, W100, 80, 100, Limited R.H.	C.S.E. (Aviation Services) Ltd. (Kidlington 4321, ATC ext. 227). Variable circuits. Gooseneck flarepath. Apron Elevation is 240 ft. Ad. not available for use by acft. over 2,730 kg. MAUW engaged on journeys for the public transport of passengers. Certain Customs facilities are available—see AGA 3-37. PPR for non-radio aircraft. Intensive helicopter training in designated areas on the aerodrome.
			03 21		1,097 × 47	G		246 255	1,044 1,074	1,044 1,074	1,257 1,105	1,044 1,074	244 250	250 244	250 244	240 244			X	X†			
			09 27		960 × 47	G		259 248	884 869	884 869	972 1,006	856 853	259 248	248 259	248 259	248 259			X	X†			
			12 30	110 290	760 × 28	T		270 250	760 760	760 760	760 760	760 760	270 250	250 270	250 270	250 270				X†			
Panshanger 514800N 000935W 2·5 nm W of Hertford (Unlicensed)	250	7°W	09 27	082 262	1,167 × 122	G																F-80 & 100/130 R.H.	London Aero Club Ltd. (Welwyn Garden 30220). PPR. Apply in writing. The circuit height is 700 ft. aal. See page AGA 3-37.
			18 36	172 352	914 × 122	G																	

HOURS OF ATC AND AVAILABILITY—*See* AGA 5. AERODROME OBSTRUCTIONS AND SAFETY ALTITUDES—*See* PAGE AGA 3-39

Fig. 20-6

RHOOSE Approach 125·85

RHOOSE Tower 121·2

GLAMORGAN
RHOOSE
N51 23·8
W003 20·8
ELEV **220** FT

311
91

RS Green

Control Tower
293
73

Light A/C only

VDF
Rhoose Hmr

Landing Threshold
213

229
9

7000 x 150 ft Tarmac
2802 x 190 ft Tarmac

R/W's in Metres
04/22–854
13/31–2134

1000   0   1000   2000   3000   4000 FT
500   0   500   1000M

LIGHTING

R/W	VASIS	Approach	Threshold	Runway
13	S 3°	White H.I. centre-line with crossbars	Green H.I.	White H.I. & L.I. White centre-line with red last 1000 ft, red/white previous 2000 ft
31			Green H.I. with wingbars	
04/22	Nil	Nil	Nil	Nil

Other Lighting: Obstruction, taxiway, ident beacon, stopway, apron floods.

WARNINGS

R/W lights 13/31 elevated
R/W 04–On Take-off or missed approach, no turns to be made within the Airport boundaries.

Taxiway width–50 ft (75 ft from apron to R/W 13/31)

Circuits: 04 & 31–right hand or as instructed.

RUNWAY AVAILABILITY

31 Landing 6500 ft (first 500 ft not avail)
04/22 Visual HJ only

STOPWAYS
31–229 ft

Var 8°W Trans Alt	3000
Elevations in feet AMSL	311
Heights above aerodrome elevation	91

LANDING CHART

GLAMORGAN

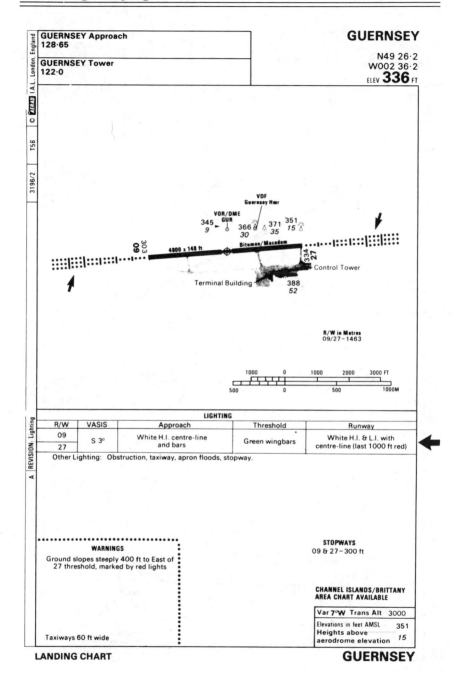

I.A.L. London, England

T56

3196/2

GUERNSEY Approach
128·65

GUERNSEY Tower
122·0

GUERNSEY

N49 26·2
W002 36·2
ELEV **336** FT

VDF
Guernsey Hmr

VOR/DME
GUR
345   366   371   351
9   30   35   15

303   4800 x 148 ft   Bitumen/Macadam
09

334
27

Control Tower

Terminal Building   388
52

R/W in Metres
09/27 – 1463

1000   0   1000   2000   3000 FT
500   0   500   1000M

LIGHTING

REVISION: Lighting   A

R/W	VASIS	Approach	Threshold	Runway
09	S 3°	White H.I. centre-line and bars	Green wingbars	White H.I. & L.I. with centre-line (last 1000 ft red)
27				

Other Lighting: Obstruction, taxiway, apron floods, stopway.

WARNINGS
Ground slopes steeply 400 ft to East of
27 threshold, marked by red lights

Taxiways 60 ft wide

STOPWAYS
09 & 27 – 300 ft

**CHANNEL ISLANDS/BRITTANY
AREA CHART AVAILABLE**

Var 7°W Trans Alt 3000
Elevations in feet AMSL 351
Heights above aerodrome elevation 15

LANDING CHART

GUERNSEY

Fig. 20-8

Fig. 20-9

Binbrook 532648N 001230W 8 nm SSW of Grimaby	373	7°W	03 21	027 207	2,286×46†	A & C	LCG IV	2,285 2,285	2,470 2,465	2,470 2,470	2,470 2,470			X		X	Ibn. VASIS	RAF (Binbrook 282). PPR to charter and private acft. †Effective length reduced to 1,920 m. for those acft. not cleared to trample book wire.
Birmingham	*See* AGA 2-5																
Bitteswell 522730N 011445N 5 nm N of Rugby	440	8°W	04 22	032 212	1,829×46	A	LCG IV	440 430	1,829 1,829	1,840 1,896	1,875 1,829	1,786 1,829	440 430	430 440	429 440	429 439	X X X	Obs. Tax. Ind. AAp.Abn.	F— JET A1 with AL 38.	Hawker Siddeley Aviation Ltd. (Lutterworth 3041). PPR. To assist pilots in effecting safe road traffic clearance lines of eight poles each carrying triangular markers 14 ft. above the road are positioned 137 m. from 36 threshold, 189 m. from 04 threshold, and 152 m. from 10 threshold. Not licensed for night use. No ground signals except light signals.
			10 28	097 277	1,280×46	A	LCG IV	429 409	1,280 1,213	1,280 1,213	1,280 1,314	1,213 1,213	429 409	409 431	409 431	409 427				
			18 36	169 349	1,289×46	A	LCG IV	422 425	1,219 1,289	1,219 1,320	1,361 1,434	1,219 1,219	422 425	428 422	428 421	419 415				

Fig. 20-10

BRISTOL/Lulsgate	*See* AGA 2-8											
Brough 534300N 003345W 6 nm W of Hull (Unlicensed)	13	8°W	12 30	113 293	1,...2×30 +192×15†	T				X	Ibn. VASIS (3½°) 152 m. and 304 m. (12/30).	F—100L. Limited R. & H.	Hawker Siddeley Aviation Ltd. (0482-667121) (0482-667330, ATC). Telegraphic address:—Propellers Brough. PPR. †Extension is at NW end. Certain Customs facilities are available—see page AGA 1-2. See page AGA 3-35.
			17 35		750×30	G		(For emergency use only).				
Cambridge	*See* AGA 2-9											

HOURS OF ATC AND AVAILABILITY—*See* AGA 5. AERODROME OBSTRUCTIONS AND SAFETY ALTITUDES—*See* PAGE AGA 3-39

Fig. 20-11

instrument runways the colour of the runway lighting over the caution zone, i.e. the last 600 metres, may be yellow and this is indicated in AGA 2 by the abbreviation YCZ. On precision approach runways at major airports flush centre-line lights may be provided over the whole length of the runway and to give an indication of the distance remaining these lights are normally coloured red over the final 300 metres and alternately red and white between 900 metres and 300 metres from the runway end. When this system is being used at the particular airfields it will be indicated in AGA 2 by the words 'colour coded'.

In addition to centre line lighting all runways which comply with the ICAO Precision Approach Category II lighting standard, are provided with Touchdown Zone lighting which consists of Barrettes (short bars) of white lights on each side of the centre line along the first 900 metres of the runway.

Threshold Lights

When these are of the flush type they normally extend the full width of the runway. When they are of the elevated type a central gap of 22·5 metres is sometimes left clear. A short row of lights (wingbars) may also be provided outboard of the runway edge lights for use in poor visibility or to mark a displaced threshold.

Approach Lighting

The distance the centre line lights extend out from the threshold will be shown in AGA 2 together with the number of lighted crossbars when provided. Unless otherwise stated, runways which have three or less crossbars on their approach lighting have the bars sited at 300 metre intervals from the threshold. When more bars are provided a 150 metre spacing is adopted.

Visual Approach Slope Indicator Systems

In order to assist the pilot in his judgement of the correct approach slope there are two types of vertical guidance system in current use:

1. The Visual Approach Slope Indicator System (VASI) or, the Abbreviated Visual Approach Slope Indicator System (AVASI).
2. The Angle of Approach Indicator System:
    (a) The Three Colour System (AAI's)
    (b) The Low Intensity Two Colour System (LITAS)

The Angle of Approach Indicator Systems are gradually being phased out and eventually only the VASI or AVASI systems will be in use.

The VASI is a system of lights which enables the pilot to maintain a predetermined approach slope during his descent to the runway. The system comprises light units consisting of metal boxes, housing three high-intensity sealed beam lamps (see fig. 20-12).

VASI LIGHT UNIT

Fig. 20-12

Fig. 20-13

Immediately in front of the lamps is a colour filter assembly, the upper two thirds of which is red and the lower third is white. Across the front of the box at the focal point of the lamps is a narrow aperture which extends across the width of the box (see fig. 20-13).

Standard installations use 12 light boxes arranged so that two split bars of light straddle the runway. On each side of the runway a minimum of two units of three light boxes are placed in lines opposite to one another (see fig. 20-14).

Fig. 20-14

These light arrays are called the downwind and upwind light bars respectively. The visual approach slope reference point is located midway between the downwind and upwind bars, and when the pilot is on the correct approach slope he will see the downwind (nearest) bars as white and the upwind (furthest) bars as red. If descending below the correct approach slope (undershooting) both bars will show red and when too high (overshooting) both bars will be seen as white.

Departure from the correct descent slope is indicated to the pilot by a transition in colour of one of the light bars. If the aircraft is becoming too high the upwind bars will change from red through pink to white, leaving a completely white display. If the aircraft is becoming too low the downwind bars will change from white through pink to red, and the pilot will see a complete array of red lights (see figs 20-15 and 20-16).

As the aircraft approaches close to the runway threshold a generally spread of light sources and narrowing of the individual colour bands may occur, this optical deterioration however will occur after the aircraft has reached a position where the pilot will be able to

TYPICAL PROFILE OF VASI INSTALLATION

Fig. 20-15

Fig. 20-16

continue through the 'landing flare' and complete the landing by reference to the runway lights. Because of this distortion in the VASI colour system during the final stage of the approach it should be appreciated that VASI is an approach aid and not a landing aid.

Under certain conditions the white bars of the VASI system may take on a yellowish colour. Conditions under which this colour change may occur are during haze or when the approach is being made into sun or at night when the indicator lighting is being operated at low intensity.

The basic principle of the VASI installation is that of colour differential between red and white. The system is aligned with the final approach to the runway and can be inclined to give a minimum of 2 degrees to a maximum of 4 degrees from the horizontal.

The VASI angle is arranged to provide obstruction clearance during the final approach to the airfield. It is particularly valuable when approaches have to be made over water or featureless terrain when other sources of visual reference are lacking or misleading.

Although the beam width is some 15 degrees on each side of the extended runway centre line, runway alignment is not a function of VASI. Heading alignment for the approach path must be obtained by reference to the approach and runway lighting system.

Those airfields which have to accommodate very large aircraft usually have a third VASI bar installed each side of the runway. This is to meet the requirements of very large aircraft in which the pilot's eye level is considerably higher than the touch down level. When using an airfield which is fitted with such a 3 bar system, pilots of smaller aircraft should ignore the extra upwind bar and use the middle and downwind bars for approach slope guidance.

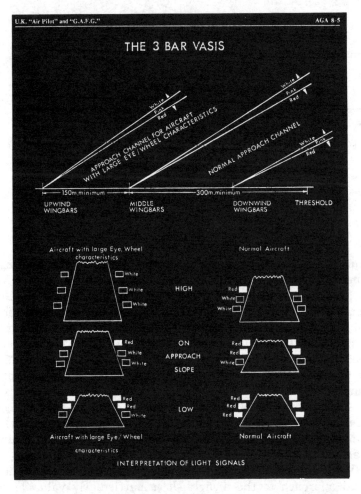

Fig. 20-17   Small aircraft should use the Middle and Downwind bars.

The range from the runway threshold at which VASI lights become visible will vary with the local weather conditions, but can normally be seen within 6 – 10 kilometres. A point to bear in mind however is that when on the approach slope at maximum range the white bars of the system may become visible shortly before the red bars.

The Abbreviated Visual Approach Slope Indicator System (AVASI) is one which utilises less than the standard 12 light units and is quite commonly used at smaller airfields. There are four types of AVASIS as follows:

  (a) 8 unit AVASIS, having two units at each of the four sites shown at fig. 20-14;
  (b) 4 unit AVASIS, having one unit at each of the four sites;
  (c) 6 unit asymmetric AVASIS, having three units at each upwind and downwind site on only one side of the runway;
  (d) 4 unit asymmetric AVASIS, having two units at each upwind and downwind site on only one side of the runway.

The installation of symmetrical systems is usually the better arrangement as better roll guidance is afforded by their perspective to the pilot. When asymmetric systems are installed they will be positioned to the left side of the runway, as viewed from the approach.

Angle of Approach Indicator Systems
  (a) The Three Colour System (AAI's).
       The indications given by the three colour Angle of Approach Indicator System are as follows:

| | INDICATOR LIGHTS | |
APPROACH SLOPE	LEFT	RIGHT
Too high	Amber	Amber
Slightly High	Amber	Green
Correct Path	Green	Green
Slightly Low	Green	Red
Too Low	Red	Red

  (b) The Low Intensity Two Colour Aproach Slope System (LITAS)
       The LITAS System is basically similar to the VASI System but is composed of lower intensity lights installed singly in the upwind and downwind VASI wingbar positions, and generally on the left hand side of the runway only.
       Interpretation of the light indications is identical to the normal VASI and although designed for use at night as a successor to AAI's the system can give useful ranges by day in other than bright conditions. When this approach slope system is used the abbreviation LITAS will be shown in column 22 of AGA 3 against the aerodrome name. When AAIs are installed it will be shown in the AGA 3 section in column 22 by the abbreviation AAI.

Regardless of the types of approach slope lighting they all have the following basic advantages:

1. They provide visual reference when approach paths lie over

featureless terrain or water and visual references are absent or misleading.
2. They will provide a safe clearance path above obstacles within the approach area.
3. They permit an easier and more precise approach path to be flown.
4. They will lead to lower noise levels being experienced by people on the ground by reducing the possibility of low approach paths with the resultant use of high power settings at low altitude.

NOTE: The foregoing information on approach and runway lighting is based upon the requirements for civil airfields. However lighting arrangements at RAF, RN, or USAF airfields may deviate from the standard installations, found at civil aerodromes. Additionally it should be noted that a fairly new approach path lighting system has become available and in use at some airfields. It is called a Precision Approach Path Indicator (PAPI) and information on its use can be found in the UK Air Pilot and AICs.

Approach Lighting
The centre line lights of high intensity systems may be coded with single lights up to 450 m from the threshold, the lights being duplicated beyond this distance. The low intensity approach system may consist only of a T in red lights, the cross bar being 150 m from the threshold with the shaft or centre line extending 300 m outwards.

Angle of Approach Indicators
Where three colour type indicators are in use the two indicators may both be sited on the left hand side of the runway and their elevation setting may be lower than that normally used at civil aerodromes.

Visual Approach Slope Indicators
These indicators are of the two colour type but at aerodromes where the main runway is less than 2,300 m in length the system may be installed nearer the threshold and the elevation settings may be lower than at civil aerodromes.

NIGHT CIRCUITS

Take-off and Climb

Line Up:
Once the pre take-off checks have been completed and the cockpit lighting re-adjusted take-off clearance must be obtained. Following this a final check must be made to ensure that the approach path is clear before the aircraft is taxied forward and lined up along the runway or take-off path.

During the final lookout into the approach path especial care must be used to search for aircraft which may only be showing their navigation lights, i.e. no flashing beacon or strobe lights.

Visual references during the take-off run:
Many pilots consciously or subconsciously use some distant reference feature to achieve heading maintenance during the take-off roll, but at night this will usually be impossible and the straightness of the take-off path will have to be achieved by reference to the lines of runway lighting.

Transference to instruments:
Immediately after the aircraft becomes airborne the pilot should transfer his attention to the flight instruments with particular emphasis upon adjusting and maintaining the attitude and airspeed required for the climb.

Establishing the initial climb:
A positive rate of climb should be established and instrument flight continued during the climb until the aircraft attitude can be reasonably assessed by observing ground lighting cues.

Use of flight instruments:
When established in the climb a combination of instrument flying and outside visual reference can be employed. This dual adaptation of flying techniques will permit correct performance in climbs, turns, straight and level flight and descents. Care must be used not to overbank during turning and the attitude indicator and airspeed will need more frequent monitoring than by day.

Instrument climb and initial turn:
At night the circuit height is usually not less than 1000 feet (a.a.l.) and when operating at airfields where the circuit height by day is normally 800 feet a straight climb to above 500 feet is recommended at night before turning onto the crosswind leg. This action will prevent an unnecessarily wide circuit being caused by the longer crosswind leg during the climb to 1000 feet.

The Circuit

Aircraft positioning – reference to runway lighting:
Checks, drills and circuit procedures are normally the same as by day but where uni-directional runway lighting is used the runway path may not be seen very clearly until the aircraft is established on the base leg. In these situations added care must be used to maintain a correct alignment in relation to the runway during the downwind leg and the centre line approach lighting will be a useful reference feature for this purpose.

The traffic pattern and lookout:
A careful lookout must be maintained and the positions and headings of other aircraft within the traffic pattern must be established by their wing and tail navigation lights. It will be important not to concentrate too much visual attention on the runway lighting or the normal lookout for other aircraft may deteriorate.

Initial Approach and Runway Lighting Demonstration

Positioning:
The aircraft is maintained on the normal approach slope by recognition of the correct angle in relation to the runway lights and the colour difference of the approach slope lighting system.

A demonstration will be given to show the student how the perspective of the runway lights will change with the aircraft's position relative to the correct approach slope. During this demonstration the colour changes of the VASI or Angle of Approach Systems will also be seen.

The aircraft will be flown further downwind than normal and a descent commenced on the base leg to approximately 600 feet. The aircraft will then be turned onto the final approach path but the height will be maintained.

Changing aspect of runway lights and VASIS:
Initially the aircraft will be well below the correct approach slope and red/red indications will be received from the approach slope lighting system, and seen from this angle the runway lights will be very closely spaced. See fig.20-18.

PERSPECTIVE OF RUNWAY LIGHTING

600'

Fig. 20-18

As the aircraft approaches closer to the runway threshold the approach slope indicator lights will change, the upwind bars will show red and the downwind bars will be white. At the same time the runway lights will open out and be seen further apart. The correct perspective and the distance between the runway lights will be indicated by the instructor. Figure 20-19 shows the lighting perspective when on the correct approach slope.

Fig. 20-19

As the aircraft gets closer still to the runway threshold the overshooting indications will be seen from the approach slope indicator lights and their colours will change to white/white. The perspective of the runway lighting will also change and the runway lights will give the appearance of being more widely spaced. This is illustrated in fig. 20-20.

Fig. 20-20

Intercepting the correct approach path:
Approach slope lighting systems are so arranged as to indicate a sloping path which will provide safe clearance above all obstructions for any aircraft approaching to land within 3 n.m. of the runway threshold and give a warning by means of red beams of light if the aircraft is below the safe approach path.

Approach slope lights do not necessarily provide clearance from obstacles when aircraft are at a greater distance than 3 n.m. therefore if an approach is commenced at a distance exceeding 3 n.m. an obstacle hazard could exist, and it will be important to remain high on the initial approach path until within a safe range. Once within 3 n.m. normal bracketing procedure should be implemented by adjusting the power whilst maintaining the correct approach speed.

The Climb Away
Following this runway lighting demonstration the aircraft should be set up for a climb straight ahead and back to circuit height. The

crosswind leg will be commenced at the correct distance upwind from the runway and the circuit completed in the normal manner.

Approach and Landing

Positioning, Base Leg and Final Approach:
At night a powered approach is used and the position to turn onto base leg is determined by reference to the centre line approach lights in conjunction with the distance from the runway threshold.

When established on the base leg power should be reduced compatible with the distance out from the runway threshold and the strength and direction of the wind.

At night it will not be possible to judge the wind direction and strength from a windsock and ATC will have to be relied upon for the this information. Care must be exercised when a headwind or tailwind component exists on the base leg, and the rate of descent monitored by the use of the altimeter to arrive at a safe height of 500/600 feet in the correct position for the final turn.

The aircraft should not be permitted to descend below this height whilst on the base leg because indications of being too low will not be seen clearly from the approach slope lighting until the turn onto final approach.

Rate of Descent and Approach Path:
The normal perceptions as used by day to relate the approach path to the perspective view of the runway will be used, but at night this will be achieved by reference to the runway lighting and Visual Approach System. Nevertheless the pilot should continue to monitor the altimeter throughout the approach until close to the runway threshold.

Note: Whereas by day ATC may give an occasional clearance to land which leads to two aircraft being on the runway at the same time, by night this practice is not permitted. Therefore unless it is fairly clear to the pilot that an aircraft which is in the process of landing or has already landed will clear the runway prior to his own landing a missed approach should be initiated and the aircraft taken round again. If this occurs the overshooting aircraft should be turned slightly so that it tracks to the right of the runway so that the pilot can clearly see the flight path of the preceding aircraft if it should take off again.

Diurnal wind effect:
Due to the surface heating during the day frictional eddies caused by the wind passing over the surface may extend upwards to 2000 feet or more. This causes the faster moving air aloft to mix with air in the lower layers, and winds at the surface will therefore veer and become

stronger. During the night, the surface cooling reduces this inter-change between the air at the surface and higher layers, and the surface wind backs and decreases in strength.

Fig. 20-21

The variation in wind strength and direction caused by this diurnal effect will depend upon the type of air mass, and whether frontal activity is present. However it is not unusual to experience a reduction of up to 50% in wind strength near the surface during the night, and in these circumstances this will result in a significant change in wind speed and direction between 2000 feet and the surface.

This wind effect will often be noticed whilst on the circuit when, for example, a crosswind component experienced on the downwind leg becomes nil during the final stages of the approach, or when a moderate wind at 1000 feet decays and becomes almost non-existent a few hundred feet from the ground.

Use of landing lights:

Initially the student will be taught to complete the final approach and landing without the aid of the aircraft landing lights. Later, and as the student becomes more competent at night landings the landing lights will be used during the final stages of the approach, from approximately 300 feet above the surface.

Landing lights will normally illuminate the runway surface quite clearly from a height of 200 feet and the procedure for the landing which follows will be virtually the same as by day.

A point to bear in mind however is that on nights when the visibility is restricted by haze or mist, the landing lights can create uncomfortable glare and reflections which will make the landing more difficult. On these occasions it will usually be preferable to switch them off and use the runway lighting to assess the aircraft height throughout the landing flare.

Although this disadvantage can sometimes reduce the value of landing lights they can be used to obtain information on the visibility conditions at night. For example, if the pilot suspects the visibility is deteriorating he can momentarily switch on the landing lights and obtain clear indications of mist or haze formation.

The flare and touch-down:
When the aircraft landing lights are not used the judgement of the flare through to the touchdown should be done by reference to the runway lighting and not by attempting to see the ground. A gentle roundout should be used and the power gradually reduced until the wheels are on the ground. At this stage any residual power should be promptly removed by ensuring the throttle is fully closed.

The use of this procedure will enable the pilot to compensate more easily and quickly for errors of judgement in levelling off, such as those caused by the restrictions in vision at night or by unfamiliar lighting effects.

The Roll-Out:
Direction should be judged by reference to the runway lighting and care must be taken to look well ahead during the initial stages of the landing-roll.

Turning off the runway – control of speed:
It has been mentioned earlier that speed can be deceptive at night, therefore extra care must be taken to ensure that the aircraft has slowed down to a reasonable taxying speed before turning off the runway.

A slower speed will also allow the pilot to adjust his vision to the change in lighting during the transition from the bright illumination of the runway to the relatively dark area of the taxiways.

Going Round Again
The same procedure is used as by day, but when roller landings are being practised or on those occasions when the aircraft is taken round again from close to the ground, especial care must be given to counteracting the positive trim change which occurs during the application of full power.

Use of instruments:
Once the aircraft is airborne instrument reference will be essential to ensure the correct attitude is established and held, until the climbing speed is reached and a safe height obtained.

Re-positioning in the circuit pattern:
Airmanship considerations dictate that the aircraft is re-positioned in the circuit so as to avoid encroachment on the flight paths of preceding aircraft.

During this phase a particularly vigilant search must be maintained in order to establish the position of any aircraft which may be entering the circuit pattern from the crosswind or downwind legs.

NIGHT NAVIGATION

The principles involved in navigation at night are basically the same as those used during the day. However, the difficulty of recognising physical ground features will necessitate giving more attention to DR navigation techniques.

When flying over populated areas the light patterns of towns and large villages will be valuable, but it must be appreciated that judgement of distance by night is usually deceptive.

This difficulty in judging distance occurs because during the day a pilot estimates distance by comparing the size of nearby and distant objects, but during the night he cannot do this.

Fig. 20-22

Particular Emphasis on Flight Planning

The success of any navigation flight will depend to a very large extent upon the care given to flight planning. During night navigation the number of available navigating aids e.g. ground features, identification of airfields, etc. will be limited, so too will be the number of operational airfields and ATC facilities in the form of VHF/DF and radar.

These restrictions will make it necessary to employ additional care in the planning of available en-route aids. It may therefore, often be more sensible to plan the route in a manner that enables practical use of these limited facilities even if it means flying by a non-direct route and increasing the distance to be flown.

When making decisions on the best route to be flown it will also be important to bear in mind that MATZs are normally only operational between 0800-1700 local time and the definition of night with reference to the activity of Danger Areas is that period between 1800-0800 local time.

A further aspect which must be considered during the planning stage is that all flights at night must be conducted in accordance with the Instrument Flight Rules. Therefore when the en-route section of the flight is planned to be flown above 3000 feet a.m.s.l. and outside Controlled Airspace the Quadrantal Rule will apply. A vertical clearance of 1000 feet above all obstructions within 5 n.m. must also be observed, whether flying above or below 3000 feet a.m.s.l.

Fig. 20-23

Fig. 20-24

When the flight commences from, or terminates at, an airfield within a Control Zone and the pilot does not hold an Instrument Rating this section(s) of the flight will have to be conducted in accordance with Special VFR.

In view of the changed circumstances and additional constraints imposed during night navigation, it will be advisable to file a flight plan for all navigation flights other than short local cross countries, where the pilot will normally be in continuous contact with the ATC facility at his base airfield.

A small but important precaution when preparing the Flight Log will be to write particularly legibly as the dim cockpit lighting used during flight will increase the difficulty of interpreting normal handwritten information.

Selection of ground features visible at night

The basic ground features used in night navigation will be the light patterns from large and medium sized towns, and aerodrome beacons.

Fig. 20-25

Areas where towns are close to one another will often give difficulties in map reading and identification of position. This is due to the light pattern of one town merging into the light patterns of those which are adjacent to it. Therefore when selecting checkpoints to use en-route, the choice of towns which are well separated will be of more value than using widely inhabited areas.

Air Light Beacons, when available, are extremely helpful to visual navigation and are also useful as a back up to radio aids, but in general a very small number of airfields will be operational during the hours of darkness.

Light Beacons are installed at many civil and military airfields, and are of two different types:

1. Identification Beacons.
2. Aerodrome Beacons.

Identification Beacons:
These will flash a two-letter morse group every 12 seconds and when situated at civil aerodromes the colour is green. The characteristics of identification beacons situated at military airfields are similar to those described for civil aerodromes, except that the colour is red.

Aerodrome Beacons:
These emit a flashing light which normally alternates white/green but at a few airfields in the U.K. they may only flash white. They are operated during the day at many civil aerodromes when conditions of bad visibility exist. They are also operated at night when operations are being conducted from that particular aerodrome. At certain civil

aerodromes and military Master Aerodromes air light beacons will be operated every night from sunset to sunrise.

In addition to air light beacons there are a large number of marine lights which are visible from the air. During navigation flights in the vicinity of coastlines these lights can be most useful.

Marine Light . . . . ● Gp.Fl.(2)15·0 Secs
Lightship . . . . ⚓ Red 20·0 Secs

Marine Lights and Lightships are shown on aeronautical charts together with their identification characteristics and when appropriate these should be noted in the pre-flight planning phase.

It is important to note that lighthouses and lightships have characteristics which are often unfamiliar to pilots in that they can be:

Gp Fl ……	Group Flashing.
Fl ……	Flashing.
Gp Occ ……	Group Occulting.
Occ ……	Occulting.

An occulting light is never out, but gives a light which brightens and fades to fit the characteristics shown on the chart.

Effect of cockpit lighting on map colours:
During day flying the colour relief used on topographical charts enables a pilot to distinguish features more clearly, but at night and particularly when red cockpit lighting is used these colours will lose their discrimination and many features will blend into the background of the map and be difficult to discern.

This point should be borne in mind during flight planning preparations and it may be useful to 'mark out' essential checkpoints to be used en-route with a pen or dark pencil.

Use of radio aids
Radio aids may be the only means of confirming the accuracy of DR navigation during flight at night over featureless or unlighted terrain. The use of radio aids during night navigation may therefore be essential. It should, however, be appreciated that VDF, NDBs and radar facilities will be limited at night due to the smaller number of aerodrome ATCUs available.

Unless promulgated otherwise the facilities provided from MATZs are normally only available on weekdays and usually cease operating at 1700 local time. However some military airfields (Master Aerodromes) operate H24 and others may be open for specific night flying periods. Therefore at night it will often be of value to call any MATZ in the vicinity of the route in case their services are available.

However, with the exception of those which are known to operate H24, these services cannot be relied upon for flight planning purposes.

NDBs and VORs will afford valuable assistance, provided the pilot has received the necessary training in their use. Nevertheless the operation of many NDBs is tied to the hours of watch of the respective airfield ATCU and when this is closed, the NDB facility will usually also be switched off.

A basic point to remember during pre-flight planning is that although the position of VORs and NDBs together with their coding and frequencies are overprinted on topographical charts, it will be advisable to check in the COM section of the Air Pilot or Aerad Flight Guide and Notams, to ensure the frequencies have not changed, or that servicing periods of these stations do not coincide with the period of the intended flight.

Effect of Moonlight upon Visibility at Night
It has already been pointed out that during the hours of darkness general ground features become difficult or impossible to identify. However during moonlight nights, such features as lakes and rivers will usually stand out well, particularly when viewed against the moon. However since cloud may well form and obscure the moon whilst en-route, it is clearly inadvisable to rely on this when planning the flight.

Emphasis on Maintaining a 'Minimum Safe Altitude'
Due to the restricted visibility which attends operating at night, the determination of a minimum safe altitude during the en-route section of the flight is of paramount importance.

Great care must be exercised to assess a safe clearance over high ground and any obstructions, and whereas by day it is common to use safety altitudes in relation to the highest obstructions 5 n.m. either side of the intended track, by night it will be advisable to extend this to encompass obstructions up to 10 n.m. either side of track.

Alternate Airfields – Restricted Availability
The number of airfields which can be used as alternates at night will be far more limited than by day. It will first be necessary to check with Air Pilot and Notams to determine the hours of watch of possible

alternates, prior to making the decision to include them in the flight log.

If suitable alternates are not available within reasonable range of the intended track it may be advisable to plan the flight other than by the most direct route.

The Restricted Recognition of Weather Deterioration

Weather deterioration is probably the greatest hazard of night flying. During the day the pilot will normally have sufficient visibility to assess the weather situation continuously during a flight.

During night operations this facility will often be denied him particularly when cloud has already created dark overcast conditions. It must therefore be appreciated that inadvertent entry into cloud can occur more easily at night and the pilot must be prepared for situations where immediate and total reference to instruments will be necessary.

The need to be particularly alert to worsening weather conditions along the route will therefore form a vital part of airmanship, e.g. heavy rain, hail, snow, turbulence, formation of ice etc. Snow is particularly dangerous at night as it often cannot be seen unless the landing lights are switched on, and unless the pilot is alerted early, he could well continue unaware of the worsening situation.

Lost Procedure

The procedure to be adopted remains substantially the same as for day flying, but the difficulties of recognising ground features and the reduced number of available airfields and their facilities will often make the problem more acute.

At night the use of ATC facilities should therefore be instituted without undue delay and it would be prudent to allow a greater reserve of fuel for diversion than that which would be planned by day.

NIGHT EMERGENCIES

During training, procedures will normally be established to cater for possible emergency situations. These procedures may vary between training organisations, and between particular training aircraft, or even between different aerodromes. The following procedures are therefore written as a guide only, but they could be employed in most aircraft and in circumstances when an emergency occurs away from the training airfield.

Radio Failure

If circumstances occur in which radio failure cannot be rectified in flight, the pilot will have to rely entirely upon visual navigation methods.

It will however be necessary to alert ATC at the airfield of intended landing and to do this it will be advisable to fly at a safe height above the runway in use and in the landing direction, whilst at the same time switching on and off the aircraft landing or navigation lights.

If using the navigation lights they should be switched off and on in an irregular manner to ensure this signal is clearly distinguishable from the flashing navigation lights with which some aircraft are fitted, as part of their normal lighting equipment.

Failure of Runway Lighting

Normally this situation will be of a temporary nature because airfield licensing regulations require that a secondary power supply be available, and capable of being switched on quickly when a failure of the normal power supply occurs.

In the event of this type of lighting failure the initial procedure will be to orbit the airfield until the runway lighting is again available. Aircraft already in the circuit should resume or maintain circuit height during their orbit and those aircraft preparing to join the circuit should maintain at least 2000 feet a.a.l.

Extra care should be exercised in lookout for other aircraft during this period, as it may be difficult to maintain an accurate pattern relative to an unlighted runway.

In the event of failure of the VASIS or AAIs the comments already made regarding a standby power source will also apply. Nevertheless all pilots should receive training in making approaches without the aid of an approach slope system, and this will normally be incorporated in the pilot's initial training at night.

Failure of Aircraft Landing Lights

During night flying training the pilot will initially be taught to land without the assistance of aircraft landing lights. Landing light failure should not therefore constitute difficulty for the pilot. Nevertheless such a failure will be easier to handle if the pilot keeps himself in practice by doing at least one or two landings without the use of landing lights during any training period.

Failure of Aircraft Internal Lighting

In many aircraft there are two internal lighting systems, one for illuminating the instrument panel and the other for giving internal light to the cabin area. With the former there are two methods which may be used. One method is to illuminate the instrument panel from a single light fixture fitted into the roof above the pilot's head or other suitable position, and the other is to fit small (post) lights adjacent to each instrument or instrument group. In either case the lighting intensity is usually controlled by a rheostat integral with the On/Off switches.

Additional internal lighting may include a map light fitted into the underside of the control column or attached by a swivel to a fuselage side member, at eye level and adjacent to the pilot's seat.

In the event of partial or total failure of the instrument panel lighting, the swivel type map light or cabin lighting can be switched on, or increased in brilliance and this together with the hand torch will usually give sufficient light for the pilot to monitor the essential instruments and systems.

It is good operating procedure to note the exact location of all internal light switches and to practise reaching for them in the dark so that they can be brought into operation with a minimum of delay should circumstances require it. For the same reason the hand torch should be stowed in a position which affords immediate and rapid access should it be needed.

Further to this the pilot must be familiar with the location of all fuses which protect the lighting circuits so that action can be initiated to rectify this type of emergency as quickly as possible. If changing a cartridge fuse or re-setting a circuit breaker does not restore the lighting, or should the same lights fail again, it will be necessary to land as soon as it is safe to do so.

It is also useful to know that on many aircraft certain small light bulbs are interchangeable e.g. the bulb in a compass light is often the same size and fit as the bulb in a 'starter engaged' light. This knowledge can be extremely useful when an instrument which requires constant monitoring is blacked out because of an unserviceable light bulb.

Failure of Aircraft Navigation Lights
In the event of the failure of any light which is required to be displayed by the Rules of the Air and Air Traffic Control Regulations, the pilot will be required to land as soon as he thinks it is safe to do so. Failure of the navigation lights is the most obvious case, and it will be necessary to land unless the appropriate ATCU gives permission for the flight to continue.

Nevertheless the immediate safety of the aircraft is the responsibility of the pilot and it must not be further jeopardised by precipitate action, and if the aircraft is equipped with an anti-collision or strobe lighting system it will usually be safe to continue to destination, unless a suitable diversion airfield is conveniently located near the route. However the need to inform ATC of the situation still remains.

Precautions must be taken when entering a traffic pattern in these circumstances, and the ATCU at the destination airfield must be informed of the situation prior to the aircraft entering the circuit.

Total Electrical Failure

A total electrical failure in flight is a rare occurrence, and at night it could lead to a serious emergency, due to the collective effects of losing external/internal illumination and all radio facilities.

Strict adherence to regular en-route checks will ensure the charge rate of the alternator/generator is monitored frequently and this will provide early warning of any impending loss of electrical supply. If indications of a discharge is shown the pilot should immediately reduce the drain on the aircraft battery by switching off as many non-essential services as possible. He will also need to take early action to re-route to the nearest alternate airfield unless the distance to destination is shorter.

The appropriate ATCU should be informed together with the name of the selected landing airfield. This will enable the Air Traffic Unit at the destination airfield to be alerted to the situation and make preparations to handle the occurrence without hazard to other aircraft.

If total electrical failure occurs without warning the generally accepted procedure is to enter a traffic pattern in the normal way but exercising extreme vigilance in relation to other aircraft. The normal circuit pattern should be followed but instead of landing from the first approach the aircraft should be flown under high power to one side of the runway in use and then climbed back up into the circuit followed by a normal approach and landing.

This procedure will normally give sufficient aural warning to the air traffic controller who can then arrange for other aircraft to orbit until the unlighted aircraft has landed and is safely clear of the runway.

Abandoned Take-off

The procedure for this situation will be the same as used by day and ATC must be informed at the earliest possible moment.

Engine Failure

The difficulties of selecting a suitable area to carry out a forced landing will obviously be far greater than by day. When moonlight is available it will enable a degree of judgement to be used in the choice of landing area, as woods and open countryside will often be faintly distinguishable to the pilot.

Judgement of height will be particularly difficult and the height of the ground in relation to the landing will have to be based upon interpreting the altimeter reading in relation to QNH or QFE as applicable.

The use of QFE will mostly be confined to the circuit and when this is set, and provided the height of the ground in the immediate vicinity is the same as the airfield, a fairly accurate indication of height will be obtained from the altimeter.

Every endeavour should be made to put out a 'Mayday' call and if height permits a restart procedure should be implemented unless fire in the engine accompanied the cause of power loss.

If the night is dark and the pilot is unable to distinguish ground features it will normally be advisable to adopt the minimum descent speed for the glide (approximately $1 \cdot 1$ V_{S1}) and head the aircraft into the prevailing wind. These actions will assist to reduce the speed at touchdown.

Although full flap will permit the use of the lowest landing speed, this will only be possible if the ground is sufficiently visible for a fairly accurate round-out to be made. In circumstances where it is impossible to judge the height of the surface just prior to touch-down, the use of full flap may only result in high descent rates, undesirable steep attitudes and increased vertical impact forces on touch-down.

When landing lights are fitted these will be an invaluable aid to judging, both height above the surface and the presence of obstacles during the last stage of the descent. They should not however, be switched on until approximately 3/400 feet a.g.l., as unless they illuminate the surface immediately, their glare will reduce the pilot's ability to see beyond the length of their beams.

Bear in mind that most engine failures occur due to pilot mismanagement of the engine or its systems, it will therefore be vital to double check any fuel tank selections or similar actions when operating during the hours of darkness.

Obstructed Runway Procedure
Most night flying operations are conducted with radio facilities and some form of ATC or Advisory Service. Therefore when a runway becomes obstructed advice will be given from the ground to aircraft in the circuit and normally it will only be necessary for the pilot to acknowledge the instructions or advice from the ground and orbit until the runway is clear.

When RTF is not available local procedures should be laid down to cover this contingency. Such procedures may vary from illuminating the obstructed part of the runway or the threshold with red lights to displaying a red 'T'.

PRE-FLIGHT BRIEFING
NIGHT FAMILIARISATION AND CIRCUITS

Aim

To acquaint the pilot with the additional considerations and the changed aspects when operating an aircraft during the hours of darkness.

What

An introduction to the different factors involved when operating an aircraft at night.

Airmanship

The need for additional pre-flight preparation. The changed visual references and the recognition aspects of other aircraft, ground lighting and obstruction lights.

How

Night Familiarisation
External Checks:

Note the aircraft position in relation to other aircraft. The need for a serviceable hand torch and external lighting checks.

Internal Checks: Starting Up.

Adjustment of internal lighting. Navigation lights switched 'ON'. Sufficient spare fuses. After starting check the alternator charge is satisfactory.

Leaving the Parking Area:

All clear around aircraft.

Identification of taxiway lighting. Vigilant lookout for other aircraft and obstruction lights. Exercise care in control of speed. Use of aircraft taxy light.

Holding Point Procedures:

Determine position of other aircraft. Power and pre-take off checks. Use and stowage of hand torch.

Student Practice.

Take-off:

Approach path clear. Use of runway lighting for directional reference. Use of the flight instruments during the initial climb.

Airfield Departure:

Combined use of external references and the flight instruments.

Night Orientation:

Identification of ground lighting. Recognition of towns, other aircraft and ground obstruction lighting.

Traffic Pattern Rejoining:

RTF procedures, circuit entry and positioning on the downwind leg.

Approach/Runway Lighting Demonstration:

A constant height will be used during the approach to show: The approach slope and runway lighting indications of being, Too Low, Correct and Too High.

Student Practice.

Night Circuits
Use of approach and runway threshold lights to assess base leg turn.
Set up a powered approach and monitor altimeter for the 5/500 feet turn in point.

Final Approach:

Judgement of the correct approach slope achieved by use of approach slope lights and/or spacing of runway lights.
The need for accurate airspeed control.
Anticipate W/V change during descent.
Below 300 feet landing lights (as applicable). Below 200 feet the approach slope lighting system becomes unreliable.

The Landing:

Use the runway lights for depth perception and complete a gradual roundout together with a gradual decrease of the power.
After touchdown check the throttle is

fully closed and direction maintained by reference to the runway lighting. Reduce speed before clearing runway.

After landing checks completed.

Student Practice.

PRE-FLIGHT BRIEFING
NIGHT NAVIGATION

Aim To teach you how to safely navigate the aircraft during the hours of darkness.

What Cross-country flying conducted at night, during which the limitations of visual navigation references will be appreciated.

Airmanship The need for additional pre-flight preparation, precautions in selecting 'Safety Altitudes' and obtaining reliable weather information.

How Pre-flight planning must take into account the reduced number of visible ground features and operational airfields. The need to operate according to 'Instrument Flight Rules', and the decision to file a flight plan when dictated by good operating practice.

Additional factors to be considered during flight planning and throughout the en-route phase:

Accuracy of weather information.

Selection of 'checkpoints' including air light and marine beacons when available.

The greater need for D.R. navigation.

Selection and use of suitable radio aids.

Determining 'Minimum Safety Altitudes' for the en-route sectors.

Selection of available 'Alternate Airfields'.

Clear and legible marking of maps and the flight log.

The available ATC facilities which can be used should a situation of being 'Unsure of Position' or 'Lost' occur.

Student Practice.

Night Flying

Flight Demonstrations

INTRODUCTION

The contents of this exercise may be conveniently divided into the following demonstration groups:

1. Night Familiarisation.
    Night Circuits.
2. Night Navigation.

Demonstration 1 will essentially be an introductory exercise in which a pilot is introduced to the various problems relating to night operations and the necessity of using a combination of external visual references and instrument references to maintain safe and precise control of the aircraft.

It will include an introduction to take-offs, circuits, approaches and landings and involve the use of additional flying techniques.

Demonstration 2 will normally be introduced after the pilot under training has completed solo night circuits.

Airmanship items which are particular to night flying will be introduced and developed at the appropriate moments during each flight.

DEMONSTRATION 1. FAMILIARISATION AT NIGHT OPERATIONS AND INTRODUCTION TO NIGHT CIRCUITS

Flight Lesson	Demonstration Sequence
Night familiarisation External checks	Note the position of other aircraft. The need for a hand torch. Check windscreen dry and clean. External lighting checks: Navigation lights.

	Anti-collision light. Taxy and landing lights. Strobe lights (if fitted).
Internal checks and Start-Up procedure	Adjust internal lighting. Hand torch in accessible position. Sufficient spare fuses (if applicable). Navigation and anti-collision lights 'ON' prior to start up. Additional care to ensure area all round the aircraft is clear before starting the engine.

	After starting:
	   Re-adjust the internal lighting.
	   Ensure the alternator/generator is
	   charging satisfactorily.
	Review taxy/landing light switch
	locations.
	Ensure handtorch is stowed in a
	convenient position.

Leaving the parking area	RTF procedure completed. Decide the correct taxying direction and use additional care to ensure the taxy path is clear of other aircraft, persons and obstructions. Check positive identification of taxyway lighting.
Taxying	Use additional care and taxy slowly. Ensure an adequate battery charge rate is maintained. Maintain a vigilant lookout for red obstruction lights and the external lights of other aircraft. If in doubt at any time use the aircraft taxy light and/or stop. Only proceed if the taxy path is clear. Care must be used to avoid dazzle to other pilots if the aircraft landing lights are used during taxying operations. During the 'Instrument Checks' the internal lighting may have to be increased in brilliance. Check a reduced number of instruments at any one time and remember to reduce the cockpit illumination to a low level when the checks have been completed.
Holding Point procedures	Additional care must be used when approaching the holding point in order to ensure the position of preceding aircraft. Following the 'Pre-Take-off Checks',

	adjust the cockpit lighting to a suitable level and ensure the hand torch is stowed in a secure position which gives immediate access.
The Take-off	RTF procedure completed. Use additional care to ensure the approach path is clear prior to lining up on the runway. Note the aircraft heading is coincident with the runway heading. Note the aspect of the runway lights relative to eye level. Focus well ahead and towards the far end of the runway lighting. Immediately after take-off and towards the end of the runway lights note the difficulty in maintaining attitude by the use of external references. There will be a need to convert to instrument flight for the initial climb.
Airfield Departure and Night Orientation	The lack of a natural horizon will require the use of a combination of external cues and instrument reference. Identification of ground lighting, towns, moving vehicles etc. Recognition of lights on other aircraft and determining their headings. Identification of ground obstruction lights, e.g. television masts etc. Recognition of the airfield and its identification beacon.
	Airfield lighting layout: Runway lighting. Approach lighting. Obstruction lighting.
Re-joining the traffic pattern	RTF procedure completed. Position the aircraft relative to the airfield and accomplish the let-down procedure whilst maintaining a vigilant lookout for other aircraft.
Night circuits	Position the aircraft on the downwind leg. Complete the RTF call and note the aspect of the runway and approach lighting. Lookout and listen out throughout the circuit. Note the normal position to turn onto base leg although the aircraft will be flown further downwind for the initial approach and runway lighting demonstration.

Turn onto base leg by reference to the approach lighting and the position of runway threshold.
Carefully monitor the descent rate to achieve the final approach turn at 5/600 feet a.g.l.

Approach and Runway lighting demonstration

Maintain a constant height and continue the approach towards the runway.
Note the perspective of the runway lighting and its position as viewed through the windscreen.

1. Initially the aircraft will be below the correct approach slope.

    Note: Red/Red indications from the approach slope system.
    The runway lights will be closely spaced.
    These indications show the aircraft is TOO LOW.

2. As the aircraft gets closer to the runway:

    Note: Approach slope indicator system will show the aircraft is intercepting the correct approach slope and the individual runway lights will be seen further apart.

3. As the aircraft gets closer still to the runway threshold:

    Note: The approach slope indicator system will show all White/all Amber and the individual runway lights will be seen to be more widely spaced.
    These indications show the aircraft is TOO HIGH.

Following this demonstration the aircraft will be placed in a climb and re-positioned on the downwind leg of the circuit.

Going Round Again

There will be a need for greater instrument reference during the initial stages of the climb.
Lookout must be re-introduced as soon as possible in order to note the position of other aircraft and achieve correct positioning in the circuit pattern.
The heading of the crosswind leg should

	initially be determined by the use of the heading indicator.
Downwind Leg	Note the distance out relative to the runway and the approach lighting. Complete the normal RTF call and pre-landing checks. Lookout and listen out. Note the position to turn onto base leg by the aircraft's relative position from the approach lighting and the runway threshold.
Base Leg	Commence a powered descent and carefully monitor the descent rate to bring the aircraft into a position to turn onto the final approach at 5/600 feet a.g.l. Wind velocity will have to be determined from ATC. Re-adjust the descent rate as required and maintain a careful lookout into the approach path.
Final Approach	Note the indications from the approach slope lighting system and re-adjust the rate of descent as required whilst maintaining the correct approach speed. Complete the normal RTF call, and continue to monitor the altimeter until close to the runway threshold. Initial approaches and landings will normally be practised without the use of landing lights. At approximately 100 feet a.g.l., the use of the approach slope lighting system should be discontinued.
The Landing	Judgement of the initial flare and the roundout through to touch-down should be made by reference to the runway lighting. Use a gentle roundout whilst reducing the residual power until the wheels are on the ground. Check the throttle is fully closed and maintain direction by reference to the runway lighting. Reduce speed before attempting to turn off the runway. Lookout for the 'turn-off point' onto the taxyway. Stop the aircraft and complete the 'after landing' checks. Adjust the cockpit lighting prior to taxying.

DEMONSTRATION 2.   NIGHT NAVIGATION

Flight Lesson	Demonstration Sequence
Pilot navigation procedures at night	The pre-flight planning is completed with particular emphasis on the reduced availability of visual aids, airfields and ATC facilities. Ensure map features are suitably marked to assist in identification of checkpoints. In Flight: Use of normal navigation methods but additionally, the need for a greater use of D.R. navigation techniques. Use of light patterns from towns, aerodrome beacons and marine lights. Note the difficulty of discerning map colours. Note the effect of moonlight (when available) and the recognition of ground features e.g. woods, lakes etc. Use of radio aids: VORs, NDBs and radar. Maintain a state of awareness in relation to weather and abide by the planned safety altitude. **Lost Procedure:** The emphasis must be on the use of radio and ATC facilities. An early declaration of the situation must be made to the appropriate ATCU.